C.2

Teaching Science in

Today's Secondary Schools

Third Edition

WALTER A. THURBER

ALFRED T. COLLETTE

Allyn and Bacon, Inc.　　　　　Boston

Library of Congress Catalog Card Number: 68–23431

Printed in the United States of America

Preface

PREFACE TO THE FIRST EDITION

Everyone who works with prospective science teachers knows that there is never enough time in a science methods course to deal adequately with all the essentials of science teaching. It is not enough merely to tell students that demonstrations are useful teaching devices, that grouping helps care for individual differences, that science teachers have responsibilities for developing skills in mathematics. Young teachers need to know just *what* constitutes an effective demonstration, just *how* group work can be organized, just *when* to bring mathematics into the science program.

The authors of this book have not felt themselves alone in wishing for more practical helps for teachers-in-training. And so they envisioned a book that would give specific suggestions for teaching procedures. But to be really useful, such a book must do more than give practical aids, because young teachers must know *why* recommendations are made in order to use them wisely, and they need help in developing a philosophy that frees them from dependence upon others for their choice of approaches.

The authors recognize that it is difficult to predict the conditions a new teacher may encounter in his first position. He may have classes of twenty-five pupils or he may have classes of forty. He may be assigned a well-planned classroom or he may be asked to share a standard classroom with a teacher of social studies. One school system may encourage him to use field experiences, while another forbids him to take his pupils from the classroom except for fire drills. This book, therefore, tries to help the beginning teacher recognize the favorable conditions that might exist. At the same time, it shows him how to present a satisfactory program without gas or running water, how to organize group activities in a room crowded with fixed, slant-top desks, and how to improvise equipment to supplement a meager budget.

Much of the advice given the prospective teacher is necessarily conservative. A teacher who finds himself in a rigidly formal school system must adapt himself or fail. Even in the most liberal of situations a beginning teacher is usually wise to be somewhat formal in his approach until he has become acquainted with his pupils and has developed a measure of self-confidence.

However, the book continually points out the limitations as well as the strengths of formal teaching techniques, and it emphasizes the weaknesses of a program that uses no other approaches. The book stresses the contributions that are made by democratic processes in the classroom. It shows the teacher how to add gradually to his program the liberal practices that give pupils increasing responsibility for their own acts.

The book does not try to steer an inoffensive middle path between the extreme viewpoints held in science education today, but the authors insist that subject matter goals and general education goals must go hand in hand, implementing and complementing each other, neither one complete by itself. The authors cannot conceive of a science program without subject matter and they have no sympathy with those who minimize it. On the other hand they believe that the only jusification for the time allotted to science is the change that is produced in the ways of thinking of young people.

The organization of the book may need a few words of explanation. The order of presentation is one that has been found especially useful when working with inexperienced teachers. The first exercises in planning are limited to such specifics as short laboratory exercises, demonstrations, brief field trips, film showings, and minor tests. After the students are acquainted with the basic techniques, they are shown how to organize these into lessons, how to organize lessons into units, and how to make units into complete programs. The remainder of the book looks ahead to the day when the teacher has developed a feeling of security and is ready to continue his professional growth.

It is unlikely that the organization of this or any other methods book can suit everyone exactly, as teaching is such an individual matter. Therefore, each chapter of this book has been made independent of the others and may be used in any order with little or no cross-referencing.

Undoubtedly the philosophy of the authors is evident from the preceding paragraphs. All that remains to say is that they would like to see young people going into science teaching with a broad vision of their profession and their responsibilities. The authors know that science teaching can be one of the most rewarding of undertakings; that with high aims the teacher always finds a challenge; and that with recognition of each small achievement as a triumph he will always find satisfaction in his work.

PREFACE TO THE SECOND EDITION

The favorable response to the first edition of this book has made it possible for us to do what most authors probably want to do as soon as their books are off the press; that is, make a number of changes. We want to thank the many people whose letters have helped us to decide what features of the book to keep, what material to add, and what to omit.

While the first edition was being written, a ferment was brewing in secondary science education. This ferment has since produced a major revolution resulting in new science programs which are of such significance as to demand their incorporation into this science methods text. This is the primary reason why a new edition became desirable.

The new programs stress science as inquiry. They recognize that learning is an internal process on the part of the learner, that teaching is not telling, and that the teacher's role is to place pupils into situations in which they can learn. This accords so well with the philosophy upon which the first edition was based, we believe not only that no changes in philosophy are needed but that our original position is greatly strengthened.

Our correspondents have been especially pleased with the suggestions for specific teaching techniques, asking for more of the same. Consequently, the material on planning has been reorganized and a new chapter on approaches to science teaching has been added.

In the first edition we assumed that teachers in training understood what science is and how it operates. Our experience has convinced us that undergraduates obtain little understanding of the nature of science in typical undergraduate science programs. The number of articles which have recently appeared in scientific journals indicates that professional scientists are also disturbed with this lack of understanding. Therefore, we have added a chapter on the nature of science which we hope will be of some service.

PREFACE TO THE THIRD EDITION

The preface to a second edition is invariably much shorter than the preface to the corresponding first edition. What, then, should be the length of the preface to a third edition? Is the decrease linear, resulting in a microscopically brief expression of gratitude? Or does the length of the preface fall off assymptotically–converging toward an irreducible minimum? Here is a matter worthy of careful investigation. Whatever the optimum length should be, this third preface will be short.

We've attempted to make this revision even more of a reference book in science education for both pre-service and in-service teachers and supervisors of science than the previous editions. It now presents a more thorough coverage of important ideas on the new science curricula as well as a critical analysis of these national programs. It contains a new chapter on the objectives of teaching science which includes a comprehensive presentation on behavioral objectives. The suggested activities, readings and the appendix have been expanded and up-dated. The chapter on the nature of science was so well accepted in the second edition that we decided to revise it to include a broader range of opinions on the philosophy of science.

The comments in the preface to the second edition still seem appropriate. Not that science education has failed to change during the past decade, for it has. But the goals remain the same and the problems of attaining these goals seem much the same despite the combined efforts of many agencies. Moreover, change in science education does not necessarily signify progress. Education as a whole is plagued by pendulum-like changes. Someone devises a "new" approach with its own vocabulary of terms, and he and his disciples push the pendulum to an extreme position. This movement gains publicity, and, to mix the metaphor, everyone jumps on the bandwagon. But the approach fails to live up to all the early claims, discontent arises and everyone dashes off in pursuit of a different approach, usually in the opposite direction.

These gyrations represent much waste of energy and enthusiasm. Almost every "new" approach has had a counterpart in the past, though operating under a different terminology. Each of these approaches met certain, but not all needs. Enthusiasts claimed too much and then the disillusioned discarded everything, throwing out the baby with the bathwater. (Now the metaphors are really scrambled.)

The authors of this book have presented a wide variety of approaches indicating the limitations of each as well as the contributions it can make.

We hope that new teachers will recognize the need for many approaches to science teaching, and we recommend that they refrain from wild enthusiasm for any "new" approach, no matter how enticing it is made to appear. There will be good in each new movement and it should be extracted, but there was good in earlier movements too, good that should all be conserved and utilized.

We would like to express our deepest appreciation to several graduate students in Science Education at Syracuse University who criticized parts of the second edition and made suggestions for improving the present edition. We are particularly indebted to Mr. James Barrett Cunningham, Mr. Harry O. Haakonsen, and Mrs. Martha Wavrinek. We also appreciate the contributions that were made by a number of individuals, as well as national study groups, for photographs and charts which are incorporated in this text.

WALTER A. THURBER

ALFRED T. COLLETTE

Contents

Acknowledgments

The authors gratefully acknowledge the courtesy of permission to reprint material that appears on the following pages.

Page 154—G. W. Allport, "Attitudes," *A Handbook of Social Psychology*, C. Munchison (ed.) [Clark University Press, 1935], New York: Russell & Russell, 1967.

Pages 9, 16, 31—From *Modern Science and the Nature of Life*, © 1957, by W. S. Beck. Reprinted by permission of Harcourt, Brace & World, Inc.

Page 152—Melvin Berger, "Using History in Teaching Science," *The Science Teacher*, 30:24–26, November, 1963.

Pages 88, 89, 175—Biological Science Curriculum Study, *Biological Science: An Inquiry into Life*. Copyright 1963 by The Regents of the University of Colorado. Reprinted by permission of the Biological Sciences Curriculum Study.

Pages 298, 299, 230—*Biological Science: Patterns and Processes*. Copyright 1966 by the Regents of the University of Colorado. Reprinted by permission of the Biological Sciences Curriculum Study.

Page 90— *BSCS Newsletter*, No. 12, February, 1962, p. 7. Reprinted by permission of the Biological Sciences Curriculum Study.

Pages 87, 88—*BSCS Newsletter*, No. 28, April, 1966. Reprinted by permission of the Biological Sciences Curriculum Study.

Pages 5, 10, 20 — R. B. Braithwaite, *Scientific Explanation*, 1953. Reprinted by permission of the Cambridge University Press.

Pages 79, 80, 99—Gordon Cawelti, "Innovative Practices in High Schools: Who Does What and Why and How." Reprinted, with permission, from *Nation's Schools*, April, 1967. Copyright 1967, McGraw-Hill, Inc., Chicago. All rights reserved.

Page 17—T. C. Chamberlain, "The Method of Multiple Working Hypotheses," *Science*, 148:754–759, 1965. Reprinted by permission.

Page 30—W. E. LeG. Clark, "The Crucial Evidence for Human Evolution," *American Scientist*, 47:299–300, 1959. Reprinted by permission.

Page 33—Robert S. Cohen, "Individuality and Common Purpose: The Philosophy of Science," *The Science Teacher*, 31:27–28, May, 1964. Reprinted by permission.

Pages 2, 6—J. B. Conant, *Science and Common Sense*, New Haven: Yale University Press, 1951. Reprinted by permission of the publisher.

Pages 560, 561, 562—Belle Cooper, "The North Fulton Science Fair," *Selected Science Teaching Ideas of 1952*, National Science Teachers Association, Washington, D.C., 1952. Reprinted by permission.

Pages 8, 9—From A. d'Abro, *The Evolution of Scientific Thought*, Dover Publications, Inc., New York, 1950. Reprinted through permission of the publisher.

Pages 581, 582—Herschel G. Dassel, "After School Science: Johnny Will Stay After School," *The Science Teacher*, 32:42–43, November, 1965. Reprinted by permission.

PAGE 254—J. R. Dawson, "Learning from the Outdoors," *The American Biology Teacher*, vol. 19, April 1957. Reprinted by permission.

PAGES 292, 293, 294—Robert M. Diamond, ed., *A Guide to Instructional Television*, New York: McGraw-Hill Book Company, Inc., 1964. Reprinted by permission of the publisher.

PAGES 508, 509, 510—Marvin Druger, "A Proposed Model for a Summer Course in Zoology for Gifted High School Students," *Science Education*, 46:447–451, 1962. Reprinted by permission.

PAGE 146—Robert H. Ennis, "Concept of Critical Thinking," *Harvard Educational Review*, 32, Winter 1962. Copyright © 1962 by President and Fellows of Harvard College.

PAGE 3—Reprinted with the permission of the publisher from Frederick Fitzpatrick, Editor, *Policies for Science Education* (New York: Teachers College Press), © 1960, Teachers College, Columbia University.

PAGES 535, 536—Emile C. Fonsworth, "The Functional Approach in General Science," *Ideas for Teaching Science in the Junior High School*, National Science Teachers Association, Washington, D.C., 1963. Reprinted by permission.

PAGE 13—O. R. Frisch reviewing S. Rozental (ed.), "Niels Bohr: His Life and Work," *Scientific American*, 216:146, 1967. Reprinted by permission.

PAGE 138—W. D. Hedges, "Teaching Science by Programing," *Science and Children*, October, 1964.

PAGE 11—Joel Hildebrand, "The Joy of Chemistry," *International Science and Technology*, 67:68, 1967. Reprinted by permission.

PAGES 151, 152—Abstracted from J. R. Jablonski, "High School Student Research: Fact or Fancy," *The Science Teacher*, 31:24–26, April, 1964. Reprinted by permission.

PAGES 12, 13—C. B. Koford, "The California Condor," *Research Report No. 4*, *National Audubon Society*, New York, 1953, p. 1. Reprinted by permission.

PAGES 580–581—Abstracted from L. M. Krause, "The Research Approach Club," *The Science Teacher*, 32:36–37, March, 1965. Reprinted by permission of the publisher.

PAGES 80, 81—Horace MacMahan, Jr., "Princeton Project or ESP: A Difficult Choice," *School Science and Mathematics*, 45:87–88, 1966. Reprinted by permission.

PAGES 28, 33—Ernst Mayr, "Cause and Effect in Biology," *Science*, 134:1503, 1961. Copyright 1961 by the American Association for the Advancement of Science.

PAGE 135—Joost Meerlo, *The Rape of the Mind* [Grosset and Dunlap, Inc., 1961], New York: World Publishing Company, 1956.

PAGES 320, 321—Archie M. Owen, "Selecting Science Textbooks," *The Science Teacher*, 29:20, November, 1962. Reprinted by permission.

PAGE 51—National Science Teachers Association, *Planning for Excellence in High School Science*, Washington, D.C., 1961. Reprinted by permission.

PAGE 18—J. R. Platt, "Strong Inference," *Science*, 146:347–353, 1964. Copyright 1964 by the American Association for the Advancement of Science.

PAGE 30—Michael Polanyi, "The Potential Theory of Absorption," *Science*, 141:1010, 1963. Copyright 1963 by the American Association for the Advancement of Science.

PAGES 94, 95— PSSC, *Physics, 2nd ed.*, Boston: D. C. Heath & Co., 1965.

PAGES 150, 151—Abstracted from Abraham Raskin (ed.), "Providing for the Teaching of Some of the Elements of the Scientific Method," *Science Teaching Ideas*, National Science Teachers Association, Washington, D.C., 1955, pp. 11–12. Reprinted by permission.

PAGES 124, 127—W. B. Reiner, "Motivation in Science Teaching," *The Science Teacher*, 30–52, March, 1963. Reprinted by permission.

observations. Science is both a body of knowledge and the process of acquiring and refining knowledge.

Inherent in this definition is the implication that science is at one and the same time a body of knowledge and an on–going, self–testing process of inquiry. This is the image which should be given to the general public, particularly to secondary school pupils who are apt to view science as dull and uninviting rather than vigorous and exciting.

The scope of science. People tend to think of science as dealing with the natural world as distinct from the worlds of music, art, and literature. Thus science certainly includes geology, astronomy, and those parts of biology, physics, and chemistry which do not deal with man and his operations. Doubts begin to arise when considering such fields as psychology, anthropology, and engineering.

Some authorities attempt to limit science to those subjects that are empirical in nature, that is, those that deal with facts obtained by the direct observation of nature.[4] This admits parts, but not all, of psychology, anthropology, sociology, economics, and even history, but excludes mathematics of the so-called pure variety.

Another attempt at limitation has been to admit those fields which are amenable to the processes of science. If expanded, this somewhat circular definition means that a subject is part of science if empirical data can be obtained, used as a basis for hypotheses, and tested objectively.

"Pure Science" and "Technology". From time to time attempts are made to divide scientific investigations into "pure science" and "applied science" or "technology." Motivation or goals have been used as distinguishing characteristics. According to Leland Haworth, basic research "seeks an understanding of the laws of nature without regard to the ultimate applicability of the results."[5] Glenn Seaborg is more impassioned: "The motivating force is not utilitarian goals, but a search for a deeper understanding of the universe and the phenomena within it."[6] However, Frederick Seitz points out that one would need "a good psychologist, perhaps even a psychiatrist, to decide what the goals are."[7]

[4] Braithwaite, R. B., *Scientific Explanation*, Harper, New York, 1953, p. 1.

[5] *Federal Research and Development Programs*, Part 1, Government Printing Office, Washington, D.C., 1963, p. 6.

[6] *Ibid.*, p. 66.

[7] *Government and Science*, Government Printing Office, Washington, D.C. 1963, p. 263.

A distinction is also made on the basis of whether an investigation is "free" or "mission oriented,"[8] or whether the work produces "new" knowledge.[9] Storer's definition has a cynical flavor:[10]

> Basic research is carried out by a scientist who hopes that his findings will be primarily of interest to his colleagues, while applied research is intended to produce findings of greater interest to his employer or the public.

The real difficulty in trying to separate "pure science" from technology rests in the fact that scientific research operates over a broad spectrum of intellectual achievement, applicability, motivation, and rewards. The Bell Laboratories, though generally mission oriented, produce work of which any university would be proud. Much "pure" research reported in the journals is certainly trivial.

The feedback within scientific research is also considerable. Some information obtained with "pure" motives turns out to have important applications, and applications often produce new information. Efforts to understand better the action of semiconductor junctions led to the invention of the transistor which in turn made possible a host of important instruments used in research. A scientist never stands alone, no matter how "pure" in approach he may consider himself.

SCIENCE AS A BODY OF KNOWLEDGE

Scientific information is often presented as largely, if not completely, factual. If we consider facts as truths, and therefore indisputable, relatively few facts are presented to students. Most scientific information is presented in the form of generalizations which sum up facts. In addition, much information is presented in the form of hypotheses and theories which attempt to explain facts.

A scientifically literate person is able to identify facts, generalizations, and speculations. As information is presented to him, he recognizes that which is certain, that which is well supported by evidence, and that which lacks convincing support. He may refuse to accept certain items or perhaps accept some tentatively pending further investigation. A beginning student, however, is not prepared to make the necessary discriminations.

[8] Waterman, A. T., "The Changing Environment of Science," *Science*, 147:13, 1965.

[9] Toulman, S., "Allocation of Federal Support for Scientific Research," *National Science Foundation Staff Paper*, 1965.

[10] Storer, N. W., *Basic versus Applied Research*, Harvard University Publication, Cambridge, Mass., 1964.

Without aid, he is forced to accept all information as truth; he develops misconceptions not only about the field he is studying but about the nature of science as well.

The facts of science. "The scientific method is marked by . . . careful and accurate classification of facts."[11] But what is a fact? According to general usage, a fact is a truth. In so far as science is concerned, this would have to be a demonstrable truth.

Demonstrable truths are necessarily limited in scope. If "fact" is equated with "demonstrable truth," as it should be in science, an appropriate definition is "a happening in time or space."[12] Thus each recorded observation of an event or condition in nature provides science with another fact.

> However great our activity, facts outstrip us, and we can never overtake them; while the scientist is discovering one fact, millions and millions are produced in every cubic inch of his body. Trying to make science contain nature is like trying to make the part contain the whole.[13]

Scientific facts can be recognized when they are obviously the products of direct observation. Conscientious scientists report not only their raw data (facts) but also the methods used in obtaining them so that others can judge the reliability of the data. However, a nonspecialist must be alert for inferences reported as facts; a report of helium in a star is an inference derived from the fact that certain lines in the star's spectrum correspond to lines in the spectrum of helium as obtained in a laboratory.

Generalizations. As facts accumulate they may begin to show certain relationships. Descriptions of these relationships, called generalizations, are powerful tools for bringing raw data into a comprehensible whole. Generalizations also serve as springboards for further investigations, first, to verify and determine the ranges of the generalizations, second, to try to find explanations for the relationships discovered. Generalizations, furthermore, make predictions possible:

> . . . to classify a whale as a mammal is to assert the generalization that all infant whales are provided with milk by their mothers. . . . It enables us to predict that the next whale we meet will be a mammal, and it singles out an important feature in which whales differ from fishes.[14]

[11] Pearson, Karl, *The Grammar of Science*, Dutton, London, 1937, p. 21.

[12] *Webster's New International Dictionary*, Merriam Co., Springfield, Mass., 1960.

[13] Poincaré, Henri, *Science and Method* (trans. F. Maitland), Dover Publications, New York, n.d., p. 16.

[14] Braithwaite, *op. cit.* pp. 1–2.

A generalization can be recognized because it deals with a class of objects, conditions or events. "Grass is green," and "Foxes eat meat" are obvious generalizations. "The earth turns once on its axis every 24 hours" may require analysis to recognize that it refers to a series of events. Similarly, the statement "Copper is a good conductor of electricity," may need analysis to recognize that it refers to all shapes and sizes of copper objects under all possible conditions.

A person with a reasonable science background probably recognizes the limitations of the above statements and applies the necessary qualifications. But a person faced with the statement. "The volume of a gas varies inversely with the pressure," needs special training to know whether this statement applies to all gases at all temperatures and pressures, or indeed if it applies to any real gas at all. Most generalizations need qualifications which unfortunately may not be provided.

In *Science and Common Sense*, Conant, unwittingly provides an example of the failure to qualify a generalization:[15]

> I venture to use the slippery word "fact" to designate not only a past experiment but the generalization that is involved in the prediction that under a given set of conditions the experiment can be repeated. Thus one can hardly avoid saying that it is a fact that a suction pump will draw water up to a height of about thirty-four feet if operated at sea level.

Conant here equates "fact" with "certainty" but he broadens its meaning from a single observation to a set of observations. His example can not convince anyone acquainted with suction pumps. The statement is more truthful if it is qualified as follows: Based on a large number of observations, suction pumps operated *at sea level* lift water *somewhat less* than 34 feet (*evaporation within the pump affects the vacuum*), the exact height depending upon *temperature, weather conditions,* and especially *upon the condition of the pump.* The amended version is obviously a generalization; it is certainly not a fact.

Perhaps Conant's example was poorly chosen, but it is doubtful if any generalization which he might have selected would have been unimpeachable. Some coastal regions have only one tide a day. Not all robins migrate. The more complex a system, the more likely will be exceptions to any generalizations that might be formulated.

Principles and laws: Generalizations that are based upon a large number of observations, all consistent within the limits of observational error, are often treated as certainties. Such generalizations may be dignified by

15 Conant, *op. cit,* p. 35.

labeling them "principles" or "laws," such as the principle of the lever or the law of the lever. However, the empirical basis of these generalizations should not be forgotten.

The term "scientific law" is used very loosely. It dates back to a period when philosophers believed that the universe was governed by a finite number of absolute laws. This interpretation is still held by some scientists.

> The regularities in the phenomena which physical science endeavors to uncover are called the laws of nature. The name is actually very appropriate. Just as legal laws regulate actions and behavior under certain conditions but do not try to regulate all actions and behavior, the laws of physics also determine the behavior of its objects of interest only under certain well-defined conditions, but leave much freedom otherwise.[16]

During the present century, the concept of "universal law" has been crumbling. Some scientists believe that regularities in nature exist, but that statements of these regularities can be only approximations. Others believe that seeming regularities are but accidents and that the term "law" is an anachronism.

Haldane dislikes the implication of a supreme law and a supreme law giver: "If a piece of matter does not obey a law of nature it is not punished. On the contrary, we say that the law has been incorrectly stated. It is probable that every law of nature so far stated has been stated incorrectly."[17]

An extreme stand is taken by those who through the principle of indeterminacy have become convinced that the seeming regularities of nature are matters of statistical probability.

> Within the past four or five decades physical research has clearly and definitely shown—strange discovery—that *chance* is the common root of all the rigid conformity to Law that has been observed, at least in the overwhelming majority of natural processes, the regularity and invariability of which have led to the establishment of the postulate of universal causality. . . . It is quite possible that Nature's laws are of thoroughly statistical character.[18]

The root of these differences in opinion about regularity in Nature is related to the underlying assumptions:

[16] Wigner, E. R., "Events, Laws of Nature, and Invariance Principles," *Science*, 145:995, 1964.

[17] Haldane, J. B. S., *The Sciences and Philosophy*, Doubleday, New York, 1929.

[18] Schrödinger, E. C., *Science, Theory, and Man*, Dover Publications, New York, 1957, pp. 136, 147.

Nature may not be rational and our logic may not be able to cope with it. If this be the case, statistical knowledge may be the only type possible, though even statistical knowledge may fail us.[19]

Hypotheses and theories.   A third class of information is made up of speculations which have been proposed to account for the observations of science. Unlike facts, which are constantly being added to but never discarded, and generalizations which are constantly being refined, the speculations of science are in a constant state of flux, being amended, discarded, and replaced. Unfortunately for the nonspecialist, the tentative nature of these speculations is not always made evident, and he cannot tell whether the information presented is well authenticated or little more than a wild guess.

Speculations in science are loosely termed "hypotheses" and "theories," the latter being better supported than the former. By this interpretation, an untested speculation is an hypothesis. A speculation which has been extensively tested, fits all known facts, and has no reasonable rival is a theory. The amount of substantiation needed to advance an hypothesis to the status of a theory is a matter of personal conviction and so some speculations are classified differently by different authorities.

> The most widespread and conclusive process of self-testing in science is testing by multiplication of relevant observations. . . . it is impossible to prove anything in the abstract sense of, for example, a proof in mathematics. Multiplication of observations can only increase our confidence within a narrowing range of probability. If confidence becomes sufficiently great and the range is encompassed by the hypothesis, we begin to call the hypothesis a theory, we accept it and go from there.[20]

The tentative nature of an hypothesis or theory should be kept in mind. The statement that it is never possible to prove an hypothesis—only to disprove it—is extreme but has some truth.

> ". . . few scientists would claim that any hypothesis, however extensively tested, was a statement of absolute, universal truth. It is more likely to be a good, perhaps excellent approximation for a finite range of circumstances the boundaries of which are not well demarcated. As further studies are made, a more accurate or more widely applicable generalization will almost surely replace it.[21]

[19] d'Abro, A., *The Evolution of Scientific Thought*, Dover Publications, New York, 1950, p. 405.

[20] Simpson, G. G., "Biology and the Nature of Science," *Science*, 139:84, 1963.

[21] Wilson, E. B., Jr., *An Introduction to Scientific Research*. McGraw–Hill, New York, 1952, p. 29.

Hypotheses and theories which appear plausible when applied to a small number of facts, often become untenable when a greater number of facts have been discovered. Everyone should be prepared for changes that result in a completely new structure for a branch of science. ". . . anomalies—phenomena for which the investigator's theory had not prepared him—accrue until the old theory becomes awkward by virtue of *ad hoc* patching; then a new theory, supported by a new generation of investigators, is constructed."[22]

The tentative nature of so much of science need not be, and should not be, a source of disillusionment or a cause for cynical rejection.

> Now it might be contended that since all finality seems to be denied a scientific theory, it would be better to cease theorizing and content ourselves with a bare accumulation of facts. But an attitude of this sort would be untenable, for scientific theories, though necessarily inaccurate from a long-range point of view, are nevertheless inevitable if knowledge is to exist. A bare accumulation of disconnected facts would not constitute a science, precisely because, the facts being disconnected, they would afford us no means of foretelling the future sequence of events. Under the circumstances, it is better to be guided by a faulty synthesis which we can improve on as experience demands, rather than be guided by nothing at all. Furthermore, coordinations and theories which have since turned out to be patently inaccurate, have yet been successful in leading to the discovery of new facts.[23]

Models in science.   A term encountered with increasing frequency in scientific literature is "model." This usually does not apply to the scale model which is so familiar, but to a device, often abstract and even *purely* imaginary, for testing ideas and predicting from hypotheses.

> Because of the complexity of higher abstractions and because of the desirability of establishing much higher generalizations, scientists are forced to devise *models* of nature, simplifications achieved by eliminating irrelevant detail, from which higher abstractions can be more easily derived. . . . The model is intended to incorporate in workable form the *essential* features of the natural system under examination.
>
> Obviously, much of the inevitable uncertainty of science lurks in the question of the admissibility and appropriateness of the chosen model. Should my chosen model be too simple or actually irrelevant, I am predestined to failure. Many chosen models are . . . astonishingly unsuitable.[24]

[22] Braverman, M. H., reviewing H. B. Aldelmann, "Marcello Malpighi and the Evolution of Embryology," *Scientific American*, 216:140, 1967.

[23] d'Abro, *op. cit.*, pp. 401–402.

[24] Beck, W. S., *Modern Science and the Nature of Life*, Doubleday, Garden City, N.Y., 1961, p. 169.

The word "model" is sometimes used as though it were synonymous with "theory." However, a distinct philosophical difference exists between the two. A theory is arrived at inductively from a set of facts. A model is arrived at deductively from a theory. There are dangers in confusing the two.

> The first danger is that the theory will be identified with a model for it, so that the objects with which the model is concerned . . . will be supposed actually to be the same as the theoretical concepts of the theory. To these theoretical concepts will then be attributed properties which belong to the objects of the model but which are irrelevant to the similarity of formal structure which is all that is required of the relationship of model to theory. Models for chemical theories with molecules as linked systems of atoms, and models for physical theories with atoms as 'solar systems' of separate elementary particles have in the past led many people to suppose that atoms, or electrons, shared characteristics of the model other than those which made the model an appropriate one.
>
> But there is a second danger inherent in the use of models, a danger which is more subtle. . . . This danger is that of transferring the logical necessity of some of the features of the chosen model on to that of the theory, and thus supposing, wrongly, that the theory, or parts of the theory, have a logical necessity which is in fact fictitious.[25]

SCIENCE AS A WAY OF INVESTIGATING

Science begins with the gathering and cataloging of facts. These are arranged and given meaning so that predictions can be made. Speculation inevitably follows to account for relationships and incongruities. The resulting speculations must then be tested and new conclusions made.

> One learns the facts of nature primarily by studying nature directly without the intervention of arbitrary preconceptions, particularly those based on social constraints. Speculation about nature can be free, but must ultimately be guided by experimental observation. This precept was never fully appreciated by the Greeks, who made enormous strides in the speculative aspects of science. . . . They did not, however, appreciate the importance of tying speculation to careful observation—their science was never truly experimental .[26]

The scientific method.   Efforts to isolate and define a scientific method have occupied science philosophers for many years. Pearson believed that the scientific method is marked by: (a) careful and accurate classification

[25] Braithwaite, *op. cit.*, pp. 93–94.
[26] Seitz, Frederick, "Science and Modern Man," *American Scientist*, 54:233, 1966.

of facts and observation of their correlation and sequence; (b) the discovery of scientific laws by the air of creative imagination; (c) self-criticism and the final touchstone of equal validity for all normally constituted minds.[27]

Another description has been included in a number of textbooks:

1. A problem is stated.
2. Observations relevant to the problem are collected.
3. An hypothesis consistent with the observations is formulated.
4. Predictions of other phenomena are deduced from the hypothesis.
5. Occurrence of the predicted phenomena is looked for.
6. The hypothesis is accepted, modified, or rejected in accordance with the degree of fulfillment of the prediction.

Research scientists may not have been greatly influenced by the above formal description of method, but science educators have been greatly impressed. Thousands of young people have memorized and chanted back the steps to their teachers, perhaps intuitively doubting their application.

Its implication of a general routine that automatically solves any scientific problem is false. It quite ignores the most difficult, the most creative, and most important elements of scientific endeavor. How does one discern a problem, or decide what kinds of questions are to be asked? How does one determine what observations are relevant? And especially, what kinds of hypothetical solutions are acceptable and where do they come from? Perhaps the most cogent objection of all is that important basic research has seldom followed the "method" just as it is stated.[28]

Perhaps the scientific method cannot be described in formal terms acceptable to any scientist who knows just how unstructured his work can be. "No scientist can expect to start from precise measurements and proceed by strictly logical steps to incontrovertible conclusions. He starts with hunches, many of which are wild, makes mistakes, going off into blind alleys before finding a road that leads in the right direction."[29]

Observation and description.

Science begins with the observation of selected parts of nature. Although the scientist uses his mind to imagine ways in which the world might be constructed, he knows that only by looking at reality can he find out

[27] Pearson, *op. cit.*

[28] Simpson, *op. cit.*, p. 82.

[29] Hildebrand, Joel, "The Joy of Chemistry." *International Science and Technology,* 67:68, 1967.

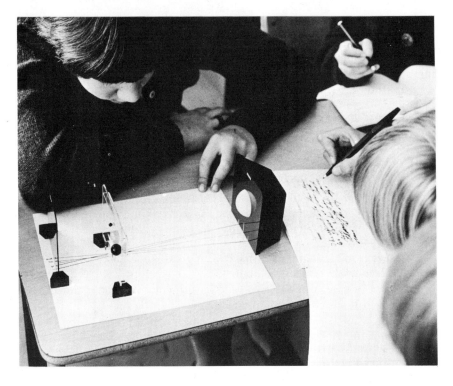

Science is observing, recording the facts, and thinking about them.

whether any of these ways correspond to reality. He rejects authority as an ultimate basis for truth.[30]

Knowledge comes to a person through the medium of his senses but we cannot assume that sensations are incorporated directly into knowledge. The senses probably do no more than provide an awareness of conditions. Judgment and inference are needed to convert sensations into knowledge. The process of observing, therefore, is subject to variation from time to time and from individual to individual. The expression "a trained observer" is no empty phrase; instruction and practice improve the ability to make valid judgments and inferences from sensory data.

The act of observing can affect the system being observed. This is obvious (if we think about it) in the study of many wild animals.

My method was primarily that of watching condors for long periods under conditions which were as natural as possible. Because condors are easily disturbed by man, observations were usually made from a considerable

[30] Wilson, *op. cit.*, p. 21.

distance with binoculars or with a 20–power telescope, and the concealment of a cave or blind was often used.[31]

Observations can also affect physical systems; an ammeter adds to the
resistance of a circuit, a thermometer extracts heat from a system, and a
light used for observing adds energy. The smaller the scale of a system the
greater the possible influence of an observer.

> It had been implicitly assumed that the state of a system could be observed
> in arbitrarily fine detail, that the position and velocity of any of its parts
> could be known as accurately as one desired. . . . In quantum theory this
> was no longer so. For a particle to be observed at least one photon had to
> be reflected from it, and that would unavoidably change the particle's
> velocity by a finite amount.[32]

One problem in scientific research is minimizing variations in observations. Practice and training are usually essential, and the employment of
two or more trained observers is helpful. But whenever possible, scientists
rely upon instrumentation. Instruments are objective, consistent, can be
standardized, and usually provide quantitative data which can be treated
statistically to reveal additional information.

Quantitative descriptions are used when possible. Units of measurement are standard and familiar to everyone, whereas words often introduce
semantic problems. Numerical descriptions can also be more precise and
meaningful than purely verbal descriptions; the statement that A weighs
more than B tells much less than saying that A weighs ten pounds and B
weighs two pounds. Even when qualities cannot be measured in standard
units, for example, the unpleasantness of sounds, rating scales can often be
devised to provide numerical values to judgments.

The role of questions. Science is in part a matter of asking questions and
trying to find answers. Most scientific questions can be reduced to such
simple forms as "What?", "How?", and "Why?" Simpson prefers to class
them as "What?", "How?", "What for?", and "How come?"[33]

"What?" questions, such as "What freshwater algae live in Antarc-
tica?" lead to research that is primarily descriptive. Explanations are not
expected. Although belittled by some scientists, descriptive research is in-
dispensable for all scientific endeavor.

"How?" questions, such as "How does the drug thalidomide affect the

[31] Koford, C. B., *The California Condor*, Research Report No. 4, National Audubon
Society, New York 1953, p. 1.

[32] Frisch, O. R., reviewing S. Rozental (ed.), "Niels Bohr: His Life and Work,"
Scientific American, 216:146, 1967.

[33] Simpson, G. G., "The Status of the Study of Organisms," *American Scientist*, 50:38,
1962.

Data are often most meaningful when quantitative.

growth of protozoa?" are relatively straightforward. The manner of attack is suggested by the question and only details of procedure need to be worked out (though these may require much ingenuity).

"Why?" questions are much more difficult to deal with. A question such as "Why does thalidomide inhibit the growth of protozoa?" contains no suggestion as to a method of attack. Trial–and–error methods are rarely profitable. So researchers usually speculate about possible reasons and then test their hypotheses.

To illustrate, three possible solutions to the thalidomide problem described above are: (1) thalidomide slows the transportation of nutrients within protozoa; (2) thalidomide reacts with certain nutrients before these can be utilized; (3) thalidomide interferes with one of the enzyme systems in protozoa. A research team working on this problem already knew that thalidomide affects metabolites in a few other organisms. They limited their efforts to the second hypothesis with positive results, thus saving themselves greatly in time and labor.[34]

"Why?" questions rarely have final answers. If experiments show that thalidomide inhibits the action of nicotinic acid (as it does), a new question arises, "Why does thalidomide inhibit the action of nicotinic acid?" Each question leads to another, more fundamental question. "It is a peculiarity of any answer to the question 'Why?' that another 'why?' always lies beyond it. We reply to conditional or intermediate 'why's' and never come to the ultimate explanation."[35]

Simpson's "What for?" questions refer to the purpose served by some structure or function such as a pigeon's tail or a robin's migration. We can also ask with regard to man-made devices, "What is a carburetor for?" and "Why is that highway curve banked?" But most "What for?" questions in the physical sciences are meaningless; one does not expect an intelligent answer to such questions as "What is a volcano for?"

Simpson's "How come?" questions refer to the origin of things such as "How did it come about that honeybees live in colonies?" These questions often invoke evolution for answers.

Questions that initiate research have usually been screened, consciously or unconsciously, to meet the criterion of answerability. "For any proposition to embody a possible truth about the world, it must also embody a possible falsehood. Since we proceed by asking nature questions, we learn nothing from her answers if the question is formulated so that the answer is 'yes'."[36]

[34] Frank, Oscar, et al., "Metabolic Deficiencies in Protozoa Induced by Thalidomide," Science, 139:110, 1963.

[35] Simpson, G. G., Horses, Doubleday, Garden City, N.Y., 1961, p. 297.

[36] Beck, op cit., p. 56.

Scientists are rarely drawn into investigations which promise little hope of success. Many important questions seem to lie beyond the scope of present-day science and investigations are not undertaken.

> . . . the great success of physics is due to the restriction of its objectives; it only endeavors to explain the regularities in the behavior of objects. This renunciation of the broader aim, and the specification of the domain for which an explanation can be sought, now appears to us an obvious necessity. In fact, the specification of the explainable may have been the greatest discovery so far.[37]

Working hypotheses.   All descriptions of the scientific method agree on one feature—the necessity for working hypotheses. A working hypothesis is a proposed answer to a question or a possible explanation of data. It is a trial idea and should have no scientific standing until it has been tested. The working hypothesis has one purpose only—to guide an investigator in his operations.

> Experiments or simple observations lead to individual facts without status as generalizations. The scientist examines these facts and attempts to make sense of them by devising some general explanation to account for them. This is the hypothesis, and if the scientist omits to frame a hypothesis . . . he can proceed no farther. For the hypothesis and not random chance should guide the scientist to his next observations. If the hypothesis is true, reasons the scientist hopefully, thus and so should be taking place in the observable world, and the hypothesis can be put to the test. If the predictions are confirmed, a new scientific generalization is on its way to being; if the test fails, the hypothesis needs to be amended or abandoned.[38]

In a publication that has been reprinted many times and should be read by every science educator and graduate student in science, Chamberlain urged researchers to propose, not just one hypothesis, but as many as the mind could invent, thus freeing the mind from bias that might result from excessive love of "one's intellectual child."

> The effort is to bring up into view every rational explanation of new phenomena, and to develop every tenable hypothesis respecting their cause and history. The investigator thus becomes the parent of a family of hypotheses; and, by his parental relation to all, he is forbidden to fasten his affections unduly upon any one. . . . Having thus neutralized the partialities of his emotional nature, he proceeds with a certain natural and enforced erectness of mental attitude to the investigation, knowing well that some of his intellectual children will die . . . yet feeling that several of them may survive . . . since it is often the outcome of inquiry that several causes are found to be involved instead of a single one. In following a single

---

[37] Wigner, *op. cit.*, p. 995.
[38] Beck, *op. cit.*, p. 56.

tice, however, there may be from several to many additional conditions that may change during the process of an experiment, thus bringing any conclusions into doubt. Much of an experimenter's time, energy, and ingenuity are spent in detecting unwanted variables, bringing them under control when possible, and estimating their influence otherwise.

> The first and indispensible condition that we demand of any process of experiment before it can be admitted into the regular procedure of physical research is that it will invariably reproduce the same results. We do not consider an experiment worthy of scientific consideration or acceptance unless it can fulfill this condition. . . . it is from . . . such reproducible experiments that the whole texture of Physical Science is woven. These classical results are the only raw material allowed to be used in the further development of scientific truth.[43]

Physicists and chemists, by concentrating upon small scale phenomena, have used experiments with great success. Biologists can use experiments in the study of small plants and animals and small ecological systems but not in the study of large organisms or systems. Geologists, meteorologists, and astronomers must depend upon other techniques.

Biologists are often faced with variables which simply cannot be controlled. In addition to the many variables present at the time of the experiment, influences of past variables may modify the structure, physiology, and behavior of the test organisms; these variables are not confined to the lives of the test organisms but may have operated in the distant past, modifying the genetic character of the organisms. Kavanau has described the distortion in behavior of white-footed mice transferred from "the stimulus- and structure-rich natural habitat to the relatively barren, highly restrictive laboratory enclosure."[44] Others have pointed out that most of the animals used in psychology laboratories are drawn from inbred strains that have certainly been modified genetically to meet laboratory conditions. Attempts to draw conclusions from experiments on the learning of children in classroom situations are even more hazardous; the children are affected not only by ambient classroom conditions, but also by genetic influences, the total of all past experiences of pupils and teacher, and the personality interactions of all persons in the classroom.

Even physical scientists, for all the niceties of their controls and the reproducibility of their data sometimes have doubts:

> . . . consider the number of experiments which have actually furnished the data on which the structure of Physical Science is based. That number

[43] Schrödinger, *op. cit.*, p. 85.

[44] Kavanau, J. L., "Behavior of Captive White-Footed Mice," *Science*, 155:1623–1639, 1967.

is undoubtedly very large. But it is infinitesimal when compared with the number of experiments that might have been carried out but never actually have been. Therefore a selection has been made. . . . That selection must have been influenced by circumstances that are other than purely scientific.[45]

Testing by prediction.   Some hypotheses in all fields are impractical or impossible to test by experiment. These hypotheses can sometimes be tested by prediction—that is, by deducing certain outcomes from an hypothesis and then looking to nature for verification. An astronomer may calculate the orbit of a comet, predict the position of the comet on some future dates, and then see how well his predictions fit the actual observations. Such testing is not limited to future events; hypotheses concerning lines of organic evolution can be tested by predicting that certain "missing links"will be found.

Successful prediction is sometimes considered strong support for an hypothesis, each success narrowing the range of probability. However, success may be attributed to uncontrolled variables which are unsuspected. Failure to predict correctly may not be conclusive evidence that the hypothesis is wrong; the deduction from it may have been faulty, or an unsuspected factor may have been operative in the situations studied.

> However many conjectures have been examined and found to confirm the hypothesis, there will still be unexamined cases in which the hypothesis might be false without contradicting any of the observed facts. Thus the empirical evidence of its instances never proves the hypothesis; in suitable cases we may say that it *establishes* the hypothesis, meaning by this that the evidence makes it reasonable to accept the hypothesis; but it never *proves* the hypothesis in the sense that the hypothesis is a logical consequence of the evidence.[46]

SCIENCE AS A WAY OF THINKING

Conant speaks of the tactics and the strategy of science, recognizing as he does so that these military terms are not exactly appropriate to scientific investigations.[47] Nonetheless, the terms do help in a general differentiation between the reasoning behind the overall campaign to obtain information from nature, and the tactics used in attacks on specific problems.

[45] Schrödinger, *op. cit.*, p. 86.
[46] Braithwaite, *op. cit.*, p. 14.
[47] Conant, J. B., *On Understanding Science*, New American Library, New York, 1958, p. 30.

Of course, scientific investigation has no clearly established and easily outlined strategical pattern; nor does the scientist fit a stereotype. The strategy of science has changed greatly through the centuries from the tight logic and deductive procedures of the scholastics to the empiricism and inductive processes of the post-Baconians, and from the search for nature's laws in the last century to the search for statistical probabilities in this. For a better understanding of past and present trends in scientific thought, and of the controversies among philosophers of science, one should turn to books on the philosophy and history of science.

Empirical basis of modern science.   One aspect of science upon which scientists now agree is that their work is founded upon empirical data.

> Science begins with the observation of selected parts of nature. Although the scientist uses his mind to imagine ways in which the world might be constructed, he knows that only by looking at reality can he find out whether any of these ways correspond with reality. He rejects *authority* as an ultimate basis for truth. Though he is compelled by practical necessity to use facts and statements put forward by other workers, he reserves for himself the decision as to whether these other workers are reputable, whether their methods are good, and whether in any particular case the alleged facts are credible. He further considers it his privilege and sometimes his duty to repeat and test the work of others whenever he feels that this is desirable.[48]

This rejection of authoritarianism is an important characteristic of modern science, contrasting sharply with the blind passivity of many scientists before 1660 and lingering on in certain institutions until our own century. Authoritarianism has an ever decreasing influence in the mainstream of scientific investigations.

> A new spirit is arising which is unwilling to accept anything on authority, which does not so much permit as demand independent, rational thought on every subject, and which refrains from hampering any attack based on such thought, even though it be directed against things which were formerly considered to be sacrosanct as you please. In my opinion this spirit is the common cause underlying the crisis of every science today. Its results can only be advantageous: no scientific structure falls entirely into ruin: what is worth preserving preserves itself and requires no protection.[49]

Empiricism does not end with the preliminary assembly of raw data but pervades the whole structure of modern science. Each new generalization, hypothesis, or theory derived must be immediately referred back to

[48] Wilson, *op. cit.*, p. 21.
[49] Schrödinger, *op. cit.*, p. 38.

nature to test its applicability. Speculations which do not pass this test, no matter how beautifully logical they may be, are rejected from the body of scientific knowledge.

Objectivity in science.   Those who describe science in uncompromising terms tell us that everything subjective is excluded on principle, that science must be purely objective so that the real truth of nature can be arrived at. However, Polanyi totally rejects the idea of complete objectivity in any mental activity. He does not believe that knowledge can be impersonal and completely detached. He regards knowledge as an act of comprehension which involves change in the person carrying out the act of comprehension so that comprehension is an irreversible process without a permanently fixed framework within which critical testing can occur. However, he does not consider knowledge to be wholly subjective; he believes that properly directed comprehension can establish contact with "hidden reality." "Even in the exact sciences 'knowing' is an art, of which the skill of the knower, guided by his passionate sense of increasing contact with reality, is a logically necessary part."[50]

Nonetheless, scientists demand all possible objectivity during scientific research and are suspicious of any obvious or fancied subjectivity. Personal bias tends to be the most stubborn problem; bias can be the result of fondness for one's own suggestions, or jealousy of a rival's, or nationalism, or ideology.

> The moment one has offered an original explanation for a phenomenon . . . that moment affection for his intellectual child springs into existence; . . . his parental affections cluster about his intellectual offspring, and it grows more and more dear to him, so that, while he holds it seemingly tentative, it is still lovingly tentative, and not impartially tentative. . . . The mind lingers with pleasure upon facts that fall happily into the embrace of the theory, and feels a natural coldness towards those that seem refractory. Instinctively, there is a special searching-out of phenomena that support it, for the mind is led by its desires. There springs up, also, an unconscious pressing of the theory to make it fit the fact, and a pressing of the facts to make them fit the theory.[51]

Rosenthal has made an intensive study of experimenter-bias in psychological experimentation. His findings imply that bias is more the rule than the exception in such experiments and one may assume that the same causes operate in other situations. Rosenthal identified two sources of bias, motivation and expectation. (A third, noticeability, might be added.) Rosenthal tested the use of neutral assistants and found that experimenters tend to bias their assistants and in turn the assistants tend to bias their

[50] Polanyi, Michael, *Personal Knowledge*, University of Chicago Press, Chicago, 1958.
[51] Chamberlain, *op. cit.*, p. 754.

subjects, not deliberately, but through some "unprogramed and unintended communication with one another."[52]

Subjective judgments cannot be entirely eliminated. "In even the simplest matching judgment, that of reading an indicator of a pointer on the scale of a meter, we encounter biases. The untutored student, ignorant of the distortions caused by parallax, may make a faulty reading because his eyes are in the wrong position. Or he may interpolate poorly between the marks on a dial. . . . When matching involves more than the simple judgments of spatial location or coincidence on a graduated dial, new sources of error emerge. The catalog of all biasing factors may remain forever incomplete, but experience with the method of free number matching has demonstrated the etiology and remedy for a few of them."[53]

Data obtained in purely subjective ways may sometimes be dependable. The question is whether the effects of perturbations have been minimized.

> It may be objected, of course, that subjective sensations have other aspects, private and elusive qualities that no laboratory test can successfully disclose. Indeed they may, but so also may electric currents continue to harbor attributes that remain as yet undiscovered. Operational definitions do not pretend to exhaustive completeness. But if by the term private the objector means that something stands, by definition, forever immune to scrutiny, then he pronounces only idle talk.[54]

Assumptions.   Science is based as much upon assumptions as upon facts, and a change in an underlying assumption may force a restructure of science just as a change in an axiom can force a restructure of geometry. Some assumptions are easily recognized. A researcher assumes that his instruments are reliable, his data without bias, and his records without error. Less obviously, he assumes that his data are pertinent and adequate for his conclusions. More subtle assumptions are also involved. Astronomers assume that light behaves in space as it does in the laboratory. Physicists make many unquestioned assumptions about time, space, force, matter, and energy. ". . . although the concepts of Newtonian physics are also by no means so self-evident, and have to be abstracted from experience, they are so familiar from our everyday experience and our early education that we are ready to accept them without questions. It requires an intellectual effort to appreciate that there are questions to ask."[55]

---

[52] Rosenthal, Robert, "On the Social Psychology of Psychological Experiments," *American Scientist*, 51:268–283, 1963.

[53] Stevens, S. S., "On the Operation Known as Judgment," *American Scientist*, 54:385–401, 1966.

[54] *Ibid.*, p. 401.

[55] Peierles, Rudolf, reviewing Max Jammer, "The Conceptual Development of Quantum Mechanics," *Scientific American*, 216:140, 1967.

Assumptions may be built upon assumptions as one hypothesis is assumed valid and used for the foundation for another hypothesis. The resulting structure is shaky; the history of science records a number of collapses. We may soon witness another as astronomers are forced to abandon the assumption that the "red shift" can be used to determine both recessional velocity and distance of far-off bodies in space.

> The conventional interpretation of the red shift of quasi-stellar objects as a Hubble shift continues to face serious problems. Each new discovery seems to rule out most previous models of these remarkable objects. . . . The usual assumption is that quasi-stellar objects are at the tremendous distances of billions of light-years given by the Hubble relationship of distance and recessional velocity. . . . The basic difficulty is that quasars are not even remotely of galactic size and nature, and thus may be local objects, with red shift due to relativistic velocities.[56]

Scientists usually discuss their major assumptions when writing for their colleagues, knowing that the latter will certainly raise these issues otherwise in critical letters and reviews. Note the following discussion in an article which describes the behavior of cells which have been separated from tissues and kept in cultures:

> I wish to examine two particular assumptions which, either singly or in combination, are widely held necessary in order to account for sorting out and for tissue reconstruction. These assumptions are (1) that the segregating cells exhibit actively directed movements, and (2) that they display qualitatively selective mutual adhesion. . . . Almost all authors who have dealt with this problem have in addition assumed that the differences in adhesiveness between the different types of cells are type specific, at least through the period during which sorting out occurs. Ample justification for this assumption is to be found in the experimental literature, as I have pointed out. Beyond this point, each additional assumption increases the risk of error.[57]

Philosophers recognize even more fundamental assumptions. For example, is our whole concept of the universe—flowing time, three-dimensional space, causal relationships—merely an artifact of our limited sensory impressions? Such assumptions may prevent us from dealing with the truth, or at least with alternatives which are rich in potentialities.

Inductive and deductive reasoning.   Modern science is often spoken of as being inductive, but deduction plays a no less important role. The inductive process seeks to establish general laws from data and can be described

---

[56] Terrell, James, "Quasi-Stellar Objects: Possible Local Origin," *Science*, 154:1281, 1966.

[57] Steinberg, Malcolm, "Reconstruction of Tissues by Dissociated Cells," *Science*, 141:401, 1963.

as proceeding from the specific to the general; it shapes a mass of raw data into a coherent, comprehensible whole. The deductive process makes inferences about specific situations from generalizations—reasoning from the general to the specific. Deduction is used for predicting and is especially important for the testing of hypotheses: "From the hypothesis consequences are deduced such that their failure to occur would disprove the hypothesis."[58]

Induction is a common reasoning process but philosophers find it troublesome because it is not a demonstrable form of inference.[59]

> Deep and troublesome questions are involved. Consider the question: When and why does a single piece of past evidence give useful information about a future situation? If one takes a single piece of copper and determines that it conducts electricity, then it seems sensible to suppose that other future pieces of copper will also conduct electricity. But if we pick a man at random and determine that his name is John, this does not at all lend credence to the idea that all other men are named John. The first of these seems to lead to a "lawlike" statement, and the second to an "unlawlike" statement; but no one, so far as I know, has ever been able to give workable form to the distinction. In fact, in spite of many attempts to make induction intellectually tolerable, the matter remains a mess.[60]

From a practical viewpoint, if not from a philosophical one, the deductive process is also flawed. Should the premises from which an inference is made be false, the inference is also false; therefore, conclusions derived by deduction should be suspect until the premises have been examined. In contrast, the inductive process always starts with truths but the reasoning may be wrong; conclusions derived by induction should be suspect until they are tested.

Two varieties of deduction in common use are interpolation and extrapolation. The calibration of a mercury thermometer illustrates both processes. After the freezing and boiling points of water have been established, the tube between the marks is divided into 100 equal spaces (interpolation). Then additional spaces of the same length are laid off beyond the freezing and boiling points (extrapolation). The calibration involves two assumptions: (1) the mercury expands uniformly throughout the range of the thermometer, and (2) the tube has a uniform bore.

Figure 1 illustrates some of the problems of interpolation and extrapolation. The data, as is commonly the case, fail to give a complete picture of the relationships. It can be assumed that the relationship is linear as indicated by the solid line or nonlinear as indicated by the dashed line.

[58] Simpson, G. G., "Biology and the Nature of Science," *Science*, 139:84, 1963.
[59] Braithwaite, *op. cit.*, p. 257.
[60] Weaver, W., "The Imperfections of Science," *Proceedings of the American Philosophical Society*, 104:5, 1960.

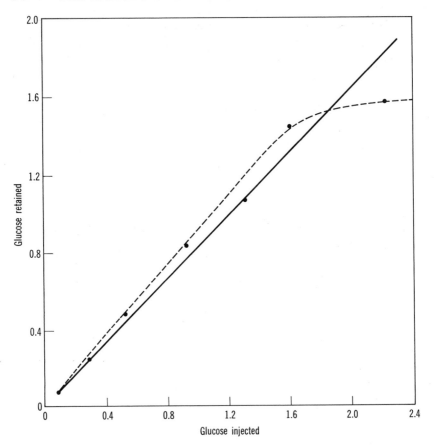

Figure 1. *Linear (solid line) and nonlinear (dashed line) interpretation of data**

However, neither line may truly describe the relationship. Interpolations based on either the straight line or the curve are probably fairly trust-worthy. Extrapolation, however, may give results that are seriously in error.

Clearly interpolations are generally more reliable than extrapolations and can be checked experimentally more easily. Extrapolations become less and less reliable and are increasingly difficult to verify as they are extended. These limitations are not always acknowledged, and some very doubtful conclusions have resulted from extrapolating into the distant past or the distant future, or into the depths of the earth, or into regions of very high temperatures.

* Data from James C. Cain and William P. Belk, "The Assimilation Rate of Intra-venously Injected Glucose in Hospital Patients," *American Journal of the Medical Sciences,* 203: 359–63, 1942.

Another variety of deductive thinking is reasoning from analogy. If a relationship is found in situation A, the same relationship might be found in similar situation B. For example, a biologist might expect to find the reproductive habits of a newly discovered species of toad like those of a closely related species. Obviously the results of such reasoning should have no authoritative value; they are useful only for guiding further investigation. The same is true for conclusions deduced from models which are also analogies.

Takahashi and Bassett have described their experiments with iron-nickel alloys under high pressures. They write, "We conclude, therefore, that the earth's core probably consists of iron-nickel alloys and is similar in composition to iron-nickel meteorites. In all likelihood, the inner core is solid and crystalline, with the atoms of the alloy packed in a hexagonal arrangement, and the outer core fluid, with the atoms closely packed but in a less orderly configuration."[61] Such a conclusion hardly seems justified; the most that has been shown is that the earth's core *could be* as described.

Cause and effect relationships.   Many believe that part of the scientist's creed is a belief that causes can be found for all conditions. Two centuries ago, David Hume pointed out that there is no intrinsic relationship between cause and effect that can be perceived by the human mind. A change in one condition and a subsequent change in a second condition can be perceived, but any relationship between the two can only be surmised. Bertrand Russell has denied that an event can have a unique cause. William Beck calls the quest "a futile search for certainty."[62] Perhaps the search for cause-effect relationships is the Holy Grail of science. At any rate, the search is difficult.

In an isolated two-component system, a cause-effect relationship ought to be detected with ease; a shift in the fulcrum of a lever is immediately followed by a redistribution of forces. The relationship would seem obvious. But a truly isolated, two-component system is only a product of the imagination; even the lever has several components and several forces acting on it.

Assume a "black box" with a change in imput A followed immediately by a change in output Z. It is logical to assume that the change in A caused the change in $Z(A \to Z)$. However, the change in Z might have been coincidental; if the operation could not be repeated exactly, the assumption would remain doubtful. Also, there is no certainty that A acted directly upon Z; the black box might contain a vast network of systems together with any number of unsuspected imputs.

---

[61] Takahashi, T., and W. A. Bassett, "The Composition of the Earth's Interior," *Scientific American*, 212:108, 1965.

[62] Beck, *op. cit.*, p .74.

It is possible that A → B → C → D → Z. It may be that A → B → Z, but that B is destroyed in the process so that the relationship cannot be verified. Or perhaps B can operate only after it matures, or under a given set of internal conditions.

Not uncommonly the black box is acted upon by more than one imput, each of which affects different internal components. Many experiments with animals are questionable because the mere presence of an observer adds an imput whose influence cannot be determined. Sometimes imputs that have acted in the past condition present output. There is evidence that the behavior of laboratory animals may be conditioned by imputs acting on the ancestors of the animals. Delbruck reminds us that "any living cell carries within it the experiences of a billion years of experimentation by its ancestors."[63]

With living organisms cause-effect relationships are the most difficult to establish. The so-called molecular biologists—the *reductionists*—work mostly at the level below the cell and their questions do not involve great complications; they have broken open the black box and are investigating the components. The *compositionists* point out that when the black box is broken life ends, and that conclusions about the interactions of the separate parts are of doubtful validity when applied to the living organism.

Problems involved in the search for causes in living organisms are formidable; one can see why many scientists are attracted by the reductionist approach. Ernst Mayr asks the cause for a single bird's migration from New Hampshire in late August:

> . . . there is an immediate set of causes of the migration, consisting of the physiological condition of the bird interacting with the photoperiodicity and drop in temperature. We might call these the *proximate* causes of migration. The other two causes, the lack of food during the winter and the genetic disposition of the bird, are the *ultimate* causes. . . . There is always a proximate set of causes and an ultimate set of causes; both have to be explained and interpreted for a complete understanding of the given phenomenon.[64]

One might assume that physical scientists have less trouble with cause-effect relationships. However, when physicists began to study the universe of elementary particles, their viewpoint towards cause and effect shifted. The practical and useful concept of a necessary causal connection between one natural occurence and another was thrown in doubt:

> We have learned to look upon the overwhelming majority of . . . processes as mass phenomena produced by an immensely large number of single

[63] Delbruck, M., *Transactions of the Connecticut Academy of Arts and Sciences*, 38:173, 1949.

[64] Mayr, Ernst, "Cause and Effect in Biology," *Science*, 134:1503, 1961.

individual entities. And we have further learned that the extraordinary precise and exact regularity which we observe . . . is due to . . . a transition from relatively well-ordered conditions among groups of atoms and molecules to less orderly conditions. . . . The exact laws which we observe are "statistical laws." . . . these laws appear all the more clearly the greater the number of individuals that cooperate in the phenomenon. And the statistical laws are even more clearly manifested when the behavior of each individual entity is not strictly determined, but conditioned only by chance. . . . And so we have the paradox, from the point of view of the physicists, that chance lies at the root of causality.[65]

Evidence and proof. Distinctions much like those found in law exist between scientific evidence and proof, and between different types of evidence. The best evidence is direct, either seen or obtained by other senses. Even the use of sensory aids may diminish the value of evidence, depending upon the amount and kind of alteration of the signal and the assumptions that must be made in interpreting the data. Direct evidence is most convincing when observations have been repeated often enough to minimize sensing errors and under conditions that minimize bias. Data obtained by neutral observers are preferred.

Evidence that can be applied only through inference and assumption is indirect or circumstantial. Grooved and scratched pebbles in a gravel bank support the hypothesis of previous glaciation only be assuming that the markings were produced by glacial action and that they could not be produced by some other agency.

Acceptance of evidence is a subjective matter. Uncritical individuals may give the same weight to circumstantial as to direct evidence and may not differentiate between the two. Critical individuals examine both the quantity and quality of direct evidence and consider that circumstantial evidence is supporting but not conclusive.

Evidence is collected for the purpose of proving hypotheses, but the question arises, "What is proof?" There is no easy answer; proof is a matter of each individual's judgment. In general, direct evidence is accepted as proof of an hypothesis though critical individuals demand evidence that is substantial both in quantity and quality. Scientists may admit partial proof of a broad hypothesis if evidence supports part but not all.

Wilson warns of the importance of distinguishing between a condition which is *necessary* for the truth of a statement and one which is *sufficient*.[66] To test the hypothesis that a falling body near the earth falls with an acceleration of 32/ft./sec./sec., one may deduce that the body falls 16 feet during the first second. To support the hypothesis, a successful test of this prediction is *necessary* but not *enough*. Successful predictions for

[65] Schrödinger, *op. cit.*, pp. 41–51.
[66] Wilson, *op. cit.*, p. 29.

other intervals of time are also necessary but are not sufficient. Obviously complete proof is impossible.

> . . . It is an interesting question, but one which is not easily answered—just at what point in the gradual accumulation of circumstantial evidence can the latter be accepted as adequate for demonstrating the truth of a proposition? Perhaps the most that we can say is that, in practice, this point is mainly determined by the multiplicity of independent sources from which the evidence is derived; if several lines of argument based on apparently unrelated data converge on, and mutually support, the same general conclusion, the probability that this conclusion is correct may appear so high as to carry conviction to the mind of unbiased observers.[67]

There are precedents for accepting circumstantial evidence as proof. Most geologists, if not all, accept Pleistocene glaciation as an unquestionable fact. Many biologists consider organic evolution proven. The notion of the particulate nature of matter underlies modern thinking in physics and chemistry. It is possible, of course, that acceptance of these hypotheses is as much because of lack of a reasonable alternative as to the weight of supporting evidence.

> The physicists of the period from 1912 to 1930 considered it as established beyond reasonable doubt that only electrical forces could account for intramolecular attraction. Arguments for the insufficiency of this explanation were rejected as unscientific because no other principles of molecular interaction appeared conceivable. This reminds me of the impatience with which most biologists set aside today all the difficulties of the current selectionist theory of evolution, because no other explanation that can be accepted as scientific appears conceivable. This kind of argument based on the absence of any alternative that is accepted as scientific, may often be valid, but it seems to me the most dangerous application of scientific authority.[68]

Many scientists expect no absolute proof. They accept ideas tentatively and utilize them as far as possible, but they keep their minds open for new and better ideas.

> "Science never proves anything in an absolute sense. It accumulates data by observation and measurement. From an assemblage of such data the scientist constructs a hypothesis, a formula that expresses the relationships he finds." As soon as further observations show that the working hypothesis is faulty, it is replaced by another which seems more nearly correct. "Fortunately, scientific endeavor does not have to be perfect to yield results. The magnificent structure of dynamics was based on a differential calculus

[67] Clark, W., "The Crucial Evidence for Human Evolution," *American Scientist,* 47:299–300, 1959.
[68] Polanyi, Michael, "The Potential Theory of Adsorption," *Science,* 141:1010, 1963.

that was, logically, full of holes." Kepler's laws explaining planetary motion were based on calculations now shown to be mere approximations. Even the Euclidean underpinnings of Newton's iron law of gravitation have become only one of the possible systems of geometry.[69]

Scientific explanation.   "It is often said that the objective of physics is the explanation of nature, or at least of inanimate nature. What do we mean by explanation?" asks Eugene Wigner, the Nobel laureate.[70] A dictionary tells us that an explanation makes something understandable but that merely leads to the question "What is understanding?" Warren Weaver says that an explanation makes a questioner feel "intellectually comfortable."[71] Braithwaite says an explanation provides intellectual satisfaction.[72]

> it is worth noting . . . that there is continuing and often hectic disagreement among philosophers about aspects of the nature of explanation. . . . Some have held that there is no real difference between *description* and *explanation*. Others have taken the position that all scientific explanation is circular. Still another conception holds that explanation consists in the systematic reduction of the unfamiliar to the familiar.[73]

Weaver says that ". . . a scientist is very likely to say that he 'understands' a phenomenon if he can predict and control it. If he can express this in mathematical equations, and if he can thus relate the phenomenon to a wide range of other phenomena, then he is likely to consider the explanation satisfactory and complete."[74] Wigner says that physicists usually seek to describe rather than to truly explain: "An explanation is the establishment of a few simple principles which describe the properties of what is to be explained. . . . It is clear that, in this sense, physics does not endeavor to explain nature."[75]

Weaver recognizes two general types of explanations: The first . . . and by far the more popular consists of explaining something by *restating or describing the unfamiliar in terms of the familiar*. . . . The second . . . characteristically describes a phenomenon in terms which are almost indefinitely *less* familiar, or in any event more basic and abstract than the phenomenon or statement being explained."[76] He illustrates the first type,

[69] Bush, Vannevar, quoted in *Time*, May 7, 1965, p. 81.

[70] Wigner, *op. cit.* p. 995.

[71] Weaver, Warren, "Scientific Explanation," *Science*, 143:1297, 1964.

[72] Braithwaite, *op. cit.*, p. 319.

[73] Beck, *op. cit.*, p. 177.

[74] Weaver, *op. cit.*, p. 1297.

[75] Wigner, *op. cit.*, p. 995.

[76] Weaver, *op. cit.*, p. 1298.

which he says moves horizontally, with an explanation of electromagnetic radiation in terms of ripples on water. He illustrates the second, which he says moves vertically, with an explanation of a geometric theorem in terms of its logical development from another theorem.

Obviously, both of Weaver's types have limitations. The first type often involves analogies which have few actual similarities with the situations being explained. The second type, carried back step by step, ends at the bottom with a set of assumptions.

Explanations are sometimes no more than giving names to phenomena. The tendency of a body to remain at rest is often explained in relation to inertia, which of course is defined as the tendency of a body to remain at rest. Beck cites another example of circular explanations: "The physical basis of life is protoplasm."[77]

Braithwaite divides explanations into two classes according to the nature of the questions asked: "When an adult asks 'Why f?' of a particular matter of fact f he is usually wanting either a *causal* explanation expressed by the sentence 'Because of g' or a *teleological* explanation expressed by the sentence 'In order that g'."[78]

Causal explanations tend to provide satisfaction, perhaps because we are so strongly endoctrinated with the axiom "every event has a cause." Nevertheless, causes remain difficult to isolate. "I doubt that there is a scientist who would question . . . that a causal explanation can be given to biological events. Yet such an explanation will often have to be so unspecific and so purely formal that its explanatory value can certainly be challenged."[79]

Teleology is the doctrine of final cause—the doctrine that the end determines the means. Explanations of rational human acts are teleological; a man plants tomatoes so that he will have tomatoes to eat. It is logical for mankind to look for similar explanations concerning the things of the world about him. However, the limitations of teleological thinking became obvious long ago in the physical sciences. A person may ask what lightning is with the expectation of arriving at a testable answer. But to ask what lightning is for can lead only to speculation and no farther. Consequently teleology almost disappeared from the physical sciences before 1800, emphasis being shifted from final causes to first causes. It became almost dogma for the physical scientist to refrain from asking "What for?"

Teleology has been a much more serious problem in the biological sciences. Inevitably, processes like food-getting, hibernation, and migration

---

[77] Beck, *op. cit.*, p. 178.
[78] Braithwaite, *op. cit.*, p. 319–320.
[79] Mayr, *op. cit.*, p. 1503.

are interpreted in terms of the ends being served. Until about a century ago, biological phenomena were commonly explained either as part of a design by "Nature" or "The Creator" or as a result of deliberate efforts on the part of an organism's ancestors.

Many professional biologists have become self-conscious about teleology and try to avoid it in their explanations. Simpson recommends a broader interpretation of the idea. He believes that it is legitimate to ask "What purpose does a structure or function serve?", and "How did the structure or function come to be?" This implies that there *are* goal-directed phenomena in nature, that through natural selection final ends (survival under certain conditions) determine the means.[80] Mayr is in general agreement:

> . . . An individual who . . . has been "programed" can act purposefully.
> . . . A bird that starts migration, an insect that selects its host plant.
> . . . act purposefully because they have been programed to do so. . . .
> Natural selection does its best to favor the production of codes guaranteeing behavior that increases fitness.[81]

Self-examination.   Scientific thinking is more than an attempt to understand nature; it is also an attempt to understand itself, to look into the ways by which men arrive at their conclusions about nature. An intelligent person cannot, to paraphrase Poincaré, believe everything or believe nothing. What then can an intelligent person believe and what must he reject, and what can he accept with varying degrees of reservation?

Scientists have always concerned themselves with these questions, indeed physics was once called "natural philosophy." But never more than today have mature scientists spent more effort in examining their processes of reasoning. Investigations into the particulate nature of matter, quantum mechanics, and acceptance of the principle of indeterminacy have undermined notions of nature that once were never questioned; even the most reluctant scientist has been forced to look closely at his ways of thinking.

Addressing the 1964 National Science Teachers Association, Cohen outlined a few of the problems (some discussed earlier in this chapter) that face thinking scientists:[82]

1. What is an explanation? Are the laws of natural phenomena descriptions or perhaps conceptual umbrellas which cover distinct types of phenomena? Are they causal?

[80] Simpson, G. G., "Biology and the Nature of Science," *Science,* 131:966, 1960.

[81] Mayer, *op. cit.,* p. 81.

[82] Cohen, Robert S., "Individuality and Common Purpose: The Philosophy of Science." *The Science Teacher,* 31:27–28, May 1964.

2. What is a causal explanation? Is cause a metaphor derived from the daily life of actions and effects? If so, where is the active agent and the causal connection? Where in the difficult indeterminacy of microphysics do we locate causal understanding?

3. Is it true that reversals of time may occur so that effects may occur at a moment prior to their sources? If so, how shall we understand our deeply intuitive feeling for past and future?

4. To what extent do successful predictions validate a theory? To what extent do negative outcomes falsify our theories? How much are present theories "stretched" to cover uncomfortable facts?

5. Can we understand the twin characteristics of every experiment—accuracy and vagueness—and can we pinpoint by experiment simple properties in the world that is so grossly complicated?

6. We work with ideally isolated factors and parts; we never seek the whole. So we must ask, is the universe the simple additive sum of the isolates? Is it to be understood as a superposition of externally described forces and effects and entities? How shall we best express the old truth of biology that function depends upon position within the whole, and that individuals run in accordance with the whole of which they form a part?

7. How has the experimenter distorted the object of his search? Do we know only what we observe, and do we observe an object only in its relatedness to our observing selves? Is there no object other than the observer?

These and a dozen more similar problems bother the men of science who look beyond the test tube and the microscope. The basic problems of science are not the discovery of another nuclear particle or another item in the DNA code, but the ways to bring our ideas about the world into agreement with what we see.

> The whole of science is nothing more than a refinement of everyday thinking. It is for this reason that the critical thinking of the physicist cannot possibly be restricted to the examination of the concepts of his own specific field. He cannot proceed without considering critically a much more difficult problem, the problem of analyzing the nature of everyday thinking.[83]

[83] Einstein, Albert, "Physics and Reality," *Journal of the Franklin Institute*, 221:349, 1936.

SUGGESTED ACTIVITIES

1. Ask the pupils of a class to write briefly their understanding of the nature of science. Categorize the results.
2. Choose a random sample of pages in a science textbook. Classify each informational statement as fact, generalization, hypothesis, or definition. Estimate the percent of the information made up by each class.
3. Many people contend that science is factual and art is creative. Debate this issue.
4. Discuss whether the statement that the earth rotates on its axis is a fact, a generalization, or a theory.
5. Set up a teaching situation in which an hypothesis is formulated and tested.
6. Prepare a laboratory activity which leads to deductive reasoning. Prepare another that leads to inductive reasoning.

SUGGESTED READINGS

Beck, William S., *Modern Science and the Nature of Life*, Doubleday, Garden City, N.Y. 1961.

Braithwaite, Richard B., *Scientific Explanation*, Harper, New York, 1960.

d'Abro, A., *The Evolution of Scientific Thought*, Dover Publications, New York, 1950.

Nash, Leonard K., *The Nature of the Natural Sciences*, Little, Brown and Co., Boston, 1963.

Schrödinger, Erwin, *Science, Theory and Man*, Dover Publications, New York, 1957.

Simpson, George G., "Biology and the Nature of Science," *Science*, 139:81–88, 1963.

Standen, Anthony, *Science is a Sacred Cow*, E. P. Dutton & Co., New York, 1950.

Weaver, Warren, "The Imperfections of Science," Proceedings of the American Philosophical Society, 104:5, 1960.

———. "Scientific Explanation," *Science*, 143:1297–1300, 1964.

Wilson, E. Bright, Jr.., *An Introduction to Scientific Research*, McGraw-Hill Book Co., New York, 1952.

Chapter 2

The Objectives of

Science Teaching

A CLASSBELL RINGS. THIRTY PUPILS HURRY FROM THE SCIENCE CLASSROOM—
thirty boys and girls who soon will be taking jobs or entering college or
serving in the armed forces, thirty adolescents who soon will be adults
and voting citizens, thirty young people who soon will be marrying and
setting up homes and having children.

What happened to these young people while they were in the
classroom? Do they know a bit more about themselves? Can they now
adjust more easily to new situations? Have they had increased practice in
meeting problems? Are they a little better prepared for what lies ahead?

Whatever happened to these pupils depended almost entirely upon
the teacher with whom they spent the hour. If he recognized the potentialities of the science program and utilized them fully, his pupils emerged
from the classroom better individuals for having entered it. But if he
viewed his task narrowly, or if he refused to accept his true responsibilities,
the time his pupils spent with him was in all likelihood largely wasted.

Teaching is more than the presentation of facts. Teaching is the
development of new ways of thinking—a development that reveals itself in
increased skills with the problems of life, in new habits of action, in more
desirable attitudes, in a benefited personality, and in an improved character.

The objectives of science education are broad. They demand a program rich in experiences that leads toward the intellectual, psychological, and social growth of young people.

A science program must be judged by its effects on individual pupils, not by the number of textbook pages read or the percentage of a syllabus covered. Science can justify its place in the curriculum only when it produces important changes in young people—changes in their ways of thinking, in their habits of action, and in the values they assign to what they have and what they do.

BACKGROUND OF OBJECTIVES

Science teachers have long recognized the need for sound objectives in curriculum planning. In an examination of over three thousand statements written from 1901 to 1950 by secondary school teachers, Paul Hurd noted that the objectives of science teaching were the teachers' first consideration in planning curriculum.[1] Objectives strongly influence the organization of the curriculum and at the same time they provide the guidelines for the

---

[1] Hurd, Paul DeHart, "The Educational Concepts of Secondary School Science Teachers," *School Science and Mathematics*, 54:89–96, 1954.

selection of teaching techniques. In the development and planning of a science curriculum it is important to know and understand the purpose for which the curriculum is being established.

To understand the present, one must know what has happened in the past. This is certainly true regarding the understanding of the development of objectives of science teaching. The history of science education reveals the conditions under which science teaching objectives were formulated and the conditions under which they changed.

The period of college domination (1870 to 1910). Between 1870 and 1910 the secondary school science curriculum was greatly influenced by the faculties of colleges and universities. It was during this period that universities began to require physics for college entrance. Shortly after, chemistry also was required for admission to college. It is easy to see how these requirements influenced the science offerings in the secondary schools. Physics became the most important science offering in the high school with chemistry as a close second. Biology courses which were really combined one-year courses in botany, zoology, and physiology were introduced. These courses had little or no integration. Geology was in the curriculum, but its popularity declined towards the beginning of the century.

The period of college domination marked the beginning of science as a formal discipline in the secondary schools. With this formalization, the popularity of science diminished. Courses were established without regard to the students' interests and need to understand their environment.

Laboratory instruction became an important part of the science offerings. The laboratory was highly specialized, often dull and stereotyped. Science was presented as a body of information in these laboratory courses and was of little or no practical value to the pupils. The main aims were to develop the ability to reason, to observe, and to concentrate.

Several Committees such as the Committee of Ten in 1892, the Committee of Fifteen in 1895, and the Committee of College Entrance Requirements in 1895 recommended that science be introduced into the curriculum earlier than the secondary school. This recommendation as well as other factors promoted the reorganization of the schools into the 6–3–3 pattern.

The period of reorganization (1910 to 1930). A number of important changes occurred in the organization of the schools between 1910 and 1930 which greatly influenced the science program. It was during this period that the high school population markedly increased. There was a rapid growth of the 6–3–3 organizational pattern in the schools and the junior high school movement was at its peak. General science was introduced in the curriculum at grade nine while biology became a tenth-year subject. Physics and chemistry were taught at either grades eleven or twelve.

General science developed very rapidly in the 1920's and was even introduced in the seventh grade in some schools. The unitary aspect of general science influenced the development of many types of integrated courses. This influence caused a de-emphasis in the specialized courses such as physics and chemistry. Both biology and general science stressed the study of the environment and the functional aspects of science.

The reorganization of the schools resulted in curriculum innovations which in turn influenced the objectives of science teaching. Although the objectives of teaching science varied throughout the country, teachers were still primarily interested in presenting scientific information. They were not interested in teaching the principles and generalizations of science. Some teachers formulated life-centered and pupil-centered objectives, but these appeared to be the exception rather than the rule.

The National Education Association "Commission on the Reorganization of Secondary Education" issued a report in 1920 which recommended the reorganization of the science program in light of the seven cardinal principles of education. The cardinal principles stated by the Commission are:

1. Health
2. Command of fundamental process
3. Worthy home membership
4. Vocation
5. Citizenship
6. Worthy use of leisure time
7. Ethical character

Attempts were made to teach general science and biology so that the seven cardinal principles could be realized. Physics and chemistry still continued to be college preparatory courses and were not concerned with life centered objectives.

Although the mastery of subject matter continued to be the primary aim of science instruction in the 1920's and 1930's, a great deal of work was done on the formulation of major generalizations that could be used as long range objectives to give continuity to the science program.

Pre-World War II and World War II (1930 to 1945). Between 1930 and 1945 the junior high school movement leveled off, and general science was introduced in the seventh and eighth grades. Advanced general science courses were proposed for grades eleven and twelve to replace physics and chemistry. Biology became a basic science offering. World War II brought about a great emphasis on the practical aspects of science, and consequently courses such as aviation, photography, and electricity were introduced into the curriculum.

Many committees published lists of objectives for teaching science during this period. The most prominent and important list of statements of objectives was published in 1932 by the National Association for the Study of Education.[2] A list of 38 generalizations which was designed to give direction to the entire science program from grades one through twelve was proposed. One of the major strengths of these statements was the balance they provided within the traditional subject matter areas and the interrelationships they promoted between these areas. These objectives represented a broad approach to the problems involved in planning.

The use of major generalizations as objectives and as outlined in the *Thirty-first Yearbook* had its limitations. Science was presented as a body of facts and pupils looked at science that way. The other benefits of science instruction derived from problem solving techniques, and the development of certain attitudes and appreciations were neglected.

The Commission on Secondary Curriculum of the Progressive Education Association in 1935, published a report, *Science in General Education*,[3] which stressed the need to correlate science with the problems of living and indicated desirability of selecting content that was useful to boys and girls. The Commission also regarded reflective thinking and economic relationships as important objectives of science teaching.

Post World War II (1945 to 1955). By 1945, about 75 percent of boys and girls of high school age were attending secondary school. More science courses were introduced to handle increasing enrollments. Courses such as earth science and physical science were offered; general science was an important offering of the science program. Biology became popular, but physics and chemistry showed a marked decline in enrollment. Science fairs and congresses became common during this period.

Science teaching placed notable emphasis on the functional aspects of science. Many organizations such as the National Association of Secondary School Principals, National Education Association and the American Association of School Administrators published statements of objectives for the teaching of science in the secondary schools. The most important statement concerning objectives of science instruction was that of the National

---

[2] National Society for the Study of Education, "A Program for Science Teaching," *Thirty-first Yearbook*, Part I, Public School Publishing Co., Bloomington, Illinois, 1932.

[3] Progressive Education Association, *Science in General Education*, Appleton-Century-Crofts, New York, 1938.

Society for the Study of Education as presented in the *Forty-sixth Year-book*, Part I.[4] The development of objectives in science education between 1932 and 1946 were summarized; during this period, science instruction followed the trends of objectives in general education. Less emphasis was placed on the memorization of information and more emphasis on teaching boys and girls the functional aspects of science. The understanding of scientific principles and developing problem-solving abilities were stressed to a greater degree than in the past. However, teaching scientific information was still considered to be the most important aim of science teaching. After World War II teachers stressed such objectives as developing scientific concepts, principles, skills and attitudes. Skill in problem solving became a primary aim of science education. An infallible scientific method that could be used as a pattern to gather information was deemed possible. The laboratory took on a new importance as the primary place where this method was used. Skills in gathering and testing data, in identification and solving of problems and in the examination of the validity of conclusions were strongly encouraged as the aims of science education. Nevertheless, the older, well established aim of teaching scientific information was not abandoned as being unworthy; instead, the relative values of the objectives were reassessed as the newer goals were added.

The National Society for the Study of Education[5] published the following categories of objectives in 1947 which reflect this type of teaching:

1. Functional information of facts.
2. Functional concepts.
3. Functional understanding of principles.
4. Instrumental skills.
5. Problem-solving skills.
6. Attitudes.
7. Appreciations.
8. Interests.

The objectives in the Forty-sixth Yearbook are stated in such broad terms that their implications to science teaching may not be immediately obvious. The professional literature of the late 1940's cites many attempts to break down these broad objectives into useable form. Curriculum groups spent a considerable amount of time on this aspect of planning.

[4] National Society for the Study of Education, *Forty-sixth Yearbook*, Part I, University of Chicago Press, Chicago, 1947.
[5] *Ibid.*

Only when a variety of experiences are incorporated into the science curriculum can pupils begin to advance toward the attainment of these broad objectives. Measuring goals of such scope is difficult if not impossible.

Revolution in science teaching (1955 to present). The most innovative and drastic changes have been proposed for the science program since 1955. It was during this time that pupil population increased significantly in the secondary schools. The enrollments in science courses also increased greatly. The Russians launched the first space satellite which made the public very science conscious. The National Science Foundation and other federal agencies became interested in the status of science teaching in the public schools with the advent of the space age. These agencies discovered that science courses throughout the country were staffed with unqualified teachers as well as teachers with outdated or poor science and mathematics backgrounds.

The National Science Foundation initiated a program to improve the science and mathematics backgrounds of teachers. Colleges and universities set up institute programs sponsored by the National Science Foundation which offered courses in science and mathematics to up-date the backgrounds of teachers. Scientists tried to stimulate changes in the science offerings. As a consequence, national curriculum committees composed of scientists and mathematicians were established to examine the content and approaches in science courses. Unlimited federal funds became available to bring about change in science and mathematics teaching.

Since 1955, a number of these national committees have been attempting to re-evaluate the aims and objectives of science instruction in a rapidly changing atomic and space age. Under the influence of professional scientists and science educators, new science programs have emerged which attempt to present science as a means of investigation and also attempt to conceptualize scientific knowledge. The new approaches such as Biological Sciences Curriculum Study (BSCS), Chemical Bond Approach (CBA), and others stress the structure of science. Pupils are provided with experiences which will make them aware of the methods and processes of science. The programs place a great deal of emphasis on laboratoy experiences which are open-ended—that is, having no known or preconceived results. Pupils spend a great deal of time in the laboratory performing experiments which are truly investigations rather than redoing the demonstrations and cook-book exercises that serve only to reconfirm previously known facts. The pupils are involved with the anticipation of things learned and to be learned. Not only is the pupil directly involved with discovering, but he also learns that science has its limitations.

A further insight into the type of learning skills which can be gained from these new programs is shown from the following excerpt from BSCS materials.[6] The statement is typical of all the recent study group programs.

The remarks are made to the pupil in a section entitled "The Logic of the Research Experience You Have Just Completed."

In these laboratory exercises we have used a variety of the general approaches employed in modern biological research. We might classify the ones we have used in this series as:

1. Observing structures and actions.
2. Correlating structural changes with action.
3. Analyzing data from experimental measurements, particularly for testing hypotheses quantitatively.
4. Designing specific experiments to test specific possibilities in specific cases.
5. Rationalizing about a structure by comparing it with concepts from other fields, such as engineering.
6. Making artificial models that will duplicate certain actions.
7. Combining data from anatomy, microanatomy (including electron microscopy), chemistry, and changes during action (functional).
8. Considering what is evidence, deduction, interpretation, and proof.
9. And last, but by no means least, giving our imagination free play for developing novel concepts and ideas for testing.

The importance of the last point cannot be overemphasized. Somebody has got to have the "bright idea" as to what can be tested that will be relevant to a particular question. Somebody or some several bodies—also have to make decisions as to which questions are worth the work of finding the answers. Data, as mere data, are sterile items. What we really want are data that bear in a discernable way on some question of interest to us.

In all research one must ask what questions may pertinently be asked. What are the pertinent observations needed? For which of these do methods exist for obtaining an answer? What will we consider (accept) as an acceptable answer? It could be said to be proverbial, that if you ask a nonsensical question, all the answers you can possibly get will also be nonsensical!

There is no question that the most significant and the most imaginative and innovative curricular changes have occurred since 1955. Many new programs have evolved and a number are still being produced. All of these approaches are attempting to lead the pupil through a series of experiences which encourage the creative process and brings him to the point where he is able to conceptualize the scientific knowledge he has obtained. He therefore ends up with an understanding and appreciation of the true nature of science and the structure and strategy of science.

[6] Richards, Glenn A., "A Laboratory Block on Interdependence of Structure and Function," *Biological Science Curriculum Study*, University of Colorado, Boulder, Colorado, 1961, p. 99.

CLASSIFICATION OF OBJECTIVES

Objectives for the science program should be determined by the needs of young people. These objectives, which may be short or long range, fall into two categories:

1. Those that can be satisfied by acquiring information and special skills. The goals may be either long or short term, and their objectives usually emphasize subject matter.
2. Those which can be satisfied by developing certain ways of thinking and acting. The goals are usually long range and represent the overall goals of the science program; they are concerned with the general education of the pupil and with his overall development over a long period of time.

The two categories of objectives listed above operate together. Each type has its special function and influence upon the program. Objectives of subject matter determine the content, give continuity to the science program, and are important in attaining the broader general education goals of the science program.

General long-range objectives provide a pattern and direction for the growth of the pupils. The realization of these objectives gives the pupil a certain level of scientific literacy, helps him develop an open-minded attitude toward new ideas, and develops the ability to interpret and draw conclusions about current controversies.

It must be realized that simply teaching an individual today's facts will not prepare him to live in tomorrow's world. If the individual possesses the abilities to think critically, to inquire rationally, and to understand and analyze scientific developments as they occur, he will then be able to adjust to living in a rapidly changing world.

Short- and long-range subject matter objectives. Pupils can learn through a single experience that a magnet can pick up bits of cobalt. They need dozens of experiences to understand that one form of energy can be converted to another. They may need hundreds of experiences to appreciate the statement, "All life comes from life."

An objective calling for the learning of the magnetic properties of cobalt can be attained in a relatively short time, perhaps a few minutes. Objectives of this type, which may be called "specific objectives," are used to govern field trips, experiments, and other limited activities. Two or three short activities may be established for a single lesson.

Other objectives of subject matter are so broad that a year's program or even twelve years of schooling are not enough for their attainment. These broad objectives should be treated as aims that give direction to a program rather than as goals for rapid attainment.

In a well-organized program specific subject matter objectives are set up so that they lead toward broad objectives. When properly related, a number of experiments with simple machines, each directed toward one specific objective, can bring about an understanding of compound machines.

Formulating short-range subject matter objectives.   Short range subject matter objectives may be used to determine the type of demonstration which will take place during a classroom period, or the reading assignment or any other learning activity which is used in day-to-day classroom teaching. A specific learning such as "Kingfishers and bank swallows nest in holes in sand banks" can be the outcome of a field trip while an outcome of a laboratory experience might be "Zinc displaces hydrogen from hydrochloric acid."

The list below gives the specific learnings set up as objectives for a unit on fire; each of these objectives may govern several activities:

1. A fire will not continue to burn in a closed space.
2. Solid and liquid fuels are frequently changed into gaseous form before combustion occurs.
3. In a luminous flame, combustion takes place when the combustible gases come in contact with air.
4. A proper mixture of combustible gas and air results in a nonluminous flame.
5. The amount of heat required to raise a combustible substance to its ignition point depends upon the nature of the substance, the amount of water present, and other factors.
6. Combustion occurs more readily when the combustible substance is in a finely divided state.
7. Fires may often be started by means of friction.
8. Heat produced by slow oxidation can ignite some substances.
9. The substance in the air that supports combustion is called oxygen.
10. Fire is chemical union of oxygen with a combustible substance.

The more limited an objective, the more likely that it can be attained within the allotted time and the less the danger of superficiality. The simpler the language in which it is expressed the more likely that the verbalizations of the pupils will approach the desired objective.

Various criteria may be used in the selection of short-range objectives:

1. *Usefulness.* The desired learnings should have value in the lives of the pupils.
2. *Timeless.* Learning should be concerned with material familiar at the present time; not with obsolete devices and ideas.
3. *Fitness.* The learnings should fit into a sequence leading towards a long range objective.
4. *Appropriateness.* The learnings called for should be appropriate for the maturity and backgrounds of the pupils concerned.
5. *Practicality.* Experiences needed for the development of the learnings should be possible.
6. *Meaningfulness.* Learnings should be meaningful. Pupils should want to know.

Sometimes teachers emphasize one or two of these criteria at the exclusion of others. Care must be taken to avoid this practice for the good of the learner. For example, a teacher who chooses fitness as a sole criterion would produce a totally unbalanced program and the result would be chaos. Sometimes "practicality" does not receive enough attention. Specific learnings are often set up as objectives without consideration being given to the means by which the learnings are to be attained.

A common technique for the selection of specific subject matter objectives employs the developmental approach. A major generalization is written down and under it are listed the learnings that are considered essential for partial or complete understanding of the generalization. For a unit on fire, the major generalization may have been written as "A fire is a chemical union of two or more substances," and the specific learnings as listed may have been considered as leading towards the generalization.

The specific learnings become tentative short-range objectives subject to evaluation by the criteria listed above. A program based on these objectives is logically organized, its pattern is more or less traditional, and its core is in subject-matter. Much good teaching has been done with this type of program.

A second technique for establishing limited subject matter objectives is more opportunistic than deliberate. An area for study is decided upon first. Then a survey of pertinent learning situations is made. From these a list of possible learnings is determined and set up as short-range subject matter objectives:

When planning a unit on garden soils for his ninth grade general science class, Mr. Barker listed as many suggestions for field work and experiments as his facilities permitted. These are given below.

Field Trips:
1. Collect samples of soils.
2. Observe top soil and subsoil.
3. Test pH of soil in nearby gardens.
4. Study compost heaps and humus.
5. Visit garden store to study fertilizers.

Experiments:
1. Test drainage of soils.
2. Test capillarity of soils.
3. Test water retention of soils.
4. Experiment with effects of leaching.
5. Discover effects of lime on soils.
6. Test soils for structures produced in drying.
7. Experiment with soil conditioners.
8. Test effects of humus on soils.
9. Experiment with growing plants in different soils.
10. Experiment with the effects of soil "nutrients" on plants.
11. Determine components of soils.
12. Classify soils.

Satisfied with the list, he turned to available reference books, slides, and films that he could use to supplement the learnings obtained from the firsthand learning situations. He also listed a number of activities that would help pupils summarize and organize their learnings.

Not until the last step in his planning did Mr. Barker list the learnings which he thought would result from the activities he had chosen. These became his specific subject matter objectives. They are listed below:

1. Soil drainage and capillarity vary in different types of soil.
2. Clay and humus help retain water in soil; sand and gravel increase drainage.
3. The structure of soil depends upon the relative amounts of sand, gravel, clay, and humus.
4. Good garden soils are neutral or slightly alkaline; the pH can be changed by adding lime, peat moss, and chemical fertilizers.
5. Humus is the product of decomposition of organic matter.
6. Top soil differs in structure and components from subsoil.
7. Fertilizers add components needed for proper plant growth.
8. Soil is an important natural resource that must be carefully used to avoid damage.

The above technique for establishing objectives makes full use of local resources. The only learnings expected are those that can be attained satisfactorily by the means at hand. Emphasis is put upon "learning by doing." With care in the selection of activities the specific learnings lead toward an understanding of broad generalizations.

Setting long-range subject matter objectives.   Long-range subject matter objectives can be used to give continuity to the science program, and they can be of tremendous value in developing science programs from kindergarten through grade twelve. In fact the list of 38 generalizations published by the National Society for the Study of Education in the *Thirty-first Yearbook*[7] was designed with this in mind. Five of these generalizations are listed here:

1. The sun is the chief source of energy for the earth.
2. Through interdependence of species and the struggle for existence, a balance tends to be maintained among the many forms of life.
3. The earth's position in relation to the sun and moon is a determining factor of life on earth.
4. All life comes from life and produces its own kind of living organism.
5. Matter and energy cannot be created or destroyed but may be changed from one form to another.

Teachers of the specialized sciences have not always recognized the application to their own subjects of long-range subject matter objectives. They tended to select only those generalizations they considered pertinent to their own subject. This sometimes resulted in narrowness in their courses.

Specialized courses are improved by having broad objectives. The modern curriculum programs such as the Physical Science Study Committee (PSSC) and the Chemical Educational Materials Study (CHEM) make ample use of such objectives. The PSSC program, for example, centers its curriculum around the concept that matter and energy are conserved; space, time and matter cannot be separated. This conceptual approach in the teaching of physics permits pupils to see how seemingly disparate facts are interrelated to form theories and principles of physics. The same is also true of the BSCS, CHEMS, and CBA programs.

The use of major generalizations as objectives for a unit may result in superficiality if they are treated as immediate goals; i.e. they cannot be quickly realized. To avoid this danger it is wise to subdivide a major generalization into segments, each of which is limited enough to be attained by the experiences within a unit. For example, a major generalization about machines could be subdivided in terms of the types of machines —inclined planes, levers, and pulleys—or in terms of efficiency, mechanical advantage, and so on, each of which would well merit a complete unit for proper treatment.

The teacher should always remember that long-range subject matter

---

[7] National Society for the Study of Education, *Thirty-first Yearbook*, *op. cit.*

objectives are not written for the pupils to verbalize. Verbalization alone does not add to understanding but does give an impression of mastery. Many teachers have prematurely ended their efforts at developing understandings because the statements of their pupils led them to believe that their objectives had been attained. We will come back to this point later when we discuss behavioral objectives.

Pupils and subject matter objectives.   The ideal situation is reached when pupils adopt the teacher's objectives as their own and work toward them. This happens in those portions of the program that are built upon their immediate needs. Adolescents want information about sex. Boys want to learn about automobiles and how to be physically outstanding. Girls want to learn about cosmetics and how to be attractive.

Outside these portions of the program, however, young people are less likely to accept the teacher's subject matter objectives. Few of them are imbued with the love of learning itself. They rarely show interest in inclined planes and protoplasm as abstract ideas.

The teacher who looks beyond the immediate needs of adolescents, towards some of their future needs, and towards the needs of society, may attain his subject matter goals by setting them up parallel to objectives which his pupils will accept readily. He may make use of the desires of adolescents to produce tangible things, to manipulate materials, or to work with close friends. As pupils work toward their own objectives, they develop the learnings and skills that the teacher believes are desirable.

Below is a list of a few teacher objectives and some corresponding pupil objectives that would result in the same learnings.

Teacher objectives	*Anticipated student objectives*
To show how fuses protect homes.	To overload a fuse and make it "blow."
To teach the principle of the photo-electric cell.	To set up a system that will ring a bell when a person passes nearby.
To determine the conditions needed for seed germination.	To make seeds grow.
To learn how to read a topographic map.	To find home and other familiar places on a map.
To learn the parts of a plant cell.	To use a microscope.
To understand the importance of good posture.	To be more popular.
To learn the names of common trees.	To make a leaf collection.
To study drainage in soils.	To set up an experiment that shows differences in drainage.

These are illustrative only. Pupils will react differently in different situations. Commonly several different pupil objectives must be set up for each teacher objective in order to provide for a wide range of pupil interests. The teacher must depend upon his knowledge of his own pupils in trying to set up pupil objectives.

OVERALL, LONG-RANGE GOALS OF THE SCIENCE PROGRAM

Although long- and short-range subject matter goals are good for purposes of planning and giving continuity to the science program, there is an inherent danger that teachers will use them solely in developing their courses. Simply using subject matter objectives alone will not provide a background of experiences to allow for the proper growth of pupils.

One criticism that has been voiced by scientists and science educators is that high school science teachers are presenting science as a collection of unrelated facts. Scientists have also expressed the criticisms that science teachers teach "technology" rather than science, and that teachers have confused science with technology. They indicate that pupils have not been given a chance to formulate their own problems and work out schemes for uncovering facts for themselves. In other words, science teaching has neglected to present to the pupils an understanding of the methods used by scientists to obtain information. These criticisms have stimulated a re-examination of the overall goals of science teaching to determine if they should be revised in the light of today's scientific developments.

The national study groups such as BSCS and PSSC have been responsible for much of the re-evaluation in setting the long-range objectives for science teaching. These new approaches emphasize the process and structure of science and de-emphasize the use of facts for the sake of facts. Their courses of study reflect this thinking. Other organizations such as the National Science Teachers Association and the National Education Association have made significant contributions in helping to set up long-range overall goals in science teaching that are important to pupils in a changing society.

The long-range overall objectives of secondary school science presented by the National Science Teachers Association[8] in 1961 are as follows:

[8] National Science Teachers Association, *Planning for Excellence in High School Science*, Washington, D.C., 1961. (A list of objectives for elementary school science is also included in this publication.)

A basic knowledge of the nature of the scientific enterprise. He (the pupil) should begin to understand the tentative, cumulative nature of scientific knowledge. He should have a healthy respect for the role of honest doubt and begin to recognize and use the elements of scientific process. At this point, he should be convinced of the observation experimentation approach. He should recognize that although intuition, imagination, and chance may play a part in the scientific process, it is the interaction of these on the prepared mind that is in reality operating. This implies that the student will have developed his reading ability so that he can carry on self-initiated work and has been motivated to begin study in depth. He should be able to analyze problem situations and use impersonal criteria for making judgments about the relevant and the irrelevant, the warranted and unwarranted claims. The student should also be aware of the international nature of science and the central importance of unrestricted communication among scientists. He should be familiar with the language by which this communication is made possible.

An increase in the mathematical, observational, and experimental skills. This necessitates a greater emphasis on laboratory work in the junior high school than has been true in the past. It calls for a familiarization and coordination with the new directions of junior high school mathematics so that optimum use is made of the knowledge and skills which are achieved by the students at that grade level.

Understandings related to the interrelations of science and society. Science is dependent on the social order and must have a large degree of autonomy to flourish. This indicates the need and desirability for public support of the scientific enterprise. In the other direction, society has become dependent on technological developments and scientific ways of thinking. Application can then be transferred to social problems and human values.

Increased understanding of the concepts and theories which describe and unify the fields of science. The junior high schools should continue to expand the dimensions of the pervasive ideas that were begun in the elementary school. These "ideas that travel" are a major criterion for the selection of subject matter. Such concepts and theories as those relating to the structure of matter, ionization, bonding, energy interchanges, and the periodicity of the elements are examples of these major ideas. Other criteria involve the selection of those areas which increase the students' understanding of the processes and products of science in keeping with his increasing maturity.

The purpose of American education is to provide experiences through which young people can acquire the knowledge, skills, and attitudes that lead to patterns of behavior acceptable to the democratic society in which we live. The science teacher is held responsible for contributing to the attainment of these goals, just as are the art, social studies, and mathematics teachers. It is the responsibility of the entire instructional staff to work toward these goals.

In terms of science education for all students, that is, "general education" in science, the National Science Teachers Association[9] has offered the following:

1. As a result of science education, students should habitually and skillfully employ sound thinking habits in meeting problem situations in the daily walks of life. They should exhibit reasonable, mature attitudes related to tolerance, curiosity, honest doubt, and the like. To do this, young people must have an understanding of, faith in, and direct practice with sound methods and attitudes of thought.

2. As a result of science education, students should recognize and accept their place in a society which is largely scientific in character. They should be in the process of developing a personal philosophy based on truth, understanding, and logic, rather than one based on superstition, intuition, or wishful thinking. To do this, students must acquire a working concept of the relations between science and society, science and individuals, and science and technology.

3. As a result of science education, students should develop and enjoy personal interests, some of which are related to science. They should recognize and enjoy some scientific aspects of their natural and man-made environment, and should appreciate and respect the efforts of those who made the latter possible. To do this, students must have varied and pleasant experiences in activities related to science, and should know something of the development of science and of the people who have contributed toward it.

4. As a result of science education, students should base their opinions, decisions, and actions on a reasonable background of principles and conceptual schemes in science. They should not only carry on sound thinking, they should have a fund of reliable knowledge with which to think. They should also be able to locate needed science information which is beyond the limits of personal memory. To do this, students must have adequate understanding of the broad generalizations and conceptualizations of science, as well as some command of the more important factual knowledge in science.

It should be recognized that these are long-range objectives. The final attainment of these objectives will depend on how well each teacher structures his instructional program. It should be obvious that these objectives will not just "be picked up along the way" by the pupil.

The Educational Policies Commission published "Education and the Spirit of Science,"[10] which lists the values of science in a modern world. The following is an excerpt from this publication:

The schools should help to realize the great opportunities which the development of science has made apparent in the world. They can do this

9 *Ibid.*

10 Educational Policies Commission, *Education and the Spirit of Science,* National Education Association, Washington, D.C., 1966.

by promoting understanding of values on which science is everywhere based. Although no particular scientist may fully exemplify all these values they characterize the enterprise of science as a whole. We believe that the following values underlie science:

1. Longing to know and to understand.
2. Questioning of all things.
3. Search for data and their meaning.
4. Demand for verification.
5. Respect for logic.
6. Consideration of premises.
7. Consideration of consequences.

Here then is a group of values which schools can promote without doing violence to the dignity of the individual. Here are values which are not intended to be accepted on the basis of external authority. On the contrary, they are themselves frankly intended to be challenged.

The Commission indicates that the addition of science courses would not necessarily achieve the goals they listed. Instead, these goals would be achieved through "an education which turns the child's curiosity into a life-long drive which leads students to consider seriously the various possibilities of satisfying that curiosity and the many limitations of those possibilities."

Many science teachers are not aware of the goals of general education and therefore do not realize how much the science program can do for young people. It is imperative that the teacher understand that he is dealing with human beings and that he must help these young people to reach their greatest potential so they will become good citizens of the world.

IMPORTANT GENERAL EDUCATION OBJECTIVES

Helping young people fit themselves into their society. Young people need extensive practice in working together, both in large and in small groups. The science program abounds in opportunities for group work within class periods. A large share of the desirable activities are best carried out by groups of two or four pupils each. There are also many opportunities for pupils to participate actively in larger groups. A class may be divided into groups of different interests, each group working on its own problem. Or the class may be divided into equivalent groups, each of which contains individuals of special abilities, one member being a good leader, another an artist, another a good writer, another mechanically skilled, and so on.

The science program can be used to encourage pupils to work in groups outside school hours. Pupils like to work on projects at each other's homes. They like arranging visits to see natural features of the region. They like to go in two's or three's to interview authorities for answers to special questions.

Special mention must be made of the opportunities for social participation provided by science clubs and science fairs. Once the pattern for conduct of these institutions has been established, pupils are able to conduct them with remarkably little supervision. They gain practice in conducting the affairs of the organizations. They have increased contacts with adults as they invite speakers, judges, and reporters to their functions.

Maintaining physical health and well-being.   As boys and girls advance toward maturity their need for information about themselves increases. They come less and less under the direct supervision of adults. In rebellion against the ways of childhood they are apt to refuse the counsel of parents. They need understandings that will help them make up their own rules for taking care of themselves.

The scientific approach to the care of the human body is more effective than indoctrination. Pupils who have made a survey of fire hazards in their homes understand better the need for precautions. Pupils who have made a study of pedestrian reactions at busy intersections are more likely to use caution themselves in similar situations. Pupils who have studied the dietary choices of their schoolmates are more conscious of the need for making wise decisions in selecting foods.

The scientific approach permits pupils to arrive at their own decisions. A boy or girl may refuse to accept an arbitrary statement by an adult, but if he understands the principles involved he is apt to accept the same conclusion for himself. And of great importance, he is able to substitute a new conclusion if he should be presented with new evidence.

The biological segments of the science program have long accepted responsibility for helping pupils maintain their physical health. Most of these courses include material on the study of the human body, on the nature of diseases, and on health practices advocated by health specialists.

Adolescents need help in adjusting to the experiences of sex that now face them. They need both knowledge and a frank attitude toward the topic. The purely physiological aspects of sex are easily handled in the science program. Basic understandings and a much needed vocabulary can be developed through a study of reproduction in plants and animals. Thereafter in a study of human reproduction young people find nothing unusual or mysterious.

The physical sciences can make equally important contributions, but full advantage of these opportunities is rarely taken. All adolescents are in great need of information about the behavior of objects in motion, including themselves, their bicycles, and automobiles. Older adolescents are in special need of understanding the behavior of automobiles at high speed. These understandings are best developed during the study of mechanics.

Helping pupils with personal adjustment. Adolescence is a difficult period for boys and girls. They are discarding the safe and tested relationships of childhood and starting out again to make completely new adjustments. Their values are changing rapidly; they want the status of adults and the approval of their fellows more than anything else. They tend to be abnormally conscious of their limitations and they often ignore their real strengths.

Probably the greatest help teachers can give adolescents is a sense of security. Teachers can help them recognize their strengths and compensate for their weaknesses. They can help them win the approval of their peers and find a place in the society of their fellows.

The diversified nature of the science program permits teachers to observe pupils under various conditions and thus determine their special strengths. Once these abilities have been discovered, teachers can provide opportunities for pupils to develop their talents and build the self-confidence that comes with success.

Helping pupils appraise themselves realistically. The school population of today is a varied one. Represented among the student body are all manner of special talents and skills. Rarely is there a pupil who seems to possess no capacity whatever. However, our schools have long preoccupied themselves with academic skills alone. The unhappy result has been that large numbers of pupils lacking high ability in academic work have become convinced that they are complete failures—that they lack all capacity for success.

Our society has in it a place for each person no matter what his type of ability. Indeed, our society must have individuals with different skills. For our schools to function properly they should help each pupil appraise himself realistically, give him pride in his special talents, and guide him into the role most suited to him.

The science program presents many opportunities for pupils to discover talents they did not suspect and thus to emerge from a feeling of general inadequacy. The science program also helps young people find compensating satisfactions when they are disillusioned with the abilities they hoped to possess.

Encouraging independence. The independent person comes to conclusions only after careful deliberation. He questions authority, not rebelliously, but in terms of the qualifications of that authority. He maintains reservations in accepting the conclusions of others until he has made his own investigations. His mind is always open and he is willing to change his opinions when confronted with new evidence. He is tolerant of the opinions of others and can prove them wrong without gloating. These characteristics are so typical of the true scientist that they are often referred to as the scientific attitude or the scientific way of thinking. However, they are not confined to the scientists, nor is this way of thinking confined to science subjects. Independence of thinking is universal in application.

Science teachers are in an advantageous position to develop this type of thinking. Much of the material with which they deal is commonplace. Students can solve many problems by experiment and by direct observations in the field. They can check the statements of books, teachers, and other authorities against reality. They can resolve conflicting conclusions by checking and rechecking data. Little of the material they study is controversial. They are able to make decisions without the handicaps of prejudice and superstition. They do not become emotionally involved, as when they are considering problems of religion, race, politics, and social relationships.

Independence of thinking is a product of increased pupil participation in the planning process. Pupils have opportunities to define their own problems, suggest methods of attack, delegate responsibilities, and accept their own results with no more than minimum guidance from the teacher. Independence of thinking is stifled in the teacher-dominated classroom.

Giving pupils exploratory experiences.   Every young person needs opportunities to explore his own strengths and weaknesses, his likes and his dislikes. He needs opportunities to study the world about him and the things in it. One requirement for exploration is freedom. No one can be forced to explore; he must follow his own interests. Another requirement is a broad range of situations in which to work. Pupils will not explore areas in which they feel certain of failure. They will not explore situations that seem to present no challenge.

Occasionally pupils express a wish to explore areas in which the teacher believes that the likelihood for success is small. They should have freedom to do so. It is far better for a person to discover his own limitations than to be told about them. Equally important, pupils often have unsuspected abilities that are revealed only when the pupils put themselves to the test. Pupils need opportunities to fail as well as to succeed. Only by failure can they discover their limitations. They should be able to balance failures with successes and failures should not result in condemnation and ridicule.

Among the incidental outcomes of exploratory work in the science program is an expanded acquaintance with the nature of scientific occupations. Vocational opportunities in the science field range from laboratory technicans who need little academic ability or training to research scientists who need almost a decade of rigorous training. Since World War II the demand for all types of scientific workers has far exceeded the supply.

It would not be wise to set up a science program as a vocational guidance program. To do so would limit its usefulness. Teachers can, however, provide many opportunities for pupils to consider the types of work being done in different scientific occupations. They can allow pupils having special interests to investigate further the nature of these jobs and the training required.

One lasting contribution of the science program is the development of healthy interests. Many of the activities—model making, bird study, collecting, gardening—lead directly into healthy, satisfying, leisure-time pursuits.

Helping pupils meet the problems of everyday living.   Adults, thinking of their own responsibilities, are apt to minimize the problems of young people, forgetting that the latter's problems are identical with their own and that practice is needed in solving these problems. The problems of high school boys and girls are no less real for being the problems of adolescents.

Although most of the problems of adolescents are primarily social in nature, many involve applications of science. They may want to know how to lubricate a bicycle, or clean dirt from under their fingernails, or use a fire extinguisher, or care for a pet, or store athletic equipment. It is better to help them practice problem solving on these situations than on hypothetical situations that may never develop. They benefit more from studying the principles of buoyancy as applied to themselves in a swimming pool than by studying submarines. They are benefited more by learning how to apply the laws of stability to themselves while dancing than by a study of gravitational forces on the moon.

Many students need help with personal grooming, particularly when the home fails to emphasize this aspect of social living. Most pupils need information about soaps and deodorants, about shampoos and hair dressing. They need understanding about procedures for cleaning their clothing. They need information about diet and its effect on appearance. They need help with posture and choice of dress. The science program, though not the only agency with obligations in this area, can provide a good part of the needed information and specific help.

Preparation for later experiences of life.   Adolescents have so many immediately pressing problems that they are little apt to be concerned with the remote future. True, they think in a vague way about their activities as adults, but they are usually more certain about what they do not want to do than about what they want to do. Even when a young person has decided upon a career it is rare that he will work toward ends that can be realized only a decade or so later; he will usually work toward more immediate ends.

Science programs have long been organized on the preparatory basis alone and have been universally condemned by educators who look at school broadly. Science programs can be effective only if they recognize the immediate needs of students. However, the preparatory function need not be neglected. It is usually possible to work toward several objectives at the same time. A boy learning about an automobile he wants to drive now can be gaining understandings of mechanics he can put to good use later in life.

When boys and girls leave school and take full responsibility for their money, they are in need of information that is sometimes taught as "consumer science." This information helps them buy wisely and take care of what they have. The study involves economics, science, and conservation. It includes a study of advertising claims, manufacturers' recommendations, testing procedures, and relative values.

The science program is obviously in a position to make some of the most important contributions to conservation education. Science deals among other things, with animals, rocks, soil, and water, and with the scientific principles that control these natural features. The science program is well adapted to help meet the three general objectives of conservation education: (1) to give information about natural resources, (2) to develop desirable attitudes towards the use of these natural resources, and (3) to give experiences with conservation practices.

RESTATING OBJECTIVES IN MODERN TERMS

Behavioral Objectives.   It is a sad but realistic fact that many teachers either formulate or adopt objectives without giving much thought as to how they will evaluate whether the learner has attained these objectives. Fulfilling objectives produces changes in the learner, but if the changes cannot be measured then the attainment of the objectives cannot be measured. However, if the objectives are stated in what are called behavioral terms, i.e., what the learner should be able to do as a consequence of the learning experiences associated with the objectives, then it is possible to discern accurately whether the objectives have been realized. In contrast to behavioral objectives, those stated in nonbehavioral terms do not specifically indicate what the learner should be able to do after instruction. In other words, nonbehavioral objectives do not focus upon the ability of a pupil to perform a specific task while behavioral objectives do.

With a little thought and effort a teacher can state his objectives of instruction in behavioral terms. To do this, he must ask himself the following: What should my pupils be able to do after instruction that they were not able to do before instruction? Behavioral objectives must be statements of observable behaviors which the teacher can see at the end of a lesson. These behaviors are what the teacher feels are necessary indications of whether and to what degree objectives have been met.

In formulating objectives, teachers tend to use phrases such as "develop an understanding," "develop an appreciation," "to demonstrate that." These may be useful in writing objectives in nonbehavioral terms, but they do not indicate specifically what a pupil should be able to demonstrate to show that he has attained the objective.

For example, the following objective is written in nonbehavioral terms: *To develop an understanding of Boyle's Law.* This statement does not explicitly state what types or levels of performance the pupil should achieve. This statement might mean several different things. For example, the teacher may expect that the student will be able to derive the equation for Boyle's Law. It might mean that the teacher expects the student to be able to interpret a graph showing the inverse relationship between the volume of an enclosed gas and the pressure exerted on the gas. It might mean that the teacher simply desires that the student be able to state Boyle's Law in words and in equation form.

It is evident that these statements do not imply identical levels of sophistication, for a pupil may be able to use the formula for Boyle's Law and not understand what it represents.

Contrast the above objective written in nonbehavioral terms to one also involving Boyle's Law but written in behavioral terms.

At the end of this lesson the pupil should be able to do the following:
1. Express Boyle's Law in the form of an equation.
2. State Boyle's Law in words.
3. Given a certain volume of an enclosed gas under a given pressure, calculate the final volume if the pressure is changed to another value.
4. Calculate the change in volume of an enclosed gas associated with a given change in pressure.
5. Calculate the change in pressure on an enclosed gas associated with a given change in volume.
6. Predict what will happen to the volume of an enclosed gas when the pressure on this gas is changed.

7. Construct a graph showing the relationship between the volume of an enclosed gas and the pressure exerted upon it.
8. Interpret a graph expressing the inverse relationship between the volume of an enclosed gas and the pressure exerted on the gas.
9. Given a pressure-volume graph, interpolate from this graph the pressure associated with a given volume and vice versa.

Notice that the objectives as stated above include such words as, construct, write, interpret, state, interpolate, graph, calculate, predict, express. These are called *action* or *performance* words. They indicate the specific types of behavior that the learner must demonstrate to show that he understands Boyle's Law. Contrast these words with those generally associated with nonbehavioral objectives, i.e., to know, to understand.

Action words which are useful in stating objectives in behavioral terms include the following:

Find	Organize	Make
Construct	Examine	Measure
Demonstrate	Classify	Suggest
Identify	Relate	Justify
Compare	Prove	Estimate
Locate	Convert	Interpret
Diagram	Devise	Infer

Note that the action words listed above indicate various levels of sophistication. For example, the word "gather" suggests what may be a relatively simple operation whereas the word "infer" suggests the need for a number of mental manipulations and thought processes. Realize that the proper selection of action words can avoid ambiguity when they are used in statements of behavioral objectives. Action words demand that the learner display his knowledge in many different ways. Hence the teacher does not have to rely simply on verbalizations by pupils as a means of measuring understanding. For example, simply stating Boyle's Law gives no indication that the student understands the law. However, if the pupil can graph, construct, calculate, interpret, etc. then we know that he understands.

It is important that pupils know the level of acceptable performance which will be required of them. Therefore, teachers should not only state the objectives in behavioral terms, but they should also tell their pupils what criteria will be used for determining acceptable performance. The performance specifications can be included as part of the statement of objectives.

Suppose a teacher has established the following behavioral objective:

that the student can identify the parts of the digestive system and state the functions of each part. The statement as written is too broad, for it does not indicate the minimum degree of acceptable performance.

To be more explicit the objective can be written as follows: that the student can identify the following parts of the digestive system and state at least one function of each part:

1. Mouth
2. Teeth
3. Esophagus
4. Salivary glands
5. Stomach
6. Small intestine
7. Villi
8. Large intestine
9. Pancreas
10. Liver
11. Rectum

Now the statement explicitly tells the student what is expected since the phrase *at least* is included. This tells him that the teacher will accept *one* function for each part listed for minimum acceptable performance.

The guidelines for constructing behavioral objectives have been given by the American Association for the Advancement of Science. Commission on Science Education Elementary Science Curriculum Project.[11] They are as follows:

A. Each objective of the exercise should be represented by at least one task. Hopefully, these tasks should be suggested by the statements of the objectives; but in any case, behaviors proposed as instructional objectives should be measured.

B. The tasks need to be designed to elicit behaviors of the sort described in the objectives. If an objective calls for the construction of something, the task might begin "draw a _____." If the learner is being asked to name something, the task might be "What do we call this?"

C. The description accompanying each task should tell the instructor clearly what to do (not just imply it). For example, an accompanying instruction might be: "Place in front of the child a dittoed sheet containing drawings of an equilateral triangle and a circle." Or, "Give the child the meterstick."

[11] Walbesser, Henry H., "Science Curriculum Evaluation: Observations on a Position," *The Science Teacher*, 33, 34–37, February, 1966.

D. The kind of performances that are acceptable should be clearly described so that a correct judgment can be made concerning the presence or absence of a particular behavior.

Mager[12] lists the following suggestions regarding instructional objectives:

1. A statement of instructional objectives is a collection of words or symbols describing one of your educational intents.

2. An objective will communicate your intent to the degree you have described what the learner will be doing when demonstrating his achievement and how you will know when he is doing it.

3. To describe terminal behavior (what the learner will be doing)
   a. Identify and name the overall behavioral act.
   b. Define the important conditions under which the behavior is to occur (given and/or restrictions and limitations).
   c. Define the criterion of acceptable performance.

4. Write a separate statement for each objective; the more statements you have the better chance you have of making clear your intent.

5. If you give each learner a copy of your objectives, you may not have to do much else.

Other ways of stating objectives have been developed. For example, Bloom[13] categorizes all objectives of instruction into three major divisions: (1) the cognitive domain (2) the affective domain and (3) the psychomotor domain. The cognitive domain is concerned with the recall of knowledge. This includes such behaviors as remembering, problem solving, concept formation and creative thinking.[14] The affective domain is concerned with interests, attitudes, appreciations and values. The psychomotor domain involves manipulative and motor skills.

Of these three categories involved in Bloom's Taxonomy, most science teachers stress the objects of instruction in the cognitive domain and place little or no emphasis upon the objectives in the psychomotor and affective domains. It is difficult to measure the attainment of objectives in the psychomotor and affective domains.

Teachers even ignore several of the important aspects of the cognitive domain. For example, teachers usually test for simple recall of information rather than for such aspects of learning as comprehension, analysis, concept formation and problem solving. Perhaps one reason is that they are not aware of the other divisions of cognitive domain. Bloom[15] lists the

---

12 Mager, Robert F., *Preparing Instructional Objectives*, Fearon Publishers, Palo Alto, California, 1962.

13 Bloom, Benjamin S. (ed.), *Taxonomy of Educational Objectives*, The Classification of Educational Goals, Handbook I: Cognitive Domain, David McKay Co., New York, 1956.

14 *Ibid.*

15 *Ibid.*

divisions of the domain in the following ascending order of complexity: (1) Knowledge, (2) Comprehension, (3) Application, (4) Analysis, (5) Synthesis, and (6) Evaluation. Teachers should be aware of all the categories in the cognitive domain and utilize them in setting objectives and in evaluating student performance. The objectives should be written in behavioral terms which will permit the teacher to measure their attainment. Hedges[16] presents a thorough discussion of Bloom's Taxonomy as it applies to measuring goals of science teaching in the cognitive domain. Many excellent ideas are presented which are useful in the construction of tests to measure the attainment of objectives in this domain.

Teachers should also be familiar with the various divisions in the psychomotor and affective domains and try to determine ways of working towards the objectives in these categories. Measuring the attainment of the objectives in these domains unquestionably is difficult. Standardized tests are available through various educational testing services which attempt to measure such things as attitudes, interests, and skills, but they are not always useful to the teacher in his own situation. Some of the National Curriculum projects like BSCS, PSSC, and ESCP (Earth Science Curriculum Project) are trying to construct tests of problem-solving skills and attitudes, but these are specifically designed for their own courses of study. It might be useful to investigate how tests of this type are constructed to see if some of the ideas can be used by the teacher to construct tests for his own courses.

The more specific a teacher is in stating objectives, the easier it will be to measure their attainment. Objectives should be educationally sound, realistic, and attainable. They should be meaningful to the pupils and should give direction to the teacher. A well defined set of objectives permits the teacher to present a course with a minimum of wasted effort.

SUGGESTED ACTIVITIES

List the reasons why you believe science should be a part of the secondary school program. Discuss your list with other prospective teachers and modify it as your ideas change. Save a list and reconsider it at the end of your methods course.

Observe a science class and make a record of all the teacher planned activities (i.e., experiments, demonstrations, projects) in which the pupils are engaged. Try to determine the beneficial outcomes of each activity. Note also the situations which do not seem to produce beneficial outcomes.

16 Hedges, William D., *Testing and Evaluation for the Sciences in the Secondary School*, Wadsworth Publishing Co., Belmont, California, 1966.

Many science teachers claim that their main job is to teach facts. Debate this point with other prospective science teachers.

List the long-range subject matter objectives for an integrated course in physical science for the twelfth grade.

Begin making a list of the general objectives that you believe should govern your teaching. Discuss your list with others and modify the list as your ideas change. Keep the list to guide you during your cadet teaching experience.

SUGGESTED READINGS

Barnard, J. D., *et. al.* "Role of Science in our Culture," *National Society for the Study of Education, 1959 Yearbook,* Part I, pp. 1–17.

Bloom, Benjamin S., *Taxonomy of Educational Objectives,* David McKay Co., New York, 1956.

Brooks, Harold B., "The Administration Looks at Science Education Objectives," *Science in Secondary Schools Today,* Bulletin of the National Association of Secondary School Principals, 37:11–15, 1953.

Curtis, Frances D., *A Digest of Investigations in the Teaching of Science,* Philadelphia, The Blakeston Co., 1931.

———, *Second Digest of Investigations in the Teaching of Science,* Philadelphia, The Blakeston Co., 1931.

———, *Third Digest of Investigations in the Teaching of Science,* Philadelphia, The Blakeston Co., 1939.

French, Will, *et al., Behavioral Goals of General Education in High School,* The Russell Sage Foundation, New York, 1957.

Grant, Charlotte, "A High School Teacher Looks at Science Education Objectives," *Science in Secondary Schools Today,* Bulletin of the National Association of Secondary School Principals, 37:16–17, 1953.

Hurd, P. D., *Biological Education in American Schools, 1890–1960,* American Institute of Biological Sciences, Washington, D. C., 1961, p. 178.

———, *Biological Education in American Secondary Schools, 1890–1960,* Bulletin No. 1, American Institute of Biological Sciences, Boulder, Colorado, 1961.

Krathwohl, David *et al., Taxonomy of Educational Objectives, The Classification of Educational Goals; Handbook II:* "The Affective Domain," David McKay Co., New York, 1964.

National Science Teachers Association, *Planning for Excellence in High School Science,* Washington, D. C., 1961.

National Society for the Study of Education, Thirty-first Yearbook, Part I, "A Program for Science Teaching," Public School Publishing Co., Bloomington, Ill., 1932.

National Society for the Study of Education, Forty-sixth Yearbook, Part I, "Science Education in American Schools," University of Chicago Press, Chicago, 1947.

Progressive Education Association, Commission on the Secondary School Curriculum, "Science in General Education," Report of the Committee on the Function of Science in General Education, Appleton-Century-Croft, New York, 1938.

Schwab, Joseph J., and Paul F. Brandwein, *The Teaching of Science, The Ingles and Burton Lectures of 1961,* Harvard University Press, Cambridge, Mass., 1962.

U.S. Office of Education, *Report of the Committee on Secondary School Studies (Committee of Ten)* No. 205, Government Printing Office, Washington, D.C., 1893.

Chapter 3

The Science Program:

Curricula and Trends

THE BASIC PURPOSE OF THOSE INVOLVED IN CURRICULUM IMPROVEMENT HAS been to see that science instruction presents recent developments in science and a reinterpretation of knowledge which has been established earlier. Curriculum experts believe that science courses should be developed which provide students with experiences that show how facts are obtained and new techniques are developed. These experts also believe that science programs developed in this manner can produce a more scientifically literate citizen who is better able to cope with the problems of everyday living.

Significant curriculum changes have occurred in science teaching. New, untraditional approaches in teaching elementary science, biology, chemistry, physics, earth science, physical science, and general science have now appeared, and more are being developed in all areas of science. The most noticeable trend in science education at the present time is the attempt to develop a kindergarten through grade twelve sequence that will coordinate and direct the efforts of science teachers to achieve the desired goals of the science program.

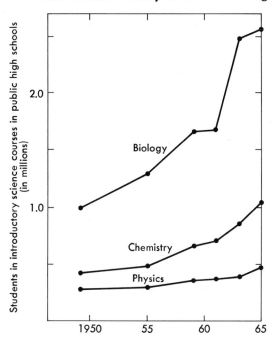

Figure 2. *Enrollments in various introductory science courses during recent years. The source of these figures is the* Digest of Educational Statistics *(1965 ed). 1964 figures from National Center for Educational Statistics, USOE.**

THE ELEMENTARY SCIENCE PROGRAM

Secondary school science teachers should become well acquainted with the science program of the elementary schools of the system in which they work. Pupils often enter the seventh grade with strong interests and a rich background of experience in science because of the elementary school program. Secondary school science teachers can utilize these interests and experiences in teaching their own courses.

Elementary teachers have a flexible schedule—no bells tell them when to start studying science and when to stop. If something of value arises in the early morning, they may take advantage of it, or they may shift the science lesson to late afternoon if this change is advantageous. They can

* Watson, Fletcher G., "Why Do We Need More Physics Courses?", *The Physics Teacher,* 5:212, 1967.

Grade and Course	All sizes	1–499	500–999	1,000–1,499	1,500 and over
Total schools	100.0	100.0	100.0	100.0	100.0
ALL GRADES					
Any science course	100.0	100.0	100.0	100.0	100.0
General Science	94.1	94.9	91.8	97.1	97.8
Life Science-Biology	24.4	9.1	32.0	31.0	17.4
Physical Science	10.2	6.6	13.3	7.6	10.8
Earth Science	11.2	2.7	15.6	11.8	13.7
Space Science	.2	.0	.4	.2	.0
Earth-Space Science	1.0	.0	1.3	2.2	.5
Health Science	2.1	1.8	2.1	2.4	2.6

School Size

Table 1. *Percent of public junior high schools offering selected science courses, by grade level and by school size: United States, 1963.* (U.S. Office of Education, *Science Teaching in the Public Junior High School*, U.S. Government Printing Office, Washington, D.C., 1967.)

extend a science lesson as long as they consider it profitable. They can weave science into areas of other subject matter.

The major objective of elementary school science is to use the materials of science to develop the individual child. Science, like all other areas, is included in the program to help pupils learn more about their own interests, abilities and limitations, to help them learn to work with others, and to give them help in solving their everyday problems.

Elementary science is not primarily designed to prepare pupils for secondary school science. It does not try to build up special vocabularies, techniques for handling specialized equipment, or ready verbalization of scientific principles. Instead, it provides the pupils with accomplishments of far greater value. It develops strong interest in science. It helps pupils approach problems intelligently and gives them confidence in their ability. The elementary science program can provide them with a rich and well-rounded background of experiences. These are the products upon which secondary school science teachers can capitalize.

Well-organized elementary science programs are not common throughout the country. Like all other divisions of the science program, elementary school science teaching varies in its effectiveness from school to school and from teacher to teacher. The variation in the elementary school may be somewhat greater because of the variation in the backgrounds and interests of the teachers. Some elementary teachers like to teach science and have an adequate background to do a good job. However, most elementary teachers feel inadequate and teach little, if any, science.

| | Number of students enrolled 1964–65 | | |
Type of course	Boys	Girls	Total
General Science, total	1,143,000	1,032,900	2,175,900
9th grade gen. sci.	1,087,400	990,000	2,077,400
Advanced gen. sci.	55,600	42,900	98,500
Biology, total	1,333,400	1,361,000	2,694,400
Tradl. biol. (gr. 9)	135,600	165,300	300,900
Tradl. biol. (gr. 10)	974,900	961,000	1,935,900
BSCS	161,300	167,100	328,400
Advanced biol.	61,600	67,600	129,200
Chemistry, total	606,100	478,500	1,084,600
Tradl. chemistry	499,200	402,900	902,100
CBA	14,200	9,200	23,400
CHEM STUDY	72,600	55,500	128,100
Advanced chemistry	20,100	10,900	31,000
Physics, total (Introductory and Advanced)	382,200	144,000	526,200
Tradl. physics	281,800	102,900	384,700
PSSC	74,900	25,000	99,900
Advanced physics	25,500	16,100	41,600
Physical Science	167,000	123,700	290,700
Earth-Space Science	138,800	106,000	244,800
Physiology	6,400	7,700	14,100
Research Science Seminar	4,000	2,700	6,700
All other sciences	111,200	95,000	206,200
Totals	3,892,100	3,351,500	7,243,600

Table 2. *Enrollments in Public High School Science by Type of Course and by Sex 1964–65* (*preliminary data*) (Watson, *loc. cit.*)

At present, elementary school science is in a state of flux. It is not a required subject in all schools throughout the country. It does not have the status in the elementary school curriculum as do the other areas. Some state departments of education and local school systems have made it a requirement for all grade levels, but they are encountering many problems. The problems in implementing programs will be overcome someday so that organized and coordinated kindergarten through twelfth grade science sequences will be common throughout the country.

A well-organized, high quality elementary school science program can help secondary school science teachers. They will know the science backgrounds of their pupils and can capitalize on this background. They will be able to teach their courses of study using the foundation their pupils acquired through the elementary program. Secondary school teachers should regard elementary science as an important part of the elementary school curriculum. They should do all that they can to help implement an elementary science program in their own school systems.

Trends in elementary science.   Many active scientists have been concerned about the errors in concept and in fact which are taught by elementary school teachers. They believe that elementary science textbooks and other science books are inaccurate and do not clearly show how the scientist finds out what he knows. Science is presented in these books as a collection of disparate facts instead of the concepts and principles which clarify the subject. These scientists are seeking to help improve elementary science by contributing to the development of units which are scientifically accurate and demonstrate the nature of scientific inquiry.

Several elementary school science projects are underway and are in various stages of development. The approaches which are being developed have several common points:

1. Less emphasis is placed on subject matter per se than is found in traditional elementary science courses.
2. Discovery laboratory experiences receive major emphasis. Pupils use the methods of science to uncover "new" facts.
3. Pupils have an opportunity to use their own materials to perform their experiments.
4. Pupils are given an opportunity to gather, record, graph, and analyze data. They draw their own conclusions.
5. The material is written for the "average" elementary school pupil.

The Elementary Science Study (ESS).[1]   This study was started in 1960 and has developed materials for teaching science from the kindergarten through the eighth grade. "The purpose is not to develop a national curriculum but to supply a variety of carefully thought out and tested materials which a curriculum director may use in developing an elementary science curriculum for the particular needs of a school system."[2]

[1] The Elementary School Science Study (ESS) Education Development Center, Inc., 55 Chapel St., Newton, Mass. The materials already produced include 19 units ranging in topics from growing seeds (K–3) to Batteries and Bulbs (Grades 5–8). Additional units on a wide variety of topics are being produced.

[2] Lockhard, David (ed.), *Report of the International Clearinghouse on Science and Mathematics Curricular Developments*, American Association for the Advancement of Science and the University of Maryland, College Park, Maryland, July, 1966.

The ESS program includes a wide variety of units which have a common approach. Materials are placed in the hands of children and through the use of these materials each child investigates the nature of his environment. The children acquire information through laboratory experiences.

The AAAS program: A process approach.   Since 1962 the AAAS Commission on Science Education[3] has been in the process of preparing and evaluating science materials for the elementary grades. These materials include a series of exercises designed to improve the child's skills in using the processes of science.[4]

In this approach, eight processes have been identified in the primary grades and are as follows: observing, clarifying, measuring, communicating, inferring, predicting, recognizing space/time relations, and recognizing number relations.

Levels four and five use integrated processes. These are formulating hypotheses, making operational definitions, controlling and manipulating variables, experimenting, interpreting data, and formulating models.

Elementary School Science Project (ESSP).[5]   The ESSP was initiated at the University of Illinois in 1960 to produce astronomy materials for grades 5 to 9. The following six units are available; each is composed of a children's book and teacher's guide.

Charting the Universe

The Universe in Motion

Gravitation

The Message of Starlight

The Life Story of a Star

Galaxies and the Universe[6]

There is a careful development, a conceptual sequence throughout the series of units "that highlights rational argument rather than conclusion

[3] AAAS Commission on Science Education, 1515 Massachusettes Ave., Washington, D.C., 20005. The materials available include: *Science, A Process Approach*—3rd Experimental Edition; A Commentary for Teachers; *The Psychological Basis of Science—A Process Approach*; A design for evaluation; Kit of teaching aids for each grade level. Xerox Educational Division, 600 Madison Ave., New York, N.Y. publishes the teachers manual and provides materials.

[4] Livermore, Arthur A., "The Process Approach of the AAAS Commission on Science," *Journal of Research in Science Teaching*, 2:271–282 1964.

[5] Elementary School Science Project, 805 W. Pennsylvania Ave., Urbana, Illinois.

[6] National Science Foundation, *Course and Curriculum Improvement Projects*, National Science Foundation, Washington, D.C., September, 1966.

and is also on the intellectual power of a few pervasive ideas rather than descriptive of loosely connected facts and phenomena."[7]

The Elementary Science Project (ESP). The Elementary Science Project[8] at Howard University has the following objective: to develop a program of compensatory science experiences for disadvantaged children and their parents. The material was developed for enrichment purposes for use after school and Saturday.

School Science Curriculum Project (SSCP). The University of Illinois initiated the School Science Curriculum Project[9] in 1963 to develop improved science materials for elementary school as well as junior high school, grades 4 to 9. Approximately 35 teachers throughout the United States used the material in 1966.[10] Materials are still being developed although no more writing conferences are being held.

The Science Curriculum Improvement Study (SCIS). The Science Curriculum Improvement Study under the direction of Robert Karplus, Department of Physics, University of California[11] is "exploring a concept of science education based on communicating scientific literacy." This kindergarten to sixth grade program started in 1962. Extensive use is made of the discovery method and of concept development. The curriculum includes both physical science and biological science and is sequential rather than graded.

Minnesota Mathematics and Science Teaching Project (MINNEMAST). The Minnesota Mathematics and Science Teaching Project[12] has devel-

---

[7] Atkin, Myron J., "University of Illinois Elementary School Science Project," *Journal of Research in Science Teaching*, 2:1964, pp. 328–329.

[8] Elementary Science Project (ESP), Department of Education and Physics, Box 574, Howard University, Washington, D.C., 2001. Fifty elementary science activity kits are available.

[9] School Science Curriculum Project (SSCP), University of Illinois, 805 West Pennsylvania Ave., Urbana, Illinois 61801. The materials already produced for the unit titles: Running Water and River Development; Beans and Biology; Motion, Photographs and Pendulums; Short Internal Timer; and others. Associated apparatus and films are being developed.

[10] Lockhard, *op. cit.*

[11] Professor Robert Karplus, Department of Physics, Berkeley, California, 94720. These materials are available for primary grades: variation and measurement systems, interaction, relativity of position and motion, subsystems, material objects, "One Physicist Looks at Science Education." Material is also available from D. C. Heath Co., 285 Columbus Ave., Boston, Mass. 02116.

[12] Minnesota Mathematics and Science Teaching Project, 720 Washington Ave., (MINNEMAST), University of Minnesota, Minneapolis, Minn. 55455. The materials produced include Science K–1 and 2–6.

oped units which focus on the operations of science (measurement, classifying, forming hypotheses, deducing, and testing). The children use these operations in the course of their investigations. The materials are designed for average elementary school pupils. Supplementary material has also been produced for the gifted child and the culturally disadvantaged.

THE JUNIOR HIGH SCHOOL PROGRAM

The junior high school science program has been the most neglected area of science education. The most poorly prepared teachers and the most inadequate facilities are usually found in junior high school science courses. This is ironical in that a recent survey shows that of the total population of students taking science between grades nine through twelve, about 28 percent were enrolled in ninth grade general science during 1964–65 (see Table 2). It is amazing that such a large percentage of the school population should be exposed to courses which are poorly developed, poorly taught, and out-dated; and very little progress is being made to change the situation.

Some schools are introducing courses other than traditional general science. For example, earth science is now replacing general science in many schools, in an effort to provide pupils with meaningful science experience. General biology and physical science courses are also appearing in the junior high school science curriculum (see Table 2).

General Science. General science occupies a critical position in the secondary school curriculum. It is required of nearly all pupils. It is the first experience most pupils have with science as a special subject, and it may be the only science course that some pupils will take during their high school experience.

General science determines the attitude that many pupils develop toward science. When the course is exciting, satisfying, and rewarding, boys and girls look forward to further science study. When the course is poorly taught, pupils are apt to look to other fields for satisfaction. General science deserves the best teaching and the best facilities that can be provided.

As its name implies, general science has a broad scope and can be applied to a broad range of interests. It was never intended, however, that general science be made up of a smattering of the specialized sciences. It has its own body of subject matter that is chosen to meet the needs of the pupils who take it. Nor should a general science course touch upon every aspect of science. To do so would result in superficiality and would cause feelings of frustration and dissatisfaction on the part of the pupils. General science is "general" only in that it is free of the traditional boundaries of the various areas of science.

General science was introduced into the curriculum as part of a general effort to humanize the secondary school curriculum. The courses offered at the beginning of the century were far from suitable for the great majority of pupils entering high school. After a brief taste of the offerings, boys and girls were leaving school in large numbers. Hunter states that during 1908 in New York City 43 percent of the enrolled pupils had left by the end of the ninth year, and 70 percent had left by the end of the tenth year.[13] The formal science courses of the time were in part responsible for the high drop-out rate.

Educators recognized the need for a different type of science course. They recognized the need for a course designed for pupils who would elect no more science, a course designed to help them understand and use the things of science commonly encountered in daily life. These educators also recognized the need for a course in science for pupils who would continue the study of science, a course that would permit exploration of interests and abilities and the building of a background of experiences.

Early courses of study and textbooks show considerable diversity in content and approach. Some teachers emphasized the exploratory function of general science, presenting samplings of the various specialized sciences loosely tied together. This type of course was of little value to pupils who would not study science further.

Other teachers emphasized the preparatory function of general science, building the course from the introductory phases of physics, chemistry, biology, physical geology and astronomy. They developed specialized vocabularies, skills in the use of formulas, and basic information. Such a general science course was of even less value to pupils who would not enter scientific fields.

A large number of teachers emphasized the practical applications of science. They taught their pupils how to repair leaky faucets, how to repair lamp cords, and how to choose a proper diet. Pupils probably benefited from this treatment, but formally trained science teachers considered the courses to be a "hodge-podge" of little value.

Gradually the idea grew that general science needed broader goals. A study made in 1930 showed that science teachers were thinking in terms of the development of interest, desirable attitudes, and certain general skills.[14]

[13] Hunter, G. W., *Science Teaching at Junior and Senior High School Levels*, American Book, New York, 1934.

[14] National Society for the Study of Education, *Thirty-first Yearbook*, Part I, "A Program for Science Teaching," Public School Publishing Co., Bloomington, Ill., 1932.

Some were still thinking of the preparatory function of general science, but most were thinking in terms of giving an understanding and an interest in the environment. It is significant that few considered general science to have any responsibilities toward helping boys and girls adjust to their social groups, find security, or explore their capabilities. General science teachers were thinking as science specialists, not as educators.

In 1932 there appeared the *Yearbook* of the National Society for the Study of Education—a publication that was to have a strong effect on general science. This *Yearbook* proposed for the twelve years of public schooling a science program based on the major concepts of science. The *Yearbook* listed thirty-eight major generalizations to be used as objectives for science instruction throughout the entire sequence of elementary, junior high, and senior high school science.

There have been objections to the proposals outlined in the *Thirty-first Yearbook* from the beginning. Hunter in 1932 said, "These generalizations completely leave out applications of science to the lives of children, no reference to health or citizenship objectives as such being found. Intellectual objectives hold complete domination over practical ones."[15]

Despite the objections of Dr. Hunter and others, general science continues to be dominated by intellectual objectives. Courses of study and textbooks emphasize generalizations rather than discovery. Demonstrations and experiments are used to "prove" that what the books and teachers say is true rather than to permit problem-solving situations.

General science has another handicap, which is a result of the times—a superfluity of material. As each major development of science has been brought to the attention of the public—television, jet planes, nuclear reactors—teachers and authors of texts have hastened to add them to the curriculum without considering the suitability of the added material. As a consequence, courses of study and textbooks are filled with information that is "up-to-date," but which has little or no function in meeting the general objectives of education.

Courses in general science vary from school system to school system and from teacher to teacher. Some are well-planned and excellently taught. Others are taught by teachers who are not prepared in science. In fact, a recent report of the United States Office of Education[16] indicates that an overwhelming proportion of general science teachers assigned to part-time teaching in science are not trained in science. This area of inadequacy, according to the report, presents a dismal picture of the staffing of general science courses.[17]

[15] Hunter, *op. cit.*

[16] U.S. Office of Education, *Science Teaching in the Public Junior High School*, U.S. Government Printing Office, Washington, D.C., 1967.

[17] *Ibid.*

Other information concerning general science is worthy of mentioning. Homogeneous grouping in general science is reported from about 60 percent of the schools. The trend appears to be towards use of ability grouping in general science.[18] Some type of laboratory facility for general science was reported by 75 percent of the schools. Because of the large size of classes, many large schools in certain geographic areas are discouraging meaningful student laboratory activities.[19] About half of the schools are using a coordinated series of textbooks for grades seven, eight, and nine. The large schools in general use recent texts and many of the smaller schools use textbooks which are fourteen years old or older.[20]

The picture which general science presents is one of a course which is not realizing its potentialities. Symptoms of this failure include a low interest in senior high school sciences, the diversion of capable students into fields other than science, and the shortage of scientific personnel in industry and government agencies. Some of the failures of general science are related to circumstances beyond the control of the individual teachers. Large classes, heavy class loads, and inadequate facilities are the inevitable results of a rapidly expanding school population.

Recent trends in junior high school science.   Some schools are replacing general science with such courses as earth science, life-science biology, and physical science. Table 1 shows the variety of courses which have already been introduced into the junior high schools throughout the country. These courses have been introduced at all grade levels—seven, eight, and nine. The courses take care of a very small percentage of the junior high school population. General science accomodates about 94 percent of the total junior high school pupils.[21]

National curriculum courses specifically designed for the junior high school pupil such as Earth Science Curriculum Project (ESCP), Secondary School Science Project (SSSP) and Introductory Physical Science (IPS) are not extensively used. The ESCP program is used in about four hundred schools and the other curriculum projects are even less common. Even though these programs have not been widely accepted, they are important for several reasons.

These new approaches involve a philosophy which is different from that of traditional courses. They stress "discovery" and "inquiry" and de-emphasize facts per se. The content of the courses is rigorous and requires that the teacher be up to date in his subject and teaching methods. These

[18] *Ibid.*
[19] *Ibid.*
[20] *Ibid.*
[21] *Ibid.*

The experiments used in the new curriculum approaches make use of simple materials to study complex phenomena.

modern curriculum programs are causing an impact that will be with us for many years to come. There is no question that science teachers will someday be forced to teach courses of this type in order to meet the demands of a rapidly changing scientific age.

Earth science.   In the 1920's, courses in physical geography and geology were taught in the high school. These courses were patterned after college courses where pupils spent most of their time identifying rock specimens, reading topographic maps, and coloring geologic maps. Many teachers are still using this traditional approach to earth science without realizing its interesting possibilities. Earth science deals with things which pupils see around them. It can be readily adapted to first-hand experience learning and can be taught entirely on a problem solving basis. Well taught, the course can be challenging to all types of pupils.

Earth science is becoming more popular; some schools are now introducing earth science in the ninth grade instead of general science. The course is recommended to pupils who are interested in science but who might not be successful in physics and chemistry.

The National Science Teachers Association recommends seventh- and eighth-grade general science courses which provide pupils with a good foundation in the principles of science and that earth science replace the traditional general science course at the ninth grade.

Table 2 shows that 244,800 students were enrolled in courses concerning Earth Space Science. This interest may be related to the availability of new course materials prepared by the Earth Science Curriculum Project Committee. The Committee has been charged with revitalizing earth science teaching in the secondary schools.

The Earth Science Curriculum Project (ESCP).   The Earth Science Curriculum Project began in 1958. The American Geological Institute appointed a committee to organize a six-week teaching-resource development conference to prepare earth science materials for the elementary and secondary schools. The conference, held at the University of Minnesota, produced a preliminary draft of a source book of earth science for teachers. In 1962, the National Science Foundation supported an initial part of a project to produce a major, interdisciplinary course in the earth sciences. The ESCP project is under the direction of the American Geological Institute. The first paperback edition of the textbook "Investigating the Earth" was prepared in 1964 and was tested in 77 schools throughout the United States.[22] The data collected from the pilot studies were used to prepare another revision in 1965. This revision was tested in 75 schools as well as 300 schools which were not a formal part of the program.[23] About 36,519 students in 44 schools used ESCP materials in 1966.[24] In 1967 the Houghton Mifflin Company published a complete hard-cover edition of the book as well as a teachers guide.

The ESCP course is designed primarily for the ninth grade level and uses an investigative approach to develop concepts and principles rather than memorization of the immutable facts.[25] The overall organization of the text book is based on the 1965 revision and has four basic units:[26] The laboratory manual which provides exercises on open-ended laboratory investigations is closely allied with the textbook.

Unit I The Dynamic Earth

    1. The Changing Earth
    2. Earth Materials

[22] Bisque, Ramon E., "Investigating the Earth," *Geo-times*, February, 1966.
[23] *Ibid.*
[24] ESCP Newsletter, No. 13, February, 1967.
[25] Bisque, *op. cit.*
[26] ESCP Newsletter, No. 13, February, 1967.

3. Earth Measurement
4. Fields and Forces
5. Energy Flow

Unit II Earth Cycles

6. Energy and Air Motions
7. Water in the Air
8. Waters of the Land
9. Water in the Sea
10. Energy, Moisture and Climate
11. The Land Wears Away
12. Sediments in the Sea
13. Mountains from the Sea
14. Rocks within Mountains
15. Interior of the Earth

Unit III Earth's Biography

16. Time and its Measurement
17. The Record in the Rocks
18. Life—Present and Past
19. Development of a Continent
20. Evolution of Landscapes

Unit IV Earth's Environment Is Space

21. The Moon: A Natural Satellite
22. The Solar System
23. Stars and Other Suns
24. Stellar Evolution and Galaxies
25. The Universe and its Origin

A study[27] concerning the 1964 edition of ESCP materials showed that 60 percent of the students thought that the mathematics in the text was not too difficult. However, the teachers thought that some of the mathematics was too advanced. The reading level of the original version was also too advanced for ninth graders. The 1967 edition has lowered the reading level as well as eliminated a number of difficult mathematical problems. About 80 percent of the students questioned would recommend ESCP courses to other students, and 70 percent would take the course again if they had a choice. About 85 percent of the students who answered the questionnaire planned to go to college.

Studies show that "the materials successfully employ a strong unifying theme and present laboratory experiences from which students experience

[27] ESCP Newsletter, October, 1965, p. 4.

growth in investigative skills,"[28] and that the program has more continuity than most general science courses with the same content.

The Secondary School Science Project (SSSP). The Secondary School Science Project[29] started in the summer of 1962 as a result of a meeting held by Education Development Center, Incorporated (EDC).[30] The objectives of the Project were as follows:[31]

1. To develop a program for junior high school grades centered on geology that will lead students through a series of their own interrelated, sequential investigations, observations and inferences—to an understanding of the earth.
2. To develop simple, inexpensive, durable materials that enable students to experience scientific inquiry at first hand.

The SSSP reported that eighty-three schools used the materials in 1965–66, but Cawelti reports that 255 schools or 3.5 percent of 7,232 schools used the materials during that academic year.[32]

The course is specifically written for grades eight and nine and covers subjects in the physical sciences (geology, astronomy, physics, and chemistry) and mathematics.[33, 34] The following summary describes the scope of the approach:[35]

> The curriculum *Time, Space, and Matter: Investigating the Physical World* (Princeton Project) consists of three parts: Part I "On the Nature of Things," Part II "Seeking Regularity in Matter," and Part III "Interpreting a World of Change."
>
> The entire course is structured on having the student "check up on what he has been told." As its title implies, the central theme is the nature of the physical world. Careful observation and critical interpretation are stressed.
>
> There is no formal textbook; the students record their observations and measurements in a Student Record Book. These record books, one for

[28] Cawelti, Gordon, "Innovative Practices in High Schools: Who Does What and Why and How," *Nation's Schools*, 79:68, 1967.

[29] Also known as the Princeton Project and the Junior High School Science Project.

[30] Formerly Educational Services Incorporated (ESI).

[31] Lacy, Archie, *Guide to Science Teaching in the Secondary Schools*, Wadsworth Publishing Co., Belmont, California, 1966, p. 46.

[32] Cawelti, *op. cit.*

[33] Secondary School Science Project, *Time, Space, and Matter: Investigating the Physical World*, Teacher's Text, Series I, II, and III, Princeton University, 1964.

[34] Materials Available: Secondary School Science Project, *Time, Space, and Matter: Investigating the Physical World*, Student Record Book Series I, II, and III, Princeton University, 1964.

[35] MacMahan, Horace, Jr., "Princeton Project or ESCP: A Difficult Choice." *School Science and Mathematics*, 45: 87–88, 1966.

each of the three major parts of the course, are definitely not of the "cookbook" type. Rather, they are comprised mostly of empty pages on which the student himself must set up his own tables for the systematic recording of data.

Each student receives a kit of materials containing such things as a simple beam balance, an uncalibrated thermometer, etc. Students are encouraged to take these inexpensive kits home to use in solving problems as they arise. In this way, the laboratory experiences are not confined to the class period.

Evaluation studies are not available for the SSSP program at this time. Plans for evaluation include (1) tests to determine the extent to which the course has reached its objectives, and (2) tests to evaluate the development of students as they proceed through the course.[36] MacMahan[37] has compared the ESCP approach and the Princeton Project as follows:

> The Princeton Project and ESCP are alike, then, in that they both restore the laboratory to its rightful place in the science curriculum. Rather than being forced to memorize and regurgitate an endless list of unrelated facts, the student works as a "scientist." He seeks answers to problems by utilizing the same methods that scientists employ. Insofar as possible, these laboratory investigations are "open-ended" in the sense that more than one conclusion is acceptable—as long as the data obtained support the conclusion given. The "cookbook" approach whereby the student merely fills in the blanks of a workbook in order to arrive at a previously revealed answer is now passé.

Both of these new science courses according to MacMahan have "missed the mark." "The Princeton Project has a limited life expectancy because of the 'aha' learnings will soon be general knowledge to many of the students before they take the course . . . yet it is generally agreed by those who have carefully and impartially evaluated them [ESCP and SSSP], that they are by far the best junior high school science curricula devised to date."

Introductory Physical Science (IPS). The Introductory Physical Science project had its origin at a meeting of the Education Development Center, Incorporated (EDC) in the spring of 1963. An outline of the course was prepared, and apparatus was designed and tested. Eight chapters of the material were used in 1963–64 by ten teachers. In 1964–65, about 60 teachers and 2,300 students of various abilities and backgrounds were involved in the pilot program. The feedback was analyzed and used to prepare the final versions of the text, teachers' guide, and achievement tests. In addition to

[36] Lockhard, *op. cit.*
[37] MacMahan, *op. cit.*

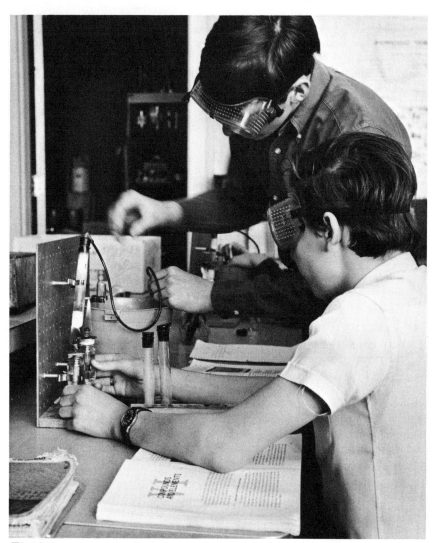

The IPS program emphasizes experimentation before class discussion. These pupils are doing an experiment out of the IPS manual.

the pilot group, the course was used by 25,000 students in new pilot schools in 1965–66 and by about 125,000 pupils in 1966–67.[38]

"The major emphasis in this course is the study of matter. Through this approach a firm understanding of the atomic-molecular theory is

[38] Haber-Schaim, Uri "Objectives and Content of the Course" from a lecture delivered at Florida State University, Tallahassee, Florida, 1966.

established. Student laboratory work is of primary importance and is integrated directly in the body of the text; the results are not described."[39]

The following is an outline of the course taken from the text:

1. Quantity of Matter: Mass
2. Characteristic properties
3. Solubility and Solvents
4. The separation of substances
5. Radioactivity
6. The Atomic Model of Matter
7. Sizes and Masses of Atoms and Molecules
8. Molecular Motion
9. Heat

The course has been used in grades eight and nine for the most part, with pupils having a wide range of abilities. Many schools are also using the course in grades eleven and twelve for students who have not had or are not planning to take physics and chemistry.[40] The course is also intended to be suitable as a terminal course in physical science and a preparatory course for chemistry, physics, and biology.

No major evaluation studies are available. Achievement tests have been prepared and are being pretested. Haber-Schaim[41] states that students with low abilities or with poor school records are often very highly motivated by the laboratory work involved in the course. He believes that the pupils will enter physics and chemistry with an excellent orientation and attitude towards science as well as with the essential skills.

THE HIGH SCHOOL SCIENCE OFFERINGS

The choice of elective sciences in most high schools is usually limited to three: physics, chemistry, and biology. Some have now introduced advanced general science courses, physical science courses, earth-space science courses, and the National Curriculum Projects in Biology, Chemistry, and Physics. Table 2 shows the enrollment of the elective sciences in 1964–65. In terms of enrollment, biology is by far the most popular science

[39] National Science Foundation, *Course and Curriculum Improvement Projects*, September, 1966.

[40] Haber-Schaim, *op. cit.*

[41] *Ibid.*

elective. Chemistry is attracting about 40 percent of the pupils who reach grades eleven and twelve; physics is the least popular, attracting about 20 percent of the eleventh and twelfth grade population. Earth science, physical science courses, and advanced general science courses are not attracting many pupils.

Biology. Biology courses have the largest enrollment. The U.S. Office of Education figures show that of the 2,694,000 pupils who took biology courses in 1964–65, about two million enrolled in a traditional biology course at grade ten (see Table 1).[42] The remainder registered in courses in biology at the ninth grade level, in advanced biology courses, or in one of the National Curriculum Approaches. The increasing percentages of students taking biology during the past sixty years attest to its appeal to young people. One can only speculate as to why biology has been more popular than physics and chemistry. Perhaps biology teachers have been less hampered by tradition and by the influence of college science. Perhaps pupils find the subject matter more meaningful than the content of chemistry or physics or earth science. Perhaps biology lends itself successfully to the teaching of classes having pupils with a wide range of abilities.

High school biology today bears little resemblance to its forebears of the nineteenth century. Previous to 1900, schools offered separate courses in botany and zoology, and later in human physiology. These courses emphasized classification and morphology. Laboratory work was primarily concerned with detailed studies of structural types. Teaching was strongly influenced by the doctrine of formal discipline which held that the mind could be trained through special exercises.

The closing years of the century saw two significant developments. Teachers began using experiments in physiology in place of studies of structure alone. The rising nature study movement, which emphasized the study of living things in their natural environment, stimulated field work and the study of interrelationships. These two factors greatly changed the pattern of biology courses.

In 1900 the move to unify the several phases of biology into a single course gained momentum. At first the resulting courses consisted of distinct sections devoted to zoology, botany, and human physiology, respectively. In these courses, type studies were often used, with perhaps an apple tree to illustrate a woody plant and a grasshopper to illustrate an insect. Field trips were taken to see these organisms in their natural environment. Laboratory exercises gave detailed studies of their structure and experiments with their physiology.

Such courses persisted into the 1920's. In many ways they were excellent courses, interesting and effective in meeting the goals of science

---

[42] Watson, Fletcher G., "Why Do We Need More Physics Courses?" *The Physics Teacher,* Vol. 5, no. 5, 1967.

education. Unfortunately, it was all too easy for type studies to become formalized into the pattern of college sciences. And the lack of integration between the separate sections of the course disturbed many educators.

The *Thirty-first Yearbook* of the National Society for the Study of Education had as great an impact on secondary school biology as it did upon general science. A number of the 38 major generalizations of science listed in the *Thirty-first Yearbook* as objectives for a twelve-year science program were derived from the field of biology.

Courses built upon these generalizations differed completely from earlier biology courses. They were well integrated. Plant and animal cells were studied at the same time to make comparisons easier. All forms of reproduction were combined into one unit. Such biology courses were systematic, highly logical, and generally appealing to secondary school science teachers. Today most high school biology courses and most textbooks are organized on this plan although in recent years modifications are increasing.

As excellent as a course based on major generalizations may appear on superficial examination, serious defects show up in actual use. The use of major generalizations as goals effectively eliminated the discovery approach to science. No pupil can possibly discover enough in one year to arrive at even one major generalization. Experiments, demonstrations, and field work must be used chiefly as illustrations of the ways generalizations apply. Indeed, laboratory and field work can be minimized or even eliminated in such a course because books, films, and slides are able to present applications of generalizations much more quickly and effectively and without the problem of introducing confusing exceptions.

Much that was good in earlier biology courses was lost in using major generalizations as objectives. Type studies were abandoned, although type studies give the best concepts of an organism as a whole, since an organism is more than the sum of its parts or the sum of its processes. Lost too has been the emphasis upon the place of living things in their natural environment, a loss that cannot be replaced by a single unit on the principles of ecology.

On the whole, the recommendations of the *Thirty-first Yearbook* improved high school biology greatly by providing an effective organization. Major generalizations and concepts are excellent centers about which to build a course, but the discovery approach to biology requires more specific objectives.

Concern over the limitations of secondary school biology has produced some interesting trends in the biology offerings in the high schools. Courses have been developed which are organized around broad concepts and present biology as a changing body of knowledge. The pupils work out their own experimental procedures in the laboratory and answer questions and draw conclusions based on the data they collect.

Biological Sciences Curriculum Study (BSCS). The Biological Sciences Curriculum Study was organized in 1958 by the Education Committee of the American Institute of the Biological Sciences (AIBS) to find ways to improve biological education in the United States. Major financial support came from the National Science Foundation.

As one approach to biology the Biological Sciences Curriculum Committee suggests the study of populations, species, and communities in habitats surrounding a school.

Three parallel sets of course materials were prepared by a team of writers working during the summers of 1960, 1961, and 1962. The materials included texts, laboratory manuals, and teachers' guides. The materials were tested during the years following each of the first two summers of work. About 1,000 teachers and 150,000 students tested the materials before they were made available commercially in 1963.[43] These were used by about 328,000 students in 1964–65 (see Table 2). Writing teams revised the materials in 1966, and these are presently available through various publishers.

The three parallel approaches are referred to as the Blue, Yellow, and Green versions. All three have certain common aims: to make clear to the student the nature of scientific inquiry, the history of biological concepts, genetic continuity, regulation and homeostasis, complementary character of structure and function, diversity of the type and unity of pattern of living things, change of organisms through time, complementarity of organisms and environment and biological roots of behavior.

"There is no indication that any one version is more suited to a rural or urban setting; to a more or less sophisticated student body, nor to a more or less well-prepared teacher. The choice among the versions is best made by the teacher on the assessment of the students' background and interest in the particular milieu in which they work."[44]

In all three versions, biological inquiry as a method of obtaining knowledge is emphasized. Once the students are familiar with laboratory materials and techniques, they are challenged with problems that they must solve by using their initiative and ingenuity.

Some teachers are using some of the materials to supplement their traditional courses while others are using an entire version. A number of local systems and state education departments are developing syllabuses in biology which are primarily based on one or more of the BSCS versions. New York State, for example, has recently distributed an experimental biology syllabus which is primarily the yellow version approach of the Biological Sciences Curriculum Study. These approaches are having a tremendous impact on biological education in the United States.

Blue version[45] (summary).

The theories of the gene, of the cell, and of evolution have been and continue to be the major unifying ideas in biology. From its inception, the Blue Version has attempted to provide and emphasize a physiological dimension to these ideas.

[43] BSCS Newsletter, No. 28, April, 1966.

[44] Biological Sciences Curriculum Study, "About BSCS Biology," Boulder, Colorado, November, 1966.

[45] BSCS Newsletter, *op. cit.*

A comparison of the early experimental editions with the current commercial publication shows that evolution theory now functions as the axial thread around which the classical disciplines of biology are organized. The physiological interpretation of the major ideas, however, still remains. It has been the author's intention to emphasize the physiological unity of life and to consider of less importance the differences between living things—differences which often become magnified in a more traditional approach. This, of course, does not mean that the rich variety of life should be slighted. It is the unifying idea of evolution which helps us to understand the fundamental similarities of living things. This same idea enables us to recognize the survival value inherent in variation.

A major goal for the future edition will be to make a solid synthesis of the text and laboratory investigations both physically and pedagogically into a single volume. Each text chapter will contain its own pertinent investigations bound within its pages. The new edition will retain the unifying approach of teaching the levels of biological organization as we assume they have evolved from the simplest to the most complex; that is, from molecules to man.

Beginning with the nature of scientific inquiry, classification of living organisms, and the principles of evolution, the text then moves to the origin of life on earth from organic molecules to the genetic code. Cell processes are taken up and followed by a discussion of reproduction and development in plants and animals. After a unit on heredity, basic tissue and organ systems of plants and animals are discussed. The final unit deals with populations, societies, and communities.

Yellow Version (summary).

The Yellow Version attempts to cover the major subfields of biology usually covered in the beginning courses in both high school and college. Nevertheless, the Yellow Version differs from conventional approaches in two respects. First, . . . emphasis on these various subfields differs considerably from conventional approaches in trying to give order to the various data of biology by treating them in relation to the (nine) conceptual themes adopted by the BSCS.[46]

In addition to treatment of the nine themes, the Yellow Version attempts to provide a "balanced consideration of microorganisms, plants, and animals,"[47] and a "balanced consideration of all levels of living organization,"[48] from the molecule through the entire world biosphere.

Also included is a "thorough, unbiased, and scientifically objective presentation of such supposedly controversial biological subjects as organic

[46] Schwab, Joseph I., *Biology Teachers' Handbook*, John Wiley and Sons, New York, 1963, p. 25.

[47] Moore, John A. and others, foreword to *Biological Science: An Inquiry into Life*, rev. ed. Harcourt, Brace & World, New York, 1963.

[48] *Ibid.*

evolution, the nature of individual and racial differences, sex and reproduction in the human species, . . . (and) the problems of population growth and control."[49]

"The Yellow Version text divides the subject matter of biology into seven sections: cells, microorganisms, plant life, animal life, genetics, evolution, and ecology."[50]

Emphasizing the unity of all living organisms, the text begins with a discussion of the basic structures and functions of cells. Diversity of organisms is illustrated in the following three sections dealing with microorganisms, plants, and animals, respectively. Bacteria and viruses are discussed from the point of view of what they are, how they grow, and how they reproduce, with emphasis on the ecological and economical importance of microorganisms to man. Photosynthesis and the major tissue and organ systems of plants and animals are the major topics of the following two sections. After a discussion of reproduction and development in animals, the text investigates the theme of genetic continuity, beginning with patterns of heredity as described by Mendel and taking up modern theories of gene structure and function. The last two sections discuss aspects of evolution and ecology, respectively. Both the biology and cultural evolution of man are covered in detail, and man's role in the biosphere is emphasized.

The Green Version (Summary). The rationale of the Green Version is based on the following statement:

> . . . the aims of the Green Version are to introduce the student to the living world, to give him some appreciation of the point of view and the ways of science, and to provide him with such biological information as may be necessary and useful in going on through life. . . . The writers of the Green Version feel that having some idea of the way in which the biological community functions is at least as important as having some idea of the way one's own body functions. . . . the problems created by growing human populations, by depletion of resources, by pollution, by regional development, and the like, all require intelligent community or governmental action for solution. These are, in part at least, biological-ecological problems, and every citizen should have some awareness of their background.[51]

The summary of the course is as follows:

> The general plan of the *Green Version* is to proceed from the familiar to the unfamiliar and from the general to the specific. However, the narrative often departs from this sequence for reasons of logic or convenience. The

[49] *Ibid.*
[50] *Ibid.*
[51] Schwab, *op. cit.*

Green Version takes the whole organism as the primary unit of study. Its first concern is with how individuals are related to one another and to the environment.

The text begins with cycles of energy and materials in the biosphere, then turns to the basic biological unit—the individual. Using the individual as a building block, it examines, in order, populations, communities, and ecosystems. There follows a section on taxonomic diversity of animals, plants, and micro-organisms. The next section deals with the ecological diversity on land, in fresh water, and in the seas; with the history of life; and with the major biogeographical regions of the world. In subsequent sections the text explores cells and the cellular structure of organisms; the physiology, reproduction, and development of plants and animals; heredity, evolution, and behavior; the structure and functioning of the human

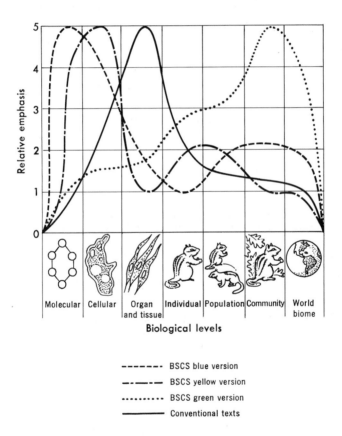

Figure 3. *Level of emphasis in BSCS biology and conventional texts.* (Biological Sciences Curriculum Study. *BSCS Newsletter*, No. 12, February, 1962, p. 7.)

animal organism in some detail; and, finally, the human animal in the midst of his biological setting.[52]

Whereas the conventional texts have their major emphasis on the organ and tissue level (reflecting the bulk of biological knowledge of forty years ago), the Blue Version has major emphasis on the molecular level, the Green Version on the community level, and the Yellow Version on the cellular level.[53]

A number of studies comparing the effects of BSCS courses and traditional courses on student achievement in biology have been made.[54, 55, 56, 57] In general the BSCS students score significantly higher on BSCS achievement tests, and slightly lower than conventional students on traditional biology achievement tests (such as the Nelson Biology Test and the test by Victor Noll, "What Do You Think?").

One appraiser of changes in critical thinking reported the following results:[58]

(1) no significant differences between achievement in critical thinking of students of the Green and Yellow Versions and "conventional" biology

(2) students of the Blue Version scored significantly higher than students of "conventional" biology

(3) students of the Blue Version also achieved significantly more than students of the Yellow Version

(4) the Yellow Version students achieved more than the Green Version students.

A study which included comparisons of student achievement between sexes, between the R and S forms of the BSCS achievement and final examinations, and among the three versions showed the following:[59]

[52] *BSCS High School Biology Green Version*, advertising pamphlet, Rand McNally, n.d.

[53] Schwab, *op. cit.*

[54] Lisonbee, Lorenzo, and Bill J. Fullerton, "The Comparative Effect of BSCS and Traditional Biology on Student Achievement," *School Science and Mathematics*, 44:594–598, 1964.

[55] Lance, Mary Louise, "A Comparison of Gains in Achievement Made by Students of BSCS High School Biology and Students of a Conventional Course in Biology." Unpublished doctoral dissertation, University of Georgia, 1964.

[56] George, Kenneth D., "The Effect of BSCS and Conventional Biology on Critical Thinking," *Journal of Research in Science Teaching*, 3:293–299, 1965.

[57] Moore, C. Olan, "An Evaluation of the Effectiveness of the BSCS Approach to Teaching Biology to High Ability Students in the Ninth Grade." Unpublished doctoral dissertation, Arizona State University, 1965.

[58] George, Kenneth D., "The Effect of BSCS and Conventional Biology on Critical Thinking," *Journal of Research in Science Teaching*, 3:293–299, 1965.

[59] BSCS Newsletter, No. 30, January, 1967.

1. Academic ability and BSCS achievement tests were appropriate in difficulty for the groups.
2. Males had higher mean scores than females on both ability and achievement groups.
3. Consistent differences appeared in both ability and achievement among groups in the three curricular versions. The Blue Version groups had the highest means, the Yellow group next, and the Green Version the lowest means.
4. Both reading tests given showed results highly related to academic ability tests and to the BSCS achievement tests.

Ausubel[60] states that BSCS materials are "reasonably congruent with the content and methods of modern biology, but except for the Green Version, are psychologically and pedagogically unsound for the majority of tenth graders."

1. Blue and Yellow Versions shows no concern with application to familiar or practical problems in biology.
2. Too much detailed biochemistry and very highly sophisticated information.
3. Thematic organization is poor. Some topics such as genetics or evolution, ecology, reproduction are treated independently with no related ideas.
4. Blue and Yellow Versions violate psychology of learning—the student first encounters unfamiliar material such as molecular biology before he comes in contact with topics as ecology and mammalian physiology.

Physics. Less than half a million pupils enroll in introductory physics courses in the senior high school.[61] This is not a very great enrollment considering that over 2.5 million pupils are enrolled in the twelfth grade in the public schools. An increase in enrollments in physics took place between 1962–63 and 1963–64, but this increase occurred when student enrollments in the twelfth grade increased by 600,000 students.[62] The percentage enrollment in physics declined steadily between 1962 and 1965 (see Figure 1 and Table 3).

The relative unpopularity of physics is not because of the nature of the subject itself. No area has more applications to everyday life. No subject deals with more exciting devices and ideas. The fault lies in the goals of the teacher.

[60] Ausubel, David, "An Evaluation of the BSCS Approach to High School Biology," *The American Biology Teacher,* 28:176–186, 1966.
[61] Watson, *op. cit.,* p. 213.
[62] *Ibid.*

Year	Introductory Physics[a]	Grade 12	Percent in Introductory Physics
1948–49	291,000	1,126,000	25.8
1954–55	303,000	1,246,000	24.3
1958–59	379,000	1,538,000	24.6
1960–61	385,000	1,820,000	21.2
1962–63	397,000	1,866,000	21.3
1964–65	485,000[b]	2,472,000	19.6

Table 3. *Enrollments in Introductory Physics and in the Twelfth Grade, 1948–1964 in Public Schools* (Watson, *op. cit.*, p. 212.)

[a] USOE *Digest of Educational Statistics*, 1965 ed., Table 16.
[b] USOE preliminary data for introductory courses.

The college preparatory function of high school physics continues to dominate the thinking of physics teachers despite the efforts of many scientists and science educators to revitalize the subject. "Physics as a college entrance requirement has been so firmly entrenched that teachers have had little opportunity to do more than follow a rather definite course of study based on factual information and laws which college professors deemed necessary as a basis for achievement in college. Physics teachers must discard the artificial standards established by colleges and universities and make physics a vital and exciting subject."[63]

The following are some of the causes for the inadequacy of secondary school physics:

1. Emphasis upon principles and "laws" rather than upon the concrete things of the environment.

2. Insistence upon memorization of formulas and standardized ways of solving problems.

3. Excessive use of mathematical exercises in order to develop skills with formal science problems.

4. Employment of stereotyped laboratory exercises and materials of the type used in formal college classes.

5. Failure to provide for individual differences.

6. Inability to stimulate original thinking.

7. Refusal to accept responsibility for social and emotional growth of pupils.

[63] Hunter, G. W., *Science Teaching at Junior and Senior High School Levels*. American Book Co., New York, 1934.

The reorganization of high school physics has been made by the Physical Science Study Committee (PSSC). Like the BSCS approaches, the PSSC course is based on broad concepts which disregard the artificial boundaries established in traditional physics courses. "The course attempts to present physics as physics appears to contemporary physicists; as a unified, but unfinished story of mankind".[64] Through laboratory experimentation the pupils discover physical laws.

PSSC Physics.   The Physical Sciences Study Committee was founded in 1956 at the Massachusetts Institute of Technology by a group of university professors and secondary school physics teachers. The aim of the committee was to develop an improved introductory course in physics. The project was sponsored by the National Science Foundation as well as the Ford and Sloan Foundations.

The materials which were developed were tried, evaluated, and revised for three years before they were released for general use in the Fall of 1960.[65] Table 4 published by the PSSC Committee shows the growth in the use of PSSC materials since 1960. The *Nation's Schools* reports that 3,100 high schools used PSSC materials as a basic reference in 1966 and that the materials are widely used throughout the country.[66]

A second edition of the PSSC textbook, *Physics*, published by D. C. Heath Co. became available in 1965. The following statement taken from the preface of the book tells how the unifying principles of physics are presented.[67]

> The PSSC course consists of four closely interconnected parts. Part I is a general introduction to the fundamental physical notions of time, space, and matter: how we grasp and how we measure them. As the student learns of the almost boundless range of dimensions from the immensely large to the infinitesimally small, from microseconds to billions of years, he finds out how these magnitudes can be measured. He learns that instruments serve as an extension of his senses. Laboratory experience shows how we first measure by direct counting and then extend our range of measurements by calibrating and using simple instruments such as stroboscopes or range finders.
>
> From these experiments measuring time and space, the student moves to an understanding of velocity and acceleration, of vectors and of relative

---

[64] National Science Foundation, "Science Course Improvement Projects," Washington, D.C., October, 1962.

[65] Finley, Gilbert C., "The Physical Science Study Committee, *The School Review*, 70:1, pp. 63–81, Spring 1962.

[66] Cawelti, *op. cit.*, p. 67.

[67] *Physics*, 2nd edition, D. C. Heath Publishing Co., Boston, 1965, preface.

[68] No footnote.

Year	No. of Teachers	No. of Students
1957–58	8	300
1958–59	270	11,000
1959–60	560	22,500
1960–61	1100	44,000
1961–62	1800	75,000
1962–63	3000	125,000
1963–64	4000	160,000
1964–65	5000	200,000
1965–66	5500	225,000
1966–67	6000	250,000

Table 4.   *Use of PSSC Materials**

* PSSC Newsletter (1966).

motion. He then goes on to study matter, which we see moving through space in the course of time. In this first examination of matter, we develop the concepts of mass and of its conservation. We then use the evidence of physicists and chemists to find that matter is made of relatively few kinds of atoms. Direct experience is provided in the laboratory. There, for instance, the students compute the size of a molecule from measurements of thin films of oil. Moving pictures extend this direct laboratory experience by showing experiments which are beyond the reach of students.

Throughout, the student is led to realize that physics is a single subject of study. In particular, time, space, and matter cannot be separated. Furthermore, he sees that physics is a developing subject, and that this development is the imaginative work of men and women like him.

The topics in the PSSC course are selected and ordered to progress from the simple and familiar to the more subtle ideas of modern atomic physics. In Part I we have looked at a broad picture of the universe. Now as we examine certain fields of physics in more detail, we start in Part II with light. We live by light, and the student moves easily into the study of sharp and diffuse shadows, reflection in mirrors, and the refraction of light at optical boundaries. The natural development of the subject leads us to develop a particle theory (or model) of light. Its discussion illustrates repeatedly the manner in which virtually all scientific knowledge develops. Again films—for instance, the film on the pressure of light—help the student to go beyond the laboratory.

Under continued scrutiny the particle model proves inadequate, and the student finds that we need another model—a wave model. The laboratory again provides an unexcelled source of experience, and here the student becomes familiar with the properties of waves. He observes the behavior of waves on ropes and on the surface of water. He begins to recognize the group of characteristics that constitute wave behavior. Knowledge of interference and diffraction comes directly from a study of waves in a ripple tank. For the first time, perhaps, the smears of light around street lamps, the colors of oil slicks, and the formation of images by lenses appear as aspects of the wave nature of light.

According to Arons,[69] the PSSC course is associated with a significant improvement in the ability of the student to learn from laboratory work in a college physics course. Verbrugge[70] compared matched groups of former PSSC pupils with former conventional high school physics students. The study showed that PSSC students obtain a higher percentage of A and B grades and about the same number of middle grades. This would seem to indicate that the PSSC course at least does not hinder the student who goes on to college. It does not necessarily mean that it prepares him either, even though many PSSC students indicate that PSSC was an extremely valuable course and did prepare them for college work.[71]

In general, few studies have been conducted using criteria which are independent of PSSC materials. Those that have been conducted indicate that students perform better on examinations based on PSSC materials than for some other physics course. Able students perform better than average students and show "behavioral changes in the direction of the objectives. But at least one major study suggests that even able students have experienced some reduction in interest in science courses in the last few years."[72]

Harvard Project: Physics, (HPP).[73] The Harvard Project is an outgrowth of the efforts of about 80 physicists and teachers to produce a one-year course in physics for use in the high school and junior college. In 1962 a feasibility study, supported by the Carnegie Foundation, was conducted. In 1964, work on the project began on a larger scale supported by the Carnegie Foundation, U. S. Office of Education, Sloan Foundation, and the National Science Foundation.

A pilot version of the course of study was used in 1967 by 2,600 students on a controlled experimental basis[74] in more than 50 schools in the United States. Tested materials as well as an evaluation report will be available by 1969.

The course is for a wide range of pupil abilities. It is intended to

---

[69] Arons, Arnold, "The New High School Physics Course," *Physics Today,* 13:20–25, 1960.

[70] Verbrugge, Frank, from a paper delivered at the Annual Meeting of the American Association of Physics Teachers, February, 1961.

[71] Friedman, F. L., *et al.* "The Relation of the PSSC Physics Course to Conventional High School Courses," *The Science Teacher,* 29:49–55, February 1962.

[72] Cawelti, *loc. cit.*

[73] Materials are available from Harvard Project: Physics, Harvard University Cambridge, Massachusetts 02138. Available materials: Basic text units, teachers' guides, student laboratory guides, filmstrips, filmloops, programmed instruction booklets.

[74] Holton, Gerald, "Project Physics; A Report on its Aims and Current Status," *The Physics Teacher,* Vol. 5, May, 1967, pp. 198–211.

attract and be suitable for half of the students in high school and is designed for the average student. Physics is presented "as a human activity" and that activity is viewed in an historical and philosophical perspective. "In doing this, a multi-media and a multi-model approach is being used in order to make flexibility of design."[75] It is expected that this course will better meet the needs of individual students.

Holton[76] indicates that the Harvard Project Physics is based on various assumptions which are different from those that were used to initiate the curriculum of the early 1960's. "We have begun to respect the role of the teacher as collaborator in making curriculum development work in the classroom on his own terms, and we have become more interested in considering the different needs of different students in the same classroom. . . . We have different assumptions of what is and is not feasible or desirable for schools to do: for example, we would not today develop a curriculum that caters only to the intellectual elite." This is a new direction for the development of curricula. The role of the teacher is playing an important part in the development of curriculum which was not the case in the 1960's. PSSC was primarily developed by research scientists who rightfully believed change was needed. When writing the materials, the PSSC Committee and others neglected to take into account the wide diversity of abilities of pupils in a classroom. Unknowingly, they catered to the above average student, while thinking they were developing a curriculum for the average student who took physics. Future committees can capitalize on the experience of the 1960's to develop courses which are needed for all levels of pupil abilities.

Chemistry. Chemistry has fared better than physics in popularity during the past few decades. It has continued to attract about the same percentage of pupils from the general school population for fifty years. In 1964–65, over 900,000 students enrolled in traditional introductory courses (see Table 2). Traditional courses are still popular although other approaches to teaching chemistry are available. As in the case of physics, however, chemistry is failing to direct an adequate number of young people into scientific vocations. Pupils take the course and then turn to other fields for their life work.

The criticisms that have been leveled at physics apply equally well to chemistry. The usual chemistry course is still concerned almost completely with abstractions. Pupils must memorize endless laws, principles, minor

[75] Lockhard, *op. cit.*, p. 251.
[76] Holton, *loc. cit.*
[77] No footnote.

facts, symbols, formulas, and equations. From the very beginning they are drilled in chemical shorthand until they assume that formulas and equations are chemistry, not merely a simplified way of expressing what is known about chemistry.

Much laboratory work in traditional chemistry courses consists of sets of exercises. Some of these are designed to teach pupils the use of chemical apparatus and procedures. Others are designed to illustrate generalizations made in books and lectures. In general, the pupils do not carry out true experiments in which they are trying to find the answers to real problems.

It is interesting that with these serious faults chemistry has been able to maintain its enrollments. Anyone who knows junior high school pupils, however, may suspect the answer. To boys and girls of the early secondary school grades, chemistry suggests all kinds of exciting things—explosions, color changes, strange bubblings, startling transformations—strongly tinted with the romance that science fiction gives to chemistry. What a pity so many of them are disillusioned!

Traditional chemistry courses have needed the same reorganization that is suggested for high school physics. More attention should be given to materials with which the pupils are familiar. True experiments should replace many of the stereotyped laboratory exercises. The problem solving approach should be used extensively throughout the course. Pupils should be encouraged to engage in extensive project work. Most important of all, the preparatory function should be minimized and pupils should be allowed to follow up special interests and develop along lines in which they show special ability. New courses have been developed using this approach, but teachers are hesitant to use them. Many teachers think that they lack the chemistry background needed to teach the new approaches as well as the training in the procedures and methods to handle the materials.

New approaches in chemistry which emphasize laboratory work and discovery are now part of the high school offerings. Like BSCS and PSSC programs, these chemistry approaches are organized around broad concepts. Two of these approaches will be described in detail.

Chemical Education Materials Study Program (CHEM).   The Chemical Education Materials Study Program began in 1959 when a committee established by the American Chemical Society examined the existing high school chemistry courses with the intent of improving the content of these courses. As a result of this meeting, the Committee obtained support from the National Science Foundation to design an up-dated introductory chemistry course for the secondary schools. Two centers were established for the CHEM Study program—one at the University of California and the other at Harvey Mudd College, Claremont, California.

Experimental texts and laboratory experiments were prepared during the summer of 1960 by a writing committee consisting of seven college professors and seven high school chemistry teachers. The first draft was ready for use in 1961–62 for a pilot program. Twenty-four high schools were involved in the first pilot study. The materials were rewritten during the summer of 1961, and 158 teachers used the rewritten materials during the 1961–62 academic year. The material was rewritten again during 1962 using the information obtained from the pilot run. The W. H. Freeman Publishing Company received the final revisions for publication in the Fall of 1963.

By 1964–65 over 128,000 students were using CHEM study materials. This was about 10 to 15 percent of the United States high school chemistry population (see Table 1). In 1966 more than 3,100 high schools or about 43 percent[78] of those which reported for a study conducted by Cawelti used the materials. The study also indicated that many schools had used the materials but later abandoned them. Many teachers use only parts of the material rather than the whole course.

> The CHEM study materials are highly integrated around the development of concepts, theories, and ideas in chemistry. The experimental nature of science is the basis for student investigation of chemical reactions.
>
> Emphasis on the structure of a chemical system, including the electron structure, the geometrical arrangement of the atoms, their relative sizes and shapes, the packing together of atoms and molecules, the forces between them, and how these affect their chemistry, is expected to guide the student in his understanding and interpretation of the complex chemical phenomena.
>
> The text material begins with an overview of the field of chemistry. Gradually, the student is introduced to major generalizations including: energy and chemical reactions, rates of chemical reactions, equilibrium and chemical reactions, stochiometry, atoms and their structure, periodicity of chemical properties, and electron structure. After the generalizations have been developed through experimentation, the students are expected to continue using what they have learned in interpreting and understanding more complex ideas.

Since the CHEM study was introduced into the schools "there has been no change in the percentage of students who elect to enroll in Chemistry."[79] However, the number of students who wish to take a post-chemistry science course other than physics has increased.[80]

[78] Cawelti, op. cit., p. 67.
[79] Chemical Education Materials Study, Newsletter, 4, No. 1, February, 1966.
[80] Ibid.

Evaluation studies have been made of the CHEM course and most show "an enthusiastic reception on the part of professional chemists and secondary school teachers."[81] Nevertheless, some teachers consider the course unsuitable for the average student who elects chemistry; the material is for the more able student.[82] The results of a testing program conducted by CHEM in 1961–62 suggest that the new course can be effectively taught to the typical student who elects high school chemistry.[83] Statements regarding the level of the course are not consistent as one can see.

In 1966 the CHEM study steering committee accepted proposals from publishers to revise the CHEM study textbook. The revision rights have been granted to publishers who will produce at least two revisions without the use of the CHEM study colophon. The CHEM study will terminate all of its activities once the project is well underway.[84]

Chemical Bond Approach (CBA).   The Chemical Bond Approach is an outgrowth of a conference held for college and high school chemistry teachers at Reed College in 1957. The purpose of the meeting was to reorganize the study of high school chemistry. The CBA committee felt that the subject of chemistry needed to be organized and presented to explore three key points:[85]

1. Chemists work in the laboratory to obtain data.
2. Chemists use their imaginations to develop ideas.
3. Chemists combine experimental data and imaginative ideas to further their understanding of chemical systems.

The project headquarters was set up at Earlham College, Richmond, Indiana, in 1958. The first trial edition of the materials was ready in the summer of 1959 and used during the summer of 1960. By 1963, the book and laboratory materials were ready for publication. The information gathered from over three hundred teachers and 20,000 students was used to prepare the final revision.[86] About 23,400 students used the materials in 1964–65 (see Table 1). Cawelti reports that from 7,237 accredited

[81] Heath, Robert W. and David W. Stickell, "CHEM and CBA Effects on Achievement in Chemistry," *The Science Teacher*, 30:45–46, September, 1963.

[82] Cawelti, *op. cit.*

[83] Chemical Education Materials Study, Newsletter, 2, No. 2, March, 1962.

[84] Chemical Education Materials Study, Newsletter, 6, No. 1, February, 1966.

[85] CBA Newsletter, 2, No. 2, April, 1963.

[86] *Ibid.*

high schools which responded to a questionnaire for a national survey, about 10 percent were using CBA materials in 1966.[87]

The following is a short description of the CBA textbook *Chemical Systems*.[88] "The major questions with which this book deals are (1) What is the nature of a chemical system—how do we recognize it, and how do we interpret it? (2) When a chemical reaction occurs, how does the change alter the surroundings of the system? (3) Why do chemical elements form certain compounds but not others? (4) What determines the conditions under which a chemical change is complete? (5) Why do reactions take time to occur?" The book is divided into five parts:

Beginning with definitions of science and chemistry, the text examines the nature of chemical change and properties of states of matter. Atomic mass, molecular mass, chemical formulas, and equations are introduced.

In Part II, the electrical nature of chemical systems is taken up, and leads to the conclusion that matter may be considered to have a structure with atoms as building blocks.

Part III considers various mental models. The charge cloud model and the atomic orbital model are proposed for the arrangement of nuclei and electrons. The roles of kinetic-molecular theory and enthalpy, as mental models, are also discussed.

Part IV deals with bonds in chemical systems. Substances are classified as covalent, metallic, or ionic, based in part on the properties of the substances and in part on ideas about the structure of each substance.

In Part V, the study of electrical systems begun in Part II is carried further to develop the idea of chemical equilibrium. Electrical potential energy, concentration, and free energy are shown to be interrelated and expressed by an equilibrium constant which describes the concentration of the components of a system in an equilibrium state.

CBA materials are not used as widely as CHEM Study materials. Cawelti[89] indicates that several states had virtually no adoptions in 1966 and that the abandonment rate for CBA was higher than that for CHEM. New York State has introduced a new experimental syllabus in chemistry in 1966 which virtually removes CBA and CHEM from the New York State Public Schools,[90] but this new experimental syllabus uses both CBA and CHEM Study materials.

The many criticisms stated for CHEM Study can also be said for the CBA approach. The material is "most appropriate for able students and

---

[87] Cawelti, *op. cit.*

[88] Abstracted and quoted in part from Chemical Bond Approach Committee, *Chemical Systems*, McGraw-Hill Publishing Co., New York, 1963, preface.

[89] Cawelti, *op. cit.*, p. 67.

[90] Communications from Robert F. Zimmerman, Bureau of Curriculum Development, State Education Department, Albany, New York, 1967.

even with them, teachers have often had to make modifications despite careful revisions made in early stages of development."[91]

Physical science.   In the 1940's physical science electives were developed for pupils who did not have the ability to handle traditional physics and chemistry. These were intended to be terminal courses and were offered in the eleventh and twelfth grades.

Many kinds of physical science electives exist today, and most are intended for eleventh and twelfth grade pupils who do not wish to pursue a scientific career. Some physical science courses have been developed to provide academically superior pupils with the background to take advanced placement programs. Courses in physical sciences for the academically talented are used in some instances as a substitute for physics and chemistry. The advantages of such courses include the elimination of duplication of a number of topics, such as "states of matter" and "atomic structure," which are found in both physics and chemistry.

Courses in physical science for pupils who are not academically talented tend to be unsatisfactory. Classes are generally large when they should be small. Most courses are dominated by college tradition and are of little value to the pupils for whom they are designed. The laboratory is centered around laboratory exercises and not on problem solving. Some courses have no laboratory period scheduled. Classes are often assigned to standard classrooms without facilities for laboratory work. The assumption has often been that these courses are for "second-rate" individuals who cannot benefit from taking science.

Physical science courses can benefit the slower reader and the less academic-minded pupils. But these courses must allow enough time for learning through first-hand experiences. Classes should be small and a great deal of the class time should be devoted to project work and to the solution of individual problems.

Some of the trends in physical science have already been discussed in the section on the junior high school program. The Introductory Physical Science Course (IPS) is prepared for pupils who have a wide range of abilities. As was mentioned, this course stresses the laboratory approach and seeks to develop basic attitudes and skills.

The Secondary School Science Project (SSSP) is primarily for pupils in grades eight and nine. Included are areas of geology, astronomy, physics, chemistry, and mathematics. Both the IPS and SSSP approaches are broad but integrated courses.

There are no extensive projects underway which are developing materials for physical science courses on the high school level. Some city and

[91] Cawelti, *op. cit.*, p. 68.

county school systems are developing kindergarten to twelfth-grade sequences which include physical science materials for grades ten to twelve. Some of these will be discussed later in the chapter (see Appendix).

OTHER SECONDARY SCHOOL
CURRICULUM DEVELOPMENTS

Many secondary school projects are in progress. One worthy of mentioning here is being conducted in the Portland Public Schools, Portland, Oregon. An experimental science program which integrates CBA and CHEM study and PSSC courses is being tried. "The goal of the integration is to avoid repetition of subject matter, consider a subject in depth from the text that offers the best treatment and help students and teachers learn "to look for similarities in rather than differences between chemistry and physics."[92]

New York State has prepared three new syllabuses capitalizing on the strengths of the recent nationwide courses in biology, chemistry, and physics:[93] Biology: An Experimental Syllabus; Chemistry: A Syllabus for Secondary Schools; and Physics: A Syllabus for Secondary Schools.

Further information concerning other elementary and secondary school curriculum projects can be obtained from the *Report of the International Clearinghouse on Science and Mathematics Curricula Developments,* Commission on Science Education, AAAS, Science Teaching Center, University of Maryland, College Park, Maryland. The report is designed to give information concerning projects which are on-going and have been influential in innovating science and mathematics curricula.

Science programs with a K–12 Emphasis.   A school system may offer twelve years of science courses without offering a twelve-year science program. A program, by the very meaning of the word, has unity of purpose, unity of approach, and unity of procedure.

In the kindergarten to twelfth-grade (K–12) science program a pupil should be provided with a carefully developed sequence of experiences. He should not repeat experiences, but he should review his understandings through encountering situations similar to those he has met previously. His understandings will be continually deepened and broadened as he finds himself in increasingly complex situations.

---

[92] Committee on the Integration of CHEMS and PSSC, *Teacher's Guide for Physics-Chemistry,* 2nd edition, Portland Curriculum Center, Portland School District, Portland, Oregon.

[93] Available from the Bureau of Secondary School Curriculum Development, State Education Department, Albany, New York.

The organizational pattern of our schools into elementary, junior high, and senior high schools has hindered the development of a sequential K–12 science program. The artificial boundaries which are created by this organizational pattern have not allowed articulation of the science program. The science program is often divided into blocks such as K–6, 7–8, and 9–12; or K–6, 7–9, and 10–12; or K–8 and 9–12, depending upon the school system. Generally there is no organization of these science program blocks into a unified and articulated K–12 science sequence.

The articulated kindergarten to twelfth-grade program is only possible through the cooperation of teachers concerned. These teachers must work closely together. They must agree to the purpose of their teaching and the methods they will use in attaining their goals. Without agreement such a program cannot be implemented.

New curricula are being developed which have this broad orientation. The Science Manpower Project of Teachers College, Columbia University, has prepared a sequential plan for kindergarten through the twelfth grade. A number of monographs are already available and many are still in preparation.[94] The Arlington County K-12 Curriculum Development Project[95] is attempting to develop an articulated science curriculum which provides extensive laboratory experiences and relates science concepts with and to specific experiences.[96] Associated with this curriculum is an enrichment program for use outside the school. This program includes materials for the slow learner at all grade levels. A laboratory course in physical science for grades ten to twelve is also included in the program.

The New York State Program is well underway. Materials for various aspects of the program have been produced. Some experimental syllabuses and handbooks for the elementary grades are now available.[97] Others are in various stages of completion. The Experimental Syllabuses in Biology, Physics, Chemistry, and Earth Science are now being used in the schools. The New Work State program will be discussed later in detail. The State of Pennsylvania Curriculum Development Program[98] is on a state-wide basis for grades kindergarten through college. New curriculum materials have been produced and used on a formal and informal basis in classrooms. The

[94] Science Manpower Publications available from Bureau of Publications, Teachers College, Columbia University.

[95] Arlington County K–12 Curriculum Development Project, 4751 North 25th St. Arlington, Va. 22207.

[96] Lockhard, *op. cit.*

[97] Bureau of Curriculum Development, New York State Education Department, Albany, New York.

[98] Commonwealth of Pennsylvania, Department of Public Instruction. Harrisburg, Pennsylvania. Materials available include: Science in Action—a series of pamphlets describing activities for units of work; A Recommended Continuum for Science Education Kindergarten Through College, *Guide for Teaching Advanced Biology.*

Minneapolis School System[99] reorganized its curriculum for kindergarten through grade twelve. Curriculum materials are being produced by teachers and a project staff. The New York City[100] science program reorganization was started in 1963. A kindergarten through twelfth-grade program is planned which stresses important concepts and critical thinking and is laboratory oriented.

"Double" and "triple" track programs.   A single science program cannot take advantage of all the range of interests and aptitudes in a school. Even with "ability grouping" and with all possible provision for individual differences, a single general science program is still a single program designed neither for the academically brilliant nor the academically retarded. The senior high school program as usually offered is made up only of courses designed for pupils with high scientific aptitudes. Were the senior high school program redesigned for the majority of the pupils, the extremes would still be neglected.

One solution to the problem attempted by some school systems is the development of two programs, each with its own sequence of courses. One program is designed for pupils with high scientific aptitudes. It anticipates that these pupils will continue their study of science in colleges and universities. The other program is designed for the great majority of pupils and is looked upon as terminal. Some authorities recommend the development of still a third program for the academically retarded, one that puts almost complete emphasis upon first-hand experiences and project work.

There are serious administrative difficulties in adopting "multiple track" programs. Small schools do not have the staff or facilities to handle two programs. In any school the problem of scheduling classes can be enormous. However, "multiple track" programs may be an answer to the problem of giving more pupils science training of a type suited for them.

The sequences below are based on a unified kindergarten to twelfth-grade program and the pattern that the secondary program will begin at grade seven.

Nonacademic Programs

Grade	Sequence 1	Sequence 2	Sequence 3
7	General Science	General Science	General Science
8	General Science	General Science	General Science
9	General Science	General Biological Science *or* General Physical Science *or* General Science	General Science

[99] Minneapolis Public Schools, Minneapolis, Minnesota.
[100] Board of Education of the City of New York, New York, New York.

Grade	Sequence 1	Sequence 2	Sequence 3
10	Biological Science		General Biological Science
11	Physical Science		General Physical Science
12	Earth Science		

Academic Programs

Grade	Sequence 1	Sequence 2
7	General Science	General Science
8	General Science	General Science
9	Earth Science	Advanced General Science
10	General Biology	BSCS Biology
11	General Chemistry	CBA or CHEMS Chemistry
12	General Physics	PSSC Physics

Academic Programs for Gifted

Grade	Sequence 1	Sequence 2
7	Earth Science	Terminal General Science
8	Physical Science	Introductory Biology and Introductory Chemistry
9	BSCS Biology	Introductory Physics and Earth Science
10	CHEM or CBA or Advanced Chemistry	Advanced Biology
11	PSSC Physics	Advanced Chemistry
12	Seminar or Advanced or Placement or BSCS Second Year	Advanced Physics

New York State is encouraging the use of multiple track programs for grades seven to twelve by preparing special syllabuses to meet the needs of local systems. The New York State recommended sequence is shown in Tables 5, 6, 7, and 8 for grades seven to twelve. Educators in New York State have developed an elementary science program[101] for kindergarten to grade six which closely correlates with the recommended sequence for grades seven to twelve.

Table 5 shows a recommended regular sequence that places major,

---

[101] The Organization of Elementary School Science for New York State is divided into six areas of study: (1) Living Things, (2) Our Growing Bodies (3) Air, Water, and Weather (4) The Earth and Its Composition (5) The Solar System and Beyond (6) Matter and Energy. Handbooks can be obtained by writing to: Bureau of Elementary Curriculum Development, State Education Department, Albany, New York.

Science 7-8-9		Orientation The Nature of Science Measurement Tools of the Scientist	Recommended Regular Sequence—1	
A Taking Care of Ourselves	**B** The Body in Action	**7** Biological Science Emphasis	**C** Living Things Around Us	**D** Living in an Ocean of Air
E Our Planet Earth	**F** The Uni- verse	**8** Earth Science Emphasis	**G** Living in the Space Age	**H** Weather and Cli- mate
I Mechanics of Fluids and Solids	**J** The Chem- istry of Matter	**9** Physical Science Emphasis	**K** Energy at Work	**L** Living with the Atom

Table 5

but not exclusive, emphasis on biological science in grade seven, earth science in grade eight, and physical science in grade nine. This sequence does not negate the "general" science nature of the program nor the spiral approach but serves to provide more depth in the total program as fewer areas are studied each year. It is particularly designed to lay a strong foundation for biology, chemistry, and physics in the senior high school.

Table 6 illustrates another possible arrangement with some biologic content in the program in each of the three years. The ninth grade program, however, again is oriented toward the physical sciences to provide a foundation for a modern biology course.

If seventh and eighth grade science is taught half-time, it will be necessary to modify the regular program so that blocks A, B, E, and F are stressed. Tables 7 and 8 illustrate possible arrangements for accelerated programs that lead to Regents earth science or biology in grade nine. In both cases, a full program is indicated for grades seven and eight with possibly somewhat extended coverage. One deficiency of many accelerated programs in the past has been the failure to plan adaptations in grades seven and eight in view of the special offering in grade nine. In both cases the eighth grade program emphasizes physical science, and is essentially the same program recommended for grade nine in the other tables. If a school offers biology in grade nine, however, some earth science content should be included in

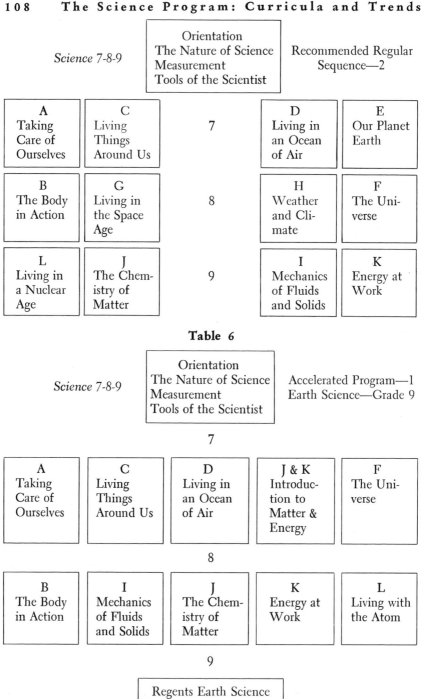

| *Science 7-8-9* | Orientation
The Nature of Science
Measurement
Tools of the Scientist | | Recommended Regular
Sequence—2 |

A Taking Care of Ourselves	C Living Things Around Us	7	D Living in an Ocean of Air	E Our Planet Earth
B The Body in Action	G Living in the Space Age	8	H Weather and Cli- mate	F The Uni- verse
L Living in a Nuclear Age	J The Chem- istry of Matter	9	I Mechanics of Fluids and Solids	K Energy at Work

Table 6

| *Science 7-8-9* | Orientation
The Nature of Science
Measurement
Tools of the Scientist | Accelerated Program—1
Earth Science—Grade 9 |

7

A Taking Care of Ourselves	C Living Things Around Us	D Living in an Ocean of Air	J & K Introduc- tion to Matter & Energy	F The Uni- verse

8

B The Body in Action	I Mechanics of Fluids and Solids	J The Chem- istry of Matter	K Energy at Work	L Living with the Atom

9

| Regents Earth Science |

Table 7

grades seven and eight. If earth science is offered in grade nine, some biology content may well be shifted from grade seven to grade eight to eliminate a two-year gap. Other plans for accelerated programs are possible, but all will depend on the major area of depth to be studied in grade nine.[102]

The standard program in New York State, which is designed for the bulk of the pupils, begins with a three-year general science program. In the senior high school, pupils may elect a biology course that is less academic than the traditional course, a physical science course that fuses the less academic phases of general physics and general chemistry, and earth science, which has always been considered the least rigorous of the usual electives.

It is also possible to provide a third program based upon these sylla-

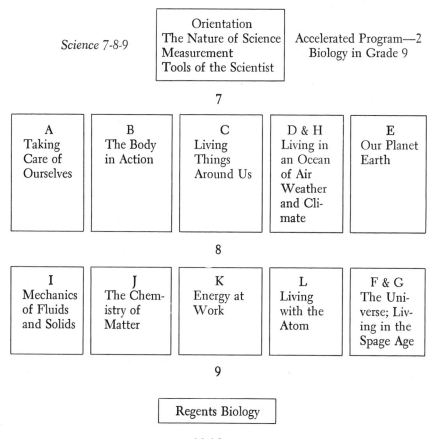

	Orientation	
Science 7-8-9	The Nature of Science	Accelerated Program—2
	Measurement	Biology in Grade 9
	Tools of the Scientist	

7

| A Taking Care of Ourselves | B The Body in Action | C Living Things Around Us | D & H Living in an Ocean of Air Weather and Climate | E Our Planet Earth |

8

| I Mechanics of Fluids and Solids | J The Chemistry of Matter | K Energy at Work | L Living with the Atom | F & G The Universe; Living in the Spage Age |

9

Regents Biology

Table 8

102 The University of the State of New York, State Education Department, Bureau of Secondary Curriculum Development, *Science 7, 8, 9*, Part I, Albany, 1962.

buses, a program for pupils who are seriously retarded readers but who are not unintelligent. The first two years of the general science program may be distributed over three years in order to provide more time for first-hand experiences and manipulative work. Of the remaining material the less academic and more practical phases may then be organized into an advanced general science elective course for the senior high school years.

Teachers who are planning double or triple track programs should be careful not to think solely in terms of subject matter. There are problems of experience background, interests, and social maturity that must be taken into consideration along with aptitude. Half a standard physics course is no better for the nonacademic minded pupil than is the whole course. And an eighth-grade pupil with an inferior experience background will benefit little from the standard physics course even if he has very high aptitude. All special courses should be planned in terms of the pupils and what will bring them maximum benefit.

Provision for gifted pupils.   The gifted student is generally recognized as an individual whose development and behavior consistently demonstrate unusual abilities, traits, and achievements for his age group. Further definition of giftedness, by statistical methods, is extremely difficult since a wide diversity of opinion exists concerning boundaries and percentile rank of IQ. The figures given by leading educators and social scientists state that the gifted students comprise from one percent to 20 or 25 percent of all educable children.

If consideration is given to the ultimate social contributions to be expected from this group, 5 percent seems to be a reasonable figure. Within this group are the pupils with a capacity for abstract reasoning and mental conceptualization that is needed in preparing for professional occupations and productive careers.[103]

A large number of this group must have a considerable amount of scientific talent, far more than is evidenced by the science talent search, science congresses, and entrance into scientific professions. The waste of this ability is the result of sheer neglect. Rarely are exceptional pupils adequately challenged to develop their superior abilities. Too few school systems make adequate provision for the gifted, although provision is made for the physically or mentally handicapped. Until recently, education of the gifted has been severely limited by insufficient supporting funds. The National Science Foundation has supported a number of programs offered by universities during the summer months which provide talented high school pupils with challenging science experiences. In addition, the Car-

[103] Hildreth, Gertrude H., *Introduction to the Gifted,* New York: McGraw-Hill Book Co., 1966, p. 25.

negie Foundation has recently allotted large sums of money to be utilized in research on the education of the gifted. Unfortunately, the schools themselves have done little toward establishing state or national programs for education of the gifted. Some of these boys and girls are able to make progress on their own initiative. The remainder are never identified and drift into mediocrity.

In recent years the critical shortage of leaders, particularly in the scientific fields, has focused attention on the problem, and experimentation in the area of educating the gifted is increasing. Fortunately, there have been educators with foresight who have blazed trails that others may now follow.

Some schools have introduced special "honors" classes in the sciences, in which pupils with unusual science aptitudes and interests can find an enriched and accelerated program. Unfortunately, such classes are often dropped by administrators because of problems in staffing, funding, and scheduling such programs. "Honors" programs have also been attempted in schools large enough to maintain a section that parallels the other sections of the regular program. In these programs, pupils pursue an entire program that is enriched and accelerated. Even in many extracurricular activities they tend to be set apart.

New York City has led the way in establishing high schools devoted to pupils with high scientific aptitude and interest. Of the total gifted group in the United States about one third live in cities large enough to support such specialized schools.

Recently a number of different kinds of programs have been instituted in various schools. The greatest amount of experimentation has been done by individual teachers who have tried to enrich their regular science classes for the benefit of the occasional gifted pupil. Through individualized instruction, science clubs, and informal guidance, these teachers have done much to provide the nation's top scientists.

An "honors" program in science.   One well-known honors program in science is the remarkable one introduced by Paul Brandwein in the Forest Hills High School. This program is past the experimental stage, having been developed in 1941 and in continuous operation since then.[104]

The Forest Hills honors program in science begins officially in the tenth year, but interested pupils in the ninth grade are encouraged to work in the science laboratories on their free time. This enables them to explore their own interests and allows teachers to become better acquainted with individuals who might become members of the honors program.

---

[104] For a more detailed account of this program together with a discussion of results, read: Brandwein, P. F., *The Gifted Student as Future Scientist*, Harcourt, Brace & World, New York, 1955.

Once in the program, the pupils are placed in special sections of biology, physics, and chemistry, designated as "honor" classes. The work in these classes is both enriched and speeded up as compared with standard courses. The pupils are required also to take additional mathematics and a foreign language so that upon graduation they have had four years each of science, mathematics, and a foreign language. After one term in the program, pupils may enter an advanced science class which permits the pupils to work upon projects of their own choosing.

That pupils benefit from their special honors classes in science is unquestioned. It seems likely, however, that their greatest benefit derives from the close contact between these young people and a group of stimulating, professionally dedicated teachers. Results are spectacular. Ninety-five percent of these students have gone to college, and ninety percent are committed to a science career. Several hold doctoral degrees in science and have made significant contributions to research.

A high school of science.   The Bronx High School of Science is one of the several specialized high schools provided by New York City for its boys and girls. It is one of four that tend to attract pupils of high academic ability.[105]

Pupils who apply for admission to the Bronx High School of Science are selected on the basis of an examination which may be supplemented by an interview that explores the applicant's interest in a science career. During the first year in the school, equivalent to the ninth grade, pupils study units which are integrations of the usual high school subjects. Trips, movies, and guest speakers are used extensively to supplement regular instruction. Pupils have opportunities to work in the laboratories on projects of their own choosing.

In the tenth grade, the curriculum proper begins. Emphasis is upon general education with opportunities to pursue special interest. Upon graduation, pupils in this curriculum will have studied four years of English, four years of social studies, three years of a language, four years of science, three or four years of mathematics, four years of health education, and courses in music and art appreciation.

In his science program, a pupil has the opportunity to follow his tenth year biology course with an elective course in clinical laboratory techniques, field biology, or nutritional science. The physical science program includes physics, chemistry, industrial arts, and mechanical drawing. These courses may be followed by electives in aeronautics, electronics, motor engines,

---

[105] For a competent description of this high school written by its principal, read: Meister, M., "A High School of Science for Gifted Students," *The Gifted Child*, Paul Witty (ed.), The American Association for Gifted Children, D. C. Heath, Boston, 1951.

elementary qualitative analysis, elementary organic chemistry, historical development of science, advanced drafting, and advanced science laboratory techniques. Each course is liberally provided with opportunities for individual laboratory work and individual projects.

Advanced placement programs. Some secondary schools offer college level courses in biology, chemistry, and physics as a means of challenging and inspiring gifted students. These courses are often accepted by colleges as an equivalent freshman course so that a student can take more advanced courses during the freshman year.

Students who enroll in these courses may take an examination administered by the College Entrance Examination Board.[106] Any student, regardless of whether he is in an advanced placement course, may take the examination. The examination is rated by a committee composed of college professors and high school teachers, who use a five point scale: 5 indicates highest honors; 4 honors; 3 creditable; 2 passing; 1 failing. Colleges may use the results of this examination in awarding either credit or placement, basing their decisions on factors such as (1) grade in the course, (2) recommendation of the high school principal, (3) examination grade, (4) a copy of the examination which was given the previous spring, and (5) a description of the advanced placement course prepared by the teacher of the course. Some colleges give their own advanced placement examinations.

The New York State Education Department offers the following guides for setting up an advanced placement program for biology.[107]

The administration of any advanced placement program is an arduous task. Special considerations must be given by the administrator in order to establish an effective advanced placement program. Adequate time must be allotted for both class and laboratory sessions. Scheduling will, of necessity, vary from school to school, but it is highly recommended that at least one and preferably two double laboratory periods be provided in addition to five recitation periods. Class enrollment of a maximum of twenty students should be faithfully observed. This permits individual pupil participation and creative "open-ended" laboratory experiences.

The availability of adequate laboratory assistance is of great importance. It is essential that certain equipment and materials beyond those that are normally used in the biology laboratory be provided.

[106] College Entrance Examination Board, A *Guide to the Advanced Placement Program*, 1964–65, Berkeley, California.

[107] Extracted from *Advanced Placement Program in Biology*, Bureau of Secondary Curriculum Development, New York State Education Department, Albany. The Bureau has also prepared advanced placement program booklets in a number of other subject areas.

Inasmuch as the teacher of an advanced placement course must devote time far in excess of that required for ordinary class preparation, every effort should be made to lessen the number of programmed hours. Program allowance may take several forms, the best one being arrived at in individual school situations. It is well to keep in mind that as a general rule, the teaching involved in an advanced placement course is equivalent to that of two regular classes. Financial assistance and released time should be given to the advanced placement teacher in order that it will be possible for him to participate in conferences relating to such courses.

The success of any advanced placement program will depend largely upon the energies of an academically superior, highly qualified, and devoted teacher for whom the program will become a truly rewarding educational experience.

A cardinal principle in planning the laboratory work of the course is to create those conditions which will enable students to work independently. The laboratory experiences must provide the students with extensive opportunities to study a wide assortment of living things. Through such experiences they will be able to strengthen the concepts and understandings developed in class recitations and supplementary readings.

The heavy responsibilities placed upon the student by the exceedingly demanding quality and quantity of a college-level course mandates the desirability for setting high standards for admission to a course in the advanced placement program. To be selected for an advanced placement course in biology a student—

(1) should have demonstrated a strong interest in, and motivation for science, especially biology, and an eagerness to work consistently at his highest level of ability.

(2) should have a minimum IQ of 125. (By no means should this particular criterion become a deciding factor and no single IQ score can be used with a satisfactory degree of reliability or validity.)

(3) should have a significantly high level reading ability.

(4) should be free of strong personal, emotional, or physical problems.

(5) should have successfully completed a first course in biology and chemistry as prerequisites. (In addition, physics constitutes a highly desirable prerequisite.)

(6) should have regular twelfth grade standing.

(7) should have demonstrated high achievement in science and mathematics courses.

(8) should have a record that contains quality recommendations from former teachers with stress placed upon objective evaluation insofar as possible.

Science seminars.   Science seminars have been used for a number of years in some schools for students who are academically gifted. They provide the student with an opportunity to do intensive research on a problem of his choice. Many of the seminars bring the students in contact with research scientists. Credit in many instances is given toward graduation if the course is a part of the school offerings. In other cases, no credit is given since the seminar is regarded as extracurricular.

A seminar course in chemistry given at Warsaw High School, Warsaw, Indiana,[108] is designed for pupils who plan to take four years of science. Although mathematics is not required of these pupils, they usually take three or four years of the subject. The following factors are used to determine participation in the seminar: intelligence, personal history of the student, history of science hobbies, scholarship, a planned vocation in science or mathematics, and recommendations from teachers.

The seminars start in the spring semester of the junior year and continue through the spring of the next year. Previous to this, students will have had a course in biology and in chemistry.

The schedule includes a double laboratory alternating with a recitation so that one week may have two laboratory periods and three recitations while the following week may have three or even four laboratory sessions. The laboratories are open-ended.

The program is prepared and conducted by the students. Project work is done after hours, at home, or in the school laboratory after school or during free periods.

Another type given at Washington Union High School, San Jose, California, emphasises research. Reports are given on research projects which are undertaken as well as on topics which are assigned. Each participant is required to enter the report on his research problem to the Westinghouse Talent Search as well as to the Science Achievement Awards Program of the National Science Teachers Association.[109]

National curriculum courses for the science talented.   Both BSCS and PSSC have developed "second" courses for the advanced student. The BSCS second course[110] is primarily for the student who has had one of the BSCS approaches and wishes to continue the study of biology in greater depth. The main objective of the course is to provide laboratory experiences which stimulate biological research. Through this approach students solve problems in areas such as microbial genetics, plant and animal growth, and animal behavior. The investigations are designed so that the student will have the successes and failures of the scientist in his work.

The PSSC advanced topic course[111] concentrates on some of the

---

[108] Communication from Harry O. Haakonsen, Science Teacher, Warsaw High School, Warsaw, Indiana, 1967.

[109] National Science Teachers Association, New Developments in High School Teaching, Washington, D.C., 1960.

[110] Biological Sciences Curriculum Study, *Biological Science: Interaction of Experiments and Ideas.* Prentice-Hall, Inc. Englewood Cliffs, N.J., 1965.

[111] Physical Science Study Committee, *Physics—Advanced Topics Supplement,* D.C. Heath and Company, Boston, Mass. 1966.

basic ideas in physics. The course is meant to be an extension of the PSSC approach and is intended to be three semesters or two years in length. It can also be used as an introductory college course. PSSC recommends that the seven advanced units which are included in this course be interspersed with the chapters found in the second edition of the PSSC book.[112]

SUGGESTED ACTIVITIES

1. Study in detail the science program of a typical school system—the required courses, the electives, the sequence, the prerequisites. Also if possible, determine the enrollment in each course. Calculate the percentage of pupils taking each science course.

2. Write to a number of institutions of higher learning for their catalogues. Determine the entrance requirements for these institutions. Using this information, plan a high school program that you would recommend for a pupil who desires to enter one of the scientific professions.

3. Select a school system using the 6–6 plan, the 8–4 plan and the 6–3–3 plan (or other variations). Compare the science programs offered by these systems. How well does each of these programs coincide with the proposed 12-year program suggested in the *Thirty-first Yearbook*, National Society for the Study of Education?

4. Examine the programs proposed by the national science curriculum study groups, i.e., BSCS to determine how well these programs meet their stated philosophies.

5. Design a science program for gifted children.

6. Compare the new junior high school programs such as SSSP, IPS, and others as to philosophy and scope.

7. Examine a state or local course of study. Note the presence or absence of such features as seasonal arrangement, use of local resources, and the like. What changes might you make in the organization to make it more effective?

8. Make a file of local teaching resources for the school in which you will do your cadet teaching. List possible field trips, outside authorities who may be called upon for help, occupations in which parents are likely to be engaged, and situations with which pupils are probably familiar.

9. Analyze the activities suggested by a textbook. In what percentage of the suggestions are the outcomes given directly or implied? Which of the activities encourage independent thinking? What suggestions may be modified to encourage independent thinking?

10. Compare a course of study prepared by a national science curriculum study group with a state or local course of study. What objectives are stated in each, and how do they work toward their goals?

[112] *Ibid.*

SUGGESTED READINGS

Barnard, J. D., "Improving Science Education," *Science Life*, October, 1962.

Bennett, Lloyd M., "A Discussion of the New Chemistry Programs (CHEM & CBA) and the Traditional Programs in High School," *School Science and Mathematics*, Vol. 66, no. 9, December, 1966.

Biological Sciences Curriculum Study, "About BSCS Biology," A Report Prepared by the Biological Sciences Curriculum Study Committee (Boulder, Colorado: Biological Sciences Curriculum Study, November, 1966).

Biological Sciences Curriculum Study, *Newsletter*, no. 31, May, 1967.

Brandwein, P. F., *The Gifted Student as Future Scientist*, Harcourt, Brace & World, New York, 1955.

Frymier, Jack R., "Curriculum Assessment-Problems and Possibilities," *Educational Leadership*, Vol. 24, no. 2, November, 1966, pp. 124–128.

Gallagher, James J., ed. *Teaching Gifted Students: A Book of Readings*, Allyn and Bacon, Inc. Boston, 1966.

Hildreth, Gertrude H., *Introduction to the Gifted*, McGraw-Hill Book Co., New York, 1966.

Hirsch, P., "How to Upgrade Your Science Curriculum," *School Management*, 6:65–8, September, 1962.

Lacey, Archie L., *Guide to Science Teaching in Secondary Schools*, Wadsworth Publishing Company, Inc., Belmont, California, 1966.

Lehman, David L., "Abstracts of Recent Research and Development: A New Dimension in the Evaluation of BSCS," *BSCS Newsletter*, no. 30, January, 1967.

MacMahan, Horace, Jr., "Princeton Project or ESCP: A Difficult Choice," *School Science and Mathematics*, Vol. LXVI, no. 1, January, 1966.

National Science Foundation, "Course and Curriculum Improvement Projects," Washington, D.C.: Superintendent of Documents, September, 1966.

Peterson, Glen E., "BSCS International Cooperation," *The Science Teacher*, Vol. 34, no. 1, January, 1967.

"Rethinking Science Education," Part 1, *Fifty-ninth Yearbook*, National Society for the Study of Education, University of Chicago Press, Chicago, 1960.

Voss, Buton, E., "The Impact of BSCS Biology," *School Science and Mathematics*, Vol. 67, February, 1967.

Watson, Fletcher G., "Why Do We Need More Physics Courses?" *The Physics Teacher*, Vol. 5, no. 5, May, 1967.

Chapter 4

How Boys and Girls

Learn Science

The earth science class quickly settled down to work. The pupils had been directed to pulverize pyrite, heat a small quantity in a test tube over a gas flame, and find out what they could about the mineral.

"See the yellow stuff on the glass. It looks like sulfur."

"It smells like sulfur."

"If it's sulfur it should burn."

Their teacher interrupted momentarily, directing the pupils to dump the residue on metal can lids to cool. At first, the class could make little of the residue except that it was black. The teacher suggested testing it with a magnet.

"Why, it's iron!"

"That's funny. Who'd ever think that pyrite has iron in it. It looks more like gold."

While most of the pupils continued to examine the residue, one pupil busied himself with a book on minerals. Soon he had an announcement:

"Pyrite is a compound of iron and sulfur," he told the class, "The formula is FeS."

This was an exciting lesson for the pupils who found in it both challenge and satisfaction and for the teacher who saw in it the growth of intellectual independence of his pupils. What makes such a lesson successful? What types of learning are involved? What outcomes can be expected?

LEARNING: PROCESS AND PRODUCT

One of the greatest mistakes a teacher can make is to define learning solely as a product. Much of the justifiable criticism of science education is attributable to the assumption that information can be poured into pupils like cream into small bottles. Learning is not information stored in the mind as information is stored in a book, available at any future time in the same form as deposited.

Learning is a process by which the mind reacts to external conditions, the reactions being modified by what has been experienced before. No two minds react identically in the same situation because each has a different history. A single mind does not react identically in two identical situations because it has changed during the interim. A teacher cannot expect his pupils to respond as he himself would respond.

An enormous amount of research has been concentrated upon the learning process during the past century. Much has been discovered about details of the process, especially about conditions affecting rote memorization. The general nature of learning, however, remains a puzzle.[1]

The nature of knowledge.   A person's store of knowledge is the sum of all the impressions he has gained by means of his senses plus the results of all his mental operations on these data. Data alone are not knowledge: "Information is but the raw material, the precursor, of knowledge. To hoard a store of unrelated items in a mental gullet by rote memory and without a sense of relevance—including the ability to regurgitate the data on a quiz master's prompting—should pass for knowledge no more than the stuffing of a hamster's pouch can be regarded as growth. Knowledge merges from the distilling, shaping, and integrating of the raw material into concepts and rules."[2]

This quotation likens the growth of knowledge to the growth of an animal. Figures 4 and 5 provide a visualization of the growth of knowledge. Knowledge begins with experience. The data thus obtained are studied, analyzed, sorted, and used as the basis for generalizations. Hypotheses that attempt to explain the generalizations are formulated, tested, and either discarded, modified, or accepted. The resulting ideas represent knowledge, which may be used for the benefit of the learner or, by a feedback process, for the accumulation of more knowledge. "A patchwork of unrelated facts

---

[1] Gleitman, Henry, "Place Learning," *Scientific American,* 209:4, 1963.

[2] Weiss, Paul, "Knowledge: A Growth Process," *Proceedings of the American Philosophical Society,* 104:2, 1960.

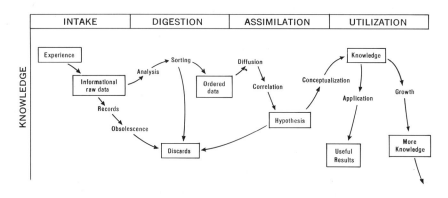

Figure 4.   *Knowledge as a growth process.**

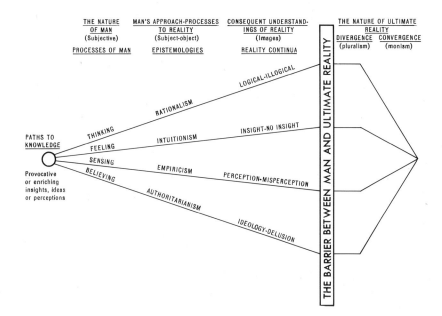

Figure 5.   *The paths to knowledge.**

* Weiss, Paul, "Knowledge: A Growth Process," *Proceedings of the American Philosophical Society,* 104:2, 1960.

has been transformed into a rationally connected thought structure of inner consistency, viable and durable. . . . As in the organism, the culminating phase is branched: as basic knowledge grows, part of the increment accrues to its own body, yielding more basic knowledge, while another part is converted into differentiated products—all that is commonly lumped under the attribute 'applied.' "[3]

Traditional education has operated on the assumption that the time-consuming steps of learning can be bypassed, that the final product, knowledge, can be transmitted by (to continue the analogy) a sort of intellectual intravenous feeding process. "It is not too uncommon to find teachers who assume that they are able to transmit curriculum content to the cognitive structure of a pupil. This assumption means that we can teach directly, that nothing intervenes between what the teacher teaches and what the learner learns."[4] The fallacy may not be obvious but it is critical; all ideas presented to a learner enter at the intake level, and must be digested and assimilated before becoming part of his body of knowledge. Advanced students have already developed skills for dealing with new information, and they have already a body of knowledge to give meaning to new information. But beginners are not prepared to cope with refined ideas; they may be able to stuff themselves with enough verbalizations to regurgitate satisfactorily at examination time, but their intellectual growth is nil.

Levels of knowing. Royce identifies four basic ways of knowing, each dependent upon a specific psychological process: (1) authoritarianism, (2) empiricism, (3) intuitionism, and (4) rationalism. These processes depend upon, in the same order, (1) acceptance, (2) perceiving, (3) insight, and (4) reasoning.[5] The degree of intellectualizing ranges from blind memorization to exercise of the highest powers of the human mind. "The scientist . . . has learned over the centuries, that, for his purpose, intuitive and authoritarian ways of knowing can be very dangerous, and that they must be guarded against. . . . He maximizes the rational and empirical approaches and minimizes the involvement of intuitionism and authoritarianism."[6] Traditional science education, however, has always maximized authoritarianism, the process which tied the hands of scientists for centuries. True, a small amount of empiricism has been practiced in laboratories and field work, but because outcomes are dictated by instructors, students have little opportunity to exercise higher powers of thinking.

[3] *Ibid.*

[4] Waetjen, W. B., "Learning and Motivation: Implications for the Teaching of Science," *The Science Teacher,* 32:24, May, 1965.

[5] Royce, J. R., "The Search for Meaning," *American Scientist,* 47:4, 1959.

[6] *Ibid.*

Boys and girls need not be limited to the lowest levels of intellectualizing. They have fine minds that by nature delight in problems which make use of their highest powers. If acceptance of authority is the only level rewarded by high grades and praise, dutiful pupils will limit their in-school thinking to this low level, at the same time becoming cautious, even doubtful, about using their ability to reason. This all-too-comon tendency can be reversed only by rewarding truly important achievements of the intellect while at the same time making pupils suspicious of authoritarianism.

Acquisition of knowledge.   Processes that take place in the human brain are far too complex for detailed analysis. In Figure 6 an attempt is made to show some of the more obvious interactions involved in acquiring knowledge, but the chart is an obvious oversimplification and does not do justice to the complete picture.

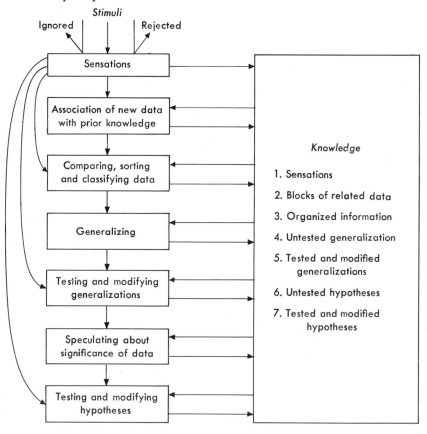

Figure 6.   *The acquisition of knowledge.*

According to this scheme, learning begins with sensing.[7] Some selectivity occurs here: many stimuli seem to make no impression, and others are rejected. Probably much depends upon the relation of the new stimuli to prior knowledge.

Information gained through the senses is almost immediately processed, being associated with and compared to prior experiences, and perhaps sorted and classified. If a new bit of information appears identical with prior information, processing may stop. If differences are noted, the person may be motivated to investigate further, seeking additional information for comparisons. Thus incongruity or novelty can serve as a motivator for learning.

Sorting and classifying lead to generalizing, that is, to formulating general statements and rules.[8] It is possible, of course, that a person begins to generalize as soon as he has two bits of information bearing some relationship. However, most generalizations are probably based on several but not necessarily numerous cases. Early generalizations tend to be broad and to involve much doubtful interpolation and extrapolation. As a person's experience background grows, he is likely to encounter exceptions that force him to contract the scope of his generalizations. The greater his background, the more limited his generalizations are likely to be. Thus generalizations undergo a continued process of testing and modification.

The processes mentioned thus far can and often do take place below the level of consciousness. Even when carried out consciously, a person may not recognize the processes as such. However, he is constantly adding the products of these processes to his store of knowledge.

Most people speculate to a greater or lesser extent about incongruities and repetitive phenomena. They ask questions and may suggest answers. Both the questions and the proposed answers (hypotheses) may lead to a deliberate search for additional information. Speculation need not be verbal; a person manipulating a strange device is obviously asking questions and checking answers.

An undisciplined search for information remains on a primitive level—simple manipulation, trial-and-error, and perhaps rudimentary experimentation. If answers are not obtained quickly, a person usually turns

---

[7] For more extensive treatment see: Russell, D. H., *Children's Thinking*, Blaisdell Publishing Co., Waltham, Mass., 1956.

[8] Two widely used words in educational jargon are "percept" and "concept." The former is usually applied to the products of comparing, sorting, and classifying sensations, but on occasion is found applied to sensations, raw data, processed data, recalled data, or images. The term, "concept," is even more broadly applied; although usually defined as "broad generalizations," it can be found to mean mental images, limited generalizations, hypotheses and theories, educational goals, and various unidentifiable ideas. Such vagueness is not helpful in communication and therefore these words are not used here, even at the expense of discarding the pleasant alliteration that goes, "Concepts are developed from percepts."

to some authority. Indeed, many people will turn to some authority, including folklore, rather than make simple tests. Perhaps this dependence to rely upon books or supposedly learned persons is a fault of our educational systems or a mark of our culture. It represents a serious lack of intellectual independence.

Efforts to obtain information and test hypotheses on a higher level require sophisticated methods and critical skills. It is at this stage of acquiring knowledge that schools can make significant contributions, teaching young people to use such processes so that their education can continue after the close of formal schooling.

MOTIVATION

The priceless drive that makes people want to learn we knowingly call motivation without actually knowing much about it. What is this drive? What causes a pupil to want to learn science? "Is it the pupil's experiences, needs, and abilities? Is it the pupil's home environment, emotional make-up, cultural background, and aspirations? Do the principles of readiness and effect influence the outcome? What emotional and social mechanisms enter in? What is the role of group dynamics, hostility, teacher dominance, emotional climate of the classroom, and pupil-pupil competition?"[9]

> When a teacher asks himself the question, "What motivates this pupil's behavior," he is asking to have identified one or several of three things. The first of these is an *environment determinant* which caused the behavior to occur. This could be the pressure of a parent to have his child learn, a provocative bulletin board display in the classroom, or a well-presented demonstration by the teacher. Second, it may be an *internal* instinct, want, desire, aspiration, plan, motive, purpose, urge, feeling, wish, or drive which precipitated the behavior. Third, it may be the *goal* which either attracted the learner or repelled him.[10]

Motivation theory.   Classic motivation theory, developed chiefly with laboratory animals, holds that behavior represents an effort to reduce some physiological need (or is associated with such an effort), and much experimentation has been carried out with rewards and punishments as motivation for learning. Many classroom practices show conscious or unconscious agreement with this theory of motivation. At the beginning of the century, control was frankly aversive—pupils worked to escape the threat of rod or

[9] Riener, W. B., "Motivation in Science Teaching," *The Science Teacher,* 30:52, March, 1963.

[10] Waetjen, *op. cit.,* p. 22.

cane. The reform movement known as "progressive education" attempted
to replace the negative approach with rewards of teacher and self-approval;
a number of the procedures were elaborate and slightly ridiculous but good
in theory. However, aversive control never ended: "The child at his desk,
filling in his workbook, is behaving primarily to escape the threat of a series
of minor aversive events—the teacher's displeasure, the criticism or ridicule
of his classmates, an ignominious showing in competition, low marks, a trip
to the office to 'be talked to' by the principal, or a word to the parent who
may still resort to the birch rod."[11]

Good teachers have always realized that motivation is not so simple as
the reward-punishment explanation would have us believe. ". . . some,
but by no means all, students learn because they seem to love learning."[12]
These pupils do not need external pressures; they seem to be self-moti-
vating. They study hard without fear of punishment or expectation of
reward, and even the most recalcitrant youngster may unexpectedly exert
himself on some problem that meets his fancy.

This drive to learn has been termed "epistemic motivation" by those
who favor jargon to simple language. "In rather simple terms, 'epistemic
motivation' can be described as the drive individuals have to seek knowledge. For generations, teachers have described such knowledge-seeking
pupils as 'inquisitive' or 'curious.' We prefer to use the term curiosity not
only because it has been used by those who research this motive but
because its simplicity communicates well."[13]

Psychologists have discovered a similar drive in laboratory animals. "It
is clear that one need not be suffering from physiological inbalance, or
anticipating that state, to become interested in . . . external objects; it is
clear that these objects of interest need not be potential restorers of physiological balance, or even associated with such servants of the homeostatic
process, in order to exert powerful impact on the individual's behavior."[14]

Dember proposes a theory which he calls the "Theory of Choice."
According to this hypothesis, every object or event has a certain information value and the complexity of the object or event is a motivationally
crucial property. Also each individual has a certain motivational property;
there is a level of complexity above which he is not equipped to deal with
comfortably and effectively. "Some objects would *for him* be excessively
complex; some would be too simple; some would be just right. . . .
Objects that are too simple elicit boredom if they are unavoidable; objects

---

[11] Skinner, B.F., "The Science of Learning and the Art of Teaching," *Harvard Educational Review*, 28:86, 1954.

[12] Probst, G. E., "Programed Learning in the Schools," *The Science Teacher*, 29:34,
November, 1962.

[13] Waetjen, *op. cit.*, p. 23.

[14] Dember, W. N., "The New Look in Motivation," *American Scientist*, 53:419,
1965.

that are too complex elicit fear, anger, and sometimes rage if one is forced to maintain contact with them."[15]

A person that is free to choose prefers objects or situations which have a complexity matching his own. "He will select these from among others if they are made available, he will seek them out when they are absent, he will work for them, and he will even *learn* what he must do to obtain them."[16] Of course, the individual may not confine himself to objects or events of exactly matching complexity. He may sample a range of situations. An individual may also choose to work with objects or events that are just a little more complex than the perfect match;[17] that is, the individual prefers a challenge to a certainty.

The "theory of choice" represents no surprise to experienced teachers. Every teacher has seen boredom and frustration in classes taught by mass-instruction methods; proponents of individualized instruction, projects, and small group activities have operated on this principle.

Motivation through rewards. On the level of animal experimentation, positive motivation has generally been in the form of food and water. Such primitive means of motivation are not available to classroom teachers so rewards have generally assumed other forms—grades, prizes, certificates, and recognition—all external determinents. Educators who may decry such motivational devices are not realistic; external determinants are natural and effective. We all work for tangible rewards and are gratified to receive them (also mortified or angered when we do not).

The unfortunate aspect of external determinants is that they may assume too much importance. It is far easier to award grades, drill for passing scholarship examinations, make out certificates, and find money for prizes than to search each day for appropriate ways to challenge a wide range of pupils. "As long as the teacher or some other mechanism of the school situation is necessary to provide reinforcement, the learner is apt to learn only 'what the teacher wants.' A far more effective teaching strategy is one which relies to an appreciable extent on intrinsic reinforcements, those which are not directly related to the intervention of the teacher."[18]

Intrinsic rewards include the satisfaction one obtains in carrying out a task to a successful conclusion. Research projects, construction projects, term papers, even care of house plants and organization of bulletin board displays are tasks in which one anticipates satisfaction upon completion.

[15] *Ibid.*, p. 420.

[16] *Ibid.*, p. 422.

[17] Earl, R. W., "Problem Solving and Motor Skill Behaviors under Conditions of Free-Choice," Unpublished doctoral dissertation, University of Michigan, 1957.

[18] Keislar, E. R., "The Learning Process and the Teaching of Science," *The Science Teacher*, 29:21, December, 1962.

The discovery approach to learning, also called the inquiry approach, depends in part upon the motivational effect of anticipated satisfaction. The reward of satisfaction is also the chief motivating device used in so-called teaching machines.

> The psychological principles of reinforcement, as used in programmed learning, are a motivational device. By letting the pupil know at once if he is on the right path to the correct completion of a task, teachers are in a sense rewarding the pupil. Informing the pupil of his progress . . . is perhaps the most effective motivation device ever invented.[19]

Such motivation is, of course, older than teaching machines. Any teacher who uses rapid-fire oral reviews and immediately-graded short quizzes is rewarding accomplishment in memorizing information. Unfortunately, this type of reinforcement encourages, even forces, pupils to accept the authority of the program maker rather than to develop his own intellectual independence and maturity.

Some educators would abandon all forms of extrinsic rewards. "Once the inquiry is initiated . . . the child must be free to decide for himself what data will be needed. . . . This means that no psychological pressures can be exerted on the child with teacher-questions. It also means that there be no competition among the children, no extrinsic rewards, no stress on grades. It is only when the child is free from pressures . . . that he can proceed with inquiry."[20] This attitude does not seem realistic or completely defensible. Few people, even the "purest" of scientists, work without expectation of some external rewards—praise or recognition. It seems wrong not to use all forms of constructive motivation as long as these lead to beneficial outcomes.

Motivation through challenge. "A common error is to assume that reinforcements are limited to such events as approval, high marks, cash, or prizes. These are relatively unimportant as reinforcers for most academic subjects. It is far more relevant for a teacher to strengthen and use the reinforcing properties of such events as the resolution of a paradox, a rigorous proof, a new set of assumptions, an intriguing question, a solution which meets certain requirements, an effective explanation, or a promising method of investigation."[21]

Challenge is a familiar means of motivation. However, challenge is not simply facing a pupil with a difficult situation. As discussed previously,

[19] Reiner, *op. cit.*, p. 52.

[20] Fish, A. S., and Bernice Goldmark, "Inquiry Method: Three Interpretations," *The Science Teacher*, 33:13, February, 1966.

[21] Keisler, *op. cit.*, p. 21.

there must be a close match between situation and subject, with the situation being slightly more complex than the complexity level of the subject. Walter B. Waetjen discusses motivation in terms of match and mismatch of curriculum content and pupil:

> [In Figure 7] . . . there is practically 100 percent match between what the teacher is attempting to teach and the pre-existing content of the cognitive map. In such situations, learning is not enhanced. . . . The type of behavior elicited from the learner is not learning behavior and is nonproductive.
>
> [Figure 8] portrays a different state of affairs in which there is, for the most part, a match between the curriculum content (including the instructional procedures) and the cognitive structure of the learners. Since there is a generous portion of match . . . it means that the youngster is familiar with the material or situation. . . . On the other hand, there is also some degree of "mismatch," meaning there are some elements of either content or instructional procedure which the learner does not know or did not predict. This is a dissonant situation which results in arousal of . . . a need to assimilate or articulate the unknown, incongruous, or unfamiliar material into his cognitive structure. . . . he engages in exploratory behavior. . . . In this condition, the learner is a seeker of knowledge. . . .
>
> [Figure 9] portrays the two things which eventuate when a great amount of mismatch occurs. In either case, information is unassimilated and usually is held in a context of anxiety. . . . To cope with this situation, the learner may engage in a variety of withdrawing behaviors. . . . Instead of integrating simple facts into higher levels of organization, the individual holds them at a lower level. . . . What is unfortunate about this type of behavior is that the learner is often judged to be at least an adequate and possibly a good learner, because he is able to retain facts even though not able to integrate them.[22]

Obviously a teacher cannot expect the same degree of mismatch for all pupils in a class. This provides a powerful argument against mass-instructional methods. However, the teacher faced with typical teaching situations can present a variety of challenging situations at different complexity levels, challenging a few with one situation and a few with another, and taking care that no pupils remain unchallenged for any great length of time. The teacher can expect that the truly challenged pupil needs little attention for some time providing he has means to follow up his interest.

Novelty has long been recognized as a motivating device. Just as a laboratory mouse is challenged to explore new surroundings, so pupils are challenged to explore new situations, providing, of course, that the mismatch is not too great. Novelty can be provided by the use of new scientific instruments; pupils are fascinated by microscopes when they first have opportunities to use them. Novelty can be provided by taking a class to a

[22] Waetjen, *op. cit.*, pp. 24–25.

Figure 7. *Close match between curriculum content and pupils' cognitive structure.*

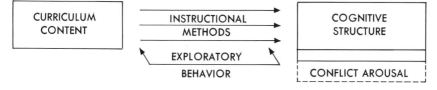

Figure 8. *A slight amount of mismatch.*

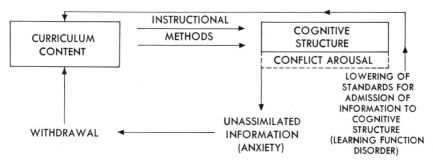

Figure 9. *A great amount of mismatch between content and structure.*

different location; a night-time class to study the sky can be very exciting to pupils. Novelty can be provided by bringing in outside speakers.

Some teachers employ "spectaculars," absurdities, and ridiculous antics as attention getters. These devices do inject novelty and attract attention but they do not provide challenge; if they do not they are at best devices to obtain temporary classroom control.

Science teachers have long used a number of intriguing devices that challenge pupils. For example, pupils entering the classroom may see water rising from one metal can through a glass tube and falling into a second can without any visible pumping mechanism (see Figure 10). This represents a mismatch with former experiences and causes curiosity. Some pupils may be motivated enough to try to arrive at an explanation.[23]

Problem-solving approaches, properly planned and carried out, provide challenge. Ideally, the problems should have strong appeal for all pupils and the methods needed for solution should lie within their ability range.

[23] Smith, A. W., "A Problem-Solving Demonstration," *Ideas for Teaching Science in the Junior High School*, National Science Teachers Assn., Washington, D.C., 1963.

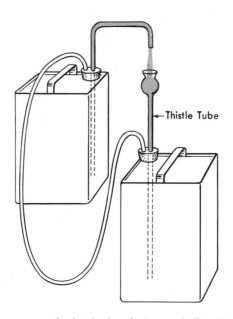
←Thistle Tube

Figure 10.   *An intriguing device to challenge pupils.*

The best problems are those that come from the pupils themselves. The teacher can help the pupils formulate the problems, divide them into subproblems, and plan methods of attack. In some cases, each pupil or small group may choose to investigate one subproblem and thereby provide a better match between problem and interests.

Part of the technique in using problem-solving approaches is asking the right questions. The following unit on mold shows how questions may be asked:[24]

> *Discuss bread mold with the pupils. They may know that it is a plant and that it is spread by spores that are produced in spore cases. These spore cases can be observed with a magnifying glass.*
>
> 1. *What else will mold grow on? (Pupils bring in specimens.)*
> 2. *Are all molds the same? Is cheese mold the same as that on jelly? Does bread mold grow on fruit?*
>   a) *How can we find out? (Students innoculate other specimens—cheese to jelly, bread to fruit, and so on.)*
>   b) *How do we know the experiments are progressing? (Help students devise charts to record size, color, and so on.)*

[24] Abstracted from Mary Blatt, "Problems of Problem-Solving," *Science for Children,* December 1963, pp. 30–32.

3. What conditions provide the healthiest colonies? (Plan with the students experiments to test these conditions.)

If pupils commit themselves beforehand to hypothetical solutions to the problems, they tend to have a vested interest in the outcomes and are more strongly motivated to carry out the investigations.

The major difficulty in using the problem-solving approach, if problems are to be presented by the teacher, is selecting suitable problems. A question is not necessarily a problem; "How do we get our drinking water?" may be answered by some pupils to their own satisfaction by referring to the drinking fountain. What represents a problem to a teacher may lack interest to pupils because they have a different background. What represents a problem to one pupil may be a matter of indifference to others.

"Open-ended" experiments can have a strong motivating function. An open-ended experiment begins with a teacher-directed activity the results of which are almost certain to open up a number of new problems along several different lines of investigation. Since the pupils discover these new problems themselves, complexity levels are more apt to be matched because what appears to be an exciting problem to one pupil may not be recognized as a problem by pupils on higher or lower motivational levels.

Pupils are shown how to measure the carbon dioxide metabolism of aquatic organisms and asked to measure this value for a fish and a water plant. To make biology interesting to the student it is essential that he be allowed to make up his own experiments. A little stimulation and suggestion by the teacher are all that are needed. A few of the more obvious experiments . . . are:

1. What is the relationship of the photosynthesis of a single aquatic plant to the amount of light it receives? [Or color?]

2. Does the presence of a predator increase the respiration of a fish? (Put a large bass in an aquarium next to the experimental chamber.)

3. What is the relation between size and respiration?

4. Does temperature affect the metabolism of organisms?[25]

The discovery, or inquiry, approach has much the same motivational value as the open-ended experiment. Pupils are put into situations in which they can make discoveries; their initial efforts are guided by the teacher towards specific outcomes, but as new problems are uncovered pupils are

[25] Abstracted from R. J. Beyers, and Bill Gillespie, "Measuring the Carbon Dioxide Metabolism of Aquatic Organisms,"*American Biology Teacher*, 25:499, 1963.

encouraged to investigate these. The motivation is the same as that which drives professional scientists in their research.

Satisfying needs.   Pupils are motivated when they sense that some of their needs are being met. Barnard speaks of our basic intellectual needs: 1) the need to belong or to identify with whatever he is dealing with; 2) the need to understand; 3) the need to be independent, to be able to do it on your own; 4) the need to be creative.[26] These needs are, of course, stated in very general terms and apply in different ways to different individuals. Creativity in one person might mean setting up a demonstration and to another breaking all the windows in a building. The need to understand might be represented by looking for the solution to a mathematical problem or for a way to steal a locked car. The interpretation of his needs depends upon the values held by the individual. The problem is to identify constructive aspects of individual needs and use them for motivation.

Probably no phase of teaching is more difficult than discovering what young people consider to be important. A teacher, even one who is very young, has adult needs which are largely concerned with the future. To the adolescent, however, the future seems very far away. His interest is in the present—himself as he is, his status with his peers, his internal and external conflicts as he demands adult prerogatives while clinging to the privileges of childhood. Teachers rarely remember how they themselves felt during adolescence, and they do not find it easy to project themselves into the minds of their pupils.

To solve the problem of motivation, a teacher must know the immediate needs of pupils so that he can plan situations in which pupils work towards fulfilling their needs while they also work towards general education goals. Close acquaintance with pupils provides the only truly satisfactory solution to this problem; unfortunately mass education systems do not usually permit extended contacts. However, some needs of adolescents are so universal that a teacher may anticipate them without knowing pupils well as individuals. Most adolescents want to drive cars. All are concerned with social acceptance. Many wish to improve their appearance.

> Each year Miss Timmons began her ninth grade general science program with a "personal inventory." The pupils listed on prepared forms their most obvious physical characteristics and made a study of such items as each desired. Besides such matters as color of hair, eyes, and skin, they filled in tooth charts with symbols indicating missing teeth, fillings, and the cavities they could locate. They tested vision. They administered hearing tests.

[26] Barnard, J. D., "What Can Science Contribute to the Liberal Education of All Children?" *The Science Teacher*, 32:25, November 1965.

A committee of girls prepared a list of things they noticed about the grooming of other girls. A second committee of girls listed things they noticed about the grooming of boys. Two committees of boys had similar functions.

All the pupils studied diet and its effect on appearance. All studied color harmonies. The girls studied hair styles and types of eyeglass frames for various types of faces. The boys studied color combinations of ties, shirts, socks, and suits.

A large triple mirror was brought into the classroom so that each pupil could see how he looked while standing and sitting. Committees judged posture while walking and climbing stairs. Bulletin boards and posters showed good and poor posture and use of clothes to minimize physical defects. The unit culminated with a school-wide "dress-up" day sponsored by all teachers and homeroom organizations. Pupils tried to dress in the best taste possible. Homerooms voted on the best dressed girl and the best dressed boy; good grooming and good taste were stressed rather than quality of clothing.

Miss Timmons' use of adolescent needs to motivate a unit on cleanliness and personal health makes motivation seem rather simple. Actually, adolescents have so many new and poorly understood needs that success in motivation is somewhat unpredictable.

Mrs. Lyons developed a unit called "Our Weather Bureau" for her eighth grade science class. It was the most successful unit of the year. Pupils made weather instruments, kept excellent records, and maintained a bulletin board in the main foyer where they posted both their predictions and those clipped from newspapers.

The following year Mrs. Lyons taught the same unit again. She followed the previous year's plans exactly, using the same approaches and the same activities. The unit was a failure. She never understood what was wrong.

It is useless to try to diagnose the causes for Mrs. Lyons' success and failure in the two situations without having been there. The unit met the needs of one group, or of a dominant few in the group, and did not meet the needs of any of the pupils in the second group.

LEARNING ON THE AUTHORITARIAN LEVEL

Authoritarianism dominates most formal education. Many people have experienced no other pattern of teaching and cannot conceive of a program in which teachers and texts do not serve as ultimate authorities. The methods of presentation are familiar to everyone. The goals are simple and demand little intellectual activity beyond memorization.

Authoritarianism should not be confused with reference to authorities. Authoritarianism is an insistence upon blind, unquestioning acceptance of information. Reference to authorities, as practiced by scientists, involves review of the data presented and the methods used for acquiring the data, a judgment as to the validity of the conclusions, and finally acceptance, rejection, or tentative acceptance of the conclusions; in short, a scientist uses his highest powers of thinking.

Instruction in the authoritarian spirit.   Authoritarian teaching is concerned only with the presentation of information without concern for the mental processes of the student. There is little or no effort to describe the empirical basis for the information, to supply needed qualifications, or to point out limitations and uncertainties. The student is not expected to reflect or ask questions.

Instructional methods include lectures, textbook readings, models, films and other audiovisual aids. Demonstrations may be used to show that what the teacher and text say is true; these usually have been set up and tested beforehand to make sure that desired outcomes are certain. Laboratory work is made up chiefly of verification exercises, these having been carefully screened to provide "correct" results. Field trips may be taken to show examples of points made in class. Authoritarian teachers depend a good deal upon analogies. The points of similarity with real situations are emphasized, particularly those that are appropriate to the material being presented. Points of difference are ignored even when these make the whole analogy somewhat ridiculous.

Teachers may ask students to apply the information to new situations. However, the steps to be followed are derived beforehand (for example, calculation of the speed of a falling body) so that the student needs only to memorize a formula or set of steps.

Testing in the authoritarian program attempts to measure the student's recognition or recall of words, statements, or steps used in applying knowledge to specific situations. The student is not expected to have any ideas of his own and may even be penalized if he presents views other than those of the instructor.

"We cannot say without qualification that memorization of scientific facts is of little consequence to the science student. We can say, however, that memorization is not of itself conducive to critical thinking or to scientific problem solving."[27] Is there, then, any argument for the authoritarian spirit in education?

[27] Strickland, W. L., "Teaching Science: by What Authority?" *The Science Teacher*, 31:23, October, 1964.

Teachers who deliberately use authoritarian procedures believe that students cannot learn enough material otherwise; they point to the need for mastery of a field, a task that grows more difficult as knowledge accumulates. Merely memorizing more information is of little value in fitting a person effectively into society:

> . . . the more you overburden the mind with facts, the more passive it may become. Intellectual erudition and book-learning alone do not make strong personalities, and in our passion for factual education and the quiz type of examination there lies hidden a form of mental pressure. The awe with which we regard the accumulation of school facts may inhibit the mind so that it cannot think for itself.[29]

Memorization, recall, and forgetting.   Learning on the authoritarian level is chiefly a matter of memorizing, and memorization is confined almost completely to verbalizations. Consequently, much of the research in learning theory has been directed towards understanding this type of memorization. Memory, of course, involves more than learning on this level, but those aspects will be considered later.

Of the several explanations of learning, the one that seems most appropriate to the memorization of verbalisms is the theory of conditioning. According to this explanation, a stimulus and a desired response are associated; through repetition, influenced by the intensity of the experience and the satisfaction obtained, the stimulus regularly invokes the desired response. Each time the correct response is forthcoming and the act is rewarded, the learning is said to be reinforced. Continued reinforcement imprints the learning more firmly.

Information can be memorized on two levels. On the lowest, or recognition level, the proper response to a specific stimulus can be recognized if presented or can be selected from a set of alternative responses. For example, the word "pepsin" might be recognized as the name of a digestive enzyme even though the word would not have come to mind in response to a direct question. On the next higher level, a specific stimulus brings forth a specific response without clues being presented. To the question for the name of a digestive enzyme, one might respond with the word "pepsin"; this is memory on the recall level. Examination questions of the multiple-choice type measure memorization on the recognition level, and completion questions measure memorization on the recall level.

Learning situations may be organized to give varying emphasis to different types of information. Relatively unimportant information may be treated on the recognition level; that is, pupils would be expected to recognize certain words and associate them with proper understandings.

[28] No footnote.
[29] Meerlo, Joost, *The Rape of the Mind,* Grosset & Dunlap, New York, 1961, pp. 266–67.

More important information would be treated on the recall level so that pupils have the words at their immediate grasp.

Research into the nature of memorization was accompanied by studies of forgetting. A well-supported theory is that of "memory decay." According to this theory, when a stimulus-response association is not exercised, it begins to weaken; in other words, a person forgets. Forgetting may be complete after a long interval. The ability to recall is lost first, then the ability to recognize.

If training is renewed, the association is again reinforced until memory is regained; relearning is more rapid than before and forgetting slower during a subsequent interval of no practice. Memorization, then, can be effected (at least until the final examination is taken) by providing an initial training period during which the learning is reinforced until a set criterion has been reached, and then providing at increasing intervals a series of retraining periods.

Another, also well supported, theory attributes forgetting to "interference" of other items of information.[30] According to this explanation, learning of one set of items has an adverse effect upon recall of another set previously learned. Interestingly enough, there seems to be little interference with memory on the recognition level. If this theory is correct, forgetting may be an inevitable consequence of memorizing much material, rather than because of lack of effort or incapacity to learn as so many teachers seem to think.

Programed learning.   Programed learning is completely directed learning with no provision for independent, original investigations. In this sense, most texts, workbooks, filmed and televised science programs, and "teaching machines" come within the classification of authoritarian instruction. All of these, of course, may be intermixed with other activities in a balanced program.

The psychological basis for programed learning as provided by teaching machines is immediate reinforcement; that is, immediate satisfaction for having arrived at the answer the program maker considers is correct. A well-designed program proceeds in a carefully tested sequence of steps "from the concrete to the abstract, from the familiar to the new, and from fact to concept."[31] The major contribution of programed learning which utilizes various types of machines are (1) automation so that each pupil can proceed on his own and obtain satisfaction immediately after he has made a correct response; (2) release of the teacher from such chores as grading workbooks and tests, and permitting him to work more with indi-

[30] Ceraso, John, "The Interference Theory of Forgetting," *Scientific American*, 217:117–124, 1967.
[31] Reiner, "Programed Learning—A Useful Tool for the Science Teacher," *The science Teacher*, 29:26, November, 1962.

viduals; (3) development of programs by experts followed by extensive pretesting before use in classrooms.

The value of programed instruction in learning on the authoritarian level is obvious; high success has been obtained in learning vocabulary and grammar of a foreign language, and in mastering certain mathematical skills. Applied to science, programed learning has doubtful features. Pupils must adopt a docile attitude and are rewarded for doing so. There can be no independence of thought because the program maker has always decided what is "correct" and what is "incorrect." Some of the programs that have been produced are little more than extended vocabulary drills (See Table 9) or application of formulas.

Class	Sentence to be Completed	Words to be Supplied
r̃u+eg	1. To "emit" light means to "send out" light. For example, the sun, a fluorescent tube, and a bonfire have in common that they all send out or _____ light.	(emit)
ẽg	2. A firefly and an electric light bulb are alike in that they both send out or _____ light.	(emit)
r̃u+eg	3. Any object which gives off light because it is hot is called an incandescent light source. Thus a candle flame and the sun are alike in that they both are _____ sources of light.	(incandescent)
ẽg	4. When a blacksmith heats a bar of iron until it glows and emits light, the iron bar has become a(n) _____ source of light.	(incandescent)
eg	5. A neon tube emits light but remains cool. Unlike the ordinary electric light bulb, then, it is not an _____ _____ of light.	⎛ incandescent source ⎞
r̃u	6. An object is called incandescent when __ ____ ____ ____ ____ ____ ____.	⎛ it emits light because it is hot ⎞
r̃u+ru	7. It has been found that an object, an iron bar, for example, will emit light if its temperature is raised above 800 degrees Celsius. Therefore we say that above _____ _____, (temperature) objects will become _____.	(800° Celsius) (incandescent)

Table 9. *Skinner's High School Physics Program Reconstructed According to the Ruleg System (Lumsdaine, A. A., and R. Glaser, Teaching Machines and Programed Learning: A Sourcebook, Department of Audiovisual Instruction, National Education Association, Washington, D.C. 1960, p. 491.)*

At least one program has attempted to include laboratory experiences as shown in Figure 11. Note that the pupil is rewarded only if he observes what the program maker wants him to see. If the pupil observes something else interesting, he cannot follow it up; if he sees something at variance with what the program maker wants, he is penalized and must go back to look for the "correct" event or condition. This is not the way to develop intellectual independence.

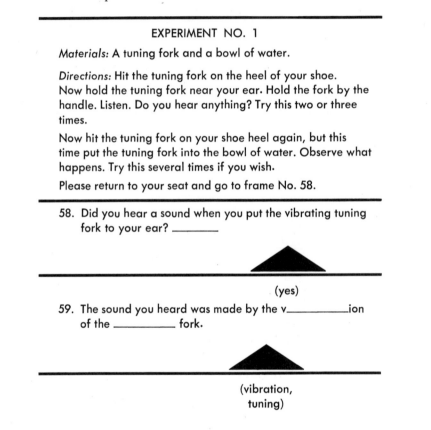

EXPERIMENT NO. 1

Materials: A tuning fork and a bowl of water.

Directions: Hit the tuning fork on the heel of your shoe.
Now hold the tuning fork near your ear. Hold the fork by the handle. Listen. Do you hear anything? Try this two or three times.

Now hit the tuning fork on your shoe heel again, but this time put the tuning fork into the bowl of water. Observe what happens. Try this several times if you wish.

Please return to your seat and go to frame No. 58.

58. Did you hear a sound when you put the vibrating tuning fork to your ear? _____

(yes)

59. The sound you heard was made by the v_____ion of the _____ fork.

(vibration, tuning)

Figure 11. *A programed experiment.**

LEARNING ON THE EMPIRICAL LEVEL

All our early learning and much that takes place in later years takes place on the empirical level. Deliberately and incidently, consciously and

* Hedges, W. D., "Teaching Science by Programing," *Science for Children,* October, 1964, p. 22.

unconsciously, we gather facts from the environment and add them to our store of knowledge. In schools, a limited amount of empirical learning is provided by laboratory experiences and field experiences, but far greater emphasis is placed upon the vicarious experiences that can be obtained from books and visual aids despite the serious limitations of these sources.

No clear boundary exists between learning on the empirical level and learning on higher levels. As soon as the mind obtains information it begins to act upon it—sorting, classifying, generalizing; but the empirical level is primarily that of fact collection.

Importance of empirical learning.   Science is based upon empiricism, that is, upon facts obtained from nature. As William Beck neatly expresses it, empiricism is "the view that says that if you wish to understand nature, look at nature, not at Aristotle."[32]

A student needs direct contact with nature so that he can understand the ways of science—the processes. He must begin with the facts and carry out some of the processes himself to see how the mind of the scientist works. To learn science only from books is to gain a distorted idea of the nature of science.

A student also needs facts so that he can interpret the information that is provided by books and other secondary sources. These sources utilize symbols, most of them words, to impart information, but one can learn the meaning of a symbol only by associating it with the thing or event or condition it represents. Too often we try to teach young people science by means of symbols that are meaningless to them.

> "Certain words may conjure up as many different images as there are students in the classroom. Much of our science instruction is being lost because of the confusion of terms. It is important to . . . provide the experiences through which words become symbols for concepts.[33]

The need for empirical learning is especially critical for the socially deprived pupils. After developing a science program for girls enrolled in a Job Corps Center for Women, Martha Allen reports: "we have found in the past months that our girls need to *see* things in order to learn about them."[34] Nevertheless, in most school programs, the culturally deprived are usually denied laboratory experiences. "If you visited the schools in our large cities, you would find most of them in the 'general' classes. . . . You

[32] Beck, W. S., *Modern Science and the Nature of Life*, Doubleday & Co. Garden City, N.Y., 1961, p. 40.

[33] Adler, L. K., "Do They Mean What You Say" *The Science Teacher*, 32:25, Feb., 1965.

[34] Arnold, M. A., "Science Education for the Socially Deprived," *The Science Teacher*, 33:28, Feb., 1966.

would find that the science program in which these 'generals' find themselves is, in the main, entirely lacking in laboratory work and teacher
demonstration. . . . The less able, the less articulate, the less verbal, need
the activity in the lab to help them learn. The more able, with a greater
power to abstract, are much more at home with textual materials and class
discussion than are the less able; but of course, they too need the experiences in scientific inquiry provided by the laboratory."[35]

Sensing and awareness. Learning begins with environmental contacts
made through the senses. Sensations are more complex than the traditional
five senses of touch, taste, smell, vision, and hearing. The human organism
has many senses, a sense of equilibrium, a sense of acceleration, a sense of
body movement and position, senses of heat, cold, pressure, and pain.
There are several sensations in connection with vision and hearing. Many
of these sensations are not well understood and it is less confusing to
classify them by stimulus than by organ:[36]

Stimulus	Examples of Sensations
Mechanical	Tactual, pain, muscular movement, tickle
Acoustic	Hearing
Thermal	Heat, cold
Chemical	Smell, taste
Photic	Vision

Sensations may be rejected. When a person is concentrating, as for
instance when driving a car in heavy traffic, he may cease to notice
irrelevant sounds such as a conversation: he has rejected the sensations
from his consciousness. Sensations may also go unnoticed; many a person
walks through the country in spring and does not notice a bird singing
although if all songs stop, the person is aware of the cessation of the
sensation. Probably much of what has been called "sense training" has
actually been making a person aware of sensations and their significance; it
is doubtful that the senses themselves can be trained.

There is a tendency for school science programs to ignore sensations
which cannot be described readily in words. This denies young people the
enrichment possible through awareness of the many sensations that constantly impinge upon us. It also seriously limits learning, because for true

[35] Lisonbee, Lorenzo, "Teaching Science to the Disadvantaged Pupil," *The Science
Teacher*, 30:19, Oct., 1963.

[36] Boring, E. G., *Sensation and Perception in the History of Experimental Psychology*,
Appleton-Century-Crofts, New York, 1941.

understanding one needs all the information that can be obtained. Odor, for example, has much more informative value than most people realize.

> No sense has so strong a power of suggestion—or is more evocative. How often has a barely imperceptible aroma instantly evoked remembrances which have been hidden away for decades? At times a highly specific incident in one's early life seemingly comes from nowhere into sharp focus. It is not unusual for a key aroma to unlock a flood of memories which lie in a remote and rarely called-upon storehouse in the mind.[37]

Association of experience. Learning is a result of association. The small baby associates his mother with the pleasures of feeding. He associates crying with attention. Later he associates a cup with drinking and a toddler car with increased independence of motion.

He learns language the same way. He associates the syllables mama with his mother. He associates no with denials or punishment. In every case, learning is the result of association of experience. The burnt child associates steaming food, or flames in the fireplace, or an unshielded stove, with pain. The unburnt child has no fear of these things. In learning language the child who has been burnt is able to associate the word hot with objects that can burn him. To the unburnt child, hot is a meaningless and somewhat pleasant syllable to repeat over and over. It is a nonsense word.

In science, as in other subjects, true learning is not a memorization of nonsense syllables but the result of association of experiences. Without experiences there can be no science learnings.

> Jack and Joe are two members of an eighth grade science class that is studying the nature of fire. Spontaneous combustion is one topic under consideration. Jack lives on a farm where a fire once leveled a large barn, destroying livestock, crops, and equipment and causing great hardships for the family. Joe lives in a large village where there have been no serious fires in his lifetime; his experiences with grass fires and chimney fires have been pleasurable and exciting.
>
> The textbook explanation of spontaneous combustion had immediate significance to Jack. He knew how hay is made and stored. He had noticed heat in fermenting manure and piles of wet grass. He could see a possible relationship to the loss of his father's barn. He turned to additional books including a chemistry text.
>
> Joe, on the other hand, had only a limited experience with hay. He could not conceive of wet hay setting itself on fire. The term spontaneous combustion was little more than a nonsense syllable and he was impatient to turn to a new topic.

[37] Freeman, S. K., "Odor," *Science and Technology*, 69:80, 1967.

Joe needed mental images of conditions in which spontaneous combustion takes place. He might have gained these by listening to Jack describe the fire in his father's barn. He might have gained them by reading vivid descriptions of fires caused by spontaneous combustion. With the images thus produced he would be better able to appreciate the importance of the topic and would thus be more ready for study.

A number of classroom experiences could have been provided to prepare him for the textbook explanations. He could have discovered that heat is generated during the fermentation of vegetable matter and the oxidation of paint oils. He could have been shown that white phosphorus can ignite itself.

Learning in science requires an adequate experience background. This applies equally well to the learning of facts and the understanding of principles. It applies to the development of skills as well as to the development of habits and attitudes.

Types of experiences.   The baby's first experiences are with things that affect him directly—the touch of a nipple to his lips, a wet diaper against his skin, the sight of someone bending towards him. He relates these experiences to the immediate sensations of pleasure or discomfort they bring him.

Later he associates present experiences with past sensations—the sight of a bottle of milk with former pleasure of feeding, the sight of a dog with previous fear of an overly playful dog. He is using memory of past experiences in making associations with present experiences.

Finally, he begins to associate mental images that are produced by words or pictures with memories of past experiences. He hears the word hot and has a mental image of steaming food which he relates to a former feeling of pain. He sees a picture of an automobile that sets up an image of a real automobile; this he then relates to his former experiences with automobiles.

Science teaching makes use of all of these various types of experiences. Direct, firsthand experiences give information about such things as the colors of flowers, the sounds of birds, the forces needed to lift different kinds of substances.

Recall of past experiences enables pupils to apply their learnings about levers to the behavior of the teeter-totter. Recall of experiences with house plants at home sets the stage for experiments with phototropisms.

Vicarious experiences help pupils visualize a hurricane from a written description and the habitat of a polar bear from a picture. The completeness of the image depends, of course, upon the previous background of experiences the pupils can draw on for association of words and pictures.

Firsthand versus vicarious experiences.   Firsthand experiences are basic experiences. A pupil may benefit from them without having a broad background of previous experiences or a certain degree of mental maturity. Pupils generally vary in their ability to interpret firsthand experiences, but most of them are well able to receive the sensations involved.

> Mr. Neuman was directing his physics class in a study of pulleys. The pupils rigged a "bosun's chair" from the framework of one of the playground swings. A single large pulley was fastened to the overhead support. A heavy rope passed over the pulley and ended in a large loop fitted with a board on which the pupils could take turns sitting.
>
> First a pupil tried to pull up another pupil of about the same weight sitting in the chair. Then he sat in the chair and tried to pull himself up. The amazed comments of each pupil indicated how little any previous experiences had prepared them for this situation.

Mr. Neuman realized that he could not depend completely on the experience background of pupils for a study of pulleys. He knew that words, diagrams, and numbers could not substitute for the sensations involved in using muscles. So he took the time to set up a firsthand experience situation.

It is possible to build a complete science program on firsthand experiences, using experiments, certain types of demonstrations, and a great number of field trips. Such a program has many advantages. All pupils, no matter what their cultural or educational backgrounds, begin on an approximately even footing. Reading ability or the ability to interpret flat pictures is not needed. The teacher has assurance that each pupil makes approximately the same observations. The teacher knows the extent of the pupil background when he begins follow-up work.

There are two major limitations of the program that uses only firsthand experiences: (1) firsthand experiences are time consuming and restrict the amount of material that may be covered, and (2) the program deals only with materials of the immediate environment.

Vicarious experiences, used so preponderantly in our schools, need much more careful treatment than they usually receive.

> A ninth grade class was viewing a film on automobile engines. The teacher, Mr. Dubois, had worked as an automobile mechanic and knew engines quite well. He considered the film excellent.
>
> Tom had twice helped his older brother rebuild a jalopy. He found the film an excellent review of the structure of an automobile engine. The animated drawings summed up for him his knowledge of the events in a four-cycle engine.

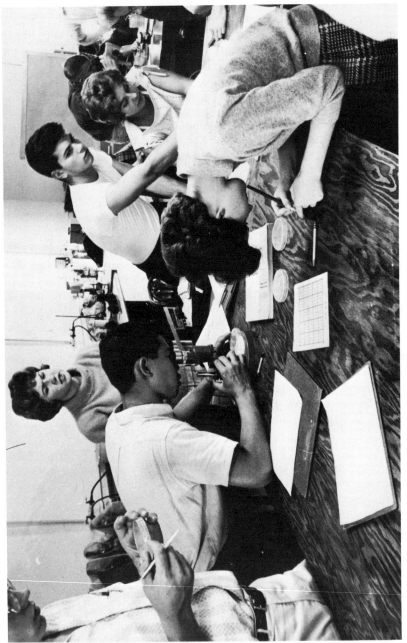

Pupils learn science best by being actively engaged in it.

Bill had never seen an automobile engine taken apart, but he had a considerable interest in automobiles and knew the names and general functions of the parts he could see under the hood of a car. All the language used in the film was familiar to him, and he learned a great deal from seeing it.

Marjorie had brothers who were always talking about automobiles. The film occasionally struck a responsive note, especially those sections dealing with the radiator, the carburetor, and lubrication.

Amy lived with a widowed mother who had no interest in things mechanical. If the family car did not operate properly, it was sent to the garage. Amy had heard the word radiator but only in connection with a heating system. "Cylinder" meant little to her except a vague recollection of a type of solid once studied in mathematics. She had heard of valves in the heart but did not understand them. "Carburetor" was a word in another language. Amy recognized the beginning sequences of the film in which an automobile drives up and stops. From the moment when the hood was lifted, however, she was in a completely strange world.

About a quarter of the general science class profited greatly from the film and carried on a heated discussion about it. This convinced Mr. Dubois that the film was an excellent teaching device and that all pupils should benefit from it. He attributed the partial understandings of pupils like Marjorie and Amy to insufficient attention or lack of mental ability.

The effectiveness of vicarious experiences in teaching depends entirely upon the nature and extent of a pupil's background. A pupil who has moved to Florida after living several years in Vermont can readily understand references to a northern winter. Those of his classmates who have never left the South may understand little. Even pictures mean little to the latter because pictures can give only limited information. Such impressions as extreme cold, stinging wind, the texture of snow, and the changed sounds are difficult if not impossible to convey.

Means for communicating vicarious experiences are extremely limited. When speech is used the listener must be able to interpret the words by forming images comparable to those in the mind of the speaker.

LEARNING ON THE RATIONALISM LEVEL

"Memory is a necessary part of learning, but it is not that which is most human. We must select, place ideas in new contexts, deduce fresh conclusions. We must create hypotheses, test them, then validate our conclusions. We must generalize. We must remain ever curious about ourselves and our world. Yet these are the things we so rarely try to teach. Did you ever hear of any teacher who gave a student a high grade simply because the student was curious and of an inquiring mind? Yet is not that the beginning of all science? Is it not significant that the computer is not curious and is never any better than the program fed into it."[38]

Elements of rational thinking.   Three basic elements of rational thinking are given by Hilda Taba: (1) the organization of specific information into conceptual systems; (2) the inductive process of developing generalizations and inferences from specific data; and (3) the deductive process of using knowledge to explain unfamiliar phenomena, to predict, and to hypothesize.[39]

To the above must be added a fourth important aspect, that of critical thinking. A number of manifestations of critical thinking have been identified:[40]

1. Grasping the meaning of a statement.
2. Judging whether there is ambiguity in a line of reasoning.
3. Judging whether certain statements contradict each other.
4. Judging whether a conclusion necessarily follows.
5. Judging whether a statement is specific enough.
6. Judging whether a statement is actually the application of a certain principle.
7. Judging whether an observation is reliable.
8. Judging whether an inductive conclusion is warranted.
9. Judging whether the problem has been identified.
10. Judging whether something is an assumption.
11. Judging whether a definition is adequate.
12. Judging whether a statement made by an alleged authority is acceptable.

Inductive reasoning situations.   The inductive method of developing generalizations has the special merit of showing pupils how scientific principles were first formulated. The pupils collect data, retain that which is pertinent to the problem, and formulate an inclusive statement from the data.

[38] Glass, H. Bentley, "The Most Critical Aspect of Science Teaching," *The Science Teacher,* 34:22, May, 1967.

[39] Taba, Hilda, "Strategy for Learning," *Science and Children,* September, 1965, p. 23. 23.

[40] Ennis, R. H., "Concept of Critical Thinking," *Harvard Educational Review,* 32:81–111, 1962.

Miss Carpenter had shown her biology class how to make microscope slides of onion tissue in order to see the cells. One boy, who finished first, asked if he could try to find cells in other kinds of plants. Miss Carpenter was pleased with his interest and showed him how to make slides of the epidermis of leaves. Interest spread rapidly through the class, and for the next few days the pupils examined almost a hundred different kinds of plants including algae. They learned how to make thin sections with a razor blade, and some used a hand microtome after a demonstration by Miss Carpenter.

One of the girls finally said, "It seems as though all plants are made of cells."

Her statement was immediately qualified by another girl, "But not all the same kind of cells."

A boy challenged the statement. "You can't say that a one-celled plant is made up of cells," he said. Several arguments centered about this point and were finally resolved in a new statement, "All plants are made up of one or more cells, usually of different kinds."

A final argument, initiated by one of the boys, restored the qualifying clause of the first statement, "It seems as though all plants are made up of one or more cells, usually of different kinds."

Miss Carpenter's class developed this particular generalization on the basis of a large number of observations, but even though no exceptions were found the pupils recognized the limitations of their statement. Their minds were open to change in case contrary evidence was presented. It is probable that they would be critical of an equivalent statement discovered in their reading.

Had Miss Carpenter made the general statement as a preliminary to the observation of the onion cells, or had she referred them to their textbook beforehand, the pupils would probably have accepted the generalization without question. The pupils would never have had this valuable exercise in reasoning.

The procedure employed by Miss Carpenter requires adequate time for development; pupils must not be hurried through the reasoning process. Teachers who are interested in covering a good deal of material in a course often try to speed up the inductive reasoning process by presenting the evidence themselves. To develop the same generalization discussed in the example, they will use microprojectors to show cells of different plants; they will display charts and models; and they will make use of films and slides. From the evidence presented they will "lead" pupils into the general statement.

This seems at first like inductive reasoning on the part of the pupils; but although the resulting generalization may be the same, the type of thinking is much different. The pupils have no choice of evidence; they cannot look for exceptions. The manner of presenting the evidence, prepared with the final statement in mind, determines the final statement. The complete procedure encourages passive acceptance rather than critical consideration.

Deductive reasoning.   This manner of thinking is sometimes called "going from the known to the known," because it involves making logical inferences from general statements that have already been accepted. It is a method that is much used in science teaching.

> Mr. Neuman's physics class had read as part of their assignment the paragraphs in their textbooks that discussed Newton's laws of motion. Mr. Neuman used the beginning of the class period to clarify the thinking of the pupils on the statements in the book, and then he illustrated the "laws" with some simple demonstrations.
>
> A few days later Mr. Neuman set up a model electric locomotive on an oval track. When he increased the speed of the locomotive beyond a certain value the locomotive jumped the track. The pupils deducted from Newton's laws that the rails did not produce enough sideward push on the wheels to make the locomotive go around the curves.
>
> The pupils then experimented with banking the rails to provide more sideward thrust. With sufficient banking they were able to operate the locomotive at top speed.

Mr. Neuman's class exercised deductive reasoning in explaining the behavior of the locomotive. It is important to note, however, that they did not stop with the deduction. They experimented to check their statements.

Formulating and testing hypotheses.   A large part of scientific thought is devoted to formulating explanations and planning methods for testing these explanations. These processes make up the very heart of what many people choose to call the scientific method. Certainly no young person has a knowledge of science if he is not well skilled in dealing with hypotheses.

The process of proposing a hypothesis and testing it involves elements of both inductive and deductive reasoning plus a good deal of critical thinking about the results. Raw data are examined, analyzed, and then brought into some form of order. A general statement is then derived by induction. The general statement serves as a hypothesis. To test the hypothesis it is used as a basis for predictions (a deductive process) which are then tested, preferably by experiment. The hypothesis is then abandoned, modified, or accepted tentatively subject to further testing.

> Tommy, one of the pupils in Miss Well's biology class, raised the question as to why there were so many flies in his attic windows on sunny days in winter. Miss Well encouraged class discussion, knowing

that some unusual behavior patterns of insects could be investigated if the pupils were interested enough.

The class decided that the flies had come in at the beginning of cold weather and were attracted to the windows by the warm sunlight. When Miss Well asked, however, how the flies could find their way into the attic, no one could propose a satisfactory explanation.

The class decided upon some experiments with the flies if Tommy could catch enough for study. A few days later Tommy brought in the flies.

The first thing the pupils noticed was that the flies did not look like common houseflies. The wings overlapped giving them a somewhat dumpy appearance.

Some of the pupils used a cardboard carton to construct a room with cellophane windows on one side. Flies in the box swarmed to the windows when the air was warm, but they clustered in a far corner when cold. Temperatures were taken and the critical point was found to be about 50°F.

The pupils then constructed another testing device by putting a partition across the center of a box. One room thus formed was given a cellophane window and the other was kept dark. A small opening in the partition connected the rooms. This time the flies went into the lighted room when temperatures were above 50°F and into the dark room when temperatures were below 50°F.

The pupils decided that flies try to get in dark places when cold and into light places when warm, or as a textbook would put it, the flies are positively phototropic above 50°F and negatively phototropic below 50°F. Tommy and some other pupils who lived in homes with open attics checked temperatures and the presence or absence of flies in attic windows on several occasions.

Later the pupils tried other kinds of flies without such positive results. They changed their conclusion to apply only to this one type of fly (the cluster fly or buckwheat fly, Pollenia rudis).

These pupils engaged in the highest level of thinking processes. They were not just learning about science, they were scientists; and they ended the project with a deepened understanding of what science is. This manner of teaching requires adequate time for satisfactory development, but in no other way can science be satisfactorily taught.

Using critical thinking. Pupils will not develop their critical thinking abilities if they are exposed only to certainty. The teacher, therefore, must provide uncertainties. This can be done by letting pupils follow a path to an expected conclusion and then raising questions about the validity of the conclusion or of the path that was followed. No new teaching situations are needed—only changed goals on the part of the teacher.

When the class was asked, "What effect has saliva on starch?" the ready answer was, "It changes starch to sugar." When asked how this could be verified, the pupils were less responsive. Most of them knew that the presence of starch could be detected with iodine solution. A pupil proposed that some saliva be added to each test tube of starch suspension. After two minutes of shaking a tube and warming it in the fist the blue colored contents of the tubes had become colorless or nearly so.

This quickly led to possible "theories" to explain the change. One pupil proposed that the iodine had been used up and suggested adding more iodine to test his "theory." Someone suggested that they test for sugar; this was done, and a positive result was obtained.

The class seemed complacently satisfied until the teacher asked, "How can we explain the presence of the sugar?" The forthcoming answer was, "The starch changed to sugar," but one pupil objected, "Maybe there was sugar in the starch suspension." The test was negative and then other questions were raised, "Is there sugar in the saliva?" and "Is there sugar in the iodine solution?" These were also tested. The findings were reviewed and listed on the blackboard.

1. The bottle labeled Starch Suspension contained starch and did not contain sugar.

2. There was no sugar in the iodine solution.

3. There was no sugar in the saliva.

4. After two minutes, the warmed mixture of starch and saliva gave a positive test for sugar.

Conclusions were called for and evaluated by the answers to the question, "If we had not tested each substance for the presence of sugar, how would our conclusion have been affected?"

This lesson provides an opportunity to use the following elements of the scientific method and scientific attitude although not labeled as such:

a) Verifying one's own work by considering the results of others doing the same thing.

b) Suspending judgment.

c) Accepting the results of exercising one's own powers instead of relying on authority alone.

d) Proposing hypotheses.

e) Gathering data for testing hypotheses.

f) *Summarizing data.*

g) *Selecting the best conclusion.*[41]

Independent Student Research. Independent research in science brings the student more closely into the spirit of scientific thinking than any other activity. He is directly and personally involved in a problem. He is intensely interested in something that is *unknown*, at least to him and to his available sources of information. Ideally, the problem has not been solved before, but this is not essential. However, there is no lack of truly original research problems.

> *Following an ecological field study by the eighth grade each pupil was asked to carry out an independent investigation. Roger chose to study the effect of goldenrod galls on the height of goldenrod stems. He began with the hypothesis that the greater the number of galls, the more stunted stem growth would be. He averaged the measurements of fifty stems with no galls, fifty with one gall, fifty with two galls, and twenty-three with three galls. "My hypothesis was wrong," he wrote, "The stems with the most galls grew tallest." Then he added, "Maybe the flies that laid the eggs chose the tallest plants."*

Jablonski describes how a simple but original problem grew into a problem of true significance:[42]

> *A group of students heard a lecture by a scientist who was conducting research in the field of animal nutrition as related to tumor growth . . . One student posed the question: "Do laboratory rats eat the same amount of three different available commercial diets?"*
>
> *A simple question on the surface, but the answer was not immediately forthcoming. The student read more about general nutrition, examined the use of proper controls and numbers of experimental animals to use and set out to find the answers.*
>
> *The student reported to the interested scientist that the rats did indeed eat different amounts of the three commercial diets. Furthermore, a second question came to his mind: "What would happen to the rats' consumption of the diets if they were given an experimental tumor?"*
>
> *The student prepared a procedural outline and with approval of his teacher and the scientist, set up his experiment. He observed that the rats changed the preference in their diet. There was considerable*

[41] Abstracted from Abraham Raskin (ed.), "Providing for the Teaching of Some of the Elements of the Scientific Method," *Science Teaching Ideas*, National Science Teachers Association, Washington, D.C., 1955, pp. 11–12.

[42] Abstracted from Jablonski, J. R., "High School Student Research: Fact or Fancy," *The Science Teacher*, 31:24–26, April, 1964.

excitement about the finding, but the scientist wished for greater verification and asked that the experiment be repeated.

Essentially, the observations of the initial observer were verified, and this led to other ramifications of the problem.

Jablonski concludes, "*Emphatically*, then, high school research can be done with the proper guidance, selection, and interpretation of information, knowledge, and ideas."

Using history to develop scientific thinking. Although most teachers and texts include a little history of science in their programs, this is usually limited to some biographical data and a summary of achievements. Struggles with unreliable data, faulty hypotheses, and blind alleys are expurgated. Such material helps little in an understanding of the ways of science.

Melvin Berger shows how an historical account can be turned to educational advantage by giving proper details and asking pertinent questions. Unfortunately, only a little of his article can be quoted here; readers are referred to the original.[43]

This dread disease (beriberi) was killing millions annually throughout the East. The medical group first set out to find a germ of some sort . . . After two years of work they were unable to report any progress. . . .

(*How would you go about looking for an unknown cause that causes a known disease? What substances from the body of the victim might you check for infectivity?*)

Eijkman . . . noticed that chickens in the prison yard were showing symptoms of beriberi . . . He also knew that . . . prisoners were suffering from the disease. Yet chickens outside the prison were as healthy as chickens everywhere else.

(*What might explain why more prison chickens were afflicted than were those outside? How might this be related to the large number of beriberi victims among the prisoners?*)

Eijkman knew that the rice eaten in the prison . . . was polished . . . Perhaps the beriberi was somehow related to the fact that the rice was polished.

(*How would you set up an experiment to determine whether beriberi is related to the polishing of rice?*)

Eijkman divided some healthy chickens into three groups. Group I was fed whole grain rice. Group II was fed rice with only the outer husk removed. Group III was fed polished rice with both the outer husk and silverskin removed . . . Those in Group III developed symptoms of beriberi. When fed the silverskins they quickly recovered.

(*The beriberi cause is now isolated. Where?*)

[43] Berger, Melvin, "Using History in Teaching Science," *The Science Teacher*, 30:24–26, November, 1963.

Berger's article continues with the development of Eijkman's incorrect conclusion and the final isolation of the vitamin factor.

DEVELOPMENT OF ATTITUDES

Attitudes developed by young people during their study of science can be as important as the skills they acquire and the knowledge they obtain. Attitudes regulate behavior, not only in the classroom but in all other areas of human experience. Strongly positive attitudes permit growth; negative attitudes hinder growth; critical attitudes aid in making wise decisions; tolerant attitudes help in adjusting to new situations.

"Attitudes have emotional content and vary in intensity and generality according to the range of objects or situations over which they apply. For the most part, attitudes are learned and are difficult to distinguish from such affective attributes of personality as interests, appreciations, likes, dislikes, opinions, values, ideals, and character traits."[44]

Importance of positive attitudes.   Positive attitudes are essential if pupils are to gain from their study of science. They must enjoy the work. They must have self-respect as well as admiration for those who succeed, and they must like the teacher. These attitudes are the direct outcome of success. Pupils participate with increased frequency in activities in which they find increasing success. They withdraw from activities in which they encounter repeated failures.

Personal pride is an important factor in developing positive attitudes. When a pupil takes pride in his accomplishments, whether these be high grades or tangible results, he is able to grow emotionally and intellectually. But if a pupil does not take pride in his work, the objectives of science education cannot be met.

The problems of negative attitudes are recognized by all who study the plight of the "culturally disadvantaged" pupils. These pupils "have limited aspirations, not commensurate with their latent abilities . . . They are not understood by their middle-class teachers. They want to learn, but resist the methods of the ordinary educational system to get them to learn. They are not interested in special favors, but they do want, like all human beings, to be respected."[45]

[44] Haney, Richard, E., "The Development of Scientific Attitudes," *The Science Teacher*, 31:8; 33, December, 1964.

[45] Lisonbee, Lorenzo, "Teaching Science to the Disadvantaged Pupil," *The Science Teacher*, 30:18, October, 1963.

Sources of attitudes. Gordon Allport suggested four primary sources of attitudes:[46]

1. General approach or withdrawal tendencies. One pupil may develop a strong liking for the study of electricity because it enables him to manipulate materials, a type of activity he enjoys. Another pupil may develop a distaste for zoology because he must handle dead animals.
2. Other people. Most young people who fear snakes have adopted this attitude ready-made from other people.
3. A single dramatic experience. Intense embarrassment resulting from an accident during a demonstration may prejudice a pupil against volunteering to present another demonstration.
4. Integration of numerous specific responses. A succession of minor rebuffs by a teacher may lead to a strong dislike for the teacher and the course.

Nature of scientific attitudes. Scientific attitudes have been variously identified and subdivided. Haney lists eight important attitudes: (1) curiosity, (2) rationality, (3) suspended judgment, (4) open-mindedness, (5) critical-mindedness, (6) objectivity, (7) honesty, (8) humility.[47]

Paul Diederich has identified some twenty components of *the* scientific attitude;[48] these are (1) scepticism, (2) faith in possibility of solving problems, (3) desire for experimental verification, (4) precision, (5) liking for new things, (6) willingness to change opinions, (7) humility, (8) loyalty to truth, (9) an objective attitude, (10) aversion to superstition, (11) liking for scientific explanations, (12) desire for completeness of knowledge, (13) suspended judgment, (14) distinguishing between hypotheses and solutions, (15) awareness of assumptions, (16) judgment of what is of fundamental and general significance, (17) respect for theoretical structures, (18) respect for quantification, (19) acceptance of probabilities, (20) acceptance of warranted generalizations.

Often the term "scientific attitude" is treated as synonymous with the term "critical attitude." The latter is then considered to have about the same aspects as those listed above although variously worded.

Fostering scientific attitudes. A suitable psychological atmosphere must be maintained in the classroom at all times if pupils are to develop those scientific attitudes we list as objectives. To paraphrase and adapt Schwab's

[46] Allport, G. W., "Attitudes," *Handbook of Social Psychology*, C. Munchison (ed.), Clark University Press, Worcester, Mass., 1935.

[47] Haney, R. E., "The Development of Scientific Attitudes," *The Science Teacher*, 31:8; 33, December, 1964.

[48] Diederich, Paul B., "Components of the Scientific Attitude," *The Science Teacher*, 34:23–24, February, 1967.

remarks about textbooks to the classroom situation: a pious preachment of generalized caution and doubt at the beginning of the school year will have no effect whatever. It is the massive influence of lesson after lesson all directed towards the goal of attitude development that will do this work if it is done at all.[49]

First, and probably most important, the teacher himself must have and constantly display pertinent scientific attitudes. "Pupils cannot learn attitudes that their teachers don't have. It may be that the first step in meeting this challenge to science education will consist of an inward look upon our own knowledge and value systems. Science teachers have a responsibility. It is to them that the public turns for an understanding of science, not just the facts of science or the skills, but also for a perspective that relates science to all other areas of human experience."[50]

The classroom must be free from the petty dictatorship that forces pupils into mute acquiescence. Schwab believes that one requirement is "a substantial component of doubt . . . nothing more than the honest statement of ignorance, uncertainty, and dubiety where these conditions are, in fact, the conditions of our knowledge."[51] To these should be added a spirit of inquiry, which encourages pupils to investigate problems for which the outcomes are not known or are uncertain, instead of a program of what Brandwein calls "problem-doing,"[52] by which he means work on problems for which the solutions are known.

Only the teacher can provide the proper atmosphere. To do so he must exercise his own critical faculties, questioning his own statements, those of pupils, and those of textbooks. He thus serves as an example and also as a challenge.

Teachers may sprinkle their statements liberally with qualifications such as, "If the air is actually made up of molecules, . . . If the earth actually does go around the sun, . . . If we accept the theory of evolution, . . . If there are genes in the chromosomes, ..." Minds are thus kept open.

Teachers may point out the assumptions on which theories are based. For instance, much work in astronomy is based on the assumption that light behaves in space as it does in the laboratory. Like the assumption that a straight line is the shortest distance between two points, this is an assumption that is rarely if ever questioned. But if the assumption were to be abandoned, a completely new set of theories would be possible.

[49] Schwab, Joseph J., "Science as Inquiry," *The Teaching of Science*, Harvard University Press, Cambridge, Mass., 1962, p. 60.

[50] Haney, *op. cit.*, 35.

[51] Schwab, *loc. cit.*

[52] Brandwein, Paul F., The *Revolution in Science Teaching*, Harcourt, New York, 1962.

Maintenance of a scientific attitude in the classroom may not be easy. University training of science teachers is not noted for its efforts to develop scientific attitudes. University professors who are very careful in their research work forget to maintain the same attitudes in their teaching. Reviewing a book on evolution, John Tyler Bonner finds himself (and many of his colleagues) guilty:

> What we have all accepted as the whole truth, turns out with some mild inspection, to be rather far from it. Apparently, if one reads the original papers instead of relying on some superficial remarks in a textbook, the affinities become extremely clouded indeed. We have all been telling our students for years not to accept any statement on its face value but to examine the evidence, and, therefore, it is rather a shock to discover that we have failed to follow our own sound advice.[53]

Lessons on scientific attitudes.   Young people are not likely to develop desirable scientific attitudes through exposure to a few lessons specifically directed towards this end; pupils need daily opportunities for contact with situations that encourage attitude development. Nevertheless, a few lessons can be used to awaken an awareness of attitudes. Although logically it may seem best to concentrate these lessons at the beginning of a course, some of the points may be meaningless at that time. It is better to scatter lessons on scientific attitudes throughout the course, making them relevant to the material being treated at the time.

A teacher may deliberately interject material which contradicts or seems to contradict ideas accepted by students on the basis of authority. It is best if the pupils discover the contradictions by examination of natural situations. For example, after pupils have accepted the definition that "Insects have six legs" they may be asked to count the legs of a caterpillar; then after they have decided either to define "leg" more carefully or have altered the first definition to "adult insects," they may be asked to count the legs of a Nymphalid butterfly which has front legs so reduced as to be almost unnoticeable.

The interjected material does not have to lead to definite answers, only questions.

> The pupils in Mr. Kane's physics class had performed a number of demonstrations illustrating the expansion effects caused by heating. In each instance the pupils applied the kinetic theory of molecules to their explanations and seemed to be well satisfied with the theory.
> Then Mr. Kane performed a demonstration. He filled a flask with colored water and inserted a one-hole stopper containing a long glass

[53] Bonner, J. T., reviewing Kerkut, G. A., "Implications of Evolution," *American Scientist*, 49:240, 1961.

tube. Instead of heating the flask, however, Mr. Kane set it in a jar of water, ice, and salt. At first the water went down in the tube, and the pupils explained the decrease in volume by the lowered activity of the molecules. After a few minutes the water stopped going down and actually began rising. The pupils were astonished and could not explain the phenomenon.

Mr. Kane's special demonstration did not destroy the pupils' acceptance of the molecular theory, but it quickly restored the theory to its true status. The pupils were beginning to treat the theory as fact and now they realized there were some possible qualifications to the general statement.

A teacher who is looking for situations in which pupils can develop their critical faculties will find many arising from the comments of pupils themselves. In the following case a teacher who had accepted unquestioningly a conclusion found in many textbooks had his eyes opened by an alert youngster.

For a lesson on the composition of air Mr. Potter chose a familiar demonstration from the seventh grade general science textbook. He floated a lighted candle on a block of wood in a tray of water. Then he inverted a glass cylinder and set it over the candle. Soon the candle went out and the water rose inside. Measurement showed that the water now occupied about one fifth of the original space in the cylinder.

The pupils had already been told that a fire needs oxygen to burn. They deduced that the candle used up the oxygen and that water went in to occupy the space. On the basis of their reasoning they wrote in their notebooks that air is about one fifth oxygen.

Mauritz, however, seemed doubtful. He finally asked, "Why did the water rise in the jar after the flame went out? I should have thought it would go up all the time the candle was burning if the oxygen was being used up."

Mr. Potter's surprise was obvious; "I think you have a point there, Mauritz. Let's try the experiment over again and we will all check you on this."

Repetition confirmed Mauritz' observation. Mr. Potter admitted his bewilderment. "I guess you and I have some studying to do, Mauritz," he added.

Anyone versed in chemistry knows that the candle flame would go out long before the oxygen supply was exhausted and that one of the products, carbon dioxide, occupies as much space as the oxygen used to produce it. The amount of water entering the cylinder because of the depletion of the oxygen content would be small indeed.

The reasoning of Mr. Potter and his pupils was logical but based on wrong assumptions. Mauritz pointed out a flaw in the reasoning. Mr. Potter was critical enough to recognize the flaw and honest enough to acknowledge it even though he had to question a firmly entrenched notion. In future classes he would be able to use the activity not to teach pupils the composition of the air but to help them recognize flaws in reasoning and develop their critical faculties.

Lessons can be built around the testing of weather sayings and proverbs and other items of folklore. "Utilization of folklore materials can provide a basis for personal experience resulting in meaningful insights into the nature of science and the scientific method. . . . Learning about folklore in areas of science leads naturally to an investigation of the use of the scientific method. Pupils may then learn the importance of getting facts from the most reliable sources available, for basing judgement on fact, of being willing to revise judgments in the light of new discoveries of more authoritative information, and of being willing to eliminate unfounded prejudices and biases."[54] But teachers should approach the subject of folklore with an open mind. Too often teachers and textbooks classify all folklore as "superstition." Even if all folklore were incorrect, which it is not, to reject it without careful testing is to act on the same level as those who accept it without question.

SUGGESTED ACTIVITIES

1. Obtain the ages, IQ's, and reading levels of one or more science classes. Prepare histograms to show the frequency distributions of these characteristics in each class.
2. Observe one pupil carefully throughout a full science period, making detailed notes on his behavior. Try to account for each of his actions as a response to the situation in which he finds himself.
3. Make a study of a pupil of high IQ and another of low IQ in the same class. Through classroom observations note differences in response to different situations. Study their written reports and their test papers. Try to determine the nature and extent of the changes in each pupil as a result of his science work throughout your period of observation.
4. Select a small segment of a course of study, and list the learnings that are expected. Classify these as (1) learnings for which pupils have adequate background to gain by lecture, (2) learnings which pupils can gain from reading, (3) learnings which pupils can gain from pictures, or (4) learnings for which pupils need first-hand experiences.

[54] Putman, J. F., "Folklore and Science," *The Science Teacher*, 30:4; 24, May, 1963.

5. At a conference a specialist in science education was heard to say, "We know far too much today to depend upon direct experience learning activities; we must depend largely upon lecturing and reading, supplemented by films and slides." Debate this statement.

6. Make a list of ways in which pupils can secure first-hand experiences in the science program. Make a list of how pupils may secure vicarious experiences in the science program.

7. You are about to begin a unit on the study of rocks in a seventh grade general science class. What motivating factors might you be able to utilize to stimulate pupil interest on the subject?

SUGGESTED READINGS

Bruner, Jerome S., *The Process of Education*, Vintage Books, Random House, New York, 1960.

Dember, W. N., "The New Look in Motivation," *American Scientist*, 53:419, 1965.

Earl, R. W., "Problem Solving and Motor Skill Behaviors Under Conditions of Free-Choice." Unpublished doctoral dissertation, University of Michigan, 1957.

Fish, A. S. and Bernice Goldmark, "Inquiry Method: Three Interpretations," *The Science Teacher*, 33:13 February, 1966.

Keislar, E. R., "The Learning Process and the Teaching of Science," *The Science Teacher*, 29:18, December, 1962.

Meerlo, Joost, *The Rape of the Mind*, Grosset and Dunlap, New York, 1961.

Probst, G. E., "Programmed Learning in the Schools," *The Science Teacher*, 29:34, November, 1962.

Reiner, W. B., "Motivation in Science Teaching," *The Science Teacher*, 30:52, February, 1963.

Richardson, John S., *Science Teaching in Secondary Schools*, Prentice Hall, Englewood Cliffs, N. J., 1957.

Royce, Joseph R., "The Search for Meaning," *American Scientist*, 47:4, 1959.

Russell, David H., *Children's Thinking*, Blaisdell Publishing Co., Waltham, Mass., 1956.

Skinner, B. F., "The Science of Learning and the Art of Teaching," *Harvard Educational Review*, vol. 24, 1954.

Smith, A. W., "A Problem-Solving Demonstration," *Ideas for Teaching Science in the Junior High School*, National Science Teachers Assn., Washington, D. C., 1963.

Strickland, W. L., "Teaching Science: by What Authority?" *The Science Teacher*, 31:23, October, 1964.

Weiss, Paul, "Knowledge: A Growth Process," *Proceedings of the American Philosophical Society*, 104:2, 1960.

Chapter 5

Pupils Should Experiment

EXPERIMENTATION IS SO MUCH A PART OF SCIENCE THAT IT IS DIFFICULT TO conceive of a science program without this type of activity. One of the major objectives of the science program has always been the development of an understanding of the experimental method; this was true even during the early days of formal science training in secondary schools. There has always been provision for some type of laboratory work and for experimentation in secondary school science.

Experiments and laboratory work are almost—but not quite—synonymous terms in the secondary school science program. There may be some experimentation done outside the laboratory, and some laboratory activities cannot be called experiments. But in practice most of the experiments done by pupils are part of their laboratory work, and most of their laboratory work involves experimentation.

Laboratory work, at its best, is an integral part of the science program, developing naturally out of other types of activities, and in its turn leading toward other forms of class work.

Mr. Johnson began a biology lesson with the question, "Does your heart beat faster when you are standing or when you are sitting?" The

160

pupils speculated that standing might represent a form of exercise but resolved that they could answer the question best by experimenting. They chose to test themselves individually, letting Mr. Johnson serve as timekeeper while they determined their respective heart rates. Results were entered in a chart on the blackboard.

Several new questions arose as the data from the experiment were being considered—sex differences, variation in rate as exercise was increased, individual variation for the same amount and kind of exercise. They chose to answer these questions by working in pairs and pooling data afterwards.

Mr. Johnson brought the lesson to a close with a general reading assignment and a brief consideration of other factors that affect heart rate—fear, anger, age, drugs, and the like. Almost immediately pupils began volunteering to conduct studies of these factors outside of school hours.

In this lesson it is difficult to draw a sharp line between laboratory work and other forms of class work. The original problem led to a general class experiment. The results gave rise to more problems best solved by small groups; procedures used were useful in suggesting a pattern for attack. The results of the small group experiments led to a general reading assignment and to continued experimentation as a permissive assignment.

THE NATURE OF EXPERIMENTS

In a broad sense many activities can be listed as experiments. A pupil mixing orange juice and milk "just to see what happens" is experimenting. His purpose is vague, his procedures are not clearly thought out, he has no controls and no plans for making observations. He may draw no conclusions. But he is trying something without knowing the outcome.

Experiments range from these simple activities to exceedingly complex attacks on problems. From the teaching standpoint, the simpler experiments are important because the attacks used are more readily adapted to the everyday situations pupils encounter. Highly formal experiments have little application in the lives of young people.

There is always danger that teachers will think only in terms of complex experiments, overformalizing the experimental method until it becomes valueless to adolescents. At its best, the experimental method is flexible and readily adapted to all types of situations. Generally, it is no more than the application of common sense to the solution of problems.

The "steps" of the experimental method.   The great majority of problems solved by experiments are so simple that no one bothers to isolate the successive steps used in the attack. There are steps, however, and these may be discovered by analyzing the procedures used.

> A pupil raised a question, "Will ice float in kerosene?" He procured a bowl, some kerosene, and a piece of ice. He dropped the ice in the kerosene, noted what happened, and made a statement.

Analysis of his procedures shows: (1) a statement of the problem; (2) a single trial with an accompanying observation; and (3) a conclusion. The pupil considered a single trial to be sufficient because he could not conceive of conditions that might affect his results differently. His conclusion was simple and direct. Though experts in science education may be critical of his procedures, their objections tend to cloud what is otherwise a satisfactory solution. Many problems can be solved by this three-step attack.

Complexities arise in situations in which several factors are operating. Conclusions that result from a single observation then need reconsideration and retesting under varying conditions to determine their validity.

> Pupils who were studying the bleaching effect of sunlight recalled that newspapers left outdoors turned yellow rather than white. Two pupils volunteered to set up some experiments to see whether yellowing is the result of exposure to sunlight.
>
> A few days later the pupils displayed strips of newsprint that had been left in a sunny window. From the appearance the class concluded that sunlight was responsible. Their teacher, however, hinted that other factors might have caused the yellowing. The pupils listed some of these factors and devised experiments to test their effects. After these experiments had been tried out a final conclusion with needed qualifications was proposed and accepted by the class.

Sometimes the need for retesting as illustrated above can be anticipated and made a part of the original experiment. This results in what is known as a "controlled experiment"—a device that will be discussed in the section that follows.

When attacking complex and difficult problems, researchers usually add another step. They investigate the findings of others who are working in the same or related fields. These investigations may suggest methods for the attack upon new problems. Sometimes they reduce the amount of information that must be gathered. Occasionally they reveal that the problem has already been solved in whole or in part. This step is not one of general use in the secondary school science program because of the lack of library facilities. It may be used by occasional pupils who can visit nearby colleges and large public libraries.

Controlled experiments.   Many science teachers prefer to restrict the term "experiment" to the type of investigation known as the "controlled experiment." In the controlled experiment, every effort is made to control the factors involved. All factors but two are held as nearly constant as possible. Of the remaining two, one is varied and its effect on the other is determined.

Two high school physics pupils were working with a direct current motor. They applied a uniform voltage to the rotor. They varied the voltage impressed on the field coils by uniform steps and determined the speed of the motor for each step. They plotted their data on a graph.

Sometimes two parallel experiments are set up so that comparisons can be made. One of the two experiments is often called a "control" or a "check."

Two seed flats containing soil from a lawn were planted with a standard lawn grass mixture. One flat was watered with rain water, the other with rain water containing a little ammonium sulfate. The flats were kept in the same place to insure identical conditions of temperature and light.

In the above experiment, the seed flat watered with rain water alone is termed the "control." It would have been possible to conduct a large number of parallel experiments using flats watered by solutions of different concentrations of ammonium sulfate. The flat watered with rain water would still have been termed the control.

Sometimes it is difficult to identify a "control" in a set of parallel experiments.

A pupil was attempting to discover the effect of temperature on the rate with which sodium chloride dissolves. First he put a measured quantity of salt in water at 20°C and stirred the liquid until the crystals disappeared, noting the time required. He repeated this experiment using water of different temperatures. He graphed his findings as a curve of time against temperature.

In the above experiment, if the pupil used identical containers for each phase of the experiment, if he measured out equal quantities of water and salt each time, and if he standardized his pattern for stirring the liquid, he controlled all factors of his experiment. There is, however, no "control" as illustrated in the previous experiment.

It is usually difficult to control the factors involved in experiments with living things because of the variation of individuals.

A general science teacher proposed an experiment with white rats to show the nutritional value of milk. Two rats were procured and kept in similar cages. One was given a diet of bread and milk; the other was given a diet of bread and water. Plans were made to keep records of the increase in weight of the two rats. However, the rat on the milk diet actually lost weight and died at the end of the fourth week.

Individual variations may be averaged out by using large numbers of individuals. Generally, the samples tested should be as large as possible, involving dozens if not hundreds of individuals.

Sometimes it is not practical to experiment with large samples. Smaller groups may be used if careful attempts are made to equate the groups in size, weight, general health, and other observable characteristics.

For an experiment to see if the movement of the sun causes the twining growth of certain climbing beans, fifty beans were planted in identical containers and given constant conditions until the seedlings were about three inches high. Then three groups of ten each were selected, the individual plants being as nearly alike as could be judged by their appearance. One group was put in a window where they re-ceived direct sunlight all day. A second group was kept in a north window where no sunlight was received. A third group was kept in darkness.

When it is necessary to work with a few individuals only, it is possible to expose the individuals to first one set of conditions and then another, comparing changes noted under the two conditions.

A young chicken was fed a standard balanced diet for three weeks, then a diet deficient in Vitamin B for three weeks, and then the balanced diet for three weeks. Weight was determined daily and con-clusions were drawn from the comparison of weight changes.

Laboratory exercises.   Many activities carried out in science laboratories and labeled "experiments" are little more than exercises with laboratory equipment. Some are frankly designed with a single purpose—to famil-iarize pupils with certain pieces of apparatus or with certain skills. Many are designed to demonstrate certain principles.

The chief distinction between an "experiment" and an "exercise" lies in the information given to the pupils. In an experiment, a pupil does not know what the results of his investigations will be. In an exercise he is told precisely what the outcomes of his work should be and how to attain them.

> Mr. Mulvaney directed his physics class to balance unequal weights on meter sticks and then calculate the moments in each case. He emphasized that in each case, clockwise moments must equal counter-clockwise moments, and that pupils should repeat measurements until equality was attained.

Pupils vary greatly in their reactions to situations in which they are told what to do, what to see, and what conclusions to draw. Some work patiently and conscientiously and are pleased when their results come out as expected. They seem to enjoy the feeling of security that this type of work gives them.

Other pupils demand more challenge. They want to find out things for themselves. They are stifled by cut-and-dried exercises. The ideal program provides opportunities for both personalities.

Standardized laboratory exercises probably owe their misuse to the relative ease with which they are conducted. A teacher need only provide his class with materials and a set of directions. After a little experience he is

Pupils are able to make or assemble much of their own equipment. They understand the investigations they are carrying out better because they thoroughly understand the equipment they are using.

able to anticipate almost all the difficulties and need give little attention to his class during the laboratory period. His program conforms with the traditional concept of laboratory work and he feels no compulsion to provide more challenging problems for some of his pupils. A conscientious teacher, however, recognizes the strengths and limitations of standardized laboratory exercises. He makes use of them to enrich his program and he provides other types of activities for pupils who need them.

The introduction of new techniques and new apparatus provides an element of discovery that appeals to pupils. Early experiences wth microscopes are stimulating to pupils in a biology course. An introductory exercise with glass bending helps create a favorable attitude toward general science.

Standardized laboratory exercises can be used to initiate independent work for those who have the inclination to do so.

> *Mr. Weissman provided his physics class with duplicated sheets that gave direction for determining the coefficient of friction between a block of wood and a board. As the pupils worked on the exercise, Mr. Weissman moved from group to group, chatting informally about results and occasionally asking such questions as "Would the force needed to move the block be different if the block were on edge rather than on its face?" and "What is the friction between a gym shoe and the gym floor?" and "How much force could Tom exert in a tug-of-war if he were wearing leather soled shoes on a polished maple floor?" Soon most of the groups were working on such problems. Two groups, however, continued to work with standard laboratory materials, checking their results against data given in a physics handbook.*

Contributions of laboratory work. Real scientific experiments, originated and carried out by the pupils themselves, involve high level thinking. The students gain practice in recognizing and defining problems. Their ingenuity is challenged and exercised in devising methods of attack. They become familiar with the limitations of data and the need for caution in drawing conclusions, and they develop the habit of critical thinking.

Some pupils are not ready to undertake original experimentation but they are interested in following up suggestions given by their teacher or the books available to them. If they are allowed to work independently, without continued interference from the teacher, they will benefit as mentioned above, though to a lesser degree. And as they mature and gain experience, they too may undertake original research.

Some pupils seem to lack ability for original work. These may benefit from standardized laboratory exercises by learning to follow directions, to keep good records, and to take responsibility for careful work. They will learn much about their strengths and limitations. They may find that the work of laboratory technicians appeals to them.

An important contribution of laboratory work is the broadened appeal this type of work gives to the science program. Adolescents enjoy activities in which they can work together. They like the excitement of the unknown, the opportunities to manipulate materials, the comparative freedom of action, and the satisfaction of tangible achievements. An exciting laboratory program can do much to draw young people into science courses and ultimately into scientific vocations.

PROVIDING UNIFORM LABORATORY EXPERIENCES

Teachers must expect to plan most of the laboratory work done in secondary school science. Occasionally pupils have original suggestions but for the most part are dependent upon the teacher for their ideas. Until pupils have had experience in working alone and following up their own ideas, uniform laboratory activities must be provided.

Uniform laboratory activities have certain advantages. All pupils gain a common background of experiences. Directions and guidance are easier to give when starting a new topic. And out of the uniform work may develop special interests that the pupils may pursue individually.

Selecting laboratory activities.   Excellent suggestions for laboratory activities can be found in textbooks and laboratory manuals. Popularized science books also contain excellent suggestions that may be adapted readily for the school laboratory; some of these suggestions are especially valuable because they call only for simple materials and straightforward procedures.

All suggestions for laboratory activities need careful analysis before they can be included in the program. Some points that should be considered are as follows:

1. Is the purpose easily understood?
2. Can clear-cut directions be given?
3. Are the procedures simple and direct?
4. Can results be obtained in a short time?
5. Are the materials familiar to pupils?
6. Are the materials inexpensive, readily procured and easily stored?
7. Are applications of the findings obvious?

The following are some types of activities that are generally successful in secondary science laboratory work.

Type	Examples
Operation of devices	electric bells, telegraph sets
Testing chemical properties	starch tests, acid-base tests
Finding physical properties	focal lengths, hardness of minerals
Microscopic examination	hay infusions, feather structure
Gross anatomy	flower structure, crystal shapes
Internal anatomy	sections of stems, vacuum tubes
Analysis	soil composition, hard water
Simple experiments	heart rates, solutions
Identification	keying leaves, identifying rocks
Preparations	carbon dioxide, conductivity tester

It is essential that the purpose of an activity be readily understood, and even more important that the purpose be such as to challenge pupils.

Mr. Hewitt provided each pair of pupils with a sauce dish to be filled with water, a needle, and a razor blade. He directed the pupils to float the needle and the razor blade on the surface of the water.

Obviously, Mr. Hewitt had surface tension in mind when he planned this activity, but he did not force this purpose on his pupils. Instead he presented them with a problem that genuinely challenged them. Out of the inevitable "why's" would come the development of the desired concepts.

It is common to find teachers forgetting the nature of their pupils and planning activities that have little significance to them.

For an introductory experience with lenses, Mr. Phillips directed the pupils in his physics class to determine the focal length of a set of convex lenses, using the relationship:

$$\frac{1}{D_o} + \frac{1}{D_i} = \frac{1}{f}$$

The pupils followed the directions he gave them but showed little strong interest in the processes. They were careless in their work. They wasted a good deal of time talking and "fooling around."

Mr. Phillips' pupils did not have the background to be interested in this problem and they found little excitement in the procedures used. They would have been far more interested in studying the relative sizes of the images produced. Then, when they recognized the effects of lens curvature, they would be ready to study focal length.

The selection of laboratory activities should be influenced by the need for concise, clear-cut directions. Many an activity, otherwise suitable, fails because the directions are too complex for pupils to follow. Such activities are better suited for special assignments for talented pupils.

Another factor important in selecting activities is the length of time needed to attain results. Pupil attention is apt to drift markedly after fifteen or twenty minutes of one type of activity. Experiments in which results can be attained in less time are best suited for uniform laboratory assignments.

Teachers should consider also the problem of "dead" intervals. Serious problems of discipline may arise while pupils are waiting for water to boil or for filtration to be completed. When such activities are necessary, supplementary activities should be assigned to fill the time.

A deciding factor in the selection of a particular activity may be the type of materials required. Some activities utilize materials that are too expensive to provide in quantity, or too delicate to withstand rough usage. There is also the problem of storage which may prevent the use of bulky or awkwardly shaped items.

In general, it is best to make free use of commonplace and familiar items. Pupils feel at ease with such materials and they see more clearly the applications of their work to everyday situations. They see possibilities for doing equivalent experiments at home.

Complex and specialized equipment has its place in the program but not for introductory experiences. The best use of such materials is in follow-up work when the need for more precise measurements and better controls have become evident.

> *The pupils in Mr. Stanhope's physics class began a determination of the latent heat of fusion using glass jars for containers. Consideration of the possible errors in the preliminary measurements, however, showed the need for better control of heat transfer. Mr. Stanhope then displayed and explained the action of a calorimeter. The pupils repeated their measurements, this time using calorimeters. Two pupils, however, thought that a thermos bottle would be even more effective and were given permission to use one instead.*

The need for obvious applications of laboratory work is not always considered by teachers because of their concern with the learning of scientific principles. Pupils are often set at tasks that to them seem to have little relation to reality. This is one common cause for dissatisfaction with traditional laboratory work.

Laboratory activities utilizing commonplace devices usually show immediate applications. When siphons, candles, electric bells, xylophones, and garden soil are studied, pupils rarely question the value of the work.

Over the years Mr. Jordan had acquired a number of damaged thermos bottles that still held water. He supplemented these with several bottles that were intact. Each year his physics class experimented with the bottles to determine the importance of the vacuum in reducing heat transfer. They plotted both the temperature drop against time and the calorie loss against time.

Giving directions for laboratory experiences.   The directions for uniform laboratory activities must be explicit; often they outline in cookbook form exactly what to do. There are times, however, when the problem is so simple that procedures can be discovered by trial-and-error. Then no directions need follow the statement of the problem.

Mr. Adams set before his seventh grade science class a carton of dry cells, a number of miniature lamps and sockets, some wire, screw drivers, and pliers. He asked the pupils to work in pairs trying to light a lamp from a cell.

The teacher should anticipate all situations that demand safety precautions.

Mr. Adams put additional lamps and sockets in his pockets and moved about to check progress. As soon as a team had lighted a lamp he gave it a second lamp with the suggestion that the pupils try to light two lamps from the same dry cell. If the second task was accomplished he gave out a buzzer or a bell in exchange for the lamps. He stopped the activity before all pupils had finished but he provided time later for interested pupils to work by themselves.

Oral directions may be adequate for one-step activities if the directions are simple enough to be remembered.

Miss Stassen told her earth science class that dilute hydrochloric acid reacts with substances containing carbonates. She gave each pair of pupils a dropping bottle of acid and a tray of assorted rocks, minerals, bones, and shells. She directed the pupils to test the several items for the presence of carbonates.

Sometimes it is wise to summarize on the blackboard directions that have been given orally.

Mr. Bruhn set out test tubes, medicine droppers, a soap solution and a liquid detergent. He showed the pupils how to test the effect of these on hard water. He then summarized the directions on the blackboard as follows:
1. Fill two test tubes nearly full of tap water.
2. Add four drops of soap solution to one test tube.
3. Add four drops of detergent to the other test tube.
4. Shake each test tube well.
5. Hold the test tubes up to the light and observe.

When pupils participate in planning an experiment it is also a good idea to summarize on the chalkboard the directions finally agreed upon.

Mr. Bertone's physics class was studying the pendulum. Mr. Bertone had suspended an iron ball from a long thread. He set the ball swinging and raised questions about the factors that might affect the period of swing.

Pupils suggested such factors as the length of the thread, the weight of the ball, and the amplitude of the swing. They planned several short experiments to test the effects of these factors. As each experiment was planned, Mr. Bertone wrote down the steps to be followed.

Previously prepared direction sheets can be great time savers, but these must not be used mechanically if the desired goals of the science program are to be attained. Such sheets are rarely stimulating in themselves. They need the same careful introduction as has been described for oral directions. Perhaps the best use of prepared sheets is for giving "recipes" for doing things that appeal to pupils.

Miss Gilmore introduced her ninth grade science class to the study of photography with an exercise on the development of photographic paper. Four sets of trays containing developer, fixer and stop bath were placed on the laboratory tables. Eight printing frames and several envelopes of printing paper were also provided. Then Miss Gilmore passed out sheets containing the following directions:

TO MAKE A PHOTOGRAPHIC PRINT

Work only in a darkened room or in a dark room lighted by a photographic safelight.

Materials Needed:

A tray of developer	A printing frame
A tray of stop bath	Printing paper
A tray of fixer	Ferrotype plate or blotters

Procedures:

1. Put a sheet of printing paper, glossy side up, in the printing frame.
2. Put something opaque, a rubber band, a leaf or a cut-out on the printing paper and close the frame.
3. Expose the paper to strong daylight for 1 minute.
4. Put the paper in the developer for 45 seconds.
5. Wash the paper in the stop bath for 20 seconds.
6. Put the print in the fixer for 10 minutes.
7. Wash the print in running water for 30 minutes.
8. Dry the print on the ferrotype plate or between blotters.

Miss Gilmore read through the sheet with the pupils showing them the materials to be used and indicating certain cautions about some of the problems that would be encountered. Volunteers were selected to return later to take the prints from the wash water and put them on the ferrotype plates. The shades were then drawn and the pupils began work.

If the directions for an activity are at all complex, and particularly if many cautions are necessary, it is usually well for the teacher to perform portions of the experiment on a demonstration basis before setting the class to work.

> Mr. Stillwell assigned his class the task of preparing oxygen from potassium chlorate following the directions given in the laboratory manuals. He displayed the materials needed and showed the pupils how to assemble them. He followed the printed directions and gave the reasons for using the required angle for the combustion tube, for the specified way of heating the tube (he demonstrated with an unlighted burner), and for the method of ending the heating process in order that water be kept out of the combustion tube.
>
> Then Mr. Stillwell asked different pupils to repeat the reasons for each of the special procedures. Only after this did he permit the pupils to begin work. Over the years he has had little breakage and no serious accidents during this particular exercise.

Open-ended experiments.   An open-ended experiment does not have a predetermined outcome that the pupil is expected to obtain in order to consider the experiment a success. All experiments, if they are truly experiments, are open-ended.

The following are characteristics of an open-ended experiment:

1. The experiment is used to answer a question.
2. The pupil performing the experiment does not know the outcome of the experiment before performing it.
3. The design of the method for the experiment is frequently determined by the pupil.
4. The pupil makes his own observations and draws his own conclusions.
5. The conclusions drawn by the pupil serve as a basis for formulating new hypotheses which are similarly tested.

Before attempting to perform an experiment, it is important for the pupil to thoroughly understand the problem and the reasons for the problem. The pupil should also think of a number of possible methods which can be used to attack the problem.

When the pupil has performed the experiment and has drawn his conclusions from the data that he has collected, he can then be asked to predict experimental results for related experiments. In this way, more thinking can be required on the part of the pupil to interpret his observations and data. Pupils will see that open-ended experiments will lead to other experiments. Pupils will also realize that an experiment should be observed and questioned from every viewpoint. The open-ended experiment is adaptable to laboratory periods of varying lengths. Experiments can be devised so that pupils can continue the experiment as a homework assignment.

Many different types of experiments have been produced by teachers, for different subject matter areas. The national study groups such as the BSCS,[1] PSSC, and CBA have also produced interesting types of experiments in their courses of study. The following is an example abstracted from the BSCS Yellow Version laboratory guide:[2]

Exercise 22–1: *The Living Invertebrate Heart*

In this lesson you will be given the opportunity to witness the working heart of a living water flea, *Daphnia,* an arthropod commonly found in freshwater ponds and lakes. A *Daphnia* is so small and transparent that, when placed under the low power of a microscope, its beating heart can be seen and studied.

The purpose of this exercise is to observe the beating invertebrate heart and through your own observations and experiments to determine its rate and the effects of changes in the environment and the effects of drugs on the rate of heartbeat.

Materials (Parts A, B, and C):

A small beaker of pond water containing *Daphnia*
Wide-mouthed medicine-dropper pipette (for "fishing out" a single *Daphnia*)
Slide and cover glass
Some bristles or pieces of broken cover glass to support the cover glass and prevent *Daphnia* from being crushed (CAUTION: if you use pieces of glass, handle them with a pair of forceps, not with fingers)
Thermometer
Large beaker of ice, water, and salt into which the small beaker containing *Daphnia* will fit in order to lower its temperature
Similar beaker containing warm water (36° C)
Small dishes into which to transfer the cooled or warmed *Daphnia*
Watch with a sweep second hand
Stereoscopic dissecting microscope
Dexedrine sulfate solution
Chlorpromazine solution
5% alcohol
Graph paper

[1] The Biological Sciences Curriculum Study Committee has published four paperbound books (*Research Problems in Biology*, Series 1–4) which include a few hundred suggestions for experiments of the open-ended type. See list of *Suggested Readings* at end of chapter.

[2] Biological Sciences Curriculum Study. *Biological Science: An Inquiry into Life, Student Laboratory Guide.* Harcourt, Brace, and World, New York, 1963.

Procedure:

Work in teams of two students, following the special instructions below.

Student A: Take the temperature of the water in the container of *Daphnia* and record it in your notebook.

Student B: Place one of the *Daphnia* on a slide in a drop of water. Place three or four pieces of broken cover glass or bristle in the drop and cover with a cover glass. Place the slide under the microscope and bring the heart into focus.

Student A: Look through the microscope at the beating heart and get ready to count heartbeats.

Student B: Look at the watch (with sweep second hand) and, when ready, say, "Go."

Student A: Begin to count the heartbeats using the method outlined for you by your teacher.

Student B: At the end of 15 seconds, say, "Stop."

Student A: Count the dots on your piece of paper and give the count to your team-mate.

Student B: Multiply the count by 4 (15 seconds $\times$ 4 equals 1 minute) and record the calculation.

Repeat this procedure at least three times. Calculate the heartbeats per minute and take the average of your three trials. Record this average count in your notebook.

Parts B and C of the exercise continue in similar fashion to investigate the effect of temperature changes and certain chemicals on the heartbeat of *Daphnia*.

The experiments below were written by Mr. John Glover, biology teacher, the Fox Lane High School, Bedford, New York. They were designed to give students practice in stating problems, forming hypotheses, and determining possible methods for solving problems. The following are directions given to pupils:

You will work in teams of four. When you are ready to carry out your experiment (after you have written down the statement of the problem, the hypothesis you wish to test, and the design of the experiment in your laboratory notebook), check with me.

There are four experiments which you must perform. Finish one completely before you go on to the next.

1. Use the manometer apparatus and a living mouse and try to determine if the temperature affects the rate of breathing.
2. Determine the effect of breathing air containing much carbon dioxide on the rate of breathing of the members of your laboratory team. Plastic bags are available for performing the experiment.
3. Use soft glass test tubes, snails, and elodea to show that snails give off carbon dioxide and use oxygen. Hint: soft glass can be bent and pulled when heated.
4. Use steel wool, test tubes, and water to see if you can determine if there is more carbon dioxide in the air at the beginning of a breath, in the middle of a breath, or at the end of a breath.

The conclusions that the pupils form from their observations almost always lead to other problems, which they are encouraged to solve.

Another interesting type of approach is given below. Here the pupil is required to learn certain techniques before he can perform an experiment. These are the directions given to the pupils:

The tablets are pure ascorbic acid. You can prepare various concentrations of solutions of acid by dissolving certain amounts of ascorbic acid in varying amounts of water. For example, a 50-percent solution is made by adding 50 gm to 100 ml of water. When this concentration of solution is made, it can be further diluted to 25 percent, 10 percent. How?

Important Calculations

1 gram (gm) = 1000 milligrams (mg)
    1000 grams = 1 kilogram (kg)
    1 liter (1) = 1000 milliliters (ml) = 1000 cubic centimeters (cc)

How many milligrams per milliliter (mg/ml) in the 50-percent solution? _____

How many in the 25-percent solution? _____ In the 10-percent solution? _____

Indophenol may be used as an indicator for ascorbic acid. If ascorbic acid solutions which you have made are placed in burettes and allowed to drip slowly into beakers containing exactly 5 ml of indophenol solution, you will notice that a certain amount of the ascorbic acid solution will cause the indophenol to change from blue to colorless. (There is an intermediate pink stage which may be disregarded.) This process is called titrating.

Procedure

1. Make up three standard solutions of ascorbic acid (i.e., the number of mg/ml of each are known to you)

2. Titrate each solution

3. Record your results in tabular form

Percent solution in burette	Ml required to change indophenol
1.	1.
2.	2.
3.	3.

4. Graph your results (mg/ml on x-axis, ml required on y-axis)

5. You are now ready to perform an experiment. Here is your problem. How much ascorbic acid is found in fresh orange juice? In canned orange juice? In frozen orange juice?

WARNING: This experiment requires extensive planning on your part. There are a couple of possible wrong turns that could cost you a great deal of time and energy.

6. Your conclusions to this experiment should be as quantitative as possible.

Open-ended experiments can be designed for all areas of science and for a wide range of pupil ability. The results a pupil obtains can be interpreted on his level of ability.

Providing materials for laboratory work.   A rich program of laboratory experiences calls for materials in sufficient quantities so that each pupil is able to participate. Usually duplicate sets of materials are needed. In some teaching situations the problem of obtaining and storing adequate materials is difficult to solve but is never so critical that laboratory work has to be eliminated altogether.

In a well-balanced program, laboratory experiences will be provided only two or three times a week at most, other class periods being built around field experiences and project work. Of these two or three periods a week, some will certainly be organized to permit pupils to work on different problems. Sets of duplicate materials, therefore, are needed somewhat more than once a week. There are countless activities that require only the simplest of materials, and, when special equipment is needed, there are various rotational plans that make it possible to get along without duplicate sets.

A number of books suggest experiments that can be carried out with materials commonplace in the home or inexpensively purchased in variety stores.[3] These experiments, though using simple materials, involve the

---

[3] To appreciate the wealth of suggestions for laboratory experiences with commonplace materials, investigate the following three books: *Science Experiences with Home Equipment, Science Experiences with Inexpensive Equipment, Science Experiences with Ten Cent Store Equipment*, all by Carleton J. Lynde, Van Nostrand, Princeton, N.J., 1950. For additional materials, see *Suggested Readings* at the end of this chapter.

Many fascinating experiments can be carried out with the simplest of materials. Pupils realize that science does deal with the things around us. This group of pupils is carrying out one of the SSSP experiments.

same high level thinking as their equivalents carried out with conventional laboratory equipment.

A surprisingly large number of items can be contributed by the pupils. Other useful pieces of equipment can be obtained from articles that have been junked, such as radios and automobiles. Tin cans of all sizes and glass jars have unlimited uses. Pupils can make much of their own equipment, some of which may be added to the general supplies for future use, thus building up laboratory stocks.

The pupils in Mr. Timball's ninth grade science class were studying radiation from different surfaces. To compare radiation from surfaces of different colors, the pupils painted fifteen number 1½ (one pint) food cans with quick drying black paint and an equal number of identical cans with quick drying white paint. During the next period the pupils, working in pairs, filled the cans with hot water, covered each with a cardboard square, and noted the decrease in temperatures.

When the experiment was over, Mr. Timball put the cans in a shipping carton designed for number 1½ cans. He labeled the carton suitably and put it away for later use.

Storage need not be a serious problem if the laboratory experiences are selected with this point in mind. In many instances the materials, when disassembled, occupy little space.

Mr. Timball planned an exercise on copper plating as one of his ninth grade science laboratory activities. The dry cells needed for the experiment were part of his regular teaching supplies and had been used for many other purposes. These were stored in their shipping cartons. Half-pint glass jars, also used for many other purposes, were stored in a suitable shipping carton. Wire and battery clips were part of his regular electrical supplies. All that remained were metal strips which he kept in a cigar box labeled "Copper Plating Experiment."

It is always advantageous to keep special items in labeled cartons or boxes as just described. A great deal of time and energy is saved when the teacher can produce a container earmarked for a certain experiment and know that all the things he needs are in that container.

Sometimes a teacher believes that pupils should have experiences with certain materials that cannot be provided in quantities. In such cases there are various rotational plans that may be employed. In one system, several different experiments are set up about the room. Groups of pupils move from one experiment to another, working at each in turn.

Miss Hotaling set up equipment in her classroom so that when the pupils entered, they found fifteen different experiments set up on the laboratory tables. These experimental set-ups, designed to provide varied laboratory experiences with minimum equipment, were as follows:

1. *A ball-and-ring apparatus*
2. *A taut horizontal wire to show lengthening when heated by an electric current*
3. *An electric toaster to show lengthening of the element wires when heated*
4. *A bimetallic thermostat*
5. *A bimetallic bar*
6. *An air thermometer*
7. *A balloon on a flask to show expansion of air*
8. *Gallon cans balanced on a scale to show relative weights and cool air*
9. *A convection box*
10. *A convection operated lamp shade*
11. *A wafer-type brooder thermostat*
12. *A flask with one-hole stopper and glass tube to show expansion of heated water*
13. *A pulse glass*
14. *An automobile radiator thermostat*
15. *Soaked sawdust in a large beaker of water to show convection caused by unequal heating*

After a few preliminary instructions the pupils divided themselves in groups of two each and drew numbers from a box to indicate the experiment with which each team was to begin. As pupils finished their experiments they moved to the one bearing the next consecutive number.

Beside each set of apparatus Miss Hotaling had previously placed a typewritten sheet bearing directions for the activity to be carried out. She included any needed cautions to reduce breakage or injury.

The pupils were able to carry out a little more than half of the experiments the first day. They completed them the second day.

Miss Hotaling encountered a few problems. Pupils were able to complete some of the activities with comparative rapidity and by moving on prematurely caused some confusion. Also one experiment gave pupils trouble and Miss Hotaling found it necessary to spend most of her time with it.

Ideally, in the type of organization Miss Hotaling used, the experiments should require the same amount of time for completion. Actually this is impossible because pupils work at different rates, but if the activities selected are relatively short, there is less variation in time needed for completion than when lengthy exercises are provided.

Despite the problems Miss Hotaling encountered, her efforts were justified. She was able to provide first-hand experiences with materials that are not effective in demonstrations and that could not be provided in duplicate.

There are several ways that Miss Hotaling could have varied procedures to avoid some of her problems. She could have divided the class in groups of three's, thus reducing the number of separate experiments to ten. By doing so, she could have equated the experiments a little better. On the other hand, opportunities for individual manipulation would have been reduced.

Perhaps Miss Hotaling could have set up seven or eight exercises in duplicate. Then two halves of the class could work in parallel. Or Miss Hotaling might have set up five experiments to be supplemented by seat work. The groups of pupils would then take turns working on the experiments, returning to their seats when they were finished. She would have encountered some administrative problems but these would not be serious.

Sometimes it is possible to permit individual pupils to work at their own speeds. Variation in rate of work quickly separates the pupils so that after the first few exercises, it is unusual for two pupils to be ready for the same exercise at the same time. Use of this technique is most successful in specialized subjects that permit the teacher to set up a long sequence of individual problems.

Mr. Smith teaches a very successful course in electricity for ninth grade boys. The walls of his laboratory are lined with deep shelves that hold large numbers of "breadboards" standing on edge. On each breadboard are directions for an exercise together with the items of apparatus needed. The exercises range from simple doorbell circuits to the study of rotating electromagnetic fields.

Mr. Smith's pupils start with some of the simpler exercises for which he has duplicate breadboards. As a pupil completes the exercise he returns the breadboard and takes another with a more advanced problem. After the first two or three exercises, the pupils are usually in different portions of the sequence and duplicate materials are not needed.

The size of laboratory groups. The major contributions of laboratory work result from the opportunities for manipulation that are provided each pupil. Opportunities for manipulation are at a maximum when pupils work alone. However, most adolescents prefer to work in groups and there are advantages in allowing them to do so.

Pupils working in pairs usually share manipulation experiences, although one pupil may dominate the other to some extent. But when pupils work in three's or larger groups, many pupils find it impossible to work

The number of persons in a group should equal the number of possible tasks. If there are more pupils than tasks, the unoccupied pupils are apt to cause trouble.

with the actual materials. One pupil in each group is generally aggressive and dominates all activities. He may allow one pupil to help him but the remaining pupils are left with little to do except observe passively, take notes, or wander off to see what others are doing. Careful planning is needed to provide worthwhile activities for each pupil in larger groups.

The teacher's role during laboratory work.   One of the chief objectives of laboratory work is to allow pupils to learn for themselves, by solving the problems that they encounter in their work. After purposes have been defined and procedures outlined, the place for the teacher in the laboratory is in the background. A teacher may move from group to group, giving encouragement, clarifying procedures, straightening out misunderstandings, and stimulating fast-working pupils to undertake new problems. But his presence in the classroom should not be required for successful operations.

A teacher should try to avoid interrupting the work of his class with announcements. Separate groups are in different stages of their work and thinking; if announcements are made, the progress of their activities will be broken, so that time and continuity are lost.

Record keeping.   Records are important in so many ways that pupils should know how to keep them well. Science laboratory work may be used to acquaint pupils with several different ways of keeping records.

The form that records take may vary with the needs that they are to fill. No research scientist would handicap himself by adopting one stereotyped format for his records. He might choose one form for one situation and another form for another situation. Nonetheless, many science teachers have done irreparable harm to the cause of science education by insisting that pupils adopt the following single, highly stereotyped form:

1. object
2. apparatus
3. procedures

4. observations
5. conclusions
6. applications

Such a form may result in boredom for a large number of pupils. However, it should be recognized that certain pupils like to follow set patterns in their work, possibly feeling more secure than when they have to make decisions about forms to be used.

Simple experiments need only simple records. Indeed, in some cases, written records are superfluous. There would be little point in requiring pupils to make notes on an experiment to find out whether pumice can float on water.

Labeled diagrams are often sufficient for recording experiments. Arrows drawn on a diagram of a beaker of water being heated along one side show the convection currents set up by the unequal heating. Labels indicate the apparatus used. Procedures are self evident. No broad conclusion is possible from this limited experiment.

Graphs and tables often serve as satisfactory records either with or without additional notes. An experiment that shows variation of heart rate after exercise and rest needs only a table of the data collected. The headings on the chart indicate the purpose, the materials used, and the procedures. The reader draws his own conclusions from the data.

Except when special materials are used, diagrams or pictures are more effective than words in describing apparatus. Itemization of the component parts of an assembly is rarely needed. Commonplace items such as funnels and gas burners are generally assumed to be used in familiar processes such as filtration and heating.

Procedures need elaboration when they cannot be inferred from diagrams, charts, and graphs. An experiment to discover the effect of air circulation on transpiration rate may require an explanation of how the twig is prepared to maintain an unbroken column of water in the xylem tubes.

Duplicated sheets for use when collecting a large amount of data can be great time savers. Sometimes these sheets may contain directions for gathering the data as well. Such record sheets insure uniform organization of data and are helpful in carrying out discussion of the results. However, these sheets encourage mechanical procedures and may discourage individual initiative. Before prepared sheets are adopted for any particular experiment, the advantages and disadvantages should be carefully weighed.

A form of record keeping that is little used but that seems to have value is an exhibit of materials actually used. Dried and pressed leaves showing the effects of starch tests in phototropism experiments may be mounted on charts as a class project or in notebooks for individual records. Nails that show the factors affecting rust formation may be exhibited with appropriate labels.

Use of data collected.   Data are collected in order that questions may be answered. Generally, summaries must be made and certain conclusions drawn. Summaries may be made orally, by filling in the data on charts or by setting up exhibits. Summarization is the usual prelude to drawing conclusions.

Conclusions that may be drawn from laboratory experiences are necessarily narrow. They should be limited to the conditions under which the experiments were carried out. There is a tendency to allow broader conclusions than are justified, particularly in the physical sciences.

The pupils in Mr. Dunlap's physics class were directed to compare the forces needed to draw a metal roller and a wooden block, respectively, across a wooden table top. The pupils collected the data and concluded that rolling friction is less than sliding friction. Mr. Dunlap accepted this conclusion.

Actually, the only valid conclusion that Mr. Dunlap's pupils could draw was that it takes less force to draw a metal roller across a wooden table top than to draw a wooden block across the same table top. The experiment did not deal with other types of rollers, blocks, or surfaces, nor did it deal with large-scale materials. The pupils could infer that their findings might apply to other situations, but they should not have been permitted to assume that the application is automatic. Actually, there are important situations in which plastic surfaces such as wet clay are involved, when sliding friction is less than rolling friction.

Pupils should be encouraged to gather considerable data before drawing conclusions. Rarely can valid conclusions be drawn from single instances. When time is a factor, pupils may pool their data, thus providing themselves with a broader base on which to draw conclusions.

Each group in Mrs. Camp's physics class made three trials in determining the latent heat of vaporization of water. As they made each determination they entered the results on a chart on the blackboard. Later they copied this chart in their notebooks. At the close of the exercise, the pupils averaged the figures and drew a conclusion from the result. Since there were twelve groups in the class, and each group made three trials, the final conclusion was based upon thirty-six separate determinations.

Statistical procedures in the laboratory.   The questions of how long, how much, how many are constantly being answered in the laboratory. Much of this quantitative information becomes more meaningful if given statistical treatment.

A biology class was studying variations in living things. Several pupils observed that the heights of corn plants in a field adjacent to the school grounds varied considerably. They measured the plants in a section of the field to determine to what extent the plants varied in height. They collected the data shown in Table I.

The pupils found that they could learn little by casual inspection of the data except that the tallest plant measured was approximately sixty-

eight inches and the shortest was twenty-six inches. Mr. Johnson directed the pupils to a book on statistics to see what could be done to make the data more meaningful.

68	52	48	45	41
65	52	47	45	40
64	51	47	45	39
58	50	47	44	39
57	50	47	44	38
56	49	46	44	37
56	49	46	43	36
54	49	46	43	34
53	48	46	42	31
53	48	46	42	26

Range: 42   Average: 46.92   Median: 46.5

Table I.   *Height of corn plants in inches*

The pupils first determined the range of heights. The range indicated the variation between the extremes. They then obtained the average height. The pupils were already familiar with the word average and knew how to obtain it. The data were becoming more meaningful to them since they could use the average height as a reference to see how much each plant deviated from this value.

The reference book showed the pupils that they could also give more meaning to setting up a frequency distribution. They used the range of the data as a basis for dividing them into subgroups or classes. They produced the frequency distribution shown in Table II by tallying each measurement into one of the classes. The pupils used the rules that were suggested by the book to determine the size of each class and the number of classes. The frequency distribution condensed their data and made them more orderly.

From the frequency distribution they found the interval 45 to 47 had twelve tallies. This was at the interval which contained the average and contained more measurements than any of the intervals. They learned that this could be called the modal interval. They also calculated the median, the point which divided the data into equal halves. This was the point above and below which 50 percent of the cases were found.

In order to see how the measurements were distributed around the average they plotted a histogram. The base line of the histogram consisted of the midpoint of each class interval in the frequency distribution (class 24 to 26 has a midpoint of 25, 27 to 29 a midpoint of 28, etc.). The vertical axis was the frequency scale. The completed histogram (Figure I) presented a picture of all the data, showing the scatter of the measurements in picture form.

Class sort	Tallies	Frequency
66–68	/	1
63–65	//	2
60–62		0
57–59	//	2
54–56	///	3
51–53	/////	5
48–50	///// ///	8
45–47	///// ///// //	12
42–44	///// //	7
39–41	////	4
36–38	///	3
33–35	/	1
30–32	/	1
27–29		0
24–26	/	1

Total 50

Modal Interval 45–47

Table II. *Frequency distribution of data in Table I, Height of corn plants in inches.*

Reporting experiments. In reporting experiments, pupils should be directed to write up their reports so that the reader of the report has a clear picture of the problem and the procedures used to arrive at the answer to the problem. That is, the statement of the problem should be clearly stated and the description of the procedure should be complete. Other suggestions for a good experiment report are:

1. The data collected are in a form that permits ease of understanding.
2. All measurements included in the report have their proper units attached to them.
3. All diagrams, if they are used, should be large enough for clarity and carefully labeled.
4. Graphs should be properly labeled, titled, and neatly drawn.
5. Conclusions should give some answer to the problem based on the data obtained.

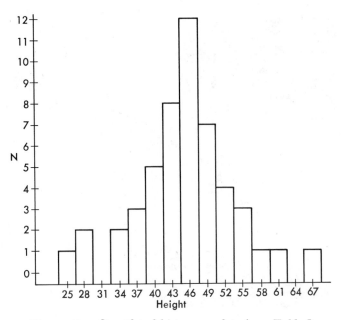

Figure I.   *Completed histogram, data from Table I.*

The evaluation of an experimental report should take into consideration the pupils and the nature of the experiment. There are a number of criteria that can be modified depending on the areas of science, the specific class, and the type of experiment. The main criteria for the evaluation should be: (1) Is the report written well enough so that a person who has not been involved in the experiment can see exactly what has been attempted, how the experiment was performed, and what conclusions were reached? (2) Could the experiment be duplicated based on the report?

INDIVIDUALIZING LABORATORY WORK

Independent laboratory activities confer on pupils certain benefits that are not permitted by uniform laboratory assignments. Pupils become best acquainted with their own interests and abilities when they are working on problems of their own choosing. Their special needs and special talents are best provided for through individualized assignments.

Teachers must know their pupils well before attempting to set up completely individualized laboratory situations. Much must be known about a pupil's likes and dislikes, and his abilities and limitations, before he is encouraged to work with a minimum of supervision. A teacher cannot hope to control the unrelated efforts of a roomful of strangers.

Individualization may begin in a limited way, however, almost from

Individualized laboratory experiences are more challenging to pupils than teacher demonstrations or other mass education techniques.

the beginning of the school year. As soon as a pupil displays a special talent or a strong interest, he may be encouraged to begin work on a special problem while others continue with their regular assignments.

Individualization of laboratory work demands of the teacher a certain flexibility of thinking. He must abandon the concept of uniform outcomes and remake his objectives to permit one pupil to learn one set of facts while a second pupil is learning a second set of facts.

Initiating independent work. Pupils do not often suggest completely original problems that they would like to undertake in the laboratory. Their teacher usually finds it necessary to provide them with specific suggestions. However, once pupils learn that they are free to adapt these suggestions or to originate their own, they become much more independent.

Some pupils display more originality in proposing problems than do others. Undoubtedly the nature of the experience background is important. Practice also seems to be a factor. Pupils who are used to taking the initiative are more productive of ideas than pupils who have always been compelled to follow directions.

One technique for encouraging pupils to work independently is to give them a list of problems from which they may make choices. It is wise to suggest more problems than will be selected so that some pupils do not feel forced to work on a problem just because it has not been chosen by anyone else.

Mr. Bowen passed out duplicated sheets to his earth science class, listing experiments on the characteristics of soils. He instructed his pupils to organize themselves in pairs and select problems on which to work. The following is the list from which they were to choose:

1. Compare the water retention in gravel, sand, and clay
2. Determine the effect of humus on water retention in sandy soil
3. Compare the drainage of sand, clay, and gravel soils
4. Compare the capillary rise of water in sand, gravel, and clay
5. Compare capillarity in packed and loose clay soils
6. Determine whether water percolating through soil dissolves minerals from the soil
7. Determine the effect of lime on the structure of clay soils that are drying
8. Determine the effects of small amounts of clay on the structure of sandy soils
9. Calculate the amount of organic matter in a garden soil and a woodland soil
10. Analyze a garden soil for its sand, gravel, and clay content
11. Determine the effect of added humus on the structure of a clay soil
12. Determine the effect of added ground limestone on the pH of a soil
13. Determine the effect of peat moss on the pH of a soil
14. Determine the organic content of a top soil and the underlying subsoil
15. Test light and dark soils for heat absorption in sunlight

This approach to individualized laboratory work requires a large selection of suitable activities, closely related and somewhat equivalent in time demands. Needed materials should be readily procured. The techniques required should lie within the capabilities of the class.

Often in a class, some pupils are not challenged by any of the problems stated. If these pupils have strong science interests, it may be easy to encourage them to propose their own problems even though these may not be so closely related to the topic as a teacher might think desirable. If the pupils are deterred by lack of general interest, a teacher can sometimes help them make a choice from the list by describing in some detail how a certain problem may be attacked. The vision of carrying out the activities involved may stimulate them to begin work even though they are not particularly interested in the outcomes.

Somewhat greater flexibility and initiative are possible if pupils are permitted to discover for themselves suggestions for their laboratory work.

> Mr. Scarry directed his seventh grade science class to organize themselves in pairs and begin looking in textbooks for experiments on the control of fire. He provided additional references for pupils who were not challenged by the suggestions in the textbooks.
>
> After the pupils made their selections, a planning session was held during which the pupils wrote down the materials they would need and decided who would be responsible for obtaining these materials. The understanding was that the pupils would bring most of the items from home the next morning. Actually an additional day was needed before the pupils remembered to bring everything required.
>
> At the beginning of the next class period, Mr. Scarry gave a few cautions and set the pupils at work. He moved from group to group giving a little help but not giving any general directions. The pupils tried out their experiments and in some instances improvised variations. They demonstrated the same experiments to their classmates during following periods.

To use Mr. Scarry's techniques, a teacher must have sources of teaching suggestions. Some textbooks are excellent for this purpose. Textbooks need not be confined to a single grade level. Many seventh grade pupils can read high school texts and others benefit more from elementary science texts. The many popularized science books are excellent sources for ideas. Some teachers keep card files of experiments and allow the pupils to browse through these.

Permitting deviations from assigned work.   Pupils doing assigned laboratory problems often discover interesting problems they would like to follow up. Generally they benefit more by being permitted to deviate than by being held to uniform assignments.

> Bob was more interested in knowing how much material was dissolved in tap water than in determining the relative hardness of different samples of water. So while the remainder of the eighth grade group tested samples provided by the teacher, Bob began boiling down a gallon of water.
>
> Bob took his sample home that night and continued the boiling process until a scant cupful remained. During his next science period he completed the evaporation process and ended with an evaporating dish nearly full of solids.

Bob's independent work certainly gave him a better concept of hard water than would the activities he was supposed to carry out. It is likely that the remainder of the class benefited also from his efforts. Commonly, discoveries made by an individual pupil have great impact on the remainder of the class.

Isabelle, who had ambitions to be a nurse, brought a dead snake to her biology class. She asked that she be allowed to dissect it instead of continuing with a study of the frog. Her discovery that the snake had but one functional lung gained more attention and initiated more discussion of vestigial organs than anything the teacher had been able to present on this topic.

Independent work growing out of assigned laboratory activities generally involves one or two pupils. Sometimes, however, a large share of the class may be stimulated to work on separate problems. On page 166 is described the way Mr. Weissman used a standardized laboratory exercise on the determination of the coefficient of friction to initiate independent work on the part of most of his pupils. This technique can be applied best in situations in which moderate sized classes are made up of enthusiastic pupils. Experienced teachers who know their pupils well use this procedure with large groups.

Encouraging original research.   Teachers who do not realize the possibilities for original research by high school pupils do not appreciate the richness of the science field and the capabilities of young people. There are thousands of unsolved problems involving plants, insects, earthworms, fungi, and other organisms. And even when there has already been research on a specific problem, a pupil's efforts may represent original thinking and perhaps a new approach.

Science teachers need an understanding of the limits of scientific knowledge to help their pupils find problems for original research. Thus equipped, a teacher can make suggestions that are practical for the circumstances in which the pupil must work. Unfortunately, few college courses give much attention to the limits of scientific knowledge and often give the impression that everything about familiar subjects has been completely explored. But possession of a critical attitude will help a teacher find problems that encourage pupils to do some original investigation.

Ninth grader Pat stated that exhaled breath contained no oxygen. Mr. Lowell, his teacher, criticized the statement.

Pat could find nothing on this topic in the limited library facilities so he planned an experiment to see if a candle would burn in a bottle containing exhaled breath. He discovered that a candle would burn about as long in exhaled air as in his control.

Pat's work did not contribute anything to the body of organized scientific knowledge, but it did represent original thinking on his part and showed him a way to attack problems. It is equally easy to turn the attention of pupils to areas that have been practically unexplored.

> Miss Appleby set up an experiment to show the effect of thyroxin on the metamorphism of tadpoles. Sally asked if thyroxin affected the development of insects. Miss Appleby suggested that Sally try its effect on some aquatic insects. After some discussion of problems of maintenance, they decided upon dragonfly nymphs as likely subjects.

Pupils may need much encouragement before they realize that they can do original research. Schools do not generally emphasize this approach to learning. But pupils will freely undertake little problems for which they can see immediate outcomes. With increased self-confidence they undertake more complex problems.

Some teachers exert pressure on pupils they think capable of original work.

> Mr. Gardiner operates a science fair for his own and neighboring schools. Each fall he tries to talk individually to those junior high school pupils who seem capable of meeting the standards he sets. "How about entering a project in the science fair next spring?" he asks. Sometimes he has to check on an individual several times. He is not impatient for he realizes that these are but early adolescents who might really like to do the kind of research demanded but who think that spring, the time of the science fair, is a long way away.

> Mr. Gardiner finds it necessary to suggest problems in a large number of cases. He tries to provide ideas of things close to the pupils. "How does a dandelion plant grow?" "Is there any difference in the average blood pressures of children of German ancestry and of Italian ancestry?" "How does the strength of different kinds of paper compare?"

> As a result of his efforts, Mr. Gardiner has in his fair a number of entries that represent work far in advance of that usually expected of junior high school pupils.

At least one teacher sets aside a block of time during which he expects all pupils to undertake independent work. Some independent work continues as original research once the pupils find they can do this.

> Mr. Klein includes in his plans for his general science program a "unit" during which each pupil is supposed to work on a problem of his own choosing. Many of the problems are relatively simple and

some pupils fail to accomplish much, but each year a few pupils are stimulated to do research that continues long beyond the time allotted to the "unit."

Ideas for original research projects may come to teachers as they are planning uniform laboratory assignments, demonstrations, field experiences, and project work. Pupils may discover problems from their science work, and from readings in books, magazines, and newspapers. Both teachers and pupils can find many ideas for independent investigation at science fairs and congresses. Some pupils like to repeat work other pupils have done. Others prefer to carry out modified procedures. Sometimes a pupil finds that an approach used in one problem suggests a problem and an approach in a related field.

Pupils who do original work of this type need help in terms of laboratory facilities, released time, and advice about sources of information. Usually these pupils are superior in an academic sense and need not spend as much time on assigned work as others in their classes. They generally pass the same examinations without giving more than casual attention to the work of the class. They benefit far more from their independent work than they could ever benefit from stereotyped classroom procedures.

LABORATORY MANUALS

Many forms of laboratory manuals have been published and many teachers have taken advantage of duplication processes to prepare their own versions. Early manuals, often bound between hard covers, were limited chiefly to giving directions for laboratory activities sometimes accompanied by brief discussions of procedures and by suggestions for reporting data—tables to be filled in, sentences to be completed, diagrams to be labeled, spaces for sketches, and facilities for making graphs.

Laboratory manuals are unquestionably time savers. The teacher is freed from the preparation of directions for each laboratory period. He need not use class time for giving directions. Pupil time is saved because the directions have been worked out so carefully that positive results can be obtained without fumbling. And if a manual with record forms is used, pupils need spend little time organizing and reporting data.

Nevertheless, laboratory manuals are not necessarily efficient even though laboratory work progresses more rapidly. Manuals tend to stereotype the laboratory program. They work toward uniform outcomes and do not provide for pupils with special interests and abilities. Commercial manuals cannot recognize purely local resources and needs.

The activities proposed by laboratory manuals are commonly "verification" exercises rather than true experiments. The manuals make little or no provision for independent thinking. Pupils are expected to follow directions carefully to attain results, but they may do so blindly. Pupils gain little practice in formulating problems, planning methods of attack, assuming responsibilities for their work, criticizing their data, and drawing justifiable conclusions.

Pupil reaction to laboratory manuals is varied. Some pupils like definite assignments which need only to be carried out carefully to obtain success. Others like the forms for reporting data because they need not concern themselves with the type of organization to be used. However, some pupils fret at the lack of freedom; they find no challenge in working toward outcomes they recognize in advance.

Use of laboratory manuals may be justifiable in some situations. Teachers with exceptionally heavy teaching loads must look for all types of labor saving devices. A chemistry teacher with six sections of thirty pupils each undoubtedly needs some type of manual, either a commercial form or one which he has prepared. He could not keep up with his work otherwise.

A beginning teacher who has had little training in the subject assigned to him may find needed security in a manual. His background does not provide him with a knowledge of tested activities. His inexperience handicaps him in recognizing and taking advantage of situations that arise during his teaching.

A laboratory manual is also useful for pupils who must work under self-direction, such as those making up work lost by long periods of illness.

However, laboratory manuals must not be allowed to dominate the science program. Teachers who for one reason or another are dependent upon them should work toward the day when they are free to use them only for the special contributions they may make.

SUGGESTED ACTIVITIES

1. Begin making a card file of suggestions for laboratory experiments and exercises in the major science areas, giving preference to those that require materials that are inexpensive and easily procured in quantities. Include a list of needed materials with each activity.
2. Prepare a direction sheet to guide pupils during a uniform laboratory exercise.
3. Analyze an experiment suggested in a laboratory manual, determining the independent and dependent variables and methods used to hold other variables constant.

4. Set up an experiment described in a textbook, and show how it can be made "open-ended."

5. Plan a simple laboratory exercise. Procure the necessary materials, and administer the activity to the others in your science methods class. Afterwards ask for criticisms.

6. A distinction should be made between a stereotyped laboratory exercise and a true laboratory experiment. Plan and carry out a true laboratory experiment of the type suitable for secondary school pupils. Report your findings to your methods class for criticism of your procedures and your conclusions.

SUGGESTED READINGS

Barrett, Raymond E., *Build-It-Yourself Science Laboratory*, Doubleday and Company, Garden City, N. Y., 1963.

Biological Sciences Curriculum Study, *Biological Science: Interaction of Experiments and Ideas*. Prentice-Hall, Englewood Cliffs, N. J., 1965.

———, *Biological Science: Patterns and Processes*. Holt, Rinehart and Winston, New York, 1966.

———, *Laboratory Blocks: Plant Growth and Development; Animal Growth and Development; Microbes—Their Growth, Nutrition, and Interaction; The Complementarity of Structure and Function; Field Ecology; Regulation in Plants by Hormones—A Study in Experimental Design; Animal Behavior; Life in the Soil; Genetic Continuity*; D. C. Heath & Co., Boston.

———, *Research Problems in Biology: Investigations for Students*, Series 1 and 2, Doubleday & Company, Garden City, N. Y., 1963.

———, *Research Problems in Biology: Investigations for Students*, Series 3 and 4, Doubleday & Company, Garden City, N. Y., 1965.

Miller, Bruce, and Merton B. Osborn, *Free and Inexpensive Materials for Teaching Science*. Bruce Miller Publications, Box 369, Riverside, California, 1964. (15-page pamphlet—$ .50)

National Science Teachers Association, *Ideas for Teaching Science in the Junior High School*, National Education Association, Washington, D. C., 1963.

National Society for the Study of Education, "Rethinking Science Education," *Fifty-ninth Yearbook*, University of Chicago Press, Chicago, 1960.

Rogers, Eric M., *Physics for the Inquiring Mind*. Princeton University Press, Princeton, N. J., 1960.

UNESCO, *700 Science Experiments for Everyone*, Garden City, N. Y., Doubleday and Company, 1961.

———, *Source Book for Science Teaching*. Oberthur-Rennes, France, 1962.

Chapter 6

Demonstrations

DEMONSTRATIONS ARE USEFUL TEACHING DEVICES. THEY SERVE SEVERAL POS-
sible functions, often two or more at the same time. Generally, teachers
should use demonstrations more freely than they do; however, demonstrations do have certain limitations. Demonstrations should not be used
indiscriminately nor to the exclusion of other teaching techniques. Improperly used, they defeat the purposes of the science program. Used to
the exclusion of other techniques, they prevent the full realization of the
potentialities of the science program.

CHARACTERISTICS OF DEMONSTRATIONS

As the word implies, a demonstration is a showing. When a teacher
shows his class how to cut a pane of glass, he is presenting a demonstration.
When he shows the reaction of sulfuric acid and sugar, he is presenting a
demonstration.

Many demonstrations are called "experiments" when according to the strict meaning of the latter term they should not be. To be an experiment, a demonstration must be built about a problem the solution of which is unknown to the pupils. The teacher who demonstrates the electrolysis of water to show that water is composed of oxygen and hydrogen is *not* performing an experiment. The teacher who demonstrates electrolysis of water to find out what constitutes water *is* performing an experiment. There is a subtle but important difference.

By custom, demonstrations are presented by teachers, but those presented by the pupils themselves, either acting alone or in small groups, can have valuable outcomes. The teacher should broaden his concept of demonstrations to include pupil presentations.

Special functions of demonstrations. Demonstrations may be used in several ways, each of which makes its own special contributions to the teaching of science.

1. *To set a problem.* A demonstration may be presented without previous discussion. From the results arise problems of interest to the class.

> Mr. Cassidy used the traditional "water to wine" trick to introduce a study of chemical indicators. As he poured water containing a little phenolphthalein from a bottle into a drinking glass containing traces of sodium hydroxide, the liquid became bright pink. The startled pupils demanded to know the cause and thus the topic was introduced.

2. *To illustrate a point.* This is the most common use of demonstrations.

> During a discussion of a recent eclipse of the moon Miss Appleby set up a model to demonstrate the relative positions of the sun, earth, and moon during an eclipse.

3. *To help solve a problem.* Sometimes a problem of general interest arises spontaneously. If the answer can be discovered by an experiment that lends itself to demonstration, it may be advantageous to employ this technique.

> During a discussion of safety practices the question about the electrical conductivity of water arose. Mr. Knuth needed but a few moments to assemble the equipment needed to provide an answer to the question.

As a review. After pupils have carried out an experiment or have seen one performed, a follow-up demonstration of the same or closely related experiment makes an excellent review, usually much better than an oral review.

A chemistry class had tried copper plating by electrolysis during a laboratory period. Two weeks later during a discussion period Mr. Wexler set up the same materials. As the experiment was in progress Mr. Wexler asked questions about the reactions involved. Several pupils were able to clear up points that had confused them and all pupils understood the process better.

5. *To serve as a climax.* An exciting demonstration is an excellent way to end a unit.

Mr. Kuhn regularly ended a general science unit on the nature of air with a demonstration of the preparation of oxygen and the combustion of such chemicals as sulfur and magnesium in an atmosphere of pure oxygen. At the close of the demonstration he explained that this activity is typical of the work done in high school chemistry.

Some advantages of demonstrations.   Demonstrations have several advantages that make them highly favored as teaching devices.

1. A demonstration guides the thinking of all the pupils into approximately the same channels. Problems may be raised and defined; solutions may be proposed and tested; and conclusions may be drawn—all as a class activity. If the subject has been carefully chosen and if the situation is properly developed, all pupils gain approximately the same understanding. It must be pointed out, however, that the technique of getting all pupils to participate fully is far from simple.

2. A demonstration is economical of materials. Some items are too expensive to buy in quantities. For example, the mercury needed for barometers and the vacuum pumps needed for atmospheric pressure experiments are very expensive. Other items may be too delicate for use by pupils. An example of this is the Hoffman apparatus used for electrolysis of water.

3. Demonstrations enable a teacher to utilize activities that would be too dangerous for pupils to carry out themselves. Work with high voltage condensers is typical of such an activity.

4. A demonstration may be economical in teacher time and energies. It is simpler to prepare material for one experiment than for fifteen duplicate experiments. It is easier to perform one experiment than to supervise fifteen. And it is much more convenient to store the materials needed for one demonstration than for fifteen experiments. However, the objectives of the science program must not be neglected in the interests of economy. If the substitution of demonstrations for individual experiments results in lessened interests and understandings, the savings in time and energy may actually be expensive.

5. A demonstration may be economical in class time. Materials used for a demonstration can often be set up and tried out before a class period begins. The teacher, being experienced, can perform the demonstration more smoothly and more quickly than the pupils. On first thought, demonstrations might seem to be the most efficient way of teaching. But the very smoothness and swiftness of the pace of a demonstration may defeat the ends desired. A demonstration seen is not necessarily a demonstration understood.

The limitations of demonstrations. Demonstrations have several serious limitations that make them useful only for certain types of learning situations.

1. Visibility is always a problem. Pupils must be able to see all details of the apparatus being used and all details of the reactions that take place if they are to profit by a demonstration. Visibility is a much more serious problem than most teachers realize.

> Miss Coleman, wearing a bright red dress, set up an air thermometer to show the expansion of air when heated. To make the liquid visible she colored it with red ink. But when she stood behind the apparatus, the red liquid was almost completely invisible against her red dress.

2. Pupils have little opportunity to become familiar with the materials. The apparatus may be presented already assembled or may be assembled so rapidly that relationships cannot be grasped. Elements that are simple alone may appear complex in combination. Irrelevant items often distract attention.

> To demonstrate the action of a photoelectric cell, Mr. Johnson assembled on his demonstration desk the following materials: a step-down transformer, a light source with condensing lenses, a photoelectric cell in its housing, a vacuum tube amplifier, a sensitive relay, a rectifier, and an electric bell. The pupils enjoyed the demonstration but they considered the topic difficult to understand.

3. Much scientific information cannot be grasped adequately by sight and sound alone. Odors require close-up observation. Texture is best determined by touch. Forces are more significant when muscular action is involved.

4. A demonstration is apt to go at such a rapid pace that pupils do not grasp each step. Unfortunately many pupils are reluctant to raise questions when they fail to follow the steps in a demonstration.

Mr. Jones used a large scale model to explain the action of the commutator in a direct current generator. After he turned to another topic, a girl, somewhat timidly, raised a question about the commutator. Mr. Jones in evident exasperation returned to the first topic. Upon questioning he discovered that a large share of the class had not grasped the concept of the alternations of current in the rotor and had understood little about the purpose of the commutator.

5. During any discussion which results from a demonstration, there may be instances when certain pupils tend to "carry the class along," to the detriment of the others. It is not unusual for a few pupils with special interests or abilities to dominate the discussion, leaving the remainder of the class to flounder along or to drop by the wayside.

6. There are few opportunities for active pupil participation during a demonstration. It is difficult to insure complete mental participation while the body remains inactive. In consequence, attention is readily distracted by irrelevant influences both internal and external to the pupils. Such loss of attention, unless accompanied by disturbance, may go unnoticed by the teacher.

7. Elaborate demonstrations tend to be too convincing. The use of professionally made apparatus, in particular, adds a note of authority and makes the results difficult to question.

Mr. Reeves fastened a large U-shaped electromagnet to a hook in the ceiling of the physics classroom. When the science period began he energized the magnet, mounted a stepladder, attached a steel ball to one pole of the magnet and a cork ball containing a tack to the other pole. Then he descended and de-energized the magnet. The two balls, falling through a distance of about twelve feet, seemed to land at the same time. No one in the classroom questioned the conclusion that heavy and light objects fall at the same rate.

PLANNING A DEMONSTRATION

A demonstration is "produced" much as a play is produced. Attention must be given to many of the same factors as stage directors consider—visibility, audibility, single centers of attention, audience participation, contrasts, climaxes.

Preliminary considerations in demonstrating. The first consideration when planning a demonstration is whether with all its limitations it is the best way to deal with a certain topic. For instance, to use demonstration procedures in testing foods for starch would be poor technique, for individual experimentation could be so much more effective.

A second consideration is whether the subject material lends itself to the demonstration technique. Are there, for instance, elements of suspense? Will the action move along with sufficient speed? Is there adequate variety within the procedures to maintain interest? Is there a satisfactory climax? Must there be long periods of inactivity while water is heated to boiling or liquids are filtered?

A third consideration is whether the materials being utilized can be made visible to each pupil in the room. A demonstration is worse than useless if pupils do not know what is occurring.

The primary objective of any demonstration lesson is to bring about important changes in the pupils. A demonstration should be presented, not because it fills in a gap in some conventional and arbitrary organization of subject matter, but because it may result in real benefit to the pupils.

Insuring visibility. Simple, large scale apparatus is best for demonstration purposes. When small items must be used, special provisions should be made for making them visible, perhaps by some form of projection. Even when large pieces of apparatus are used, consideration must be given to making small but important details visible.

The position of materials on the demonstration table may be critical. There are often blind spots on a standard demonstration desk. Some of these blind spots are caused by the relative positions of the pupils and the table. Some are because materials are placed on the table. The only way to avoid these blind spots is to view the demonstrations from the seats that the pupils will be occupying.

The background behind the apparatus is important. A dingy, half-erased blackboard makes the worst possible background. Large sheets of white or colored cardboard, or backdrops of cloth, together with suitable supports, are valuable in demonstration work.

Constrasting colors within the apparatus itself help to distinguish the various elements, but care should be used lest these colors detract from reality or give incorrect concepts.

Proper lighting is also essential. Too often demonstration materials are inadequately lighted. Contrasts may be too low. Or there may be disturbing highlights, such as the reflection of windows from glassware, which obscure the contents of the vessels.

Backlighting to silhouette apparatus may be useful. A brilliantly lighted white backdrop behind unlighted apparatus increases the contrast between opaque and transparent objects. A similar effect can be obtained by setting apparatus on a window sill. This technique is especially effective for showing action inside glass containers.

One or two spotlights properly focused on demonstration apparatus make a startling difference. In some modern schools spotlights are built into the ceiling above demonstration desks. These provide good top lighting. Sidlighting is effective in many instances. Color filters may be used with spotlights for dramatic effects.

Demonstration materials need not always be placed on a demonstration table. Materials placed on the floor or on low tables enable pupils to look down on them. Materials suspended from the ceiling permit an upward view. Large scale materials may be set up outdoors where pupils may walk around them.

Focusing attention on the demonstration. An uncluttered setting focuses attention on the important details of a demonstration. Often it is wise to begin a presentation with a completely bare table. As each item is needed it is taken from a box, a drawer, or a convenient cupboard.

An element of suspense is introduced if the materials are kept in a box whose contents are not visible to the pupils. The pupils keep wondering what next will be withdrawn and how it will be utilized.

If a large piece of apparatus must be assembled beforehand, it may be covered with a cardboard carton. As the apparatus is "unveiled" it is certain to attract attention.

Another technique for attracting attention is to set in operation some device that pupils will notice as they come into the classroom.

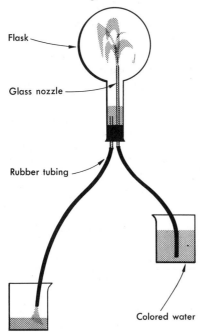

Flask

Glass nozzle

Rubber tubing

Colored water

Figure 12. *A fountain in a vacuum. This attention-catching device is in reality a siphon. Atmospheric pressure forces the colored water up into the low pressure region in the flask, from which the water drains into the lower container. The fountain is started just as is the flow in a siphon.*

One day when Mr. Goff's pupils came into their classroom they saw the scientific novelty which Mr. Goff later termed a "fountain in a vacuum" (see Figure 12). A bright red liquid was jetting upwards in a large flask, seemingly of its own volition. The first few pupils who noticed it began to discuss it, and soon most of their classmates were clustered around, trying to account for its behavior.

Planning for variety in demonstrations.   As in all other phases of work with boys and girls, variety in using demonstrations is desirable. Variety can be achieved by modifying basic techniques slightly. Each modification may have an entirely different effect on the pupils.

Variety can be provided by using different techniques of presentation, by utilizing special apparatus, by using different demonstrators, by taking advantage of situations that arise spontaneously, and by varying the setting of the demonstration.

1. The teacher may present a previously prepared demonstration. This is the type most commonly seen in science teaching and needs no description.

How many poor demonstration techniques can you find in this picture? What might the teacher have done to improve the presentation? To what extent should the pupil in the picture be participating?

2. The teacher acting on the suggestions of the pupils may set up and present a demonstration to solve a problem that has arisen in discussion. To be effective, such demonstrations require immediate access to demonstration materials.

3. A pupil may present a previously prepared demonstration. The pupil may have set up the materials after school, at home, or during time allotted from the class period. Unless the pupil is exceptionally able, it is wise to keep such demonstrations simple and direct.

4. A group of pupils may present a previously prepared demonstration. This group may have worked after school or during time allotted from the regular class period. The subject should be simple and direct.

5. A pupil may carry out a demonstration under the direction of the teacher. In this situation a pupil has no idea of what he will be doing until he is given oral directions from the teacher. Again the subject of the demonstration should be simple and direct, but a number of pupils in succession may be directed to carry out a series of related demonstrations.

6. An outsider—a pupil from another room, another teacher, or an expert not connected with the school—may present a demonstration. Demonstrations by outsiders are often difficult to control and may be too difficult for the pupils to follow. Adults who are not trained in teaching are particularly apt to go too fast, to fail to give basic understandings, and to depend upon a technical vocabulary.

7. A demonstration may be presented with some special piece of apparatus such as an opaque projector. The use of unusual apparatus adds novelty and a bit of suspense.

8. A demonstration may be presented in some new setting such as outdoors. Although there are special problems in these demonstrations they are very effective in capturing and holding attention.

9. A demonstration may involve spectacular noises, lights, or motions. The occasional use of such devices is justified in terms of attention and favorable attitudes.

The importance of preparation and pretesting.   Last minute preparations are apt to result in confusion and embarrassment. If a teacher must scurry around to look for a stopper, to cut a suitable length of glass tubing, or to find a misplaced carton of a chemical, valuable class time is lost.

Even the simplest demonstrations sometimes involve unexpected complexities. Should a demonstration pulley have a damaged bearing, or a dry cell have too much internal resistance, or a siphon become air bound, the trouble may be hard to locate. How often a teacher is heard to say, "Well, it should have worked this way."

The only way to be certain that a demonstration will proceed smoothly and with expected outcomes is to set up the apparatus beforehand, try them out, and use these same materials during the demonstration.

PRESENTING A DEMONSTRATION

The nature of a demonstration is such that ordinarily few pupils have opportunities to participate actively. Participation must be mental. Thus the science teacher is faced with problems very different from those encountered in laboratory work.

Establishing the purpose of a demonstration. Recognition of the purpose of a demonstration is essential for maximum participation on the part of the pupils. Insofar as possible the purposes of a demonstration should be kept simple so that they may be given in short, direct statements. If the statements are at all complex, they should be written on the blackboard or in the pupils' notebooks.

Sometimes a verbal statement of purpose by the teacher is adequate if the demonstration deals with a situation of special interest to the pupils.

Mr. Blair set up a mechanical "smoker" for his biology class to draw the smoke from a burning cigarette through filters to extract the tars.

"Today I am going to show you what is in cigarette smoke," he announced. He described the action of the apparatus and proceeded immediately with the demonstration.

Pupils readily accept the purpose of demonstrations that promise the possibility for minor explosions, odd sounds, and other unusual events. They enjoy the feeling of suspense.

Mr. Cooke displayed a "breadboard" on which was mounted a fuse block and several appliance outlets.

"Let's see how many things we can plug in before the fuse blows," he said.

A technique commonly used by experienced teachers is to ask the pupils to commit themselves as to what they think the outcome of a demonstration will be.

Mr. Kimball displayed a wooden disk and a brass ring of the same diameter to his physics class. With a balance he showed that the two

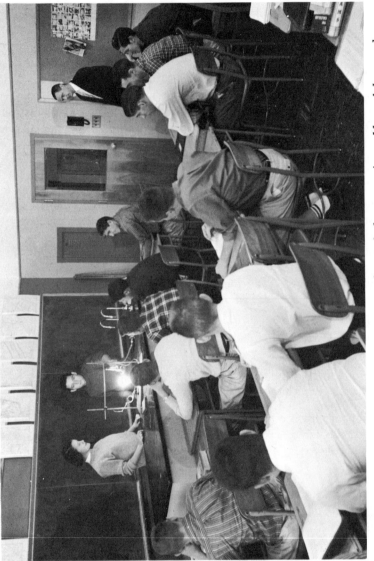

For meaningful demonstrations, use an uncluttered demonstration table and large-scale equipment which is visible to all pupils in the room.

items weighed the same. Then he held the two at the top of an inclined board.

"Which one will roll down the slope faster?" he asked the class.

Some pupils thought the disk would roll faster while others thought the ring would reach the bottom of the incline first. Most of the pupils, however, thought that the two would roll at equal speeds.

Interesting problems can arise from the action of the demonstration materials themselves. From the problems the pupils discover the purposes of the demonstrations.

Before her class convened, Miss Parry clamped one end of a copper tube to a laboratory support. The other end of the tube almost, but not quite, touched another support. Wires connected the supports to a dry cell and electric bell.

In presenting her demonstration, Miss Parry directed a pupil to heat the copper tube with a gas burner. In a few moments the bell began to ring and then later, after heating was ended, it stopped.

The pupils speculated on the reasons, one suggesting that the heat produced electricity, a suggestion that was shouted down because of the presence of the dry cell, and another pupil suggested that the metal became a better conductor when heated. Miss Parry acknowledged the contributions and then directed a pupil to trace the circuit. The gap was discovered, a new hypothesis was raised, tested and verified.

Some teachers have the unfortunate habit of telling their pupils in advance what the outcomes of the demonstrations will be. Occasionally the practice is justified but whenever it is used it denies pupils opportunities to formulate their own problems, to speculate, to plan methods of attack, and to draw conclusions in terms of their findings.

Acquainting pupils with materials and procedures.   Much has been said about the need for making demonstration materials visible. Equally important is the need for helping pupils recognize the materials being used and the function that each item plays in the demonstration.

The first two items Miss Carpenter drew from a box were a spark plug and a "hot shot" battery, both of which the pupils identified. Two pupils connected the plug to the battery without producing a spark.

The third item was a spark coil which Miss Carpenter identified. Two other pupils connected this to the plug and battery following a circuit diagram Miss Carpenter drew on the chalkboard. This time a spark was produced.

The fourth item was a friction-top metal can in which a hole had been made to hold the spark plug. Pupils succeeded in producing a spark inside the can.

The fifth item was a bottle of gasoline, a few drops of which Miss Carpenter used in blowing the lid from the can.

During this demonstration, Miss Carpenter made no assumptions about the understandings of her pupils. She made sure that each item was identified and its purpose made clear.

During demonstrations that involve several steps or several associated activities it is usually well to stop occasionally for summaries of results. Such results may be given orally or they may be recorded in tabular form on the blackboard. The recording of results in the form of graphs is also helpful.

Pacing a demonstration.   The audience must not be forgotten during a demonstration. Facial expressions, obvious inattention, questions, laughter, and exclamations—all these are helpful clues in judging the effectiveness of a presentation.

A teacher should remember that it is difficult for young people to sit quietly for any great length of time. He should provide opportunities for relaxation. In general, it is best for demonstrations to be short and fast moving. If a demonstration must be extended over a considerable period, it may be possible to break it up into various phases separated by brief intervals during which pupils engage in other activities.

Suspense is a useful device for holding attention. The moments leading up to a dramatic climax—an explosion or the fracture of a loaded wire—can be very exciting. Races of various types have their moments of suspense.

Humor can play a part, too. Laughter is an excellent way to relax tensions. Adolescents tend to favor absurd situations and many demonstrations can be devised to end with ridiculous outcomes.

Insofar as possible pupils should be permitted to participate physically in demonstrations. There are relatively few situations in which the teacher must do all the manipulation, and even then pupils can often serve as assistants. It is usually possible for first one pupil and then another to carry out certain phases of a demonstration under the direction of the teacher.

Insuring understanding of events.   Things are apt to happen so rapidly in demonstrations that a pupil misses some of the important points. He may have had a momentary lapse of attention, his vision may have been blocked at a critical moment, or an exclamation may have drowned out an essential word. If he dislikes calling attention to his failures, he may say nothing and thus fail to grasp the significance of the demonstration.

A teacher should utilize all possible techniques to help pupils keep abreast of events. One such technique is to ask a pupil to describe what he saw and then, without signifying approval or disapproval, to ask another pupil if he made the same observations. If arguments result, it may be necessary to repeat all or part of the demonstration.

Pupils are not always sure of the procedures used even when a teacher has used utmost care in describing them. Brief reviews may help these pupils to clarify their thinking. A review may be broken into several parts with one pupil reiterating the purpose, another describing the materials, and still another giving the procedures.

Summaries, both oral and written, are essential. When demonstrations are made up of a number of distinct phases, interim summaries are desirable. Whenever possible, data should be summarized in chart or table form on the blackboard. This is often done by a class secretary.

If materials or products which result from a demonstration need to be examined or handled by the pupils, these may be passed out to the class in duplicate, or labeled properly and exhibited for later examination.

Working toward general objectives.   No matter how valuable the subject matter outcomes of a demonstration may be, equally important are the physical and mental changes which have been brought about in the pupils through their participation in the activity. Because mere passive acceptance of results produces few changes, pupils need maximum opportunities to manipulate materials, to perform before the group, to speculate about possible results, to defend viewpoints, and to modify opinions when presented with contrary data.

A teacher can well afford to adopt a "hands in pockets" attitude in all his teaching, demonstrations included. Each time a teacher manipulates materials that pupils should manipulate, each time he gives pupils an answer to a question that they could solve themselves, each time he forces a ready-made opinion upon his pupils, he is denying them the opportunities to benefit fully from his teaching.

The technique of keeping one's hands in one's pockets, both physically and mentally speaking, is not an easy one to master. Tradition makes the teacher a fountainhead of all wisdom and common teaching practice encourages a teacher to dominate classroom activities. But habits can be broken and tradition can be ignored.

The "hands in pockets" technique demands that a teacher give directions without predicting results. It demands that he ask questions that encourage careful observations and intelligent speculation without telling pupils what they are to see or what conclusions they are to draw. It demands that he be critical of pupils statements without letting himself be influenced by what he thinks they should say.

The "hands in pockets" technique has certain advantages. It frees the teacher to move about the classroom to notice how pupils react, to give help here and encouragement there. He is better able to check on visibility and audibility. He can see whether all pupils are responding desirably.

> Mr. Jones set a carton on his demonstration table and took from it a box of baking soda, a bottle of vinegar, a spoon, and a drinking glass.
>
> "Has anyone done an experiment with these four things?" he asked.
>
> Several hands went up.
>
> "All right, Bob," he said to one of the boys. "Come up and show us what you have done."
>
> As Bob came forward, Mr. Jones moved to the side wall out of the center of attention. After Bob had demonstrated the action of vinegar on baking soda, Mr. Jones invited a pupil who had never tried the experiment to come forward and carry out the same activity.
>
> Mr. Jones took other things from his box—a lemon, a tomato, a can of grapefruit juice, a box of alum—and in each instance asked for suggestions for experiments. The pupils proposed the things to do, carried out their suggestions, and kept records on the blackboard.

During this lesson Mr. Jones did no manipulation save to take items from his box, and he gave no information save to introduce the word "react." His hands were in his pockets, figuratively speaking, at all times. The pupils proposed most of the things to do and they learned by making their own discoveries. They ended the lesson with a limited but valid generalization that could serve as a basis for more extensive work.

This lesson illustrates other important points. It moved swiftly and with several different approaches. There were moments of suspense in waiting to see what would happen, and satisfactory climaxes when the solutions bubbled over the top of the glass. The closed box produced a feeling of anticipation. Best of all, there was opportunity for most of the pupils to participate actively at one time or another during the period.

Some special presentations.   There are several general patterns for demonstration procedures and each pattern is capable of infinite variation. The more that a teacher can adapt general procedures to fit special circumstances, the closer he can come to meeting the goals he has set up for his program. This often calls for considerable ingenuity.

One situation that may be encountered is the need to discuss with pupils the characteristics of certain specimens.

Mrs. MacWilliams found that the pupils in her earth science class were having difficulty distinguishing between gneiss, schist, and some of the banded sandstones. She planned to discuss the characteristics of some of the different gneisses with her class but she wanted to call attention to characteristics that could be seen only in large specimens and to characteristics that could be seen only on close examination.

She prepared several large specimens of the gneisses, each a foot or more across. She also prepared fifteen sets of chips from these same gneisses, each numbered to correspond with the large specimen from which it came. She was able to point out characteristics on the large specimens placed on a table in front of the group. She was also able to refer to characteristics in the small specimens by referring to each by number.

It is not uncommon to find a teacher beginning a demonstration only to discover that the pupils have already seen the demonstration previously. It is not always necessary to discard one's plans if such an incident occurs. Sometimes the same demonstration can be used to illustrate a more advanced idea.

Miss Hull planned a "candle race" for her seventh grade class to find out whether the size of a jar covering a candle affected its burning. The pupils protested that they had watched the same demonstration the year before.

"Let's try it anyway," Miss Hull said and appointed three pupils to handle the jars, and another pupil as timekeeper. As expected, the candle under the smallest jar went out first.

"Can anyone tell why this happened?" Miss Hull asked. The first responses were the usual ones—"air used up" and "oxygen used up." Then pupils began to speculate about carbon dioxide and heating effects. Miss Hull proposed that they try the experiment again to see if they could discover any clues as to the correct answer.

This time, to everyone's surprise, the candle under the smallest jar burned longest! On a third trial all candles went out at once! The effect was more speculation, more hypothesis formulation, and more attempts at verification.

Eventually the pupils understood. Miss Hull had carefully lifted the larger jars from the extinguished candles and had placed them, mouth down, on the table top. But during the second trial she had held the smallest jar in her hands inconspicuously while the pupils were talking, thus interchanging the air inside.

Sometimes a teacher can anticipate undesirable reactions from his pupils and plan demonstrations to startle these pupils into more favorable ways of thinking and acting.

Two boys in Mr. Pratt's physics class had an annoying "know-it-all" attitude that disturbed the smooth operation of the classroom. They reacted as expected when Mr. Pratt exhibited a Cartesian diver, in this case a miniature test tube floating inverted in a glass cylinder.

Mr. Pratt asked one of the boys to explain the diver, which he did creditably enough. He then asked the boy to demonstrate it. But the diver refused to cooperate. The diver behaved properly for other pupils but not for the two boys.

The remainder of the class was at first quietly amused but became boisterous when the diver began a series of strange antics. The diver would continue to float while pressure was applied but sink when pressure was released. Once the diver bobbed up and down insultingly as soon as a pupil had turned his back.

Mr. Pratt revealed the secret. The inverted test tube was weighted with a ring of iron wire. Under the table top was a strong electromagnet. When Mr. Pratt pressed his kneee against a button he could make the diver descend independent of any pressure applied.

Novelty in demonstration serves to attract and hold interest. Novelty also makes classwork more enjoyable.

Mr. Martin entered the general science classroom a few moments late. Without a word he picked up a ball-and-ring apparatus and showed that the ball could pass through the ring, weighed the ball, and entered the information on the blackboard. His very silence began to attract attention.

Mr. Martin heated the ball, showed that it could no longer pass through the ring, weighed it again, and entered this figure beside the other one. He wrote on the board "What is the purpose of this experiment?" and then left the room.

The pupils who had been merely puzzled before now began to argue. After a few moments of confusion one boy took charge of the class, appointed a secretary, and by the time Mr. Martin returned a few minutes later, had guided the class in making a record of the experiment.

SPECIAL EQUIPMENT FOR DEMONSTRATIONS

Special teaching techniques usually require special equipment. Demonstrations are no exception. Sometimes a teacher needs basic apparatus that he can assemble to meet his needs, then take apart and reuse in other demonstrations. Sometimes he needs apparatus specially designed to emphasize a point or set of related points.

Apparatus for demonstrations. Special apparatus is useful for the following:

1. *Demonstrations that involve weight and other forces.* Scales with large dials are a necessity for comparing forces. Platform scales of the spring type are excellent for weighing objects and determining downward forces. Dairy scales, designed for weighing pails of milk suspended from them, can be used to determine both weights and other forces.

It is desirable to have two of each type so that comparative readings can be taken simultaneously. Two platform scales, for instance, may serve as the piers of a model bridge to show the change in forces as a loaded toy truck moves across the bridge.

To indicate slight changes in weight, a sensitive balance is needed. Figure 13 gives details for building a demonstration balance that reacts readily to forces of less than a gram. This balance may be used to show the changes in weight of air as it is being heated and to compare the densities of carbon dioxide and air.

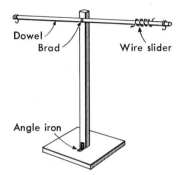

Figure 13. *This diagram shows details of construction of a simple balance. The beam is a quarter-inch dowel thirty inches long; the upright is about thirty inches long, and the base, a foot square. The hooks are made of #24 copper wire. A spiral of wire serves for a rider. Counterbalance weights can be made from loops of wire. (From Walter A. Thurber, "A Demonstration Balance," School Science and Mathematics, April, 1941)*

2. *Atmospheric pressure.* Demonstrations of atmospheric pressure require a vacuum pump, which may be either hand or electrically operated, a pump plate, and an assortment of bell jars. To show pressure changes, a direct reading dial-type pressure gauge is desirable.

3. *Submerged and floating objects.* The best device for showing what happens under water is a large, rectangular aquarium. An aquarium should be reserved for this purpose alone.

4. *Chemical reactions.* Glassware for chemical demonstrations should be big. Specific gravity cylinders and gallon battery jars make good test tubes for cold reactions. When heat is involved, oversized test tubes and large flasks are needed.

5. *Electric currents.* A large scale galvanometer is needed for demonstration work in electricity. The galvanometer is a versatile instrument. It

has an added advantage in that suitable shunts and series resistances placed in the circuits convert it to a voltmeter or an ammeter as desired. The scale is visible at a considerable distance.

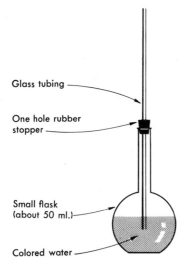

Glass tubing

One hole rubber stopper

Small flask (about 50 ml.)

Colored water

Figure 14. *An air thermometer*

6. *Temperature changes.* Suitable equipment for demonstrating temperature changes by direct reading instruments is not available for secondary school teachers. In college demonstration work, elaborate thermocouple and galvanometer combinations are used, but these are obviously too complex for general science and probably not desirable for physics and chemistry.

Direct readings can be made from dial immersion thermometers, but the dials are too small to be read at a distance. To show temperature changes the air thermometer shown in Figure 14 provides fair visibility but no readings. Unfortunately, the air thermometer does not resemble a standard liquid thermometer and pupils must become thoroughly acquainted with its behavior before it can be effectively used in demonstrations.

Building special apparatus for demonstrations.   Science teachers have opportunities to display a great deal of ingenuity in the construction of apparatus for their demonstrations. Professional literature contains many examples of intriguing, exciting, and instructive devices.

The advantages of these teacher-constructed devices are several. Most important is the fact that they are designed to illustrate a specific point that the teacher wishes to emphasize. Thus they fit into his teaching plans and correspond with his patterns of instruction. A teacher uses these devices with a special flair because he is so well acquainted with them, and with a special enthusiasm because he has created them himself. His pupils respond to this personal interest in the materials.

Added advantages result when pupils construct demonstration apparatus themselves. They benefit directly from the experiences of planning and construction, and from the presentations they make. Their classmates benefit by increased interest.

Teachers may suggest demonstration equipment which pupils can make. Pupils will also make suggestions themselves.

Fred was in the process of "junking" an automobile when he asked his general science teacher to help him understand the differential. While the teacher was explaining, Fred recognized the need for a model and proposed making one. He removed the differential gears from their housing and made a wooden framework to hold them. He sawed off a drive shaft and attached a crank for turning the gears. He sawed off the axles and attached disks of plyboard to simulate wheels. By the time he had completed the model he understood differential action himself and had helped some of his classmates understand it. Incidentally, the teacher gained a valuable piece of demonstration apparatus.

More commonly pupils need ideas for constructing apparatus. They may follow directions given in a professional journal or adapt ideas given in a photograph. Sometimes they need only the description of a device seen by or conceived by their teacher.

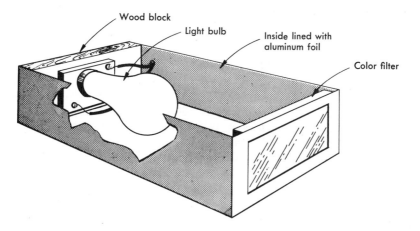

Figure 15.   *A demonstration color-mixing box*

Mr. Hall needed a device to demonstrate the nature of reflected colors. He told three pupils about the apparatus he had in mind. In a short time they had produced the device shown in Figure 15. For a light source they used a shoe box lined with aluminum foil and fitted with a lamp socket on a block of wood. For filters they used several thicknesses of colored cellophane sandwiched between panes of glass. They used the colored light to illuminate sheets of colored construction paper to see how each type of paper appeared in light of different colors.

Demonstration apparatus tends to fall into two general categories— those used to illustrate the workings of some commonplace devices and those used to illustrate certain scientific principles. Fred's model of the differential falls in the first category. The following is an example of the second:

Figure 16 shows a device used by Mrs. Borodino to demonstrate to eighth grade pupils that the strength of an electromagnet depends upon the number of turns in the coil and upon the current flowing through the coil. The two electromagnets, made from stove bolts wound with insulated wire, are connected in series so that the same current goes through each. They are mounted in a frame to improve visibility.

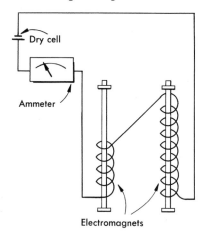

Pupils determine how many paper clips each electromagnet is able to hold when a single dry cell is used. They then repeat the experiment using two dry cells. The ammeter is used to indicate the change in current.

Figure 16. *A device for demonstrating that the number of turns of wire on an electromagnet determines the strength of the magnet*

Demonstration apparatus should be designed to be as simple and straightforward as possible. It is very easy to introduce confusing elements while attempting to emphasize certain points. Even with Mrs. Borodino's excellent device for illustrating the principles of electromagnets it should not be forgotten that many pupils do not realize that the current is the same in both electromagnets.

Pupils generally understand apparatus that is closely related to things with which they are familiar. A device for showing the effect of tension on vibrating strings can be made similar to a guitar or banjo. Models of cranes and slide projectors are usually effective.

Apparatus used to demonstrate abstract principles, however, may be less readily understood and are more appropriate for the advanced sciences where pupils are more used to thinking in abstract terms than are pupils in general science.

Presentations involving miniature materials.   Sometimes it is desirable to use miniature materials during demonstrations. Then special procedures must be developed so that all pupils can see the materials involved.

Microprojectors may be used for such microscopic materials as thin tissues and one-celled organisms. Since the viewing is somewhat unreal, it is best if pupils have had an opportunity to view the same or similar materials through a microscope beforehand.

> *Mr. Shaw's biology pupils had already prepared and viewed slides of paramecia from a hay infusion. To introduce amoebae, Mr. Shaw prepared a slide of several of these organisms and projected it with a microprojector. The class was able to view some of the characteristics of amoeboid movement and structure. Afterwards, interested pupils tried to find amoebae for further study.*

A standard 2¼ by 4¼ slide projector can be used to project thin materials such as leaves in silhouette, or to show some details of structure of specimens that are sufficiently translucent.

A water cell can be made for the same type of projector. A short length of rubber tubing is arranged in "U" shape between two glass slides and the whole is clamped tightly with tape (Figure 17). Liquids in the cell are projected on a beaded screen. Opaque objects within the liquids appear in silhouette. Unfortunately all images are inverted—a fact that pupils should be made aware of before the demonstration is started.

The opaque projector has some important uses, providing the room can be darkened sufficiently. The greatly enlarged images enable all pupils to study rather small objects. Certain manipulations may also be viewed.

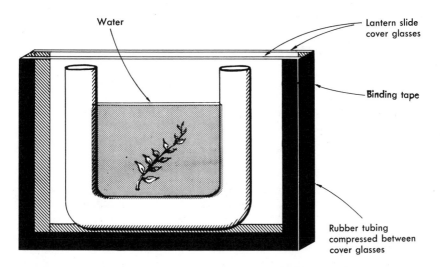

Figure 17.   *Water cell for the projection of small aquatic organisms, chemical processes, and the like, with a standard lantern slide projector*

Mr. Hurt wanted to show the action of sodium on water without using large quantities of the metal. He placed a pan of water in an opaque projector and sprinkled bits of sodium in it. The intense activity of the sodium was immediately apparent and the flames of burning hydrogen were distinguishable.

Dramatic effects can be achieved through the use of shadow projection. A strong light source with a condensing lens, such as a slide projector, is placed low in front of the apparatus. Shadows of the apparatus are cast on a white screen behind the demonstration table. By using a diverging beam of light from the projector, the shadows are much larger than the objects which cast them.

Four pupils from Mr. Hull's ninth grade science class prepared a demonstration as part of a unit on aerodynamics. They suspended two flasks about an inch apart, hanging them from strings attached to an overhead support. During the demonstration one of the pupils blew through a long glass tube pointed at the space between the flasks. The action of the flasks was made visible by projecting greatly enlarged shadows of the apparatus on a beaded movie screen.

Audibility is as important as visibility in many demonstrations. Sounds can be picked up and amplified by means of a microphone, an amplifier, and a loud speaker.

Mr. Shippley placed a microphone on a pupil's chest and amplified the sound of his heartbeat with the sound projection apparatus of a sound movie machine. He was able to point out the nature of the different sounds and he was able to demonstrate the effects of various conditions such as exercise. Later he purchased a special stethoscope-microphone which gave more satisfactory results.

SUGGESTED ACTIVITIES

1. Make a check list of points to guide you during the presentation of a demonstration. Observe a science teacher present a demonstration, and apply your check list.
2. Prepare a demonstration and present it to your methods class. Afterwards ask for criticisms.
3. Prepare a demonstration that pupils will be able to present by following your oral directions. Carry out this demonstration using the members of your science methods class to gain practice in this technique.

4. Continue to build up your activity card file by adding suggestions for demon-strations.

5. Prepare a demonstration that makes use of the true experimental approach.

SUGGESTED READINGS

Biological Sciences Curriculum Study, *Biology Teacher's Handbook*, John Wiley and Sons, New York, 1963.

Brandwein, Paul F., Fletcher G. Watson, and Paul E. Blackwood, *Teaching High School Science: A Book of Methods*, Harcourt, Brace and Company, New York, 1958.

Joseph Alexander, *et al.*, *Teaching High School Science: A Sourcebook for the Physical Sciences*, Harcourt, Brace & World, New York, 1961.

Miller, David F., and Glenn W. Blaydes, *Methods and Materials for Teaching the Biological Sciences*, 2nd edition, McGraw-Hill Book Company, New York, 1962.

Morholt, E. P., P. F. Brandwein, and A. Joseph, *Teaching High School Science: A Source Book for the Biological Sciences*, Harcourt, Brace & World, New York, 1958.

National Science Foundation, *Tested Overhead Projection Series* (TOPS), Washington, D. C., 1962.

Richardson, John S., and C. P. Cahoon, *Methods and Materials for Teaching General and Physical Sciences*, 2nd edition, McGraw-Hill Book Company, New York, 1962.

Tested Demonstrations in General Chemistry, compiled by Hubert N. Alyea, and *Chem Ed Tested Demonstrations*, Frederic B. Dutton (ed.), re-printed from the 1955–1958 volumes of *Journal of Chemical Education*, Division of Chemical Education of the American Chemical Society, Easton, Pennsylvania.

Chapter 7

Excursions Outside the

Classroom

THE CLASSROOM IS A LIMITED PLACE, BOUNDED NARROWLY BY FOUR WALLS and meagerly equipped for the task of providing pupils with worthwhile experiences. The world outside the classroom knows no bounds; it has almost every conceivable situation that a teacher might wish to utilize. In the school corridor pupils may study fire control measures or the effectiveness of a megaphone, or may determine the horsepower they develop when they run up a flight of stairs. Still within the building they can gain important experiences in the school shops, in the cafeteria, in the heating plant, and in the nurse's office. On the school grounds there are almost always plants, insects, birds, soil, paved surfaces, playground equipment, sunshine and shadows, flagpoles, building materials, bicycles, and automobiles. And just beyond the bounds of the school property lie the limitless resources of the community.

Many field experiences need only a few minutes for completion and nearly all can be accomplished within the limits of a period. Time need not be a limiting factor. Nor does transportation need to be a problem. A full program can be built from the experiences within a few minutes' walk of a school.

One of the BSCS approaches emphasizes field investigations.

Miss Busch teaches biology in a high school in the heart of Brooklyn. She finds ample material for a field study program and has no sympathy for urban teachers who argue that field work is possible only in suburban and rural areas. "The challenge is naturally greater in the city," she says, "but that means that an urban teacher can do much more for pupils."

Her trips take the pupil "no farther than one's feet can take him." She believes that arguments about transportation difficulties are apologies, not reasons, for failing to take advantage of the resources around the school.

For administrative reasons she takes her trips on Tuesdays. "As a result," she says, "our biology periods on Mondays are very exciting planning periods." The pupils must not only plan what they are going to do but also what they are going to wear because they have agreed not to let the weather interfere with their activities.

Her pupils have studied the way dandelions crowd out the grass in the school lawn, the secondary sex characteristics of city birds, and protozoa in puddles. "It is one thing to establish a culture in a battery jar in the classroom," says Miss Busch, "and quite another to look for protozoa in places which are part of our everyday environment."

In winter her pupils have studied temperature distribution in snow and have looked for insects. They have examined plants that stay alive and plants that died completely and have observed ways that plants make provision for new plants the next spring.

"Note that none of these trips are meant to extend beyond a regular period," Miss Busch points out. "We simply adapted our program to our allotted time. We worked in an outdoor laboratory."[1]

FIELD EXPERIENCES

Field experiences are first-hand experiences. They arise from direct learning situations. They play the same role in the learning of science as do experiments and demonstrations.

Special contributions of field experiences. Field experiences are generally much more closely related to the out-of-school experiences of young people than are the experiences gained in the classroom. Field experiences tend to be much more meaningful and permit easier transfer of learnings to the solution of real-life problems. Field work awakens many interests that

[1] Busch, Phyllis B., "I Am Prejudiced," *The American Biology Teacher*, January, 1957.

classroom work cannot arouse. Field work is the study of actual objects, and objects stimulate more curiosity than do ideas. Out of almost any situation encountered in the field can develop a host of challenging problems.

The best place to study the reactions of plants and animals is in the field. Most living things do not react normally when brought into the classroom. Native plants are adversely affected by unnatural light and indoor humidity. Animals do not have proper diet, exercise, and seclusion. Whatever observations are made of living things indoors should be considered as supplementary, not basic, experiences.

Field work permits first-hand study of many things that cannot be brought into the classroom because of size or inconvience. It is only in the

An important part of modern ecological field work involves such quantitative procedures as sampling, counting, and measuring.

field that pupils can study real apple trees, power shovels, and waterfalls. It is only on field trips that they can see songbirds. It is only outside the classroom that they can investigate the operation of complete automobiles.

Field work permits a class to engage in activities that are too noisy or too violent to be used in the classroom. A soda-acid fire extinguisher must be operated outdoors. Model airplane gasoline engines demonstrated in a school building would disturb classes on every side.

Outdoors, pupils are able to work with large scale materials. A teeter-totter makes a more impressive lever than a meter stick, and erosion is better demonstrated with a stream of water from a garden hose than with a tiny trickle from a faucet.

Field experiences and the senses.   During field work, all senses are brought into action. Thus pupils gain a more complete picture than from any other known method of teaching.

> Genevieve is watching a huge derrick lift a steel girder into position for a new building. She has fixed her attention upon the graceful sweep of the great load through the air, but though she is not truly conscious of them, her senses are aware of much more. Out of the corners of her eyes she sees the erratic movements of men and machines—urgent gesticulations and ponderous obediences. Her ears are filled with the stuttering growl of hoisting machinery, the roar of truck engines, the clang of dropped steel, the shouts of workers. In her nostrils are the scents of raw earth, new concrete, sun-heated boards, tarred cables, motor oil and the prevailing stench of engine exhaust. Beneath her feet the ground quivers as trucks roll by. All these sensations pile one upon another with almost frightening intensity and blend into the final picture Genevieve has of a large building under construction.

What comparable experiences could a teacher provide within the limits of the classroom? A model may give Genevieve an understanding of the mechanics of a derrick but it can give no impression of the magnificent power. A film may show the relative sizes of men and machines but fail to give the picture of everything working together. A recording can produce noises that approximate reality in pitch and rhythm but not in intensity or direction. Odors, so much more important than most people realize, cannot be duplicated in the classroom. And the interaction of all the senses, the blending of sensations into the final impression, is pitifully incomplete.

True learning is the result of many sensations interacting and merging with one another. If one or more sensations is omitted during the learning process, the final impression is weakened, not only by the absence of the missing sensations, but also by the absence of their effect on each other.

Using field experiences to set problems.   One of the most important ways to establish problems in science classes is to bring pupils into contact with things. Field work, of course, emphasizes the observation and manipulation of things. From the contacts thus made questions inevitably arise. Attempts to find answers to the questions give rise to new problems and thus horizons continue to expand.

> Mr. Schmidt took his earth science class to a gravel pit in a glacial moraine. He directed the pupils to shut their eyes and pick up the first ten stones the hands of each encountered. The first question was, of course, "What kinds?"
>
> The pupils classified the specimens by type and identified as many as possible. Mr. Schmidt helped with the unknowns. The pupils were then asked to total the numbers of each type and calculate the percentages represented.
>
> New questions immediately arose. "Why should there be so many different kinds of rocks in one place?" "Why should 72 percent of the specimens be shale?"
>
> Back in the classroom Mr. Schmidt directed the pupils in a study of glacial movements and the distribution of bedrock in the region. Pupils made maps of the possible origin of their specimens and the probable flow of ice that brought them to the gravel pit.

Outdoor laboratories.   Teachers may consider the world around their classrooms as their laboratories, where they can carry out experiments on a scale and of a type impossible within doors.

> Mr. Wilson's physics class planned a demonstration of the speed of sound. Two pupils were to carry an automobile tire rim as far away as could be seen from school, a distance of about 350 yards. There one pupil was to hold the tire rim suspended by a cord while the other pupil hit the rim with a hammer to which a white cloth was attached.
>
> On the day of the demonstration the boys carried the tire rim to the place planned. Two others measured the distance to the school where the remainder of the class waited. By watching the white cloth the observers could tell when the hammer struck the rim. The interval before the sound arrived represented the time needed for the sound to travel the distance between the two points. Some of the pupils tried to estimate the time with a stop watch.

Many other sound experiments are best carried on outdoors. Studies of echoes can be made if there is a clear area of 100 yards or more at the base of a large building. Megaphones are most effective outdoors. Doppler effects can be demonstrated by a boy blowing a whistle as he rides past on a

Good field work requires advanced planning so that the pupils know what they should be doing. The teacher's role in the field is to encourage, help when needed, but not to lecture.

bicycle or in a car. The Doppler effect is also noticeable when pupils bow over and straighten up as they listen to a passing airplane.

Much of the study of mechanics is more effective outdoors where large scale equipment can be employed effectively. An experiment with a bosun's chair in which a pulley is suspended from a playground swing framework and other pulley problems may be studied the same way. The outdoor laboratory makes possible the use of large levers, wheelbarrows, bicycles, and large inclined planes.

Laws of motion can be best investigated where there is space for things to move. Falling bodies may be studied by dropping different kinds of objects from fire escapes or high windows. Stopping distances of runners, bicycles, and even of automobiles—if a driver-education car is properly equipped—can be determined on playgrounds and streets. Principles governing projectiles may be discovered. The effect of trajectory angles can be shown with a stream of water from a garden hose and with a bow and arrow. Horizontal and vertical motion can be related.

> The boys in Mr. Jordan's physics class wanted to measure the speed with which a pitcher could throw a ball. Mr. Jordan took the class outdoors and lined most of them up about ten feet from the base of the building. One boy was selected as the pitcher and directed to throw the ball between the row of observers and the building, trying to start the ball on as nearly a horizontal path as he could. The observers checked to be sure that the ball did not rise above the horizontal, using the rows of bricks as reference lines. Two pupils noted the height of the ball as it left the pitcher's hand. Another pupil noted where the ball landed.

> The pupils then measured the vertical drop of the ball and the horizontal distance it covered. From this data they calculated the time the ball was in the air and with this figure they calculated the horizontal speed of the ball.

Many earth science activities should be carried on in the outdoor laboratory. Contour maps are much more meaningful when taken to a hill top or other observation point and related to the actual features of the landscape. Most weather measurements must be done outdoors. Erosion experiments need large scale equipment to approach accuracy.

> At the Audubon Nature Center in Greenwich, Connecticut, experiments with soil erosion are carried on with two large wooden troughs about 6 feet long, 2 feet wide and 6 inches deep. These troughs are filled with soil and propped up on an incline. Measured quantities of water are sprinkled on the soil and run-off is collected from holes pierced through the lower ends of the troughs. One trough may

contain bare soil while the other is heavily sodded, or there may be other combinations. Effects of different slopes can be shown by propping up one trough more than another.

Centering instruction about field experiences.   It is possible to build many instructional units about materials that are available in the field. This places field experiences at the core of the learning activities.

Less than half a mile from the school where Mr. Dean teaches chemistry is the Portland Cement plant that is the chief industry of the community. Early each year Mr. Dean introduces a unit on the manufacture of cement and its properties. He takes his classes on trips to the quarries, to the plant, and to the testing laboratories. Nearly all laboratory and classroom work is an outgrowth of experiences gained in the field.

Within a short distance of most classrooms there are different but equally effective learning situations around which complete units may be centered. Sometimes a single trip can provide enough material for days of study.

Miss Dale gave her eighth grade science pupils kitchen strainers, flat pans, and glass jars, and took them to a nearby stream. In a few minutes the pupils had collected a rich variety of aquatic life to take back to the classroom for study. Aquariums were first set up. Then the pupils began a series of observations and experiments with their specimens, followed by references to books for information on life histories.

Units based upon field experiences do not differ in organization from those based upon classroom experiences. There are the same opportunities for experimentation, for reading, for summary and organization, and for project work. The only real difference is in the source of the basic experiences upon which the unit is built.

Field trips as follow-up experiences.   Field work may be used in science units to show applications of the information gained through previous study.

Mr. Swanson's physics class had studied transformers in the laboratory, experimenting with models, dissecting a bell-ringing transformer, and testing a small commercial transformer. Near the close of the unit, Mr. Swanson took the class to a transformer station that serviced the community. Here the pupils saw the three large step-down transformers hooked into a three-phase network. Their attention was directed to the variation in size of conductors and insulators in the primary and secondary circuits.

The pupils also noted the cooling systems of the transformers, the lightning arrestors, the circuit breakers, and the voltage regulators. Upon their return to the classroom they read about these devices and discussed their operation.

Mr. Swanson's use of field experiences made excellent follow-up for laboratory experiences. The pupils had gained a knowledge of the construction and operation of miniature transformers from their laboratory work. The field trip showed them large transformers in actual use. The relative sizes of the insulators in primary and secondary circuits pointed out the "step-down" action of the transformers. The relative sizes of primary and secondary conductors emphasized the reciprocal relationship of voltages and current in a transformer circuit. The cooling system and the hum illustrated the energy losses in coils and cores.

In this instance, the field trip was more meaningful used as a follow-up activity rather than as an introduction to the study of transformers. Commercial installations tend to be complex and to contain accessory devices that confuse the beginner. A preliminary understanding of basic components makes it easier to trace events and processes in commercial installations.

Field trips for review and drill.   Few teachers recognize all the potentialities of field work. Rarely does one see a teacher using field work for review and drill purposes.

Miss Birdsall took her eighth grade science class to see a sawmill as part of a unit on the growth and uses of trees. Two weeks later, in a review of the learnings of the trip and subsequent readings, Miss Birdsall brought the class back for a return visit. The pupils had an opportunity to review their understandings in a more impressive way than an oral review could have been.

Identification of things studied in the field can also be reviewed and tested in the field.

Mr. Martin gave his biology pupils duplicated sheets bearing numbers corresponding to numbers on tagged trees in a nearby park. At the park, he started the pupils, one at a time, on a circuit of the trees. As the pupils moved from tree to tree, they wrote down the names of the trees in the appropriate blanks on their sheets. Then Mr. Martin took the class around the same circuit so they could correct their answers.

Review work in the field can take the form of games and contests.

Mrs. Adams divided her biology class into two teams and announced a scavenger hunt. To the leader of each group Mrs. Adams gave a list of items to be collected. The list contained such items as the following:

1. A piece of a plant that reproduces by means of spores.

2. An arthropod that is not an insect.

3. A perfect flower.

The region in which the pupils must collect was defined and the time limit was established. The pupils were then dismissed to begin their hunt.

GETTING READY FOR FIELD WORK

A teacher encounters certain special problems in planning field work. For one thing, programs given in courses of study and in textbooks rarely emphasize field experiences as basic learning situations. A teacher must make certain adaptations in his program if he is to use field experiences effectively.

The teacher must also search for school and community resources for use in field work. Community resources have rarely been inventoried by a teacher's colleagues or predecessors.

Finally, the teacher must know school policy about field work and adjust his plans to any regulations established by the school administration. If he plans to take his pupils beyond walking distance from the school he must investigate the transportation facilities available.

Adapting the program for field work.   Conventional planning procedures usually begin with the setting of subject matter objectives, followed by decisions as to the most suitable activities for attaining these objectives. Field experiences have a place in a program so planned. With conventional planning, however, many opportunities for field work are neglected because their contributions seem insignificant.

Miss Busch describes an urban field study thus: Many city children never saw a clover plant growing, although it is certainly very common. They are found on lots and borders. Direct the pupils to measure off a square foot and then count the number of plants. How many four-leaved clovers can they find? Compare the shapes and sizes of leaves. Dig up a plant to see the root nodules.[2]

---

[2] Ibid.

If Miss Busch were teaching a conventional unit on reproduction, she might feel little enthusiasm for walking her pupils down three flights of stairs merely to see clover plants spreading by means of trailing stems. And for a conventional unit on interrelationships she might prefer to dig up a clover plant and take it into the classroom to show the nodules.

Most units built around field trip experiences cut across conventional subject matter boundaries. A field study of clover plants involves reproduction, nutrition, symbiosis, inheritance, soils, and economic biology. The contribution to any one area is small. The total contribution is impressive.

A different planning sequence is recommended in order to emphasize field work. First, a survey of possible field experiences is made, then the learnings that may be gained from these experiences are determined, and finally plans are made with these learnings as objectives.

The resulting plans are necessarily unconventional, but they are adapted to the local situation and are profitable because of this. Experienced teachers have discovered that in the total program they cover almost the same material through plans based on field work as through conventional plans.

Mr. Moose planned an experiment to compare the effectiveness of a conventional program and a program based on field experiences. One class was exposed to the conventional method of teaching biology— classroom discussions and laboratory exercises. The other biology class was taken into the field throughout the school year. Insofar as weather permitted, pupils went to parks, gardens, and vacant lots where they could study such plants and animals as they encountered. All field trips were planned, of course, but if something interesting caught the eye of one of the pupils, Mr. Moose stopped to elaborate on it. The group exposed to conventional teaching methods was very conscious of the final state examination. The second group was not informed about the examination until the time came for review. Both groups reviewed for the examination for the same amount of time. Both groups performed about the same on the examination. Both attained approximately the same average grade.[3]

Surveying resources for field experiences.   "Study indoors the things that are best studied indoors; study outdoors the things that are best studied outdoors." This is an excellent precept to govern all field work.

Within and around each school are hundreds of things worthy of study—resources far more valuable than are available in the most expensively equipped laboratories. Little things that are so common make the best things to study; one does not need a volcano, a blast furnace, or a botanical garden for effective field work.

[3] Personal communication from Dr. Carleton Moose, Professor of Biology, State University of New York Teachers College, Albany, June 12, 1957.

To make a survey of resources it is well to begin within the school building and on the school grounds because there are comparatively few problems when taking trips inside school boundaries. One may then explore the immediate neighborhood. Long trips are advisable only when the learning opportunities justify the additional time and effort needed. The list below may be of service in suggesting some possible field study situations.

Administration of field trips. Trips taken within the confines of the school property present few administrative problems. Most school systems permit teachers to take their pupils anywhere within these limits without special permission. Sometimes, however, a principal wishes written notification of intent to leave the classroom.

Trips off the school property, however, involve the problem of liability for accidents. Policies governing such trips have usually been established by the school officials. Most principals justifiably insist upon a written notice which includes the names of the pupils and the destination of the trip. Some systems require written permission from each parent before pupils can be taken from the school grounds. This last requirement is a serious handicap in the case of short trips and teachers should try to obtain blanket permissions for trips within the immediate vicinity of the school.

SUGGESTED FIELD STUDY SITUATIONS

The school building

Heating plant: transfer of heat
Wood shop: electric motor ratings
Metal shop: gears in lathe
Art dept.: temperatures in pottery kiln
Cafeteria: diet choices of pupils
Kitchen: bacterial counts on dishes from dish washer
Corridors: emergency exit patterns
Music dept.: wind instruments
Medical office: blood pressure measurement
Auditorium: acoustics

School grounds

Lawns: habits of lawn plants
Shrubs: effects of light and shade
Trees: seasonal changes
Flagpole: shadow studies
Concrete walk: friction studies
Macadam pavement: absorption of heat
Soil around building: spatter erosion

Teeter-totters: lever action
Swings: centers of gravity
Snow bank: insulation effect of snow
Bicycles: gear ratios

Streets

Automobiles: analysis of exhaust
Bicycles: Doppler effect
Pedestrians: pedestrian safety habits
Driver-training car: stopping distances
Intersections: traffic patterns
Traffic lights: control mechanisms
Fire box: method of signaling
Electric lines: pole transformers

Neighboring homes

Gardens: top soil and subsoil
Flower beds: phototropisms of flowers
Porch boxes: slips for regeneration
Lawns: earthworm castings
Lawn sprinklers: rainbows
Outdoor fireplaces: convection around fire

Community services

Water system: chlorination of water
Fire station: fire extinguishers
Police station: short wave equipment
Hospital: sterilization procedures
Churches: pipe organs

Rural areas

Woodlands: analysis of soil
Ponds: temperature distribution
Streams: transportation of sediments
Fields: collection of insects
Roadsides: seed distribution
Ploughed soil: animals in the soil
Hillsides: erosion effects
Cliffs: rock structures
Beaches: wave action

Small businesses

Service stations: hydraulic lift
Garages: differential pulley

Music store: electronic organ
Radio shop: oscilloscopes
Plumbing store: water softeners
Building suppliers: insulation
Appliance store: refrigerators
Lumber yard: kinds of lumber
Transformer station: circuit breakers
Coal yards: types of fuel
Junk yard: electromagnetic crane
Gravel pit: sedimentary deposits
Quarry: rock specimens

Hobbies

Astronomers: telescopes
Fish fanciers: aeration of water
Radio hams: antenna characteristics
Hi-fi enthusiasts: speaker characteristics
Bee keepers: life history of bees
Gardeners: fertilizers
Photographers: dark room techniques
Rabbit raisers: inheritance

Construction projects

Excavations: soil-moving equipment
Foundations: concrete making
Bridges: derricks
Small homes: electric wiring
Office buildings: air conditioning
Schools: plumbing

Small manufacturing plants

Bakeries: action of yeast
Sawmills: structure of tree trunks
Dairies: Pasteurization
Ice plants: use of ammonia gas
Greenhouses: photoperiodism
Foundries: metal casting

Long trips, particularly those requiring the use of buses or automobiles, are a different matter. Parents should know when their children are leaving the school for extended periods. Because long trips require considerable advance preparation, the request for parental permission imposes little hardship.

The majority of field trips should not require transportation. However, there may be some highly desirable experiences that could be given if some form of transportation were available. Schools that own their own buses commonly provide the buses for field work without question or limitation. Some allot a certain number of miles to each teacher, giving the individual teacher the option of using the mileage for a few long trips or several short trips. Other systems allot the use of buses on an hour basis. Small systems are generally more flexible than large ones.

Occasionally, a system budgets money for hiring buses for field work. Individual teachers must anticipate their needs for bus travel in making up their budgets for the following year.

When public carriers are available, as is the case in metropolitan areas, teachers may ask pupils to bring money for transportation unless school policy forbids this. The teacher must always anticipate the problem of those pupils who cannot afford the cost.

Parents may be willing to transport pupils in their personal automobiles. It is essential that these automobiles be properly insured.

Miss Donaldson, seventh grade teacher in a non-departmentalized school, used field trips extensively. She made requests for transportation through her "Mothers' Club," an organization that provided a number of services. There was rarely any problem in finding half a dozen mothers free to drive when field trips were planned.

Time for field work should rarely be a problem because so much can be accomplished within twenty or thirty minutes. Trips to distant places, however, may require travel time in excess of that provided by the schedule.

Some school principals look with favor upon field work and gladly excuse pupils from all classes for long trips. Other principals hesitate to excuse pupils arbitrarily but do not object if two teachers agree to exchange class time. Thus a science teacher and a mathematics teacher having successive periods with the same group may alternate classes on two different days, providing each with a double period.

If a science period precedes or follows the lunch period, it may be possible to extend a long trip through the lunch period by asking the pupils to bring their lunches.

Mr. Anderson wanted to take his earth science class to the local airport to see the weather station. Because his class met immediately after the lunch hour, he was able to give his pupils almost an hour at the station by having them bring lunches to eat enroute.

Teachers must find time in their own busy schedules for field trips that take more than one period. Some schools provide these teachers with substitute teachers during the hours they are missing. Sometimes arrangements can be made with other teachers who have vacant periods. Sometimes pupils in unmet classes can be sent to the study halls with special assignments. In smaller schools the principal or vice-principal may help out.

Teachers may be concerned about supervision of the pupils during field trips. If the trips are to places where there are special hazards, it is desirable to have one or more adults along to help out. Sometimes a principal or a special teacher will consent to go along. Sometimes other teachers who are free go gladly. Parents may be asked to participate in such trips.

One teacher solved her problem in an entirely different way. She divided her class in two parts and took only one half at a time. The other half was sent to the study hall and to the library to work on special problems. By alternating the groups, she was able to have a much more manageable group in the field.

PLANNING AND CONDUCTING FIELD WORK

Four parents with cars were helping Miss Hunter take her seventh grade to study the plants and animals that live in and near water. The cars were driven to a small pond, and the pupils rushed off in several directions around the pond. Miss Hunter and the parents strolled along a path to the edge of the pond, chatting casually about the pupils and their activities. Within fifteen minutes the pupils began to move toward Miss Hunter. The first arrivals promptly displayed the specimens they had collected.

"Why don't you show that to Mrs. Bouton?" Miss Hunter told one girl. "That's an interesting find, Sylvia," she told another pupil. "Let's show it to the mothers who brought us out here."

Within twenty-five minutes all the pupils had returned and were getting into the cars for the trip back to the school.

"Miss Hunter," said one of the mothers, "how can you keep so calm? I used to be a teacher and I wouldn't have dared let the pupils go off in all directions by themselves. I would have insisted that they stay together."

Miss Hunter looked faintly surprised at the question and a bit puzzled too. "Why, I don't know," she said hesitatingly. "I guess I just expect them to behave properly and they do."

Miss Hunter greatly oversimplified her answer. It is true that she did expect the pupils to control themselves but that was because she had given the pupils a great deal of practice in self-control and she knew what she could expect of them. In addition, the trip had been very carefully planned to keep each pupil so busy he had little opportunity to do things that would have been undesirable.

Preparations had been made well in advance. The pupils were interested in finding out what kinds of plants and animals live around water. They had organized themselves into several groups, one group to look for submerged aquatic plants, another group to look for aquatic plants growing up into the air, a third group to look for aquatic birds, a fourth group to look for amphibians and reptiles, a fifth group to look for aquatic insects, and a sixth group to look for aquatic mammals or signs of their presence.

Within each group there was a division of responsibility. One pupil carried the special equipment, such as dip nets or field glasses. Another pupil carried containers for specimens that might be collected, while a third carried a field guide. One pupil took notes and another drew sketches for the frieze on aquatic life that had been planned.

Before making the trip the pupils had examined a map and decided where to go and the limits within which to stay. They had worked out procedures to be followed on the trip. They had written notes asking mothers to drive and they had assigned themselves to the several cars.

The pupils knew how to prepare for a trip in this fashion because they had taken many shorter and less elaborate trips. They were fully accustomed to taking responsibilities for their own activities during field work. They, too, "just expected to behave themselves."

Teaching in the field is no more difficult than any other kind of teaching. Miss Hunter had mastered the techniques and used them so naturally that she could not understand why anyone was surprised at what she did.

Applying psychology to the planning of field work.   The boys and girls that a teacher takes on field trips are the same boys and girls that a teacher has in the classroom. Only the surroundings are different. It is the impact of these new surroundings that causes them to react differently.

Gone are the four walls and the patterns of behavior that were established during six or more years within them. Gone are the reflecting surfaces that throw back their own noises and make them conscious of their actions. Gone are the reverberations that give strength and authority to the voice of the teacher.

Lectures in the field are a practical impossibility unless the teacher has a megaphone, a public address system, or the voice of a bull. Discussions generally fail because pupils cannot hear each other and because there are so many distracting things to look at. Reading is difficult in bright sunlight. Writing is done under severe handicaps. And pupils are too exhilarated to sit passively as they might be able to do in the classroom.

But there are plenty of constructive things that can be done in the field. Pupils can be set to work on any number of problems. They can explore, collect, take measurements, experiment, or do anything else that demands physical effort.

When considering problems for field work it is generally wise to select those that permit pupils to work with their hands in some way. One should assume that if no provision for this type of activity is made, some of the pupils will probably find things to do with their hands, things that teachers would just as soon not have them do. During a five-minute walk on the way to a park, pupils in a seventh grade class were observed to do the following things unrelated to the purpose of the trip:

1. Two girls walked along with their arms about each other.
2. Four girls picked up colored leaves.
3. Five boys picked up black walnuts and threw them.
4. Two boys tripped the girls ahead of them.
5. One girl chased the boy who tripped her.
6. One boy punched the boy ahead of him, was punched in return, and grappled with the boy momentarily.
7. Two boys continually jostled each other as they walked along side by side.
8. One boy broke twigs from bushes and a low branch and threw them at others.
9. One boy jumped up and pulled some leaves from a low hanging branch, then wadded up the leaves and threw them at pupils ahead of him.
10. One boy pretended to put a caterpillar down the necks of the girls ahead of him.
11. Three girls ducked and squealed at the pretended caterpillar. A fourth girl slapped the boy's face.
12. One boy snatched the "beanie" from another boy's head but was forced to return it by the teacher.

These are the normal reactions of preadolescents and early adolescents. The experienced teacher expects such behavior and is not upset by it. He does, however, try to provide substitute activities that are more constructive than those just listed.

Each year Mr. Walther took his chemistry classes to visit a junk pile. His pupils worked in pairs, each pair being provided with a strong magnet and a file. The purpose of the trip was to study corrosion of metals. The magnets enabled the pupils to find pieces of iron, both rusted and unrusted. The files enabled them to investigate the metals hidden by corrosion and protective coatings.

The pupils collected samples of the metals to study in the classroom. During follow-up work they read about the nature of rust, performed experiments on the conditions causing rust, and investigated the types of coatings found on other metals. They also read about methods for coating steel with various other metals, paints, and enamels. Some carried out experiments with the processes involved.

Teachers should remember that the attention span of young people is no greater in the field than in the classroom and that there are many more distracting influences. Pupils should not be held to one type of activity for long intervals. There should be considerable variety in types of activities carried out.

Miss Gibson's biology pupils were determining soil temperatures in a number of different places—in bare, packed soil; in luxuriant clover-bluegrass associations; in a poorly fertilized lawn; under a tree; and on the north side of a building. They worked in pairs, one digging a hole for the thermometer and taking readings, the other locating the site on a map of the area and recording the temperatures.

Miss Gibson's plans gave each pupil a sequence of several short activities to do, with the sequence repeated five or six times, not enough to become monotonous. No single activity required over a couple of minutes for completion, there were no long waits for results, and there were opportunities for the pupils to move about between readings. There were also opportunities for interested pupils to do more than the minimum expected.

The overall time element of a period in the field must be considered. Generally, several short trips are more effective than one long one. Preparation and follow-up for a short trip is concentrated upon a small problem instead of being distributed over several problems. The fatigue factor is negligible during short trips.

Preparing pupils for field work.   Little preparation is needed for the "Let's go see—" type of field trips: "Let's go see the blossoms on the elm trees in front of the school," "Let's go see whether the sun is causing the tar to squeeze out from between the concrete blocks in the sidewalk." The purpose of these trips is simple and easily stated; pupils understand quickly what they are to look for. Long discussions are not needed.

Short field studies that involve simple comparisons are also easy to prepare pupils for. Such problems as, "Does the color of the surfaces on an automobile affect the absorption of heat from sunlight?" and "Does plantain grow better in a shaded part of the lawn or in sunlight?" are readily understood by pupils. A little more preparation may be needed for this type of activity than for the preceding. The pupils usually work best in teams of two and may choose partners. They need to know the limits of the territory in which they are to work. And they must recognize a time limit for their study.

As the complexity of the field problem increases, the preparations become more elaborate. The problem of soil temperatures, referred to earlier in this chapter, requires that the pupils understand the steps of the procedures and that they have an adequate system for recording data. As the length of time needed for a field activity increases, so will the differences between the rapid and the slow workers. Provision must be made to take care of those who finish early, perhaps by permitting additional measurements as was done in the soil study just referred to.

Very complex field studies require special assignments and sometimes carefully written-out directions. Careful attention to organization is seen in the account of Miss Hunter's aquatic life study on page 236. Each of her groups acted independently of the others because each had its own problem. Within the group there were individuals with particular responsibilities. In group work of this type there may be a chairman from each group who acts as liaison with the teacher and who directs the others in his group. There may be secretaries, artists, collectors, and librarians.

The pupils in a class may not be ready for highly organized field work that involves much individual responsibility. They first need practice with short trips and limited responsibilities.

Trips to collect specimens are generally easy to conduct. Pupils need to know specifically what they are to collect, any special techniques needed for collection, the limits of the area in which they are to work, and the time limits that are set.

> Mrs. Bayles arranged a fossil hunting trip to a nearby quarry for her earth science class. The pupils were divided in pairs but each person had a cloth bag for his own specimens. One hammer was provided for each two pairs of pupils.
>
> Mrs. Bayles listed on the blackboard the names of the major groups of fossils commonly found in the quarry. She also showed some of her own specimens collected in previous years. She gave the pupils references to the fossils in their textbooks so they could look up their specimens themselves.
>
> At the quarry the pupils immediately scattered and began searching through the loose rocks. Mrs. Bayles began hunting too but was soon forced to give her time to pupils who discovered specimens that puzzled them or that seemed especially interesting. Within 25 minutes

most of the pupils were satisfied with their collections and willingly returned to school. A few, however, planned to return after school and continue their search for unusual specimens.

Visits to industries and other large scale operations are apt to involve serious problems. Rarely are the pupils permitted to operate devices or manipulate materials or make collections. Commonly, they must go single file past machines, and thus become separated from the leader by a distance that makes control difficult. Pupils are often at such a distance from the leader that they cannot hear him tell about machines or processes. Sometimes there is so much noise that only a few of the closest pupils can grasp the leader's words. When the leader is not accustomed to working with young people, he may use technical language that handicaps them in understanding what he is talking about. Careful preparations help make such visitations more effective.

> Before taking her biology class to visit a local bakery Miss Brown gave her pupils an understanding of the way bread can be prepared in the home. For laboratory work the pupils prepared dough with and without baking powder so they could see the leavening effect of the gas produced. By putting the dough in glass jars they could see the bubbles being formed in the dough.
>
> Several girls volunteered to bake biscuits at home, using dough with and without baking powder so that the final effect of leavening could be studied. Two pupils prepared a demonstration that showed the evolution of carbon dioxide from yeast in a sugar solution. Miss Brown prepared a yeast dough which she let rise for a few hours before class in order that the pupils could see the effect of the yeast. Then she kneaded the bread and explained why this was done. All pupils had an opportunity to view a yeast suspension under a microscope.
>
> These experiences enabled the pupils to prepare a list of questions on the problems of large scale bread making. The questions were duplicated and were used to guide their observations at the bakery.

It is often helpful to prepare work sheets for the pupils to fill in while visiting an industrial plant. In addition to guiding observations, they give the pupils something to do with their hands. Work sheets may contain sentences with blanks to be filled in, questions to be answered; tables to fill in; or spaces for sketches, diagrams, or maps. These sheets may be prepared by the teacher or by the pupils themselves. More time for preparation must be allotted in the latter case but the time is generally well spent.

Below are the questions from a work sheet used by an eighth grade science class when visiting the pumping plant of the city water supply. The sheet was prepared by the teacher.

1. What is the source of Cortland's water supply?
2. What type of pump is used?
3. What kinds of motors operate the pumps?
4. Why isn't the water filtered?
5. Why is chlorine added to the water?
6. How does the chlorine look as it is added?
7. How is the chlorine brought to Cortland?
8. How is the proper amount of chlorine measured?
9. How does the operator know how much water is being used?
10. How much water does Cortland use every day?
11. At what times of day is the most water used?
12. How much water might be used for putting out a large fire?
13. How much water do the storage tanks on Prospect Terrace hold?
14. What would happen if the main pump should break down?
15. What would happen if the electrical supply to the pumping station were cut off?
16. What would happen if the water supply began to dry up?
17. What would happen in case of a large fire?
18. How long would Cortland have water if the pumping station were destroyed?

"Flow diagrams" are helpful in keeping in mind the sequence of operations in a complex industry. Pupils need advance instruction in the meaning of the symbols. Figure 18 shows a flow diagram prepared by the teacher of a chemistry class for its visit to a wire products manufacturing plant.

Museum visitation may require less advance preparation than a trip to industrial plants. Museums are set up as educational institutions with the nature of pupils in mind. Most modern museums provide opportunities for boys and girls to manipulate things, to operate devices, and to observe things that move or change in some way. Special attention is given to the language on labels and to the types of problems set up. Many museums also provide specially trained guides for school groups.

Nonetheless, certain preparations make museum visits more meaningful. Pupils should certainly have a well defined objective for their visit, preferably a problem that they want to solve. They may also have planned to take certain notes or make certain sketches for use in class at a later time.

Mr. Smalley's ninth grade science class planned to construct miniature dioramas showing the habitats of animals in which they were inter-

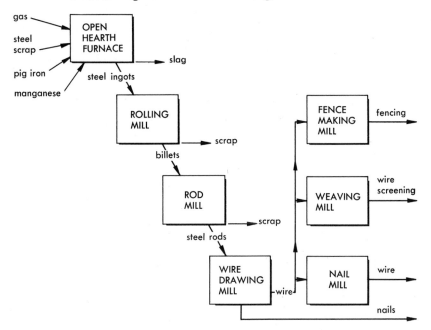

Figure 18.   *Flow diagram of a wire products factory.*

ested. To get ideas for their projects and to check on the accuracy of the work already started, the class visited the city museum to view some of the superior dioramas of the major habitats of the state—plains, foothills, high mountains, deserts, and irrigated fields. The pupils made notes and sketches to help them after they returned to the classroom.

The teacher's role during field work.   The account of Miss Hunter's field trip as given at the beginning of this section illustrates the proper role of a teacher during field work. Miss Hunter served as a consultant for the pupils as they brought in their materials. She did no lecturing. She did not interrupt the work of the pupils with loud voiced comments or last-minute directions.

If a teacher can be free of instructional responsibilities during field work he may watch his pupils more closely and give specific help and encouragement when needed. He is able to provide proper recognition for pupil achievements. And he can sense general progress, so that he will be prepared to bring the field work to a close at the optimum time.

Personal enthusiasm for field work is a great asset to a teacher. If he can greet unusual finds or accomplishments with expressions of strong interest, pupils are stimulated to continue their efforts. Often a teacher needs to work along with the pupils, displaying by his own example how interesting the work is.

Generally a teacher should not interrupt the work of the pupils. Occasionally, however, something unusual arises and justifies an interruption.

A seventh grade class was making a study of the blooming habits of dandelions on a park lawn, measuring lengths of stems and marking specimens to be measured on succeeding days. As they worked, a flock of grackles in a spruce tree became very noisy.

"If those were crows I would say that they had discovered an owl in that tree," the teacher said to a couple of pupils near him.

"May we go look?" they begged.

"Why, I guess so," the teacher told them.

A moment later they shouted, "There's an owl up here. Come quick!" The teacher motioned them to be quiet and, calling the pupils together, led them as inconspicuously as possible to the tree. There on a limb sat a barn owl, less concerned about the pupils than with the grackles who pestered him until he flew away.

The pupils returned to their work, possibly less enthusiastic about dandelions but enriched by the experience.

There are occasions when it is justifiable to change the purpose of a trip. Not infrequently, some temporary condition arises, something that can be utilized at the moment but which cannot be seen again.

Mr. Dutter was taking his biology class to compare the vegetation in a woodland where cows were pastured with a woodland from which cows were excluded. He stopped at a farm to explain that he was going into the woodland, having requested permission previously. He learned that at that moment a cow was being inseminated artificially. He immediately asked if his pupils could watch and they stayed until the act was completed. Mr. Dutter felt that the experience was a valuable one and should be utilized. The woodlands, on the other hand, would wait until another day.

Follow-up activities for field work. The value of field experiences is greatly strengthened by providing suitable follow-up activities. Pupils need opportunities to sum up and organize their learnings. Oral and written discussions, so often used, have some value, but various types of project work leave more lasting impressions.

A general science class visited the municipal water supply system. After their return the pupils constructed a large working model of the system.

In addition to models, pupils may make charts, friezes, and posters. They may prepare exhibits of materials collected. They may organize bulletin board displays of pertinent pictures. Sometimes they can dramatize conditions seen during the trip.

Most field observations give rise to numbers of problems. Some of these problems can be answered by follow-up experiments.

A trip to a swift stream showed seventh grade pupils a gorge dug in bedrock and, farther downstream, deposits of rounded pebbles. After returning to the classroom, the pupils experimented with the erosional forces of moving water. They put freshly broken fragments of soft rock in glass jars of water. They then shook their jars vigorously for a hundred times. The fragments now showed slightly rounded edges, the water in the jars was clouded with sediment, and the jars showed scratches on their inner surfaces.

Other problems may be solved by reference to books, magazine articles, or other authorities.

A chemistry class visited a bottling plant to see how water is carbonated for soda pop. The pupils wondered how the carbon dioxide in the pressure cylinders was obtained. As part of their assignment, the teacher asked them to read about the commercial production of carbon dioxide.

Sometimes problems raised during one field trip are best answered by a second trip.

After a ninth grade science class had visited an ice cream plant, the pupils raised a great number of questions. "Was the method used for pasteurizing the milk the same as was used for their bottled milk?" "How was the butterfat content measured?" "How was the cream used removed from the milk?" "What is homogenized milk?" The teacher believed these questions could best be answered by arranging for another trip, this time to a milk processing plant where bottled milk was produced for table use.

BROADENING THE OPPORTUNITIES FOR FIELD EXPERIENCES

Although the possibilities for field work within a short distance of the school may be numerous, time may not be sufficient to take advantage of them, or they may be of some special value to certain pupils but not to others. Some may exist beyond practical travel range for a class. And occasionally a teacher wishes that certain possibilities existed where they do not. Solutions have been found to all these problems.

Optional field trips.   Enthusiastic teachers may arrange optional trips for their science pupils.

> On the average of once a month, Mr. Kendall invited his general science pupils to go with him on Saturday morning hikes. There was no special objective for the hikes. They might lead to a pond, a stream, a woodland, a field, or a swamp, just to "see what was going on." Only a small number of pupils took advantage of the opportunity, perhaps a dozen or so each time, depending upon the weather, but their enthusiasm was high and stimulating to other pupils.

Night trips appeal strongly to young people, possibly because of the excitement of going out after dark and partly because young people like to get away from home into the company of their peers.

> Each spring Miss Barber took her seventh grade science pupils on a "peeper hunt" to catch some of the tiny tree frogs that enliven temporary pools of the northeastern states during the months of March and April. The pupils were asked to come dressed in warm clothing and boots, and to bring a flashlight and a glass jar. Parents provided the transportation to the puddles where the pupils were to begin the hunt. A few peepers would be carried back to the classroom for study.

Astronomy "hikes" are popular. The pupils are asked to meet at a central location from which they walk to an open place where street lights do not interfere with star finding. The pupils are cautioned about dressing warmly. They may bring flashlights, "tin can planetariums," and other devices to help in finding the stars and constellations.

Parents often enjoy participating in optional field trips and will drive if transportation is needed.

> Mr. Davenport arranged a series of Saturday morning trips for his junior high school science pupils. Parents were invited and some of them provided the transportation. Trips were taken to a ledge rich with fossils, a museum showing the development of the local salt industry, a beaver dam, a fish hatchery, and a foundry. Parents said they enjoyed the trips as much as their children did.

Voluntary field work.   Pupils voluntarily undertake field problems that specially interest them, spending long hours in field work outside of school hours. Sometimes these problems are suggested by teachers as optional assignments; sometimes the problems grow out of work done in class.

Miss Jones took her eighth grade science classes on field trips to an open field where they collected wild flowers. Returning to the classroom she showed the pupils how to press and mount the specimens. Within a few days a large number of her pupils had taken independent trips to gather additional specimens for their collections.

A teacher may ask pupils to investigate devices within their own homes. This is a form of field work.

Mr. Frier's science classes were studying homeheating systems. He asked each pupil to investigate the heating system in his own home, making diagrams and writing up a report for his notebook.

Pupils can also be asked to make visits to places where they may study material being taken up in class. Care should be taken not to send them to places where there is danger.

Mr. Tremont wanted his ninth grade science class to see an automobile motor block so they would know what cylinders, pistons, and valves are like, but he had no motor block available in the school. However, a large general merchandizing store had motor blocks for sale. Mr. Tremont asked each pupil in his class to visit the store and look at the displays.

Pupils generally like to work together on out-of-school projects. If teachers suggest a number of practical problems, pupils often undertake them eagerly.

Mrs. Dale knew of a man who raised orchids as a hobby. She suggested that two pupils might visit the man and report back to the biology class on his activities. June and Sylvia volunteered.

The girls found the visit very interesting. The man was experimenting with raising his own plants from seeds. He not only told them about orchids in general but was able to demonstrate the problems of germinating the tiny seeds.

After the visit the girls made an excellent report to the class. They were able to illustrate their report with pictures from catalogs, with two blooms, and with some samples of seeds and seedlings that were given them.

Young people commonly engage in such activities as hiking and camping with scout groups, picnics with parents or clubs, and hunting and fishing. Teachers can make suggestions for things to do during these activities and thus enrich the science backgrounds of the boys and girls engaged.

> Henry and Charlie were probably the most avid fishermen in the school. They went out at every available opportunity. Mr. Medhurst asked the boys to keep track of some great blue herons that were beginning to nest in a swamp where the boys often fished. The boys kept good records of the progress of the colony for several years.

Parents may help pupils with their field work, particularly in providing transportation to places beyond walking distance.

> Mr. Dunlop discovered a newly opened road cut where an anticline and a fault were plainly visible. Along the fault plane were rock fragments bearing slickensides, veins of calcite, and crystals of both quartz and calcite. Mr. Dunlop told the pupils about his discovery and gave precise directions for reaching it. Over the weekend more than a quarter of his earth science class had persuaded their parents to take them to the site.

Recognition for voluntary field work.   Pupils need recognition for the field problems they undertake after school hours. One way to give such recognition is to provide opportunities for them to report on their activities.

> Mr. Jenning set aside the beginning of his general science classes each Tuesday morning for "scout" reports. At this time pupils could tell about their observations during the preceding week, particularly those made over the weekend. Most of these reports dealt with observations of plants and animals.

It is helpful to provide a table on which pupils can display things associated with their field work—specimens collected, experiments, and models. These need have no relation to the regular classwork.

A science column in the school newspaper gives pupils opportunities to report on their field work, and thus to gain recognition from other pupils outside their science classes. One teacher sponsored a weekly mimeographed bulletin titled "Nature Notes" to publicize the field work of her junior high school science classes. One science club gave a fifteen-minute radio program on field observations each week.

Sponsors for field activities.   Many people with no direct connections to secondary schools can provide rich field experiences for young people.

Some of these laymen work in scouting and are trained in helping adolescents. Most laymen, however, lack such training and have only their own enthusiasm to depend upon. They work best with boys and girls who also have strong interests.

In many communities there are bird study groups that meet regularly for early morning bird hikes and for exchange of field notes. The leaders of these groups are happy to add interested young people to their numbers.

Camera clubs often enroll young people. Of course it is necessary that these young people be financially able to bear the expenses involved in photography. Amateur astronomers commonly put themselves and their equipment at the service of teachers. When they find interested young people they often extend invitations for continued work and they sometimes help these young people build their own telescopes.

Local industries are opening their doors more and more often on "Let's Get Acquainted" days. Sometimes the general public is invited, sometimes only the families of workers are invited. Science teachers should encourage pupils to take advantage of these opportunities.

Science clubs and field experiences.   Science clubs commonly include field trips in their programs.

> Mr. Decker's science club plans four or five major trips a year. Some of the trips are taken during the regular meeting time and run over into the hours after school. Some are taken on Saturday. The administration allows the club to take one full day a year from classes and provides a bus for transportation.

A science club may devote its entire program to field work.

> The Wyandotte High School Field Club sponsors seven yearly field trips, some one day in length and some lasting through the weekend. Out of these trips and out of their own special interests, the members become engaged in individual research projects which they write up and present at the Club meetings or to scientific organizations if possible.

School gardens.   School gardening has been an established part of the elementary school program in a number of cities since early in the century. In some instances special supervisors are employed to give continuity to the program through the summer months.

The school garden is an equally good laboratory for the secondary school sciences. Many important problems that do not lend themselves to indoor study can be investigated in a garden. The garden also instigates problems that can be worked on through the winter months and projects that individual pupils may carry out through the summer vacation.

Any part of the school grounds may be utilized as a school garden if it does not interfere with other activities.

Mr. Tillman was a general science teacher in a new school that had just been landscaped. He asked for permission to use the space between the newly planted shrubbery for some special studies. During the fall his pupils planted several kinds of bulbs and watched their development the next spring. The pupils learned about the dormancy of bulbs, the reactions of flowers to temperature and sunlight, and the methods of pollination.

The major problem in school gardening is the care of the gardens during the summer months. Where there is a special supervisor, such care is assured. In other situations, a custodian may be given the responsibility for the plot. Privately owned gardens, from which sections are loaned for experimentation, receive the needed care by their owners.

Mr. Miller uses portions of privately owned gardens for his laboratories. Problems that pupils have worked on include: (1) how to replace Kentucky bluegrass with Winter Rye; (2) how to irrigate a small garden properly; (3) how to start a compost pile; (4) how organic matter changes into humus; (5) what the life cycle of the common cabbage butterfly is; (6) what effects various gardening techniques have on the growth of mustard plants.[4]

Wildlife laboratories. One penalty paid for suburbanization is the loss of natural areas where boys and girls can become acquainted with native plants and animals. All the movies, television programs, expensive laboratories, city parks, and supervised playgrounds cannot compensate for the loss. Science teachers, if for no more than selfish reasons, should be among those most vigorously active in trying to preserve or to restore natural areas near their schools.

Sometimes a school district already owns the land that can be used if teachers will press actively for it.

The West Lafayette, Indiana, schools owned about three acres of undeveloped land in a residential area. The land had become littered with trash and was an eyesore to the community. Undoubtedly pressures would have been exerted upon the school board to clean it up and convert it into lawn or playground. But Mr. Bush, the biology

[4] Miller, M. C., "The Garden Laboratory," *The American Biology Teacher*, vol. 17 November, 1955, p. 223.

teacher, and Mr. Floyd, the superintendent, could see reasons for developing the area as a natural outdoor science laboratory.

Mr. Bush initiated a number of class projects designed to make the area useful. First the pupils cleaned up the trash. Then they planted native trees and shrubs and started wild flower gardens. They put up signs identifying interesting features. They built bird houses, bird feeders, and provided suitable types of cover for concealment. They began a number of soil conservation practices.[5]

When school systems acquire land for buildings and grounds, some parts are often excellently suited for nature areas if they can be preserved before bulldozers begin to operate. Again, science teachers must be alert to the possibilities.

Miss Larsen persuaded the trustees of the Carmel, California, High School to set aside two and a half acres of land for science work. Among the problems undertaken in this outdoor laboratory have been: (1) the nature of soils and the effect of weather on them; (2) rates of plant growth; (3) kinds of plants and animals living on the tract; (4) location of examples of interdependence; (5) the prevention of gully erosion.

From the first there has been much individual project work on the plot. Bill chose to study the rate of growth of Monterey Pine seedlings. Francis made a study of the nesting habits of the wood rat. Melinda began a plant collection for the use of future classes. Susan prepared soil profile charts. Tam and Melinda studied the habits of some of the birds.[6]

Sometimes the school district is willing to acquire land solely for the purpose of outdoor laboratories.

The Norwich, N.Y., school board purchased an abandoned farm as a science and conservation laboratory. Mr. Anderson, general science and biology teacher, has been responsible for the project from the beginning. Trees have been planted, erosion control measures have been adopted, and a pond has been constructed. Mr. Anderson has a science club that has been responsible for many of the improvements.

City parks are often large enough to contain a few acres of natural area, but park authorities usually think in terms of neatly clipped lawns

[5] Floyd, William, and Kenneth Bush, "School Homesteading—Viewpoint of the Biology Teacher," *The American Biology Teacher*, vol. 18, May, 1956, p. 189.

[6] Larsen, E. A., "Opportunities for Exploration and Discovery," *The American Biology Teacher*, vol. 17, December, 1955, p. 260.

and ornamental plants. Sometimes, however, they can be convinced that natural areas are needed.

> An estate was willed to the city of Brookline, Massachusetts, to be used as a park. About five acres of this tract, containing two ponds, was excellently suited for an outdoor laboratory. Mr. Keene, of the Brookline High School, and chairman of the "Natural Areas for School Grounds in Massachusetts" sponsored by Nature Conservancy, tried to get the park authorities to set aside the plot for school use.
>
> "Working alone for the establishment of the Conservation Center did not prove very successful," he says. "This was something new for this region. I was pioneering and the road was rough at first. I enlisted the aid of our Garden Clubs. These ladies saw the value of natural areas for our boys and girls. Finally, after much hard work on the part of many, the Park Board granted the use of this five-acre plot as a plant and wildlife conservation center."[7]

School camping.   One interesting development in modern education is school camping. It is a movement in which science teachers can find the answers to many problems. In camping programs, boys and girls encounter at first hand situations they merely talk about in school and rarely encounter in everyday life. The problems of fire building and elementary sanitation and nutrition become real rather than academic problems. Young people develop the backgrounds of experience so necessary for much of what they read about and study in secondary school science.

School camping programs range from day camps to two-week experiences far from home. Sometimes trips are taken on weekends and holidays only; sometimes the program is given during the summer vacation; occasionally camping becomes part of the regular curriculum.

More and more schools are buying property specifically for their camps. Others are renting or leasing land. Many schools make use of public lands in state and national parks.

Few school camping programs are set up specifically to teach science, nor do they need to be. Experiences gained in camp are largely basic science experiences no matter how the program is designed. There is the chemistry of fire-building, the mechanics of rowing a boat, the natural history of the organisms encountered, the geology of stream, and wave action.

However, many opportunities for science experiences are neglected in school camps that are operated solely by physical education and recreation

[7] Keene, I. C., "Establishing a Plant and Wildlife Area in a City," *The American Biology Teacher*, vol. 19, February, 1957, p. 44.

The school camping program puts pupils into constant contact with science materials—giving new experiences, awakening strong interests, and providing a background that makes classroom work more meaningful.

staff members. Science teachers have not always shown the interest in school camping that they might. When they take the initiative some very fine programs result.

Mr. Dawson of the St. Clair High School in Michigan sponsors a science camping program. He takes as many as 55 boys and girls to public lands where they live in tents, do much of their own work about camp, and engage in an intensive study of natural science.

The program of the camp is given below. Speaking of the outcomes of the program, Mr. Dawson says, "Each individual had some unique experience and awakening that was strictly his own . . . Almost without reservation it can be said that each individual progressed in some way. In some it was greater, but even the student who just took part was making great strides."[8]

PROGRAM OF THE ST. CLAIR HIGH SCHOOL SCIENCE CAMP

4:45 AM	The group leaders were awakened.
5:00	Groups having bird observations were aroused.
6:00	The other half of the camp was awakened for detail and breakfast preparation. These groups alternated activities each morning.
7:00	The bird observation groups returned and breakfast was served.
7:30	General clean-up for the duty half of the camp. (Bird observation groups had this time free for personal care.)
8:00	The groups mustered at the bus loading area to begin the day's activities.

The soils group, upon arriving at their area, experienced problems in soil management, erosion, bank control, etc. The forestry unit was concerned with types and uses of trees, growing and planting of these, in an actual work situation. The wildlife group combined both the practices of game management and the proper method of handling firearms and conduct in search of game. The nature study group, using the general camp area, was able to study the topography from lake shoreline to open fields. They were able to make comparisons of plants and animals within these areas. This group, because of the lack of transportation time, was able to return to camp and set up for the next meal preparation.

12:00 N	Lunch
12:30 PM	Work details
1:00	Back to work areas
5:00	Supper
5:30	Half the groups were on bird observations and the others were on camp details.
6:00	The work details mustered for a lecture on camping, particularly survival camping.
6:30	All returned to the area for recreation, such as volley ball, swimming, capture the flag, etc. Parents helped supervise.
8:00	All gathered on the beach for a bonfire, songs, and a general good time.
9:00	Back to the tents. Group leaders met.
9:30	Lights out.

[8] Dawson, J. R., "Learning from the Outdoors," *The American Biology Teacher*, vol. 19, April, 1957.

SUGGESTED ACTIVITIES

1. Visit a typical secondary school and make a list of the field experiences that are possible in and near the school building.
2. Go with a science class on a field trip. Make notes on the actions of the pupils. Try to analyze the reasons for their behavior.
3. Take a group of pupils on a short field trip. During planning make certain that each pupil has meaningful activities to keep him busy. If this cannot be done with a group of high school pupils, conduct the field trip with members of your methods class.
4. Make plans for an extended field study in which pupils work in groups of four or five. Make sure that each pupil in each group has meaningful activities to busy him at all times.
5. Go through a standard textbook in each of the major areas of science. Suggest one or more practical field experiences to enrich each chapter or unit of the textbook.

SUGGESTED READINGS

Abraham, N., et al., "High School Biology Field Expedition," American Biology Teacher, 28:381–387, 1966.

Anderson, J. E., and M. C. Neeley, "Attitude of Science Camp Students toward Various Sciences," Science Education, 51:273–275, 1967.

Biological Science, An Inquiry Into Life (BSCS Yellow Version), Harcourt, Brace & World, New York, 1963.

Busch, Phyllis B., "I Am Prejudiced," American Biology Teacher, 19:10–11, 1957.

Cranston, E. J., "Swamp Stompers," American Biology Teacher, 29:123–134, 1967.

Greene, K. L., "Classroom Without Walls; Outdoor Education Project," American Biology Teacher, 29:211–216, 1967.

Jacobelli, A., "Summer Program Offers Recreation Through Science," Science Teacher, 34:50–51, March, 1967.

Keene, I. C., "Establishing a Plant and Wildlife Area in a City," American Biology Teacher, 19:43–45, 1957.

Miller, M. C., "The Garden Laboratory," American Biology Teacher, 17:223–224, 1955.

Polizzi, L., "Worthwhile Biological Adventure," School Activities, 34:74, 1962.

Rowley, J. V. and J. B. Galford, "Fieldtrip Checklist," The Clearinghouse, 41:426–428, 1967.

Smith, Julian W., *et al.*, *Outdoor Education*, Prentice-Hall, Englewood Cliffs, N. J., 1963.

Totman, D. M., "Denny Lake Project," *Science Teacher*, 33:24–25, January, 1966.

Wagner, G., "What Schools Are Doing; Utilizing Community Resources," *Educator* 87:186–189, 1966.

Wood, C. G., "Summer Science Programs for High School Students," *Journal of Chemical Education*, 39:647–648, 1962.

Chapter 8

Audiovisual Aids and

Other Instructional Media

THERE ARE TIMES WHEN FIRST-HAND EXPERIENCES CANNOT BE PROVIDED FOR pupils. An earth science class cannot be taken to Greenland to see an ice sheet. A biology student cannot sit patiently watching a bud while it opens. A physics student cannot see what goes on inside a vacuum tube. It is then that a teacher must use substitutes for reality—photographs, drawings, models, recordings.

Most of these substitutes make use of the pupils' vision; a few depend upon the sense of hearing. In consequence, the term "audiovisual aids" has been coined. The term is not a good one because these same senses are involved in all good learning situations and the term can be applied to all apparatus used in experiments and all materials studied in the field. However, in this chapter common usage will be accepted and "audiovisual aids" will refer only to those devices used to provide substitutes for first-hand experiences.

257

CLASSIFICATION OF AUDIOVISUAL AIDS

For convenience in discussion, audiovisual aids may be grouped under four headings: (1) photographs and reproductions of photographs; (2) paintings and drawings, and reproductions of these; (3) models; and (4) recordings.

The contributions of audiovisual aids.   Each of the four types of audiovisual aids makes its own contribution to the educational process. Sometimes, when two or more types can be brought to bear on the same topic, their strengths are pooled and their limitations are minimized. Following is a discussion of the situations in which audiovisual aids may be employed profitably.

1. *To present exotic material.* Chiefly through photography, but to a limited extent through paintings and dioramas, pupils can be given understandings about science materials in distant places. Some sound films and recordings also help enrich the experience background of pupils.

2. *To present historic material.* Since the introduction of photography a wealth of authentic photographic records of important events, places, and people has become available. Most of these are in the form of still photographs but there are an increasing number of films.

To provide information about events and people prior to the invention of photography there are reproductions of contemporary paintings and drawings. There are also modern paintings and drawings that reconstruct conditions and events of the past. Museums sometimes contain reconstructions as dioramas.

The library of tape recordings and records of the sounds of historical events is growing. Some are available today and many more will be available in the future. Teachers may make tape recordings of radio reports and thus build up their own libraries.

3. *To present information about inaccessible places.* It is often impossible to visit local industries and other prohibited places in the region. In such instances photographs and films are the only visual means possible for giving pupils information.

4. *To give a "bird's-eye" view.* Many machines, industries, and topographic features are too large to be grasped from the usual viewpoint. Aerial photographs are useful in showing the relation of parts or features to each other. Scale models have the advantage of including a third dimension. Both scale models and working models show the relation of the component parts of large machines.

5. *To summarize a series of observations.* After a field trip to an industry, a suitable film presents a quick summary of things seen on the

trip. Flow diagrams and bulletin board displays of relevant pictures serve the same purpose.

6. *To present information about microscopic materials.* There are many materials which pupils cannot prepare for examination through a microscope. Photographs and projected slides are useful for presenting information about these materials. Films can be used to show the behavior of microorganisms that are difficult to obtain. Large scale models are especially valuable to give pupils a concept of the third dimension that is lacking when viewing objects through high power microscopes.

7. *To amplify sounds.* Faint sounds such as heartbeats can be picked up with a stethoscope and amplified with a radio amplifier so that an entire class may hear them. There are also recordings of amplified sounds available.

8. *To acquaint pupils with elusive organisms.* Few pupils have ever seen a mole or a shrew, common though these animals are. Photography makes it possible to acquaint pupils with these and other seldom seen organisms. Recordings of the calls of frogs, insects and song birds help pupils associate commonly heard sounds with the rarely seen animals that make them.

9. *To present things usually seen by inadequate light.* Bats are often seen but are seen too indistinctly for the observer to comprehend their details. Flash photography has done much to acquaint people with nocturnal creatures.

10. *To acquaint pupils with infrequent phenomena.* Such phenomena as rainbows are rarely seen at the time a teacher wishes to deal with them in class. Photographs and paintings recall the past experiences of pupils and give opportunities for study of formerly unnoticed details.

11. *To acquaint pupils with dangerous conditions.* An explosion of gasoline fumes is not a suitable large scale demonstration for science classes, but a film of such an explosion can be used effectively.

12. *To acquaint pupils with materials that are difficult to keep.* Many desirable teaching materials cannot be kept in satisfactory condition long enough to justify their cost. Organs from the human body, for instance, are expensive to buy and difficult to keep. Colored photographs are often to be preferred to "pickled" specimens. Better yet are full-scale models.

13. *To help pupils make comparisons.* Two or more sequential photographs permit comparisons of changes that might otherwise go unnoticed. Still pictures permit more detailed comparisons than do films. Recordings permit comparisons of sounds that ordinarily might not be heard together.

14. *To speed up gradual changes.* "Time-lapse" moving pictures make such normally slow changes as the growth of a seedling seem to occur very rapidly. Thus changes not usually noticed become obvious.

15. *To slow down action.* The wing motion of a hummingbird is too rapid for the eye to analyze. By the use of "slow motion" moving pictures it is possible to study the movements of the wing and even the behavior of individual feathers.

16. *To stop action.* The development of electronic flash has made it possible to take pictures with an exceedingly short exposure. These pictures can be used to analyze conditions that last for no more than a few thousandths of a second; for example, the distortion of a tennis ball when it strikes the floor.

17. *To show the action of devices not easily studied.* Working models are useful for showing how machines operate, indicating the basic parts, often simplified, and their action. When complex machines are studied, a series of models, each illustrating a portion of the total organization, helps to clarify understandings.

18. *To show the interior of things normally enclosed.* Cut-away drawings and phantom drawings are excellent for showing the relationship of interior structures. Sectional drawings are useful for those who know how to interpret them. A series of photographs or drawings made while an object is being constructed or taken apart may give desirable concepts. Animated drawings, either sectional or in phantom view, give the relationship of moving parts.

Cut-away models and dissectible models are often to be preferred to pictures because they give a concept of the third dimension. Phantom models having exterior coverings made of transparent plastic are expensive but are finding increasing use.

Limitations of audiovisual aids. The chief limitation of audiovisual aids is their lack of reality. Pupils are faced with the problem of interpreting—producing images representing actual conditions. A pupil who has seen an apple undoubtedly interprets correctly the photograph of an apple. But the pupil who has never seen stylolites might have considerable difficulty in realizing what a picture of these structures represents.

The science teacter often forgets that his special background makes it possible for him to interpret audiovisual aids in a way that his pupils cannot do. For instance, he may grasp quickly the meaning of a cross-section diagram of an aneroid barometer but to his pupils the diagram may be no more than a set of lines.

Photographs and drawings have two dimensions, but they must be interpreted in three dimensions. When they represent familiar objects pupils have no trouble adding the third dimension. If they have never seen the object represented they may not be able to see more than two dimensions.

Diagrams are much more difficult to interpret. So much detail has been eliminated from a diagram that it ceases to resemble anything real, save as the mind is able to supply the missing portions. Cross-sectional diagrams are particularly difficult for many pupils to interpret.

All images produced from audiovisual aids are necessarily incomplete. Two senses alone are involved and these may give distorted impressions. The fusion of all the impressions gained by all the senses is lacking.

Audiovisual aids tend to give distorted images. Pictures may give no clue as to size: pupils seeing equal sized photographs of a cat, a cow, and an otter would probably recognize the relative sizes of the cat and the cow but might think of the otter as being as large as the cow if there were nothing in the picture with which to make comparisons.

Photographs are often distorted deliberately for "artistic" effects. The camera may be held at an unusual angle, or provided with special lenses, or altered to increase the foreshortening. The resulting photographs are likely to produce incorrect or confused images in the minds of many pupils.

Photographers distort the information provided by a photograph in order to emphasize a point. They blur out the background, provide artificial backgrounds, use unusual lighting. Sometimes they deliberately falsify; propaganda films commonly cut out all scenes giving contradictory evidence.

Models are commonly distorted. Topographic models generally have an eight-to-one distortion, making mountains seem higher and steeper than in reality. The distortion in astronomical models is generally so great that most people have totally wrong concepts of the size of the solar system and the distances between its components.

Models may give wrong impressions because of the materials of which they are made. A model of a human heart, made of rigid papier-mâché or plaster, does not give at all the image of a mass of muscle—flexible, vibrant, pulsating.

Miniature working models may give wrong impressions because not all forces can be reduced accordingly. A miniature landscape being eroded by a miniature stream flowing across it does not illustrate large scale erosion with any precision. In a small model, the effects of adhesion, cohesion and surface tension play a considerable role in the movement of the water and the particles of soil. In large scale erosion, as is seen outdoors with rivers, these same forces are negligible.

Sounds can be distorted too. Recording equipment cannot record the full range of sounds audible to the human ear. Most play-back equipment found in public schools is even less faithful in reproduction. Lost are the high and low frequency vibrations. In addition, low quality amplifiers and speakers overemphasize some frequencies and underemphasize others. Intensities must be distorted because very loud sounds cannot be recorded or reproduced by most equipment. This results in sounds that are perhaps identifiable to the person who knows them but that may be confusing to others.

Devices needed for use with audiovisual aids. Although some of the audiovisual aids, such as photographs, may be put directly in the hands of pupils for study, many of them require special projection equipment. All science teachers should master the operation of each of the following devices as soon as possible; all are highly useful to him and some, such as film projectors and tape recorders, need trained hands lest serious damage result.

1. *Bulletin board*. This is used for displaying photographs, drawings, and other flat materials.

2. *Chalk board or blackboard*. The teacher uses this most commonly for line drawings.

3. *Duplicating machines*. Copies of line drawings can be produced in quantities by standard office duplicating machines.

4. *Photographic and photostat equipment*. This equipment produces copies of photographs and line drawings in quantities. The former gives the better quality of reproduction; the latter produces copies more rapidly.

5. *Overhead projector*. Permanent or temporary transparencies may be projected on a screen or blackboard.

6. *Opaque projector*. This machine makes it possible to project an image of photographs and drawings on a screen for class study.

7. *Microprojector*. Microprojection materials range from animate to inanimate. Prepared microscope slides include both live material and commercial slides.

8. *Slide and filmstrip projectors*. These two machines are commonly combined and may project either slides or filmstrips by slight adjustments. With a beaded screen, the room need not be darkened, but it is well not to have the light intensity too high.

9. *Hand viewers*. A single pupil may view slides through one of these without disturbing the others in the class.

10. *Stereoscopic viewers*. These give the illusion of a third dimension to paired photographs. Some are designed for transparencies and some for opaque prints.

11. *Motion picture projectors*. Most motion picture projectors in schools today can also reproduce the sound on the sound track of films. They may also be used with silent films.

12. *Phonographs*. Modern phonographs play records at 78 RPM, 45 RPM, 33 RPM, and 16 RPM, and have both large and small needles for standard recordings and microgroove recordings.

13. *Tape recorders*. Most tape recorders both record sound and play back recordings. On some machines headphones may be plugged into the external speaker jack for individual listening.

14. *Closed circuit television* (if available). The camera may be mounted on a stand over a demonstration table, and the image greatly magnified on receivers distributed at convenient locations in the classroom.

Fitting audiovisual aids into the curriculum.   Despite the claims of enthusiasts, audio-visual aids do not call for new methods of teaching nor do they call for the elimination of already existing methods. Audiovisual aids should fit into the work of the class as a logical, sequential step in the learning process. One of the primary aims of the science teacher should be the integration of these aids into the over-all instructional program so that they are regarded by the pupils as the best possible way of learning about the topics under study.

One of the first considerations is to make certain that an audiovisual aid is not replacing a first-hand experience situation unnecessarily. It would be poor teaching indeed if a film on experiments with bar magnets were to displace the experiments themselves. Audiovisual aids may supplement first-hand experiences but should not substitute for them save when the latter cannot be provided.

Another consideration is to make sure that pupils are ready to benefit from a specific audiovisual aid. They may not have the background needed for interpretation of a chart. They may not understand some of the words used in a sound film. They may not recognize the point of view from which a photograph is taken.

The situation must govern the type of audiovisual aid to be used. There is no one best type; a film is not necessarily better than a filmstrip, nor a model better than a chart. Sometimes one has advantages over the other and vice versa. Because all types have their limitations, and none are as good as reality, often the best solution is to use several devices together in hopes that the strengths of one will compensate for the weaknesses of another.

The timing in the use of an audiovisual aid must likewise be governed by the situation. When it is used to supplement a first-hand experience it must of course follow the latter. When used as a substitute for a first-hand experience, it can be used whenever the latter would have been used. In filling other functions it may come at any time; it may open a unit to set problems or it may end a unit to summarize it.

DISPLAYS OF SCIENCE MATERIALS

Any display, to be useful, must be looked at; it is useless if pupils pass it by unseeing. Material selected for display should both be intrinsically interesting and have visual appeal. It should be colorful and large enough to attract attention. It should be arranged with artistic unity.

Displays should be topical; that is, centered about a theme. A mere display of unrelated materials is rarely interesting or of much educational value. The theme may be one related to class work or it may be independent, representing a matter of current interest or of special interest to certain pupils.

A display may illuminate class work but it should rarely try to duplicate it. A flow chart of the Solvay process in colored poster paper may be striking, but if the textbook contains exactly the same flow chart the utility of the display may be questioned.

It is important that displays be changed frequently. Nothing is more depressing than a faded or dust covered exhibit. Pupils develop a habit of looking at displays only when they expect to see new things regularly. The preparation of new exhibits may be done by the teacher, but there are many valuable outcomes for pupils when the latter prepare exhibits. The task of arranging a new display may be assigned as a group responsibility replacing other assignments or it may be suggested as voluntary work for extra credit.

The bulletin board.   The bulletin board is best adapted for displays of pictures and clippings though other flat materials may be attached where there is no danger of their being brushed off. Most classrooms today have some bulletin board space but there may not always be enough. The area above the chalkboards may be used for some types of displays. Strips of composition board to which pictures may be tacked or strips of decorators' burlap to which pictures may be pinned are attached above the chalkboards and used for poster materials and large, uncluttered pictures.

Unused sections of chalkboards may also be used for bulletin boards. Materials are attached with masking tape. The use of the chalkboard has additional advantages in that lines, labels, and diagrams in colored chalk may be used to amplify and to give emphasis to the materials displayed.

The preparation of bulletin board displays may be an outgrowth of regular class work; sometimes it can be planned to be an integral part of such work.

Mr. Marshall's eighth grade science class was engaged in the study of airplanes. Mr. Marshall suggested that a bulletin board display be prepared. Several pupils made suggestions none of which were accepted by their classmates, either because the materials would be too familiar to everyone or because the materials would not have sufficient appeal. Finally the class decided to prepare an exhibit based on famous trans-Atlantic flights. Committees were organized to do the necessary research, to find pictures in Mr. Marshall's files, and to draw maps and labels.

Pegboards.   Pegboards, designed for storage of merchandise and household items, can be useful in the classroom for displays of teaching materials. These pegboards are drilled at regular intervals to receive hooks, shelf holders, tool holders, and other special adaptors. When a board is fastened to a wall it should be separated slightly from it by means of cleats or by separators designed especially for the purpose. The boards come in several colors but they may be finished in enamel over a primer coat.

Items for display may be suspended from hooks. They may also be placed on shelves of thin plyboard which are held up by shelf supports provided for the pegboards. Obviously, one of the major advantages of the pegboard is the ease with which the various holders and supports can be rearranged to meet the special needs of the display.

Display cases.   Small cases, about 12 to 18 inches on a side and 9 to 12 inches high, may be used for display of specimens that should not be handled or exposed to dust. These cases may be made of a variety of materials: Lucite, Plexiglass, celluloid, or sheet glass. The plastics may be cemented together. The glass may be held with adhesive tape. These cases are especially useful when all sides of a specimen are to be viewed.

Wall cases.   Wall cases which may be closed and locked are needed for the display of fragile and expensive specimens. Generally, shallow cases are most convenient. A viewing area unbroken by frames is desirable. A pegboard used at the rear of the case makes possible many arrangements of the supports used to hold the specimens.

Interior lighting is especially desired; fluorescent lamps across the top, with a shade to keep light from shining directly into the viewer's eyes, are most satisfactory. When shelves are used these should be of glass or clear plastic to reduce shadows cast on specimens beneath.

In museums one will see a number of techniques that may be adapted to making the displays in wall cabinets more effective. Rectangles of colored paper placed under or behind specimens give emphasis and provide needed contrast. A mirror behind a specimen makes its rear surface visible. A large lens properly mounted magnifies a small specimen or a portion of a large one. Colored threads may lead from parts of a specimen to labels and captions or to related specimens.

Display tables.   Any science classroom is improved by the addition of a display table. On this may be placed large specimens, models, and other materials that may be handled. One important use of the table is for the display of apparatus used during a demonstration so that the pupils have opportunities to examine the material closely and manipulate it.

A small bulletin board behind the display table adds to the table's versatility. On the board may be pinned pictures, descriptive materials, and directions pertinent to the display.

The chalkboard.   The chalkboard is a familiar and much used teaching device but it is often used carelessly and without full realization of its potential. Certainly the crude scrawls and aimless scratchings seen on so many chalkboards must have little teaching value.

The use of the chalkboard should be planned as carefully as a demonstration or a test should be planned. The chalkboard is too important to be left to chance or to spur-of-the-moment inspiration. The teacher should decide in advance just what parts of a lesson are to be presented by means of the chalkboard. He may find it useful to make a layout of this material on a sheet of paper so that he can determine in advance the amount of space required, the best means for emphasizing certain points, and the details of spacing.

Carelessly made diagrams may be worse than useless. In some instances it is wise to make diagrams in advance, laying them out carefully, and emphasizing points with colored chalk. Advance construction makes possible a check on visibility from various parts of the room.

Sometimes a teacher wishes to construct a diagram a bit at a time while explaining it to the class. He may draw the diagram in advance with soft chalk which on erasing leaves a vague outline. The teacher may then reproduce the outline as he wishes.

Accessories that help realize the potential of the chalkboard are a blackboard straightedge, a blackboard compass, a blackboard protractor, a blackboard 30–60–90 degree triangle, and a blackboard 45–45–90 degree triangle. A section of the chalkboard should be ruled off into squares with a carborundum or hardened steel stylus to facilitate the construction of graphs. A teacher who has difficulty with blackboard writing will find that lightly ruled lines on a section of the board will help him level and space his writing better.

Displays using colored chalk and built around diagrams or pictures taped on the board can be very effective. Sections used for this purpose should be those that are not used regularly during class presentations.

FLAT PICTURES

Flat pictures have a number of advantages and some serious limitations. Among their advantages is the fact that they are free or inexpensive, easily procured, and easily stored. They can be used for the study of very large or very small objects, and for objects that are unavailable in the classroom. In addition they often show objects in their natural surroundings. Flat pictures are excellent for individual study, either in the hands of the pupils or as part of displays and exhibits. They may also be projected on a screen for class study.

On the other hand, pictures are rarely true to color and may have no color at all. Size relationships are often not indicated and are sometimes distorted. The use of unusual camera angles may make interpretation difficult. Because of these limitations a teacher should choose flat pictures with care.

Developing a picture file. Scattered through magazines and other publications is a wealth of material useful to science teachers. Some issues of the *National Geographic* and *Life* magazines are veritable treasure houses of valuable pictures. Catalogs, advertising brochures, and discarded books make other contributions. A number of industries print visual materials especially designed for teachers. The teacher who does his own photography may add to his collection by taking pictures in black-and-white and making enlarged prints. Standard 8 by 10 inch enlargements are a useful size.

Photographs and clippings may be stored in a standard letter file. Related photographs may be kept in a folder having a topic heading. The folders may then be filed alphabetically or under major headings that correspond to units of the course of study.

To prevent clippings from becoming creased and torn, it is well to cement the more useful ones to sheets of heavy paper or to sheets of thin cardboard such as are used in laundered shirts. Pictures that are handled by the pupils are apt to become soiled. These may be mounted on cards and covered with plastic film. One excellent film is the type used to wrap meats before freezing. It is wrapped around the card and the edges are sealed together at the back with a hot iron.

Photographs or clippings used for individualized study may be stapled inside manila covers.

Using photographs and clippings. These visual aids are better adapted for individual study than for general class use. However, an opaque projector makes possible the projection of an image of a photograph or clipping on a screen where all may observe it.

When photographs and clippings are given out for individual study, pupils need specific directions which are clearly written out so that they will not be forgotten while pupils wait their turn to examine the materials.

Mr. Williamson chose twelve colored photographs of birds to illustrate bill and foot adaptations. He stapled each picture in its own manila cover. On the facing side of the cover he stapled a typewritten sheet of questions to guide observations. The pictures were circulated during intervals of individualized work.

A similar technique has been used with stereophotographs. However, instead of circulating the materials, they are left in one place and the pupils take turns using them.

Mr. Schick purchased a set of stereophotographs illustrating successive stages in the development of a chick embryo. The photographs and the viewer were placed on a side table where the light was suitable for observation. The pupils were given guide sheets listing points to look for. They took turns looking at the pictures during portions of the period devoted to individualized work.

Bulletin board displays may be organized on the same basis. A set of guiding questions may be tacked to the bulletin board or copies may be given to the pupils. Copies given to the pupils may have spaces in which pupils are to write out their observations.

CHARTS

Charts are standard equipment in most science classrooms. They are used extensively by some teachers, little by others. The advantages of charts are several and make them desirable visual aids, but since their limitations are serious they should be used only with the greatest of care.

Advantages and limitations of charts.   Most charts present a diagram or a series of diagrams. These charts may be difficult to interpret, because diagrams have such serious limitations. If the diagrams have been over-simplified, the pupils may not know what the diagrams are intended to represent.

When the limitations are recognized and provided for, charts have some distinct advantages. The diagram on a chart is generally superior to anything a teacher might draw on the chalk board, providing visibility and contrast through prominent, sharp lines, bright colors, and bold printing.

Charts require fewer facilities and less effort for presentation than do lantern slides. Lines of diagrams are usually sharper and in greater contrast with the background. The chart may be left up as long as needed but slides cannot be projected indefinitely. Against these advantages must be mentioned the greater difficulty of storing a large number of charts.

Diagrams in textbooks and on duplicated sheets are much more difficult to follow during general discussion than are the diagrams on charts. A teacher may use a pointer to indicate each structure under consideration and lead the attention of the pupils from one structure to the next.

Using charts effectively.   The first step in effective use of charts is the selection of suitable charts. Charts should always be large for general class use. All lines should be distinct and the printing should be readable from all parts of the room. Color is effective. It can be used to emphasize important details and to lead the eye towards them. On the other hand, too much color can be confusing, and nonfunctional color, applied for decorative effects, should be avoided.

Each chart should be simple and uncluttered, with adequate space between separate items. Some charts are so crammed with details that from a distance, they resemble patchwork quilts. Some charts come with labels, some with parts indicated by letters or numbers. The latter kind are more versatile, since they may be used in oral reviews and testing.

Lighting should be considered when displaying charts. The best lighted wall should be used if the charts are hung on wall hooks. If a stand is used, it should never be placed so that pupils are looking toward the windows. A teacher should move about the room and check the visibility from several points.

The major limitations of charts can be compensated for by proper planning. The solution is often simple—pupils must know what they are seeing when they look at a chart.

Mr. Clair set up a large spark coil and produced sparks so that the class could recognize its function. He then displayed a chart on which was a cross-sectional diagram of a spark coil. Before attempting an explanation of the action of the coil, Mr. Clair took time to point out on the chart each visible feature of the appartus. He then indicated where the interior structures shown on the chart were located in the apparatus.

Sometimes it is feasible to put materials in the hands of the pupils before beginning a study of diagrams on charts.

Mrs. Dayton's biology class collected grasshoppers on a field trip. For the next class period each pupil had a live specimen in a jar. After the pupils had looked casually at their grasshoppers, Mrs. Dayton hung up a chart on which were two diagrams, one of the external anatomy of the grasshopper and one of the internal anatomy. Pupils studied the external anatomy first, comparing their specimens with the chart. Attention was then given to the diagram of the internal anatomy so that the pupils could relate some of the internal features with the exterior.

As the above illustrations show, charts have important uses in supplementing demonstrations, discussions, and the like. They may also be used for review.

> Mrs. Tatum displayed three charts with diagrams representing the life history of a fern, a moss, and a mold, respectively. She gave the pupils duplicated sheets of questions which referred by number to the structures on the diagrams. She asked the pupils to answer these questions.

Charts may be used in similar fashion for testing pupils. It is important that they have studied the same charts before so that they are familiar with the conventions used in making the diagrams.

> Mrs. Tatum asked her pupils to write down in order the ten numbers she dictated. She then displayed a chart on which the same numbers referred to structures in the human eye. She asked the pupils to write down the names of the structures indicated by these numbers.

Making charts. Sometimes teachers wish they had charts for special purposes but find none available at scientific supply houses. They can make these charts with relatively little trouble. For temporary use, charts may be made by using a felt pen on large sheets of wrapping paper. These charts are not very durable and are easily damaged during storage. Longer lasting charts can be prepared by making drawings on sheets of white poster board.

Permanent charts are made on special chart cloth sold by scientific supply houses. Outlines are drawn in pencil and traced in India ink with a ball-tipped pen, a drafting pen, or a felt-tipped pen. Colored lines, labels, and arrows may be added with colored drawing inks. Colored areas may be filled in with wax crayons, after which the wax is blended in by applying a warm iron to the reverse side.

Chart making is an excellent project for pupils to carry out either as a service to the teacher or as as part of presentations which they themselves plan to make.

MODELS

Models tend to be superior to many diagrams and pictures, because they introduce a third dimension. They possess some of the same limitations, however. If pupils do not understand what the models represent they cannot interpret them.

Models fall into different classifications. Scale models are designed to duplicate the appearance of a real object as closely as possible, but are usually larger or smaller. Diagrammatic models emphasize selected features and suppress others for the sake of clarity. Display models show structural characteristics and operating models show the action of moving parts.

Choosing models for classroom use.   A model must be of adequate size to be seen clearly from all parts of a room if it is to serve as the center of class discussion. Smaller models may be used for individualized work Generally speaking, a model should be three-dimensional, although there are exceptions in the case of some cross-sectional models. The value of a model lies in its presentation of the parts in their proper spatial relationships.

The degree to which a model resembles the real object is important. Simplification is desirable, but it is possible for a model to be oversimplified. The subject of the model and the age level of the pupils with whom it is to be used must be taken into consideration.

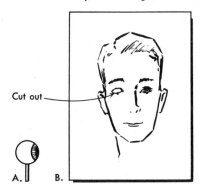

Figure 19. *Pupils often have difficulty in visualizing the relationship of anatomical models to corresponding structures in their own bodies. The model of the eye is usually shown to pupils, as in A, with no relation to the head. If a teacher draws a face on oak tag and cuts out one of the eyes (B), he can show the relationship by holding the model behind the cut-out in the proper position. (From Patricia Birdsall, "Making an Eye Look Like an Eye," School Science and Mathematics, November, 1950).*

Using models effectively.   Pupils often may lack the type of background that makes interpretation of a model possible.

> Mr. Corbin purchased a cut-away model of a gasoline engine. As the flywheel of the model was turned, the pistons moved up and down, valves opened and closed, and lamps flashed to simulate the sparking of the plugs. Pupils were fascinated by the model and operated it whenever he would let them.
>
> A test given at the end of the unit, however, gave no better results than formerly. Mr. Corbin talked confidentially with some of the pupils who had failed the test and discovered that they still had no

true concept of pistons, cylinders, and crankshafts, and they were puzzled about the lights in the model. The following year, Mr. Corbin took the pupils to see an engine block in an auto supply store. He also replaced the lamps in the model with improvised spark plugs that sparked when an induction coil was used. His pupils now interpreted the model much more satisfactorily.

Similar problems of interpretation are apt to arise with the use of biological models, especially those that deal with microscopic sections.

For several years Mr. Arthur used a large model of a three-year-old woody plant stem without much success. One year he reversed his technique for introducing the model. He took the pupils on a field trip to collect specimens of one- and three-year-old saplings. Back in the laboratory the pupils compared sections of their specimens, summed up their observations, read about woody plant growth, and discussed their learnings. Only then did Mr. Arthur bring out the model. This time interest was high and pupils studied the model carefully.

Making models.   There are certain advantages to making models. One is the reduced cost; commercial models are generally expensive. Then too models may be made to fit specific situations; an earth science teacher may prepare a relief model of the area around the school, which he could not purchase from supply houses.

Probably the chief value of model making is the construction of models as special projects. The research necessary for the production of a good model adds greatly to the development of scientific concepts. The skills developed are generally worthwhile. And the satisfaction gained is invaluable in developing desirable attitudes.

Modeling clay has several uses in the biological and earth sciences. It may be used for figurines illustrating evolutionary development, for models of anatomical structures, and for illustrations of land forms. Plasticene, which comes in several colors, has similar uses, and the combination of two or more colors gives contrast and often increased realism.

Plaster of Paris is a versatile material. It gives sharp castings; it may be drilled, sawed, and sanded; it may be tinted and painted. It is excellent for permanent models, although it chips easily and requires careful handling and storage. It may be used for casting animal tracks found in mud, for making reproductions of small objects, and for reproducing objects in relief on plaques. Blocks of plaster are easily sculptured before the material has completely hardened.

Several plastics useful for modeling are marketed by scientific supply houses. These are relatively expensive but have special uses that make them worthy of consideration.

Mechanical models are usually made of wood and metal. Supplies of these materials and the tools needed to work with them should be a part of every science classroom. Construction kits of wooden and metal parts have innumerable uses; although sold as toys they are truly educational and deserve a place in the science program.

THE OVERHEAD PROJECTOR

In most schools, the overhead projector is a useful tool for the projection of transparencies which the teacher can prepare. The device is placed in front of the classroom where the teacher operates it while facing the class. The machine can be equipped with transparent sheets or rolls of plastic on which the teacher writes with a wax pencil as conveniently as writing on the blackboard. Wax pencils of different colors are used to obtain different effects. The writing can be erased easily so that the plastic sheets may be used over and over again.

Permanent transparencies for the projector are prepared in various ways. A ballpoint pen which will scratch the surface of the plastic sheet can be used. Special types of transparent inks for writing on plastic are available in various colors to produce different effects. Wax-coated clear plastic, on which material can be typewritten, may be purchased. Transparencies can be made from stencils of the mimeograph or by spirit duplication. Directions for making transparencies by using these methods are obtainable from various companies. (See Appendix.) Photocopy machines are able to produce transparencies directly on the plastic sheet. Material to be projected is typewritten or drawn on a sheet of paper and then run through a copy machine using clear plastic sheets. Many types of photocopy machines are available. Some have more advantages than others in the preparation of transparencies. A teacher should look into a number of different machines to determine which would be the most suitable for his purpose. (Consult Appendix.)

Another type of permanent transparency is called the overlay. These are made by drawing parts of a picture or diagram in different colors, or the same color, on different plastic sheets. As one section of the diagram is being viewed, another section which is on a different sheet is placed directly over the one being shown. In this way the teacher is able to construct a diagram or picture by placing one section on another as the material is being presented.

Transparencies can also be prepared which have the appearance of motion. This technique gives the impression of gears rotating, liquids flowing, and gases exploding. Information concerning this technique can be obtained from The American Optical Co., Charles Beseler Co., and others. (See Appendix.)

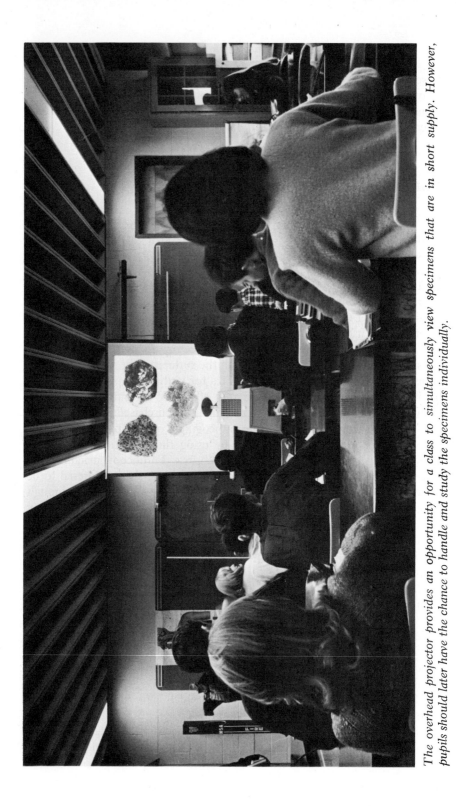

The overhead projector provides an opportunity for a class to simultaneously view specimens that are in short supply. However, pupils should later have the chance to handle and study the specimens individually.

A series of articles in the *Science Teacher* on the use of the overhead projector in the teaching of chemistry has been published. The first part of the series called "Tops in Chemistry" describes fourteen simple devices which can be made inexpensively by the teacher and which can be used to perform over 1000 different experiments viewed through the overhead projector. The articles describe how to convert projectors that are available in the school for vertical stage projection and how to prepare the demonstration material for projection. The techniques were developed for lecture demonstration purposes and were not meant to replace laboratory work.[1]

Because of the versatility of the overhead projector, and its potential in teaching science, it is advisable to contact the various suppliers to determine what equipment is available and what best serves the teacher's needs. Consult the Appendix for addresses of sources of materials, equipment, techniques, and guides for the production of materials and the utlization of the projector.

THE OPAQUE PROJECTOR

The opaque projector is the only type which can project opaque materials like flat pictures, book illustrations, raised models, and specimens. It can also be used to project pupils' work such as a dissection of an animal or a plant (overall thickness must be less than one-half inch).

The machine can project enlargements of drawings or diagrams so that they can be traced. In this case the picture or diagram is placed in the projector, focused on the chalkboard or poster board and traced.

Some teachers mount the pictures or diagrams on dark cardboard for filing. Rubber cement is not used to mount pictures because the heat produced causes the pictures to come loose. Mounted material is easily handled and classified.

The opaque projector has its limitations. The images produced are usually not sharp or defined. The room has to be absolutely dark for maximum image brightness which prevents the pupils from taking notes.

FILMSTRIPS AND SLIDES

Filmstrips and slides are not to be considered as feeble substitutes for motion pictures. They are unique teaching devices, having certain virtues

[1] Alyea, Hubert N., "Tested Overhead Projection Series," *The Science Teacher*, March, April, September, October, November, December, 1962.

as well as limitations of their own. The chief advantage of these devices is their versatility. The teacher can alter the time allotted to any scene, or series of scenes, as he wishes. He can spend one second or ten minutes on one picture, using it as a focal point for discussion, as a model for sketching or drawing some object, or as a basis for oral test questions. In addition, the teacher can turn back readily to any scene for reconsideration. In the case of slides he may present the pictures in any order and delete those that are inappropriate.

Filmstrips and slides, when compared with moving picture films, are relatively inexpensive, and the projectors are far less expensive. The projectors are so simple to operate that all pupils can use them, either helping the teacher make a presentation or making presentations of their own.

The limitations of slides and filmstrips as compared with motion pictures are fairly obvious and need no detailed discussion. They do not compel attention as does the constantly shifting action of a film. The lack of motion, however, is not so much a disadvantage as a difference that allows filmstrips and slides to fulfill different functions.

Using slides and filmstrips.   Filmstrips and series of slides may be presented in the same fashion as motion picture films. The pictures on filmstrips are arranged sequentially and they are often supplemented by captions that serve the same function as the narration of a sound film. Slides may be arranged sequentially and supplemented by oral remarks of the teacher. When slides and filmstrips are presented in this fashion, the same suggestions apply about preparation, showing, and follow-up as were given in the previous section on motion picture films.

Because of their versatility, slides and filmstrips may be used in several other ways, each with a specific purpose in mind. These visual aids may be tied in closely with other teaching procedures, perhaps to clarify a point.

> During a description of growth changes in bones, Mrs. Mooney projected a single slide showing X-ray photographs of the hands of a child and an adult.

A slide may make it possible to illustrate an application immediately after a principle has been developed.

> The physics class had completed several experiments relating weight and displacement of floating bodies. During the following discussion, Mr. Dixon projected a slide showing the Plimsoll marks on the side of a ship.

A few slides make possible comparisons that would otherwise be difficult.

The biology class had been shown calla lilies on a trip to a greenhouse in mid-winter, skunk cabbage blooms on a trip in late winter, and jack-in-the-pulpit blooms on a trip in early spring. To show that these plants are closely related, Mrs. Jorgenson projected slides of their flowers and called the attention of the pupils to the similarities of structure.

A slide may make an answer to an unexpected question much more meaningful.

John read in the newspaper that there was a good deal of sunspot activity on the sun at that time. "What's a sunspot?" he asked his science teacher.

The teacher found himself beginning a vague verbal description but then remembered that in his files were some slides showing photographs of sunspots. He took but a moment to locate one of the slides, slip it in the projector and give a description that was understandable to John and the other pupils.

Slides showing diagrams are more conveniently stored than charts, though they cannot be made available for pupil use for so long a time. Sometimes a diagram on a slide is available when a chart is not.

To help give an understanding of a cathode ray tube Mr. Meade photographed a cross-sectional diagram of one. During the study he had on his desk a television tube and an oscilloscope. On the screen behind him he projected the diagram. By making references to the television tube and to the diagram, his demonstrations of the oscilloscope were made more understandable.

Slides of tables and graphs may also be useful. If the teacher knows how to prepare his own slides he can present material specifically designed for his purposes.

Mr. Meade found that his pupils had difficulty doing problems on relative humidity because they could not determine the necessary constants from the saturation curves he provided for them. So he photographed a copy of the curves and projected it on the screen. As he worked out sample problems, he could show his pupils the exact procedures to be used in reading the curves.

Mention was made earlier in this chapter of the difficulty some pupils have in interpreting diagrams. There are various techniques for making a diagram more meaningful.

Mr. Templeton was helping his pupils understand the development of a cumulus cloud. He projected on a large sheet of white cardboard a slide of a landscape with a prominent cumulus cloud overhead. With a black crayon he traced the direction of the air currents, and the level at which condensation was taking place. When he turned off the projector the paper contained a diagram very similar to the one given in the textbook.

Slides can be used for giving directions when verbal directions, either oral or written, are inadequate.

Mr. Clemens found that many pupils misinterpreted or ignored the verbal directions he gave for dissections, so he made colored slides of each of the major steps. These were projected during the preliminary discussion of the directions. Then the corresponding slide was projected as pupils progressed through each stage.

Sometimes slides make excellent reviews. They may be used to review material presented through slides previously, in which case the same slides may be projected. Or they may be used to review material presented through first-hand experiences. The teacher who does his own photography has special advantages in that his slides can deal with the identical materials studied.

Field trips had been taken to see a number of topographic features caused by glaciation—kames, eskers, kettles, truncated spurs. On each trip Mr. Petty took colored slides of the things seen. During a review of the unit on glaciation, Mr. Petty projected the slides. The pupils identified the features and described their probable origin.

Slides may also be used for review tests in somewhat similar fashion.

A field trip to a nearby woodland introduced the pupils to a number of spring flowers. Mr. Mahon collected samples and put them on display. A week later he announced a test, asked the pupils to number their answer sheets from one to ten, and projected ten slides of wild flowers for the pupils to identify by name.

Pupils find slides and filmstrips useful when they are making reports on special investigations.

Susan and Joan chose to investigate the nesting habits of some common birds. They collected nests of some species but could not find materials to illustrate habits of nesting in cavities in trees, in tunnels in banks, and on the ground. Their teacher suggested they look at some *of his filmstrips. They found one that was suited to their needs. During their report they used both their actual materials and the filmstrip.*

Slides may be made available for individual study through the use of hand viewers. The slides may be studied as a follow-up of special interests or as part of a general assignment.

Mr. Burton gave to his earth science pupils sheets listing thir assignments. The assignments called for a number of different activities including the study of a set of slides of seacoast features. The pupils were to identify each of these features by reference to photographs and diagrams in their textbooks, and then find out how each feature originated.

Handmade slides give pupils opportunities to prepare their own visual aids for use in making special reports.

Four boys in the seventh grade volunteered to present a report on the possible origin of the earth. The reference they used described the planetesimal hypothesis in some detail with free use of diagrams. The boys copied some of the diagrams on specially etched glass slides and colored the diagrams with crayons designed for the purpose. They based their report on these slides.

Building a slide and filmstrip library.   The low cost of slides and filmstrips and the ease with which they may be stored makes it possible to develop a library that ranges widely in content and application. The immediate accessibility and the readiness with which they may be projected makes them of high value.

Filmstrips, compared with slides, are relatively inflexible. The pictures are arranged in a fixed sequence and supplemented by captions that present ideas according to a pattern devised by the producers. This makes it necessary for a teacher to evaluate filmstrips with special care. If he does not wish to present information as it is presented in the filmstrip, the strip becomes almost useless to him.

The philosophy of the producers is not always in accord with the accepted philosophies of science education. A number of filmstrips, for instance, are little more than reading lessons with the picture supplementing the captions and at times being merely decorative. Also these producers often use paintings rather than color photographs. Sometimes paintings have special value but generally photographs are much more accurate and infinitely more realistic.

Slides are available from many sources. The large slides are generally in black-and-white and include both photographs and excellent diagrams. The smaller slides are usually in color and are often made from photographs. Slides may be purchased individually or in sets, the latter at reduced rates. However, a set of slides may contain slides of little or no use to the teacher; if this is so, the actual cost of the useful slides may be higher than when purchased individually.

Making slides by photography.   The teacher who does his own photography has unlimited opportunities to build up his slide library. With a 35 millimeter camera the production of color slides is simple and relatively inexpensive. One need only follow the directions given on the packages of color film to produce successful pictures.

The purchase of a tripod and an inexpensive close-up lens enables a teacher to make close-up pictures of rocks, flowers, insects, leaves, and the like. He may also copy maps, topographic sheets, charts, diagrams, paintings, and colored slides. Books on photography give suggestions for this type of work.

Black-and-white slides may be made by printing negatives on positive film. One may also take photographs on direct positive films which upon development give positive transparencies. The Polaroid-Land camera produces black-and-white transparencies a few minutes after the picture has been taken.

Handmade slides.   Handmade slides enable teachers and pupils to prepare visual aid materials for special situations, and they represent a good medium of self expression for many pupils.

Several companies market kits containing the materials needed for slide making. The slides are invariably of the 3½ by 4 inch size, smaller sizes being difficult to work with. There are three basic types: cellophane slides, etched glass slides, and coated slides. Printed material may be typed directly on cellophane by the use of special carbon papers; these are bound between cover glasses for projection. With etched glass, line drawings may be made with a soft pencil and colored in with special crayons. Coated slides will take ink, thus giving sharper lines. The materials in each case are re-usable.

EDUCATIONAL FILMS

Educational films are used extensively and often indiscriminately in the classroom. Valuable though they may be within their limitations, they are more subject to abuse than any other type of audiovisual aid. Perhaps this is so because a film temporarily takes over the task of teaching; teachers come to feel that the film is an independent device that can operate successfully without effort on their part. Some educators have gone so far as to claim that the film can replace the teacher, perhaps envisioning schools as movie theaters supervised by projectionists.

Actually, films can do no more than supplement the work of the teacher. Experiences provided by films are severely limited. Films are designed for mass instruction and cannot provide for individual differences; they cannot give pupils practice in problem-solving.

Functions of educational films.   Motion pictures are most useful in the classroom for helping pupils gain new experiences, necessarily vicarious in nature. In addition, they have a few other limited uses—presenting problems, providing overviews, summarizing learnings, and reviewing material covered. Few films can be used for all these functions; many are suitable for one function only.

1. *Overviewing a unit.* A few films are well adapted for use at the beginning of a unit to show pupils what the possible content of the unit will be. These films are especially helpful to initiate teacher-pupil planning sessions, especially if they suggest methods of attack on problems. A film used for overview should deal with situations and materials familiar to the pupils because as yet the pupils have gained no formal background in the subject. The language should be non-technical for the same reason.

> Miss Cruickshank chose the film titled, "The Cell—Structural Unit of Life" to open a unit on cells. The action of the film starts with two boys making a stained slide of onion tissue which they view with a microscope. They then view slides of other tissues, both plant and animal. The only technical words used are "cell," "nucleus," and "protoplasm," each of which is carefully introduced.
>
> Following the showing, Miss Cruickshank asked for suggestions as to how the unit might proceed. One pupil suggested that they begin by making slides of onion tissue; the others voted for this approach. Then, feeling the need for more information about cells, they determined a general reading assignment by reference to the index in their textbook. The pupils decided to delay further planning until after they had used the microscopes and discovered some questions to be answered.

2. *Supplementing first-hand experiences.* The most important function of educational films should be to broaden understandings gained by experiments and by field work. However, many films are constructed to accomplish too many purposes and are superficial in consequence. There are good films but not as many as one could wish.

Early in the fall Miss Thompson took her seventh grade class on a field trip to collect milkweed caterpillars. These were brought back indoors and kept in suitable cages.

The pupils had opportunities to see the caterpillars eat and move about. They saw one caterpillar forming a chrysalis and they saw a butterfly after it had emerged. But they did not see the butterfly emerge and spread its wings; there were other details of transformation that they also missed.

Miss Thompson then presented a film titled, "The Monarch Butterfly." The pupils already had a background of experience and a vocabulary suitable for appreciating the film, and the film answered many of their questions.

3. *Setting problems.* Although most films attempt to give solutions to all the problems they raise, a few films are well adapted to problem setting. In general these films deal with situations familiar to pupils, calling attention to things the pupils have experienced and awakening their interest in them.

Mr. Chesney presented the film, "Story of a Storm," near the beginning of a unit on weather prediction. This film describes the passage of a typical cyclonic storm over a community, describing the advance indications of its coming, the development of the storm, and its concluding phases.

During the discussion that followed, the pupils compared the storm described in the film with storms they had experienced themselves. In attempting to summarize learning, arguments grew so heated that a reshowing was necessary to satisfy everyone. Many questions remained unanswered, however, and these were listed for further study. Among these questions were:

1. How fast does a storm move?

2. Why are cirrus clouds thinner than other clouds?

3. How low is the pressure in the center of a storm?

4. How can you tell when a cold front is coming?

5. What makes a storm start?

6. How does an aneroid barometer work?

These and other questions were used in the organization of the work of the unit.

4. *Summarization and review.* Most of the commercial educational films are best adapted for summarization and review purposes. This is because they tend to deal with broad topics in superficial fashion. This superficiality is no special handicap if the pupils have already had an

adequate experience background and have drawn limited conclusions in advance.

Preparing to use a film.   An activity that occupies fifteen or more minutes of class time should be carefully planned lest that time be wasted. Teachers tend to neglect planning for films because, unlike other activities, film showings present few discipline problems whether well planned or not. But class time is too valuable to be spent in an activity that provides only entertainment.

1. *Previewing the film.* The preview of a film indicates the best use to which the film may be put—whether it should open a unit, overviewing or setting problems, or whether it should be used later in the unit. From the preview the teacher may determine what preparation pupils need to benefit from viewing the film. He may decide upon preliminary experiences to be provided. He may list words that need careful introduction. He is able to decide upon follow-up activities that should come immediately after the showing.

2. *Using the manual.* Most educational films are accompanied by a manual that gives a synopsis of the film and usually suggests preliminary activities and follow-up activities. There is commonly a list of words to be studied and a list of suitable references. Teachers will find it useful to reread the manual in advance of later showings. The synopsis will refresh their minds about the contents of the film and the preparations needed, thus reducing the need for additional previewings.

3. *Making pupils ready for the showing.* Relatively few films should be used without preliminaries designed to make the viewing more meaningful to the pupils. Sometimes the pupils need first-hand experiences in advance in order to undersand the significance of what they see.

> Mr. Willis intended to use a film on the general subject of erosion, including an excellent section of animation showing the effects of frost action. To be sure that his pupils realized the expansion forces caused during freezing, Mr. Willis set up several days in advance an experiment showing the results of freezing a bottle of water in a mixture of salt and ice. He also encouraged his pupils to try the same experiment at home in their refrigerators.

Sometimes pupils need advance help with words. Technical words used in films commonly receive little or no special introduction but if pupils do not understand these words, they have difficulty interpreting the material in the film.

> Mrs. Meyers wished to use a film featuring some excellent animation describing the fertilization of ovules. However, the term "tube nu-

cleus," used by the narrator and as a label, would be unfamiliar to her pupils. Two days in advance of the showing she described the origin of the pollen tube and its function, introducing the term as she did so. The following day she reviewed the topic and the term. During the showing her pupils had no difficulty with the topic.

Sometimes pupils have never seen some of the materials shown in a film. They may have difficulty interpreting the pictures without help. The following technique was seen applied in an elementary classroom; there are times when it would be equally useful in science classes in the secondary school.

Miss Donahue was about to show a film describing conditions on some of the Pacific Islands. But first she displayed a coconut in its husk, some fragments of husk, some coconuts, and some palm fronds. She opened the coconuts to show the meat and the milk inside, and gave the pupils a little of each to taste. When the film was shown, the pupils were better able to appreciate the importance of the coconut to the inhabitants of the Islands.

To be truly effective, a film should help pupils solve problems of importance to them. One of the major advantages in having films always available is that they may be used whenever problems arise. However, rented films must be used during the short interval between arrival and required return. Sometimes the teacher can stimulate the thinking of his pupils enough to cause them to formulate problems.

A film describing experimental work with lightning in a high voltage laboratory became available unexpectedly. Mr. Fitch, the physics teacher, set apart a few minutes of class time for a consideration of lightning. His pupils raised a number of questions which he did not try to answer but which he asked the pupils to write down. He then set up the film projector and presented the film. Afterwards the pupils decided how many of the questions had been answered satisfactorily and which needed further investigation.

Sometimes teachers prepare a summary of a film and talk over with the pupils the nature of the film. Sometimes they list questions for the pupils to answer. There is some danger that these procedures will become formal and without challenge to the pupils. Much depends upon the nature of the topic of the film and the backgrounds of the pupils.

Showing a film.   It is important that the presentation of a film proceed smoothly. Much time can be wasted bringing the image into focus, adjusting the sound, and arranging the framing. Whenever possible, the projector should be set up and tested beforehand, perhaps between periods. Sometimes it may be set up while pupils are busy with other problems.

It is usually well to let the first showing of a film proceed without interruption. The pupils should be allowed to concentrate fully upon the new material being presented. After the first showing many questions may arise. An immediate reshowing may be desirable.

Reshowings at later times may be used to follow up discussions and may be used for review. For these reshowings pupils may list questions to be answered or points to be noted. During reshowings it may be desirable to turn off the sound while the teacher or a pupil calls attention to important points. With some projectors it is also possible to stop the machine and project a single frame for special discussion.

Follow-up activities. Much of the value of a film results from what is done about it after the showing. A discussion period should always be provided. During this time pupils are able to ask questions about points that puzzle them and to refer to related previous experiences. Because so many films end on a falsely positive note, pupils may not feel like asking questions. The teacher can stimulate discussions by asking a few questions about details given early in the film.

A short test using multiple-choice or true-false questions helps the pupils realize the extent and limitations of what they learned from the film. A discussion given after the test is often profitable. If problems have been listed, the discussion may center about how well the film helped solve them. A useful technique to be used occasionally is to conduct a review of the film, outlining the major points on the blackboard. Some teachers put this task in the hands of a temporary chairman and secretary.

If experiments have been described in the film and conclusions have been drawn from them, pupils should be encouraged to repeat these experiments to see if similar results are obtained.

> An advertising film showed some remarkable characteristics of heat-resistant glass. During the follow-up discussion the physics teacher mentioned casually that through photography such results could be faked. The pupils became suspicious immediately and wanted to carry out the experiments themselves.

Often certain phases of a film are not developed adequately because too much is attempted in the film. Attempts to follow up these topics may be more profitable than the viewing of the film itself.

> A film on the life histories of some lepidoptera referred briefly to a caterpillar which eats aphids. Some of the pupils recognized

immediately the unusualness of this habit and from their discussion came questions about other insects that are carnivorous. The teacher encouraged the pupils to plan an attack on this new problem.

Single concept films (film loops). Motion pictures are usually in the form of complete film productions. Within recent years, segments of complete film productions have become available. The so-called "film-clip" is a portion of a complete film production which can be used independently of the remainder of the entire production. Along this line, the short 8 mm single concept film which is packaged into its own cartridge has been developed. The film cartridge system requires no threading or rewinding. One simply inserts the cartridge in a slot of a special projector, and the machine is ready for use. The film can be used effectively for large and small groups and for individualized instruction.

Single concept films, both silent and sound, which are now on the market can be obtained for all areas of science—biology, chemistry, physics, and elementary science. The length of the films vary from thirty seconds to four or five minutes. Two or more cartridges are used for concepts which require more time.

A number of companies such as McGraw-Hill and Encyclopaedia Britannica are producing film loops in large numbers. Science Research Associates[2] has produced an entire Inquiry Development Program for junior high school science based on single concept films. This program is designed to help students formulate and test their own theories and hypotheses.

Selecting films for rental or purchase. The price of a film represents a substantial investment. Even rental charges add up rapidly. The selection of films demands careful consideration. All films should be previewed and, if possible, should be used at least once before purchase. Catalog descriptions and manufacturers' claims cannot always be trusted to give true pictures of films. A good method for becoming acquainted with a film is to obtain a copy from a renting agency; the decision to purchase is then based upon actual trials.

When possible, films should be previewed before renting. There are usually film showings at teachers' conferences and during summer session workshops. A card file of films listing titles and producers and commenting on general usefulness helps in choosing films for rent.

[2] Science Research Associates, Chicago, Illinois. The program has been developed by J. Richard Suchman. Materials available include materials kit, teachers' guides, student guides, and phonograph records of actual inquiry session.

One of the first things to consider is the general *usefulness of the film*. The teacher should decide how and if he can use it. Commonly a film may be too difficult or too elementary for the pupils who are to see it. Producers' claims about grade placement cannot always be trusted. It is also possible that the film cannot be related to the experiences of the pupils. Much of the film then becomes meaningless to them. Experience is the best guide in determining this characteristic of films.

A second point to be considered is *whether the film is worth the cost*. A film that merely describes experiments that the pupils could do in the classroom is certainly uneconomical. So too is a film that describes experiences the pupils have already had so often as to need no review. A film based on lengthy classroom discussion is apt to be of little worth.

A film may contain sections of valuable animation, time-lapse photography, or other special features. If, however, these take up but a small percent of the total footage, the remainder being easily duplicated in the classroom, the film under consideration becomes very expensive.

Color in films is often effective and sometimes absolutely necessary for the development of the content of the film. It is also expensive. If color adds nothing to a film except attractiveness, black-and-white films might better be purchased.

Sound has come to be accepted as a great asset to educational films. True, sound films have great potentials but they are rarely utilized. Few films use synchronized sound. Sound effects are occasionally dubbed in. Generally, however, the sound track is used only for the voice of a narrator who gives a running commentary on what is essentially a silent film. The narration is frequently not so useful as the teacher's own remarks, and some teachers simply turn off the sound and make their own comments.

A third point to be considered is the *technical quality of the film*. The pictures should be sharp and distinct. If there is color, the colors should be true; many copies are pale or lean heavily to the red end of the spectrum. The sound should be of good quality, with the narrator's voice distinct and understandable.

A fourth point to be considered is the *accuracy of the film*. Errors of fact often creep into films. Even when there are no errors there may be misleading ideas. The makers of a film are sometimes lacking in the scientific attitude and present theories as facts, draw conclusions from limited evidence, or make sweeping generalizations that cannot be justified. These weaknesses seriously impair the usefulness of a film.

Amateur films.   Amateur films have the special advantage of being able to deal with local situations. Pupils have heightened interest and they quickly see the applications of the points made. The imperfections which are almost inevitable do not always detract from films and sometimes give it a more personal touch.

In the production of an amateur film the best procedure is to start with writing a script. Because the film is silent, the script is merely a description of the desired scenes and of the needed subtitles. The scenes are numbered for convenience.

Then photography begins. Scenes are not necessarily shot in the order given in the script, but rather as is convenient. For instance, all close-ups of maps, posters and the like might be done at once so that the camera need be set up only once for this type of work. If, during the photography of the required scenes, unexpected opportunities for unusual scenes present themselves, these too are photographed. Later the script will be rewritten to include these scenes.

After the photography is completed and the film developed, some rephotographing may be needed to replace scenes that do not show up well. When all the scenes are satisfactory, the scenes are cut apart and spliced together in the order of the script. Titles and end matter are added. The film is now complete, faulty perhaps in places and obviously amateur work, but often far more valuable than a corresponding commercial film.

> Mr. Jordan, a science teacher in a New England community, produced a film on the manufacture of maple syrup. Some of the scenes he shot while on field trips with his pupils. Some he took during special visits to local farms.

A film written, directed, and produced by the pupils themselves has double value, partly from the teaching value of the film and partly from the experiences the pupils gain while producing it.

> A science class in Greenwich, Connecticut, produced a film on the local water supply. The pupils carried out the needed research, wrote the script, planned the shooting schedule, and acted in many of the scenes. The school board supplied the film. One of the teachers did the camera work. The result was an attractive, informative film that was very useful in all science classes in the system.

RECORDS AND TAPE RECORDINGS

At present there is only a limited library of records that reproduce natural sounds such as waves on a beach, jet planes, and frog calls. The most successful of these have been the recordings of bird calls and songs.

Teachers use the latter to help pupils learn to identify birds by their songs. Ordinarily they play the records and at the same time project pictures of the corresponding birds on a screen to enable pupils to associate both sound and sight. Undoubtedly this technique could be used for other recordings.

Recordings of musical instruments may be used in science classes to study changes in pitch and the quality of sounds produced by different types of vibrating materials. For physics students there are records designed to help test the fidelity of phonographic equipment; such testing helps pupils develop understandings of the characteristics of sound.

Many musical masterpieces are based upon the sounds of nature. Perhaps these could be used more in the science program to add to the interest of the subject and to the meaningfulness of music. For instance, the section depicting a storm in Rossini's *William Tell Overture* could be compared with the sounds of a real thunderstorm and its sequence analyzed.

The portable tape recorder is a versatile machine that enables one to pick up sounds almost anywhere and reproduce them at will. Science teachers can make good use of them.

> Mr. Bradshaw, a student teacher, was teaching a unit on weather to an eighth grade. To emphasize the west to east movement of storm fronts in the region, he took tape recordings of the "Weather Round Up" of the New York State Rural Radio Network. Stations beginning at Buffalo and ending at Albany reported on the local weather. If a front was passing over the state there were marked differences in weather to the east and the west of the front. Soon Mr. Bradshaw had a number of good examples to play to his pupils.

Some of the best science broadcasts are given evenings or weekends. Even when these are broadcast during the school day the number of pupils who can listen to them is limited. Tape recordings made of these broadcasts can be played over and over.

The pupils in one science class can produce a radio program or a play which is then recorded and played to other sections. Pupils gain practice in language arts in the process. Some elementary teachers have sent their tape recordings to pupils in distant schools with whom they have correspondence. Perhaps this would be an interesting project for science clubs.

Tapes are easily edited; portions can be clipped out with a razor blade and the ends spliced with cellulose tape. Or the tape may be cut apart and another section spliced in. Editing gives the tapes additional versatility.

> Mr. Wilson wanted to play the songs of a limited number of birds. He prepared a tape recording from all his records and cut out the sections

that he wanted. These he spliced together in the order he thought most useful.

Later for review and testing, he prepared a similar tape, this time without the announcer's voice naming the birds.

RADIO IN THE CLASSROOM

Radio in the short space of about forty years has grown into a teaching tool which should find its way into every classroom. A number of important qualities of radio make it an important tool. It is inexpensive, and the students become emotionally involved in real live broadcasts. The terse description of an atomic explosion, the report from the center of a hurricane, and the words of a spaceman miles above the earth are experiences of tremendous value.

Radio schools of the air have been refined and improved over the past few years. The Empire State School of the Air in New York State, Wisconsin School of the Air, Minnesota School Broadcast Service, Indiana School of the Sky, and the Ohio School of the Air are among the many radio networks broadcasting programs for in-school listening. The majority of the programs are produced by school systems and are on a variety of subject areas.

An interesting and recent innovation is found in the University of Wisconsin's radio-vision project. Radio-vision is a method of using the strengths of an expert radio teacher and a well-planned and developed series of film strips. The film strips are sent to the participating teachers well in advance of the radio broadcast. These are projected in the classroom at certain times during the radio broadcast. "How-to-do-it" explanations are made verbally and visually.

Another example of how radio broadcast lessons can be used in the classroom is in St. Louis, Missouri. In this case, science lessons are prepared by script writers, teachers and other experts. The classroom teacher gathers the science materials which are needed in association with the broadcasts and uses them while the lesson is being broadcast.

TELEVISION

Television has developed very rapidly since 1960. In this short span of time it has become a valuable classroom tool.

Learning experiences not normally available in the classroom can be provided through television. Television can be valuable as a supplement to classroom work.

Television has a number of advantages for classroom use. Pupils can hear and view events as they are happening. The programs or events can be viewed by an unlimited number of pupils in many classrooms at the same time. Closed-circuit television permits the use of all types of audiovisual materials without losing the personal contact with pupils. Closed-circuit television has a tremendous range of uses including the magnification of devices, specimens, and other materials, and can even be a foundation for an entire science course.

There are three types of television: commercial television, educational television, and instructional television. Programs of scientific interest are sometimes broadcast on commercial television stations, but most of them are transmitted when school is not in session. Commercial television is a relatively unimportant classroom tool in comparison to the other types. Educational television concerns certain stations which broadcast on a special frequency specified by the Federal Communications Commission

(F.C.C.). These stations produce programs of special interest to children and adults on a variety of topics including science. Some presentations are correlated with school curriculums; others can be used to supplement courses of study. Courses for credit and in-school instruction are but a few types of broadcasts which are being transmitted by educational television stations. Commercial and Educational television are broadcast on open-circuit systems whose range covers an area of 40–50 miles. Instructional television programs can be transmitted by open systems or in some cases through a closed-circuit system. Closed-circuit television is limited to a small geographical area and does not require a license from the F.C.C. The system may be installed in a single classroom or in a number of classrooms within a school or school system. Several channels can be utilized simultaneously to permit a number of broadcasts to be transmitted at the same time.

Closed-circuit television installed in individual classrooms does not necessarily involve an excessive expenditure and has a number of important uses. The installation can be used in the classroom to enlarge small items used during a demonstration which is taking place in the front part of the room. Monitors are placed in advantageous parts of the room for optimum viewing—front, back, sides and at various levels so that the pupils can see what is taking place at the demonstration table. For example, a dissecton of the eye of a calf or of a frog performed at the demonstration table can be viewed in detail by all pupils as it is taking place. Microscope attachments are available so that the equipment can be used as a micro-projector.

The problems of teaching science to a large number of pupils either in a single classroom or in many classrooms can be overcome by using closed circuit television. Hassur[3] has cited a number of examples of the use of television to improve science instruction:

Biology: In the study of human physiology the television unit was used to demonstrate the use of a standard sphygmomanometer in measuring blood pressure. Close-ups of the equipment and in the method of attaching the cuff to the patient were effectively shown. A special microphone was attached to the stethoscope used by the instructor, which enabled the students to see the pressure change on the manometer and also to hear the change in the sound of the pulsebeat when the diastolic and systolic pressures were reached.

Every one of the students in the large lecture hall could actually record the blood pressure of the subject as if they were taking it themselves. Normally when working with small groups this same exercise requires an hour or

[3] In Diamond, Robert M. ed., *A Guide to Instructional Television,* McGraw-Hill Book Co., New York, 1964. Mr. Hassur is a Professor of Science Education at San Jose State College, San Jose, California.

more for the instructor, each student sharing a number of expensive instruments. With television, less than fifteen minutes is required.

Physiology. An area in the field of physiology in which the television system was found to be very helpful was a demonstration of the techniques for typing human blood. The television camera was used for close-ups of the microscope slide preparation. Then the camera was coupled with a standard microscope with extra bright substage illumination. In this way the students got a laboratory-technician's-eye view of the clotting of blood in response to the testing serums. The student response was overwhelming. Actually seeing the blood cells clotting was much more effective than all the blackboard and flannelgraph diagrams in the world.

Physical sciences. The effect of the temperature of a solvent on the dissolving rate of a solid was very effectively shown by the television system. A closeup was shown of two labeled breakers, one of hot and the other of room-temperature water. Sugar cubes were added, and students could time the rate of breakdown and solution of the sugar in each container.

To demonstrate single-replacement reactions in chemistry usually calls for a large-scale operation with great quantities of solutions. Using the television system, on the other hand, standard, even semimicro, glassware is sufficient. Adding a coil of copper wire to a crystal-clear solution of silver nitrate produces in a few minutes mounds of white mossy silver forming on the wire as the entire solution darkens with copper nitrate.

Physics. In the field of physics the television system makes possible many demonstrations which would normally be far too small to be attempted in a large lecture hall. These include a study of the air currents around a candle flame in a convection box. Dense smoke introduced into the system could be seen to rise above the candle as cooler air laden with smoke rushed in from all sides to take its place.

Televising the oscilloscope trace of a sound which the students can also hear is an easy way of showing the relationships between its frequency and pitch and the amplitude and volume of sounds.

The presentation of Ohm's law, a basic concept of electricity, to large groups of students is more easily done by utilizing the magnification potential of the single-room television system. Using a simple resistance board and inexpensive laboratory-type meters, students can easily record, by means of television, sufficient data to derive the equation for Ohm's law. This same technique would be nearly impossible without television; that is, unless huge, very expensive demonstration meters, visible from the back of the room, were available for use.

Climatology. In the study of weather perhaps the most difficult area of instruction is the construction of weather maps and their use in weather prediction. Using television as an opaque projector, weather maps—isobars, fronts, and all—can be constructed, starting with a blank weather map. Of course this can also be done with transparencies on an overhead projector. Where television really has the advantage is that the latest weather map, hot off the presses, can be placed in front of the camera, and each student can examine it under the direction of the instructor's pointer. Transparencies for the opaque projector, on the other hand, take some time to prepare.

Closed circuit television has its limitations. A teacher who uses this tool must prepare materials well enough in advance so they can be pretested. This requires a great amount of time. Much experimentation has to take place before one can use instruments like a microscope or other shiny materials which require special lighting. Special training is required to use closed-circuit television effectively. Training is needed to learn lighting techniques, lens selection, and proper camera angles.

VIDEO-TAPE RECORDINGS

Equipment is now on the market which is capable of recording both the audio and visual parts of a television broadcast. This equipment, called a video-tape recorder, can be a useful aid to classroom instruction.

Video-tape recorders make it possible to record programs of educational value for future use. These programs can be shown by the teacher at a time when it is most relevant to the instructional program. For example, many national networks transmit science documentaries during a time when classes are not in session. These documentaries when taped and later shown to the class could be the basis for a science lesson.

Lectures by visiting scientists presented to a class can be recorded, stored and then shown to similar classes in the years following. Copies of the tape can also be made for distribution within the entire school district.

There are a number of others uses for video-tape recordings. Pupil demonstrations, reports, seminars, science lessons, and other presentations can be taped and presented as examples to pupils in succeeding classes.

Video-tape equipment can also function as a closed-circuit television unit. The equipment does not have to record which makes it more versatile than ordinary closed circuit installations.

AUTO-INSTRUCTIONAL APPROACHES

Much has been written in recent years about self-instructional approaches to learning. These approaches are often called "programmed learning," a controversial term because all formal instruction is programmed in one sense or another. The term "teaching machines" is also sometimes used synonymously with auto-instruction, but it is better to limit the term to the mechanical devices used.

Auto-instruction is not new. Several programs of the 1920's, such as the "Dalton Plan" and the "Winnetka Plan," experimented with self-instructional methods. A self-teaching machine for use with multiple-choice tests was described by Pressey as early as 1926. Many other devices, such as flash cards and programmed workbooks, can be classified as teaching machines in use for half a century or more.

However, the auto-instructional methods being devised today are based upon comparatively recent findings in the laboratories of experimental psychologists. These methods promise significant results if used wisely and with full knowledge of their limitations.

Principles of reinforcement. Experimental biologists have learned to shape the behavior of many animals almost at will. Simply by presenting food to a hungry animal at the right time, three or four consistent responses can be developed within a short period. Extremely complex performances can be attained by successive stages, reinforcements being changed progressively in the direction of the desired behavior. Furthermore, psychologists have learned to maintain patterns of behavior throughout the life of an organism merely by providing a suitable schedule of reinforcements.

Flushed from their successes in animal laboratories, experimental psychologists have looked at classroom procedures with dismay. They point out that positive reinforcements are few and far between and often too late to be effective.[4] Educational control remains chiefly averse in character, with pupils seeking to avoid the displeasure of teachers and parents, the ridicule of classmates, low grades, and poor showing in competitions.

These psychologists explain that the content of a program should be broken up into tiny bits to be mastered first singly and then in combinations, with immediate reinforcements for correct responses and a schedule of reinforcements to maintain the correct responses. However, science teachers should realize that these psychologists are usually discussing elementary arithmetic, spelling, or foreign languages in which responses are labeled right or wrong. The present stage of our knowledge in science does not permit so ready a classification of answers, and there is no evidence that computer-type responses should be the ultimate goal of the science program.

[4] Skinner, B. F., "The Science of Learning and the Art of Teaching," *Harvard Educational Review,* 24:86–97, 1954.

The nature of programmed instruction.

By programmed instruction we mean the kind of learning experience in which a "program" takes the place of a tutor for the student and leads him through a set of specified behaviors designed and sequenced to make it more probable that he will behave in a given desired way in the future; in other words, that he will learn what the program is designed to teach him.[5]

Educational psychologists believe that the best learning environment is one in which five factors are operative:

1. The learner is active.
2. The learner gets frequent aid and feedback on his performance.
3. Learning proceeds gradually from the less complex toward the more complex in an orderly fashion.
4. The learner is allowed to develop his own best pace of learning.
5. The teacher's strategies are constantly reappraised on the basis of an objective analysis of the learner's activity.[6]

One group of professional programmers believe that they can provide such an ideal environment through

(1) an ordered sequence of stimulus items, (2) to each of which a student responds in some specified way, (3) his responses being reinforced by immediate knowledge of results, so that he moves by small steps, (4) therefore making few errors and practicing mostly correct responses, (5) from what he knows, by a process of successively closer approximation toward what he is supposed to learn from the program.[7]

An example of the above type is reproduced in Figure 20. Notice the sequential arrangement of the material and the nature of the content.[8]
Another type of organization for programmed instruction has a branching pattern. Here, the responses are used as a test to determine whether the student has grasped the essential point of passage of the text. If the student selects the incorrect response to a multiple-choice item, he is referred to a section of the program where a number of remedial items can

---

[5] Schramm, Wilbur, *Programmed Instruction: Today and Tomorrow*, The Fund for the Advancement of Education, November, 1962, p. 1.

[6] Komoski, Kenneth, "Programmed Instruction: "A Prologue to What?" *Phi Delta Kappan*, 44:292, 1963.

[7] Schramm, *op. cit.*, p. 2.

[8] See Appendix for addresses of commercial firms involved in producing programmed materials and hardware.

11 | In the center of an atom is the nucleus (NEW-klee-us).

The arrow points to the _____ .

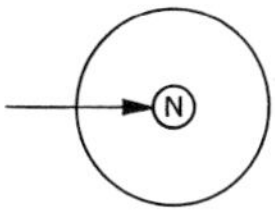

nucleus

12 | A molecule is composed of _____ .

atoms

13 | The plural of nucleus is nuclei (NEW-klee-eye). When we speak of more than one nucleus, we call them _____ .

nuclei

14 | The nucleus contains a number of particles called protons.

This nucleus has 2 _____ .

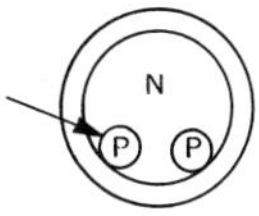

protons

15 | The protons are found in the ═══════════════

nucleus of an atom

3

Figure 20.   *An example of programmed instruction* (courtesy Teaching Machines, Inc., Albuquerque, N. M., 1961).

be found. After successfully completing the remedial items, the student is brought back into the sequential order of the programmed material.

Advantages and disadvantages of programmed instruction.   The advantages of programmed instruction can include the following:

1. More effective presentation of subject.
2. More efficient presentation of subject.
3. More adaptable to rate of learning of students of different abilities.
4. Immediate feedback of results to the learner.
5. Greater range of courses can be offered in the school.
6. More efficient utilization of teacher time.

The courses of study in science already programmed seemed to be concerned chiefly with subject matter outcomes, these being verbal in nature. Techniques have not been devised as yet for attaining the broad goals of science education. Therefore a teacher should be cautious in employing programmed materials. Teachers could, however, use segments of programmed courses to supplement other classroom procedures.

Example of a linear program.   Below is an example of a linear program which is based on Skinner's plan of recognition or recall of information.

PROGRAM S-63: ENERGY RELATIONSHIPS, PART II*

In an earlier Program you and a woman pushed a sports car up a hill. Both of you were energy-containing systems. What kind of energy did you have? Where did it come from? When the stored energy in your systems was spent, how could it be restored?

A human being or any other organism uses chemical energy. Chemical energy differs from the position energy of the car-hill relationship (system), but, as you recall, they are both forms of stored energy.

Stored energy may be available because of the position of one object in relation to another object, such as the position of the car in relation to the hill.

Molecules in your body have energy. Molecules are made up of atoms joined together in a definite pattern. When the pattern of atoms is changed so that new molecules are formed, which may involve a loss or gain of atoms by the molecule, energy may be stored or released.

It would be difficult to have all the molecules in your body "sitting on a hill" in order for them to have stored energy. However, because they are made of atoms joined together they can have stored chemical energy.

	1. The energy contained in a molecule is a result of the joined atoms. Thus, two atoms together such as carbon and hydrogen (C-H) have chemical energy because they are _____ together.
joined	2. The relationship of one atom to another in a molecule can be a source of (stored/radiant) _____ energy.
stored	3. The form of stored energy available because the *atoms* are joined together is _____ energy.
chemical	4. Carbon and hydrogen in their form (C-H) have chemical energy because their atoms (are/are not) _____ joined together.
are	5. Chemical energy of the molecule can be changed to other forms of energy *if* the connection between the _____ _____ is broken and new connections are formed.
atoms	6. Often, something is needed to break the connections between the atoms. Shall we try to (heat/cool) _____ the connection in order to break it?
Let us try heating.	7. By heating the molecule, a few connections between the atoms can be broken. (Go on to the next frame.)
* * *	8. As a result, the chemical energy can be changed from stored to (active/inactive) _____ energy.
active	9. A common example of this process is combustion, or burning. The small flame of a match or a spark (cannot/can) _____ start a fire and the breakup of the molecules. Note that parts of the fuel must recombine with oxygen in this reaction.
can	10. The small flame of the match starts the breakup of the molecules. The roaring flame continues until no more _____ _____ break up and no new ones are formed.

molecules	11. In the case of the fire, the change from chemical to heat and light energy was caused by the movement of the atoms in the molecules. This movement of atoms and the breaking of the connections is associated with (heating/cooling) _____.
heating	12. Heat is used to start a fire, and the fire produces more heat as more and more of the _____ between atoms in the molecules are broken and new connections are formed.
connections	13. However, in living cells, heat is not used to give the breakdown reaction of a molecule its start. ENZYMES are used instead. (Go on to the next frame.)
* * *	14. The energy used by a living organism is obtained by enzymes helping to break the _____ between the atoms of a molecule.
connections	15. Heat is not used to start the process within the living cell. Instead, _____ help the connections to break and new ones to form.
enzymes	16. There are several advantages in using enzymes. One of them is that *some* of the chemical energy can be kept in the form of chemical energy rather than changed to *other* _____ of energy.
forms or kinds	17. When enzymes control the release of chemical energy from a molecule, some of the energy released is heat; but some of it is _____ energy.
chemical	18. The chemical energy released by enzyme action is used by cells for work. Two kinds of work accomplished by your body are 1. contraction of muscle cells and 2. secretion by gland cells. Copy the statements from above that describe the two kinds of work accomplished by the cells when enzymes change chemical energy. 1. _____. 2. _____.

* Biological Sciences Curriculum Study, Biological Science: *Patterns and Processes,* Holt, Rinehart and Winston, New York, 1966.

TEACHING MACHINES

Teaching machines are designed to provide immediate reinforcements at a rate impossible for the classroom teacher. The machine asks a question, the pupil replies, and the machine either announces that the answer is correct or gives the correct answer for comparison.

Teaching machines are not necessarily complex devices. A pack of flash cards with answers given on the reverse sides represents a simple machine. The cards are usually in random order and so the machine is not programmed. However, the user can program it crudely by replacing cards with questions answered incorrectly at the rear end of the pack and cards with questions answered correctly at the far end.

There is some divergence of opinion about the design of teaching machines. Some designers ask multiple-choice questions; others ask pupils to write down their answers. Obviously the design of the machine depends upon the type of question asked, but no one seems to have investigated the type of learning that results, whether on the recognition level or the recall level.

Developments in teaching machines have occurred at a rapid rate. The more sophisticated types provide for re-teaching if errors are made and for by-passing simple material if competence is indicated. Electronic computers are employed in some of the more advanced machines, but obviously these machines will not make their way into secondary schools for some time.[9]

Fry[10] has cited a number of specific characteristics of teaching machines which make them useful in the learning process.

1. Provide immediate student knowledge of correctness of his response.
2. Offer opportunity for the student to try again until a correct response is obtained.
3. Prevent students in most cases, from progressing until the correct response is made.
4. Provide the correct response before moving on to the next questions or problem based upon the student's last impressions.
5. Indicate the number of incorrect responses preceding the correct response.

[9] Use of computer assisted instruction (CAI) in science is being developed at the Department of Science Education, Florida State University at Tallahassee, Florida. Programmed text material is of the linear form. The computer program has been prepared to match the text and a laboratory program is associated with the course.

[10] Fry, Edward, "Teaching Machine: The Coming Automation," *Phi Delta Kappan*, vol. 62:28–31, 1959.

6. Enable the student to proceed at his own pace—however slow or fast this may be.

INSTRUCTIONAL KITS

The combination of the teaching machine and other instructional media is producing a trend towards the production of instructional kits for a course of study. These are self-contained units which make use of programmed materials, teaching machines (computer or other types) 8 mm cartridge type projectors, tape recorders, 2 × 2 slide projectors, and science materials.

The teacher who uses this type of auto-tutorial system will not necessarily be involved in designing a course of study. Most likely, he will be responsible for implementing the system. He will have to organize the materials, handle the equipment and scheduling.

An auto-tutorial system set up at Syracuse University for a freshman course in biology has proved successful and has implications in teaching high school science.[11]

A specially designed area which contains a number of study booths is available for the course. Each booth is equipped with its own tape recorder, an 8mm film loop projector, a microscope, microscope specimens, and other materials. Materials which are large or difficult to handle or too expensive to purchase in quantity are placed on a table located in the area. The lectures and laboratory instructions are taped. These tapes include assignments for homework, laboratory procedures, directions for handling specimens, directions for viewing material under the microscope and procedures for an experiment. The students "sign up" for a three-hour period any time during the week. The area is open between 8 A.M. and 10 P.M., and an instructor is always available for advice and help. A weekly seminar session is held by the instructors of the course. Problems which arose the week before are discussed. Discussions are also conducted on topics pertinent to the week's work during this seminar period.

An informal evaluation of the course shows that students prefer this approach to old systems. Better grades are also earned by students through this system in comprison to grades obtained in traditional courses.

Postlethwait[12,13] has evaluated an auto-tutorial course in botany

[11] Personal communication from Dr. Marvin Druger, Associate Professor of Science Education and Zoology, Syracuse University, Syracuse, N.Y.

[12] Postlethwait, S. N., "A System's Approach to Botany," *Audiovisual Instruction*, vol. 8, April, 1963 p. 244.

[13] Postlethwait, S.N., "Audio-Tutoring, A Practical Solution of Independent Study," *Medical and Biological Illustration*, London, July, 1965, p. 187.

Specially designed areas which contain a number of study booths or carrels are made available in many schools to facilitate independent study programs.

offered at Purdue University. He cites a number of advantages of the system:

1. There is more student contact with instructors than through traditional approaches.
2. Students can work at their own rate. This takes care of a wide range of student abilities in a class.
3. Students can take tests whenever they feel they are prepared.
4. More material is learned through this system in a shorter amount of time than through traditional courses.
5. Students have an opportunity for reinforcement. They can repeat what they do not understand.
6. Students earn better grades through this approach than through traditional approaches.
7. A large number of students can be handled in a relatively small area.

Courses of the auto-tutorial type permit pupils to work at their own rate. They allow for individual differences. The bright students are not held up and the slow students can work at their own levels of competence and abilities. A student doing work at his own rate can gain a great deal of self-confidence as well as a feeling of accomplishment.

Before embarking on courses using this approach teachers should consider the type of facilities which are needed to do the job well. The facilities must be flexible enough to allow all kinds of activities to be happening at the same time. Testing, program taking, projecting films or slides, experimental work are but a few of the kinds of activities which could be taking place in the facility devoted to auto-tutorial work. Proper storage facilities should be adjacent to the work area so that pupils have access to equipment and materials as they are needed.

Before adopting an auto-tutorial course, teachers should carefully weigh the merits of such a course over classroom instruction. Careful consideration should be given to objectives of instruction. Well planned auto-tutorial courses place emphasis on "learning behaviors" rather than subject matter objectives.

SUGGESTED ACTIVITIES

1. Begin a file of flat pictures.
2. Prepare an attractive and meaningful bulletin board display. Submit it to the criticism of others in your science methods class.
3. Plan a lesson which is centered around materials prepared for use with an overhead projector.

4. Practice using the chalkboard effectively, including the making of diagrams, straight writing, and printing.

5. Assume that you are to show a class a filmstrip or set of slides. Write out the comments you would make for each frame in the strip. Present this to the methods class.

6. Analyze a motion picture film carefully to determine the length of the portions that (1) duplicate or review experiences pupils have already had, (2) provide experiences that could well be provided at first-hand by the teacher, and (3) provide experiences that could not well be provided otherwise. Using the total cost of the film, determine the cost-per-foot of the portion that justifies its purchase. Compare several films on this basis.

7. Study a film carefully and make plans to use it wisely, with provisions for whatever background (including first-hand experiences) is needed for its interpretation and follow-up activities to add to the effectiveness of the film.

8. Examine in detail a course which has been programmed for use with a teaching machine. What science teaching objectives can the programmed course fulfill?

9. Compare an auto-tutorial course using instructional kits with a traditional course. The comparison should include the types of objectives involved for each approach as well as the outcomes expected.

SUGGESTED READINGS

Alyea, Hubert N., "Tested Overhead Projection Series," *The Science Teacher*, March, April, September, October, November, December, 1962.

The Audio Visual Equipment Directory, National Audio Visual Association, Fairfax, Virginia, published yearly.

Brown, James W., Richard B. Lewis, and Fred F. Harcleroad, *A-V Instruction, Materials and Methods*, 2nd edition, McGraw-Hill Book Company, New York, 1964.

———, *A-V Instructional Materials Manual*, 2nd edition, McGraw-Hill Book Company, New York, 1964.

DeKeiffer, Robert E., *Audio Visual Instruction*, The Center for Applied Research in Education, Inc., New York, 1965.

———, *Manual of Audio-Visual Techniques*, 2nd edition, Prentice Hall, Englewood Cliffs, N. J., 1962.

Diamond, Robert M. (ed.), *A Guide to Instructional Television*, McGraw-Hill Book Co., New York, 1964.

Erickson, Carlton W. H., *Fundamentals of Teaching with Audio-visual Technology*, Macmillan Company, New York, 1965.

Horkheimer, Mary Foley, and John W. Diffor (eds.), *Educators Guide to Free Films*, 26th edition, Educators Progress Service, Randolph, Wisconsin, 1966.

————, *Educators Guide to Free Filmstrips*, 18th annual edition, Educators Progress Service, Randolph, Wisconsin, 1966.

Kemp, Jerrold E., *Planning and Producing Audio-Visual Materials*, Chandler Publishing Company, San Francisco, California, 1963.

Minor, Ed., *Simplified Techniques for Preparing Visual Instructional Materials*, McGraw-Hill Book Company, New York, 1962.

Sanderson, R. T., *Teaching Chemistry with Models*, D. Van Nostrand Company, Princeton, N. J., 1962.

Vrana, R. S. "Filmstrip Projectors for Science Experiments," *Educational Screen and Audiovisual Guide*, 41:658–9, November, 1962.

Wittich, Walter Arns, and Charles Francis Schuller, *Audio-Visual Materials, Their Nature and Use*, 4th edition, Harper & Row, New York, 1967.

Chapter 9

Science Textbooks, Notebooks,

and Workbooks

THE TEXTBOOK IS THE MOST WIDELY USED OF ALL TEACHING INSTRUMENTS, not excepting the teacher's own oral presentations. Indeed, the textbook is almost synonymous with schooling. Few teachers attempt a program without one and many administrators require that one be used. Student notebooks are likewise well established teaching devices and in widespread use save where replaced by their printed equivalents, workbooks.

Any devices used as extensively as these are certain to be misused on occasion and to be the subject of harsh criticism in consequence. But the criticism should be leveled at the way they are used rather than at the devices themselves because each has certain merits that makes it useful in the science program.

These devices may also be overused. It is important to remember that textbooks, notebooks, and workbooks are but three of the many tools available to the science teacher. There is no justification for allowing one to dominate the program. Over-dependence upon the textbook, for instance, limits the program to the advantages possessed by the text and excludes the advantages unique for experiments, films, and projects. Well-balanced utilization of all the tools of science teaching gives pupils the advantages of each.

SCIENCE TEXTBOOKS

The concept of the textbook has changed greatly in the last century. Once used chiefly as a source of information, the textbook has today become a course of study, a set of unit plans, and a learning guide as well. Once employed most commonly in the textbook-recitation method, it is today employed in many other and more stimulating ways.

Structure and function of a science textbook.   The modern science text is a complex publication. Its characteristics can be discovered only by careful study and by classroom use. The present-day textbook is usually divided into sections which are roughly analogous to chapters. But these sections are more than chapters, they are unit plans built around specific topics. Thus a textbook becomes a course of study which may be used in its entirety or with such additions and deletions as a teacher may wish to make.

The book invariably begins with an introductory section that may overview the contents of the book, attempt to define science, describe the scientific method, and illustrate the scientific attitude. Thus the book attempts to set the stage for the year's program.

Each section or unit opens with provision for some activity that prepares the pupils for the work to follow. This might be a pretest to acquaint pupils with the extent of their knowledge. It may be a recall of past experiences to establish the foundation upon which later learnings will be built or a brief historical background to show the developments that have led up to present knowledge. It may be a discussion designed to establish problems for the pupils to solve.

The body of each section more closely resembles the body of a typical chapter. It provides printed information and is supplemented by photographs and drawings. Captions given with the illustrations may be informative; they may suggest ways to study the illustrations, or they may ask questions about them. Textbooks commonly include in the body of each section many suggestions for supplementary activities: experiments, demonstrations, readings, and the like. These are tied in closely with the printed matter.

Each unit ends with at least one special feature. There are always questions for self-evaluation. There may be a list of expected learnings and a list of technical words used. Commonly there are suggestions for additional experiments and projects. A few textbooks supplement each unit with material in boxes and with footnotes. The boxes may contain short biographical sketches of scientists or accounts of the history of specific scientific developments. Footnotes are used chiefly to give the meaning and pronunciation of technical words.

Science textbooks invariably close with an index. Sometimes there is a glossary. Occasionally there is a concluding review section with provisions for self-evaluation.

The use of a textbook in a course of study. Textbooks are designed to sell to a broad market. They must be usable anywhere in the country, in any type of school and in any type of teaching situation. A program suggested by a textbook program does not truly fit any specific situation. It cannot take advantage of resources unique to one community. It cannot anticipate local events. It can at best be only approximately seasonal in organization. Textbooks tend to contain much more material than can be treated adequately in the time available. This is because authors are under strong pressures to meet every interest and every demand.

Generally a textbook program must be modified for maximum effectiveness in any single teaching situation. Superfluous material must be deleted. The remaining material must be rearranged to take advantage of local events and local situations. New materials must be added to take care of deficiencies.

Many texts which are used today are encyclopedias of scientific information. The authoritarian approach to teaching is emphasized. They answer all questions. They solve all basic problems. They detail all the steps of essential experiments and tell the pupils what should be observed and what conclusions should be drawn. Pupils have little or no opportunity to speculate, to devise methods of attack and to draw their own conclusions.

The authoritarian approach permits rapid coverage of material. In addition, the material can be so organized that pupils can recall and apply it quickly. But certain assumptions are made when attributing these virtues to the authoritarian approach.

1. The pupils must be willing and able to assimilate information.
2. The information must have intrinsic value (since the process of memorization is not in itself believed to confer benefits), and the pupils must have some basis for evaluating what they have learned.

The above assumptions do not always hold on the secondary level of education. Authoritarian methods have satisfied college teachers with limited subject matter goals because college students have sufficient incentive to try to master the materials presented to them. Secondary pupils on the other hand usually have definite goals and are less affected by threats of low grades or failures. The authoritarian approach with its insistence upon blind acceptance does little to help pupils make their own decisions about information presented to them.

Some modern textbooks use the discovery approach. The National

Study Groups such as ESCP, CHEM and the like base their textbooks on this approach. The major contributions of the discovery approach when properly carried out is the opportunity provided for independent thinking. Pupils are challenged with problems, they then plan and carry out their own procedures to solve the problems; they collect and organize data and draw their own conclusions. The teacher helps and encourages but does not dictate.

Mr. Kilburn, an eighth grade general science teacher asked one of his pupils to follow the directions for an experiment given in the text. The directions were as follows: Pour purple cabbage juice into several test tubes.* To the pupil's surprise and that of the class, the liquid in each test tube differed from the others in color.

The first reaction of the class was to attribute the color to slight differences in the amount of liquid in each test tube. Then someone wondered if there might be temperature differences after which the class entered into a short period of excited speculation. Mr. Kilburn acknowledged all suggestions but refused to accept or discredit any of them. Instead he helped the pupils plan methods for testing the hypotheses. Most of the actual testing was done at home during the next few days, the results being summed up and discussed during the class periods.

Contrast Mr. Kilburn's approach to that usually used in secondary schools. Mr. Kilburn's pupils thought for themselves. Pupils in an authoritarian program have little opportunity for independent thinking: they are assigned "problems"; they are directed to use certain materials and procedures; they are required to make specified observations and conclusions. Original ideas are rarely encouraged and may actually be discouraged.

The most common objective to the discovery approach is the time factor. Certainly the breadth of content covered is severely limited. However, the objectives of the discovery approach are much broader than those of the authoritarian approach. What is lost in terms of subject matter may be gained in terms of an understanding of the nature of scientific inquiry.

Before using a text, the teacher must consider a number of factors. A course which is based on the authoritarian approach does not require special laboratory facilities, special materials and equipment, and the scheduling of class time is not a problem. The discovery approach involves more class time and more materials and equipment for pupil activities. Before launching on a program of this type, the teacher must have the full support of the school administration for all aspects of the program. The

---

* Mr. Kilburn moistened the insides of the test tubes with solutions of differing degrees of acidity as specified in the teachers manual accompanying the text.

range of pupil reading abilities should also be considered in using a textbook. The range in a group may be great; some pupils read with difficulty and are reluctant to use books. Advanced readers of course can use the text without any trouble. Retarded readers will need help.

Using unit introductions.   Authors of textbooks design the introductions of the units to stimulate curiosity and establish problems. Such motivation is far superior to plunging pupils into a study of material for which they see no purpose. The introductions given in the textbooks cannot be considered as ideal. Authors are handicapped in preparing these introductions. They must write for nation-wide usage and cannot take advantage of strictly local or momentary conditions. In consequence, there are usually more satisfactory introductions that can be devised by a teacher to fit his local situation.

A reference to a local event or condition in which pupils are interested may stimulate a lively discussion out of which grow problems pupils are anxious to solve. At other times, a demonstration, a field trip, or a film may produce strong interest. The teacher will do well to examine each unit introduction carefully and try to devise a more challenging approach. Perhaps he will find such a substitute but sometimes he may find the textbook approach ideally fitted for his specific needs. Sometimes the textbook introduction has more value after the teacher's own introduction and may follow closely afterwards. Sometimes it can be assigned as special reading or used during the review and summary that ends the unit.

The problems with which an author opens a unit need careful examination also. These problems are necessarily broad and may be far removed from the lives of the pupils. Many of them are useful in the local situation. Others have little value and can well be replaced by problems that apply directly to the interests and needs of the pupils.

> The textbook unit was headed, "How do communities get their water supply?" and was introduced by a general discussion of the need for safe drinking water in large quantities. Mr. Foster changed the problem to "How does Pottsville get its drinking water?" He introduced the unit with a trip to the water treatment plant, and set up subproblems in terms of the observations made on the trip.

Reading-recitation techniques.   This is probably the oldest of the techniques used with textbooks. It was once used so extensively that it was titled the "Textbook-recitation method." As the term indicates, pupils read a section of the textbook and then recite their learnings. Employed occasionally for brief periods, it can be effective. Employed indiscriminately day after day, as it once was, it stifles individual initiative and kills interest.

Reading-recitation may be used to emphasize sections of the text that are considered highly important, and should be reserved for this use. To employ it for trivial information reduces its effectiveness in other situations.

The teacher should be certain that the material to be read can be interpreted by the pupils, so that their time is not wasted. If the language is too difficult or the ideas too complex, other forms of presentation should be employed instead. Sometimes it is advantageous to use the reading-recitation technique near the close of a unit, when the pupils have gained a suitable vocabulary and an adequate background for understanding.

Instead of following the reading of the text by pupil recitation or by oral questioning, a teacher may find group discussion more profitable. A pupil may recite on what he read, then other pupils comment on his statements, describe their related experiences, and criticize the generalities given in the book. From these discussions of the information given in the book problems often arise that the pupils are anxious to solve.

Pupil presentations of textbook material.   A teacher may delegate to a group of pupils the responsibility for presenting a section of a textbook unit to their classmates. The pupils use the same demonstrations, perhaps supplemented by additional ones, and charts or models based on textbook illustrations. They call for textbook readings and assign special problems.

Occasionally a full unit lends itself to division into sections each of which can be assigned to a group.

> Mr. Kenney divided his physics class into six sections for the study of simple machines. Each group was assigned one section of the textbook unit with instructions to prepare a presentation for the class. The pupils followed the pattern of the text, using demonstrations, experiments, charts and filmstrips. Each group worked out problems on the blackboard, assigned problems and corrected them, and prepared a final quiz.

Reading assignments in the textbook.   Teachers customarily make uniform reading assignments in the basic textbook. There are times when these assignments are justified. The material covered by the assignment should be of high importance to all pupils. The pupils should recognize the importance of the material and desire to read about it. The language and the ideas presented should be simple enough for all pupils to be able to interpret. Unless these three conditions are met, the reading assignment is apt to waste pupil time and discourage interest.

Reading assignments are more profitable if pupils know in advance what information they are supposed to be finding. The teacher may prepare a list of questions to be answered. The questions help the pupils sift from the mass of details the items that the teacher considers most important. When possible the assignment should be based on a problem which the pupils are anxious to solve. The pupils themselves may prepare a list of questions to be answered by the reading.

Assignments need not be uniform. Individuals or groups may be given different lists of questions to answer. These pupils then report back to the class on their findings which they attempt to make meaningful by explanations and visual aids of various types, including the illustrations in the textbook. Later during review all pupils may be expected to read the same section. This practice helps pupils gain the necessary vocabulary and background to understand the assigned material.

Using suggestions for demonstrations and other activities. When a textbook gives directions for demonstrations, experiments, and similar activities, it is possible for the pupils to work with a minimum of guidance from the teacher. In some instances, each pupil working alone or with others may carry out the directions. Sometimes it is better to ask groups to set up equipment and present demonstrations to the class. In this last case, one group may work apart from the class during class time or it may work during free time to make preparations. Occasionally, when there are enough suggestions, the class may be broken into groups, each of which presents a demonstration.

It is unfortunate that most authors give the outcomes for the experiments suggested by their books. By doing so they make impossible the discovery approach to science with these particular activities. A teacher may, however, think of variations on the suggested experiments and thus encourage activities in which the outcome is not known.

> The textbook suggested that a container be filled with a mixture of water, ice, and salt to produce condensation on the exterior and thus show that cooling the air sufficiently causes condensation. After the demonstration and the following discussion during which pupils stated the expected principle, the teacher interjected, "Maybe the water soaked through the can somehow." Though the pupils did not think that it did, they were challenged to set up an experiment to see whether such might be the true explanation.

Using the illustrations. The illustrations in a textbook are often one of its strongest features and should be utilized as fully as possible. Many photographs and diagrams deserve extended attention with discussion of details and applications.

Sometimes an illustration can be used to establish a problem for solution. Perhaps the pupils want to know how a device operates or perhaps they can be challenged to find out why a certain reaction occurs. Photographs showing unusual adaptations of organisms may stimulate pupils to do further reading about the life histories of the organisms. The illustrations may show applications of principles learned in class work and pupils may be encouraged to discover how the principles apply.

Some illustrations have such interesting details that they may be projected. Diagrams may be copied on chart paper or the blackboard for better control of the discussion. Pupils may sometimes take the responsibility for the presentation.

The textbook showed an illustration of a concert harp. Georgianna, whose aunt played this instrument, volunteered to explain the photograph. She used an opaque projector to give an enlarged image on the screen and then pointed out the pegs for tuning the harp and the pedals used for changing the key of the harp.

The illustrations may be used during review. As the pages of the text are turned, the teacher calls on the pupils to explain certain features in each illustration.

Utilizing historical and biographical sketches.   Some science educators believe that a knowledge of the historical backgrounds of science gives increased knowledge of the present-day status of science. Some go so far as to recommend a recapitulation of the major developments of science. Generally the sketches given in textbooks are too brief to paint vivid pictures. These may be used as beginning points from which interested pupils go to encyclopedias, biographies, and books on the history of science.

Textbooks as references.   Textbooks may be used for references, but usually the information contained in them is condensed and general. If the books are so used it is best to encourage pupils to follow their readings in the text with references to encyclopedias and specialized books or articles. The text helps them gain an overview of the topic.

Textbooks for summary and review.   This is one of the strongest uses of the textbook. After a unit has been completed, and the pupils have taken several field trips, carried out many experiments, and looked at numerous visual aids, the textbook brings together their learnings and summarizes them in meaningful fashion.

A textbook lesson.   The following is an illustration of the way in which a physics teacher built a complete lesson about a section of the textbook. It is given as an example of one of the many uses of the text but not as a recommendation for daily practice.

> Mr. Austin had asked his class to review the textbook material on the energy relations involved in evaporation and condensation. He opened the class period with a brief test to focus attention on this topic. He turned next to the subject of the day's lesson—mechanical refrigeration. He drew attention to the refrigerating unit he had taken from a discarded refrigerator and helped the pupils visualize its location in the cabinet by reference to a large chart of a refrigerator.

> Mr. Austin then directed the pupils to open their textbooks to the appropriate section. Because he considered the subject difficult, he asked the pupils to take turns reading the section aloud while he pointed out on the chart and the actual unit each structure as it was referred to. He also asked the pupils to find the same structures on the diagram in their texts.

> Brief questioning quickly revealed a number of uncertainties despite the care he had used to deal with the topic. This led to a general discussion and frequent references to the text. To make a final summary one pupil reread the section aloud while another pointed out the structures on the chart.

> Mr. Austin described the variations that could be expected in home refrigerators. He asked the pupils to take their textbooks home with them and compare the diagram and information given with the refrigerators in their kitchens.

> He then raised the topic of other applications of mechanical refrigeration. Among those suggested was air conditioning. A brief discussion of this last topic raised several questions that interested the pupils. Mr. Austin asked the pupils to read about this topic in their textbooks as a background for the next day's work.

Helping retarded readers with the textbook. If science textbooks were written for the norm of the grade in which they were to be used, then half of the pupils below the norm would have trouble with the books. Some could not read the books at all; others would have difficulty with them; many would use the books reluctantly.

Some textbooks are difficult to read. A recent study of physics and chemistry textbooks revealed the following:

1. There is need to give greater consideration to readability in the selection of chemistry textbooks.
2. There is need to obtain specific information concerning the reading ability of students for whom the book is intended.

3. None of the chemistry textbooks had a readability score that would make it useful to half of the students in the survey.

4. Readability of physics textbooks seems to be at the level of most students. The verbal content of the texts is presented in relatively simple words and sentences.

The investigators emphasize the necessity for including the readability of textbooks and the reading ability of students as part of the criteria for selecting textbooks.[1]

Until further investigations are made, extending these conclusions to apply to other texts seems reasonable. Authors of science textbooks are rarely reading specialists; they use a technical vocabulary and concise writing that causes difficulty for young readers. It is to be expected that science textbooks would be difficult for many pupils to read. Certainly the complaints of many teachers justify that conclusion.

Retarded readers need special help with their textbooks if they are not to flounder, lose confidence in their scientific ability, and develop a dislike for the program. Probably the best thing that a teacher can do is to develop a flexible attitude toward pupil achievements. He should give retarded readers opportunities to succeed in ways other than by reading. They are then able to approach their textbook without a feeling of dread and loathing but with a confidence that anything they do may add to their successes.

Retarded readers are aided if they have gained a background of information and an essential vocabulary before they approach their reading assignments. Consequently it is well to delay general reading assignments until near the end of a unit after they have had many experiences with experiments, field trips, and visual aids, and have developed a suitable vocabulary through discussion of these experiences.

The illustrations in a textbook can be very helpful to pupils as they read the accompanying sections. They are able to interpret much of the printed matter in its relation to the pictures and diagrams. It is therefore often wise to spend some time in group study of the illustrations, using the captions to aid in verbalizing the information gained.

Retarded readers are also helped by knowing precisely what they are to discover by their reading. They benefit by a discussion of section headings and what must be included in each section. They also benefit by lists of questions to answer; the teacher may prepare these lists or better, he may help the pupils prepare their own lists.

[1] Belden, Bernard R., and Wayne D. Lee, "Textbook Readability and Reading Ability of Science Students," *The Science Teacher*, 29:20–21, April, 1962.

Choosing a textbook. At some time or another nearly every teacher is called upon to select a textbook. His decision is generally an important one because so often the textbook is influential in shaping the content and organization of his course.

The teacher should strive for objectivity in making an evaluation of the several available textbooks. Merely looking through a copy is not sufficient to judge its worth. Even a careful reading may not leave the teacher with a correct impression of the book's usefulness; for instance, a teacher may favor a particular textbook despite serious defects, because it contains an abundance of material on his favorite topic.

To avoid reading his own interests and knowledge into a book a teacher should try to view it as though he were a pupil, immature and untrained in science. He should also try to apply as many objective tests as possible.

1. *Content.* The content of most textbooks, except for those produced by the National Study Groups such as BSCS, CHEM Study, is remarkably uniform. The texts of these "new approaches" include content which is not usually found in traditional texts.

The following factors should be considered in evaluating content. Lacey recommends that:

1. The content should be appropriate for the readiness of the pupils.
2. The content should be accurate and up to date.
3. The content should reflect the nature of the scientific enterprise—the incertitudes and tentative aspects of scientific knowledge.
4. The content should be reasonably consistent with state and local syllabuses that the teachers are supposed to use as guides.[2]

2. *Organization.* Two types of organization are seen in secondary school science books. In the type using logical organization, concepts and principles are developed in the way that a well educated person might organize them; this is the form usually seen in college texts and in high school physics and chemistry texts. In the type using psychological organization, the attempt is made to present the material in the order that would be most meaningful to the pupils for whom it is designed; many general science and biology texts have been given this type of organization.

Books with a psychological organization may be differentiated according to the nature of the learning segments. Some books use environ-

[2] Lacey, Archie L., *Guide to Science Teaching,* Wadsworth Publishing Co., Belmont, California, 1966.

mental units; some use problem units. Ideally, a textbook should agree with the organization used for the course of study. Otherwise it may be somewhat awkward to refer to readily.

3. *Literary style and vocabulary.* Literary style has much to do with the readability of a book. Although style is difficult to judge, some points to be looked for are: (1) length of sentences; (2) directness of sentences; (3) number of ideas per sentence; (4) use of lead sentences for paragraphs; (5) presence or absence of irrelevant thoughts; (6) continuity of thought.

When evaluating a textbook, the teacher must decide whether or not the vocabulary is excessively difficult or inappropriate. He may want to refer to a standard word list designed for secondary school texts and other publications. He should remember that new advances in science have introduced words that may not be included in some of the word lists.

The teacher should also remember that a textbook that is easy to read may not be a suitable text for his situation; readability is but one factor to be considered. Sometimes the text that is somewhat harder to read has other features that outweigh this point.

4. *Illustrations.* The quantity and quality of illustrations need consideration. Photographs should be clearly reproduced. Diagrams should be carefully made and attractive. Color in the illustrations adds to eye appeal and when properly used has considerable teaching value. The recently introduced transparencies made on plastic sheets are excellent teaching aids but because of cost can only be used in small quantities in any one book.

Most books today are profusely illustrated. However it is well to check to see if the illustrations have been well selected. The illustrations should amplify the material printed on the same page and the captions should tie in closely with the paragraphs around it. Photographs that have little or no relation to the text are "padding" and represent careless book making.

5. *Teaching aids.* The table of contents and the index should be comprehensive. Some teachers like a glossary; if so they should check to see that the glossary includes technical and difficult words used in the book. The activities at the end of a chapter should meet the needs of the teacher. If he wishes to use them to take care of some of the individual differences among his students, the range of difficulty and type of suggested activities should be great. If he wishes to use them chiefly for summary, the activities should be closely related to the content of the chapter.

6. *Mechanical make-up and appearance.* The following features are usually considered under the heading of mechanical make-up and appearance: attractiveness of the book, durability of the binding and paper, size of the book, and legibility of print. The book should have an attractive overall appearance. The cover design and the color of the binding should be attractive. The size of the book may have unsuspected psychological

implications. If the book is poorly proportioned, too long and narrow or to short and thick, it will be unappealing. If the book is excessively large, its mere encyclopedic bulk is likely to make the student feel that it will be dull and difficult reading. The size of textbooks has decreased considerably during the past few years. Texts used to be large encyclopedias. Many of the newer texts are attempting to select content that is directed toward developing an understanding of the basic principles rather than being encyclopedias of information.[3]

The length of line and the size and legibility of type are important mechanical factors that determine the ease and comfort with which the text may be read. If the book is rather wide, the double-column page will probably be more attractive. Ample space should be left between lines to provide for ease in reading. The type should be sharp and printed on a good quality paper.

Factors of little importance in choosing a text.   As previously mentioned, the educational rank and reputation of the author should not be one of the criteria used in evaluating the text. This should not be interpreted to mean that noted science educators do not usually write good books, but rather that a book should not be excluded from consideration merely because its author is not well known. It should be noted that the present trend is for teams of authors rather than a single author for science textbooks.[4] A team of authors, especially if it consists of experts on subject matter as well as experts on the psychology of education, often produce a better text than could a single author.

The *Thirtieth Yearbook* of the National Society for the Study of Education lists some of the factors which should not be considered in selecting a textbook.[5] The prestige of the publisher should not be considered. The *Yearbook* points out that wide use of a text is not necessarily a good criterion for selecting a textbook. Even though it may serve well in many schools, it may not satisfy the needs of an individual school. The cost, although it must of necessity be considered, should not be over-emphasized in selecting a textbook. A cheap textbook which proves unsatisfactory and must be discarded after a very short period of use actually costs more in the long run than a more expensive book that can be used for many years.

[3] Owen, Archie M., "Selecting Science Textbooks," *The Science Teacher*, 29:20, November, 1962.

[4] Nelson, U. R., and S. B. Brown, "Perceptible Changes in Science Education—1954," *School Science and Mathematics*, December, 1954.

[5] National Society for the Study of Education, "The Textbook in American Education," *Thirtieth Yearbook*, Part II, University of Chicago Press, Chicago, 1931.

Criteria	*Procedures for examining books*
1. The intent of the author and his point of view.	Read foreword and introduction.
2. The suitability of the material to objectives of course of study.	Analyze the table of contents in relation to topics in the course of study.
3. Degree to which the material meets the standards for effective learning.	Read one chapter, attending to organization of material, activities suggested, instructional aids, and bibliography.
4. Degree to which the book incorporates the element of critical thinking.	Read material on one selected area. Note manner of development.
5. Degree to which generalizations are stated as such and the amount of factual evidence in support of these.	Look up one important subject in the index and read all the material in the book on that subject.
6. The degree of probable interest for students.	Obtain student reactions. Examine format for eye appeal.
7. The degree of reading difficulty.	Use student opinion, language-arts teacher's opinion, information from publisher, and reading grade-placement formulae.
8. The degree to which illustrative material is helpful to learning.	Examine representative illustrations in terms of their purpose.
9. The degree to which the material is up-to-date, representative, and authoritative.	Examine authorship, publishers' blurbs, copyright date, table of contents, indexes, and illustrations. If a revised edition, determine extent of revision through changes in the table of contents, illustrations, format, comparable pages, etc.
10. The treatment of controversial issues.	Check index for a controversial topic and read material on it in book.

Table 10. *Suggestion for Studying Textbooks**

* From Owen, Archie M., "Selecting Science Textbooks," *The Science Teacher*, 29:20–23, November, 1962.

DIRECTIONS: Rate each book on the items listed below on a 5-point scale as follows: 1—unsatisfactory, 2—poor, 3—fair, 4—good, and 5—superior.

Course _____ Examiner_____Date_____

As an instructional tool:	Title 1	Title 2	Title 3	Title 4	Title 5	Title 6	Title 7	Title 8	Title 9	Title 10
How well does the book achieve the objectives of the course?										
How well does the book give satisfactory coverage to subject matter?										
How satisfactory is organization of material for effective learning and for course of study?										
How clearly is the material written?										
How effective is the material for student interest?										
How appropriate is vocabulary and style of presentation for students for whom intended?										
How accurate and up-to-date are contents?										
How helpful to the learning process are the illustrative materials?										
How adequate are study aids, suggested activities, bibliographies, and other teaching aids?										
In terms of format:										
How durable is the construction and paper?										
How clear, readable, and attractive is type?										
How adequate is the general over-all eye appeal?										
How adequate is its size for students?										

Comments_____

Recommendations in order of preference:
1._____3._____
2._____4._____

Table 11. *Sample Rating Sheets for Evaluating Books**

* Adapted from Owen, *op. cit.*

Evaluating science textbooks.   Various check lists have been devised to make the selection of textbooks as objective as possible. All the major factors considered important in evaluating textbooks are listed and assigned a certain number of points to establish the relative weight of each. Sometimes the major items are broken into specifics, each with its own point value. After a textbook has been rated according to the list, its total score may be compared with that of the following:

One example of a check list is found on page 320.[5] Associated with this list is a guide for studying textbooks which will aid in checking the rating sheet (Table 11).[6]

Another kind of score card, designed to speed up the process of evaluation, is the "spot check" method, illustrated by *Vogel's Spot Check Evaluation Scale*[7] (see below). On this score card, each item has been assigned a maximum value of two points.

Obviously the use of a score card is not truly objective, because each separate item is judged subjectively. It does have the advantage of systematically directing the evaluator's attention to each of the factors considered important. Some degree of objectivity is introduced in the totaling of the points.

The danger in the use of score cards comes with the attempts to compare books by their scores. Some important points may have been ignored in constructing the card; others are too intangible to be defined. The only real test of whether a textbook will serve satisfactorily in the classroom is actual use.

VOGEL'S SPOT CHECK TEXTBOOK EVALUATION SCALE

Textbook ————————————————————————————

Author ————————————————————————————

Publisher ———————————————————————————

Copyright year ————————————————————————

List price ——————————————————————

Score ————————————————————

I. *Qualification of author* (see title page, preface to textbook, and preface to teacher's manual)

(2) The author has taught the subject about which he is writing.

(2) The author holds advanced degrees in related fields.

(2) The author has received assistance from specialists in preparing his manuscript.

(2) The author has tried out his material in classroom situations.

[5] Owen, *op. cit.*

[6] *Ibid.*

[7] Vogel, Louis F., "A Spot Check Evaluation Scale for High School Science Textbooks," *The Science Teacher,* 18:70–72, March, 1951.

(2) The author's point of view, theory, or philosophy is in harmony with that of my school.

Partial score _____

II. *Organization* (see table of contents, the preface, the section headings through one unit, and the end of one chapter)

(2) There is a central theme which correlates the whole textbook.

(2) The textbook is organized into units which are based on student interest and probability of use in everyday life.

(2) The organization makes use of topics already taught in my school.

(2) Questions and/or problems at the end of chapters are graded explicitly in difficulty.

Partial score _____

III. *Content* (see table of contents, index, and five text pages)

(2) The texetbook contains all of the topics necessary for my course.

(2) Material from one part of the textbook is cross-referenced with similar material in another part of the book.

(2) The historical development of science is given some place.

(2) Topics dealing with the latest advances of science, such as atomic energy, are included.

(2) The social significance of science is stressed.

Partial score _____

IV. *Presentation of material* (see any five introductions to chapters, or problems)

(2) The inductive approach is used wherever possible in introducing a new topic.

(2) The problem solving aspects of scientific method is stressed.

(2) The author's style is informal and interesting.

(2) Unfamiliar scientific terms are set in italics or boldface.

(2) Important principles are set in italics or boldface.

Partial score _____

V. *Accuracy* (select any five topics in the index and look them up in the text)

(2) All the items I looked up are on the pages indicated in the index.

(2) The items I looked up are scientifically correct.

(2) Teleological expressions are avoided.

(2) Personification is avoided.

(2) No ambiguity is apparent.

Partial score _____

VI. *Readability* (see any one text page)

(2) The average number of words per sentence is below 21.

(2) Sixty percent of the sentences are simple or compound, as opposed to complex.

(2) There are at least four personal references per 100 words.

(2) There is at least one application for each abstract principle.

(2) There are not more than 42 affixes per 100 words.

Partial score _____

VII. *Adaptability* (see table of contents and any five text pages)
   (2) The textbook is satisfactory for slow, average, and brilliant students.
   (2) Students with rural and city backgrounds will find the text useful.
   (2) The textbook is arranged so that certain sections can readily be omitted.
   (2) The authors treat controversial subjects impartially.
   (2) In general the text fits my particular community needs.
                              Partial score _____

VIII. *Teaching aids* (see end of chapters, appendix, and teacher's manual)
   (2) Summaries, questions, and problems at the ends of chapters are adequate.
   (2) References for teachers and students are annotated.
   (2) Appendix material is pertinent and useful.
   (2) The teacher's manual is more than an answer book.
   (2) An annotated up-to-date film list is provided.
                              Partial score _____

IX. *Illustrations* (see any 10 illustrations)
   (2) The illustrations are relatively modern.
   (2) The photographic reproductions are large and clear.
   (2) The line cuts are well drawn and adequately labeled.
   (2) The figures are tied into the textual material by direct reference.
   (2) The legends under the illustrations are useful learning devices.
                              Partial score _____

X. *Appearance* (see cover and leaf through the text)
   (2) The appearance of the cover is attractive.
   (2) The size and shape of the textbook would not be a handicap to students.
   (2) The placement of the illustrations is pleasing.
   (2) The design of most pages is open, rather than crowded.
   (2) The size of the type makes for easy reading.
                              Partial score _____

SCIENCE NOTEBOOKS

The science notebook is a valuable teaching device, suitable for a wide range of interests and abilities. At its best, it is a place to keep records, a summarization of learnings, an exercise in organization, a medium for self-expression, an indication of progress, and an accomplishment in which to take pride.

That notebooks seem at times to have little or no value, that they are commonly viewed with distaste by teachers and pupils alike, is not the fault of the notebooks. Any teaching device improperly used may be of more harm than good.

Functions of the science notebook.   By tradition, the chief function of a notebook is to keep records. In it are to be kept records of experiments and of observations in field and classroom. Notes made of presentations by the teacher or by pupils, of assigned and voluntary readings, and of films and slides find a logical niche in the science notebook. The notebook is also a satisfactory place to keep duplicated material given out by the teacher, corrected test papers, assigned book reports, and other papers.

The task of keeping this material in order gives the pupils many opportunities to organize their learnings. As they prepare summary sheets for each unit and a table of contents for the entire notebook, they see the development of the program, topic by topic, unit by unit.

The notebook is a device for review. As pupils keep the material up to date and in proper order they constantly review the work they have done. Before tests, they find in the notebook the material on which they are to be tested.

According to more modern usage, the notebook may be a medium for self-expression. For supplementation of assigned work, a pupil may write in the notebook original stories, essays, poems, and plays. He may make diagrams, sketches, cartoons, and paintings as his particular interests and talents dictate. He may enjoy pasting in clippings, a form of self-expression favored by many pupils.

Finally, the science notebook may become tangible evidence of progress. As the notebook thickens, topic by topic, and unit by unit, pupils recognize that their learnings are growing too. The final notebook or any one of its sections may be a project in which a pupil takes great pride, winning with it the approval of his fellows and the commendations of his teacher. The quality of the contents of a notebook give the teacher another measure of the interest, efforts, and achievements of its maker.

A science notebook may not be all these things to all pupils. Some brilliant pupils are understandably impatient with the routine of keeping a notebook. Some academically retarded pupils may find no satisfaction in any of the activities involved. All pupils react differently to notebooks. For this reason, notebook requirements must be as flexible as everything else in the science program.

Providing for notebook work.   It is well to specify at the beginning of a program the exact form of the notebook that will be used. Left to themselves, pupils bring in a variety of shapes, sizes, and types. Some of these notebooks are difficult to adapt to the requirements of a good notebook program.

A loose-leaf notebook is essential for the addition of new material from time to time and for the occasional reorganization of the old material. Spiral notebooks and composition books permit no flexibility; materials must be left in the order in which they are entered.

The standard notebook size, 8½ inches by 11 inches, is convenient for the addition of any duplicated sheets provided by the teacher, which are usually of this size. Duplicated materials added to smaller notebooks must be folded and make awkward inclusions.

The exact number of rings in the notebook is not critical but all notebooks should be the same. Then duplicated materials may be punched before being given out. Pupils need both lined and unlined paper. The lined paper is best for longhand writing. Unlined paper is best for drawings and for clippings. It is also well for pupils to buy gummed ring reinforcements for the pages of their notebooks. Outer pages are easily torn out and lost without some form of protection where the rings pass through the holes.

A pupil may produce far more than enough material to fill a standard notebook during the course of a year. Some teachers require the purchase of manila covers, one for each unit, as well as a standard cover. At the end of each unit a pupil removes the material from his notebook and puts it in one of the manila covers, securing the pages with rings or paper fasteners. The cover may be decorated with designs appropriate to the unit. Thus at the end of the year, a pupil has the equivalent of several notebooks, one for each unit and each in its own cover.

There are psychological advantages to such a division of notebook materials. For each unit a pupil starts afresh. If he has taken pride in one section he is encouraged to do equally well on the next. If he has been careless on one unit, his failures are no longer visible to haunt him and interfere with the pride he might take in his work on the next unit.

A few materials kept on hand in the classroom are helpful in encouraging notebook work. A small supply of lined and unlined paper and some gummed ring reinforcements are needed for pupils who use up their own supply or forget to bring enough. A pile of old magazines, several pairs of scissors, and a plentiful supply of paste provide pupils with clippings for their notebooks. Colored pencils and crayons enable pupils to add color to their drawings. And, if possible, a teacher should provide a paper punch to make holes in the specified covers and in the inserted material.

The basic notebook. Adolescents being what they are, few of them undertake notebooks voluntarily. A teacher must provide the initial impetus by requiring a certain minimum amount of work. As the unit progresses he may offer numerous suggestions for supplementing the required work, and he may occasionally provide time for such optional work.

The teacher outlines the minimum content of the notebooks as he makes his unit plans. Most of the required material is closely associated with the basic activities he expects all pupils to carry out. He may require records of assigned experiments, planned demonstrations, and general field work. He may require short written explanations of devices or phenomena considered by the class as a whole. In addition, he may demand a table of contents and a concluding summary of learnings.

The basic notebook should be made as interesting as possible. It should never represent drudgery. Too often pupils come to hate notebook work because they are forced to do endless copying of trivial and useless material. Much record keeping can be made interesting through varying the procedures. Demonstrations are best recorded by diagrams supplemented by labels and captions. Tables and graphs are often the most effective ways for recording data obtained from experiments and field observations.

The teacher may dictate the form of the records used in the basic notebook. Or he may permit the class to work out the form to be adopted for a specific experiment or field study. The teacher may give out duplicated sheets on which there are diagrams to label, tables to fill in, or squared sections for graph making. On occasion, when a certain point seems especially important, the teacher may dictate or write an explanation on the blackboard for pupils to copy, or give out the statement on duplicated sheets. More worthwhile, if uniformity of expression and thinking is desired, he may permit the class to formulate the statements to be copied into the notebooks.

Generally, class time is used for work on the basic notebook. At the conclusion of a demonstration or experiment, or after a discussion, pupils are given several minutes to make the required drawings and write out their observations, conclusions, and explanations.

Some teachers make extensive use of work sheets. These are similar to pages found in workbooks. They contain directions for activities, blanks to be filled in, spaces for diagrams or diagrams to be labeled, and questions to be answered. These work sheets are useful for general assignments, although their use may be overdone. The finished work sheets should become part of the notebooks.

Pupils may be asked to carry out certain uniform assignments at home or in study hall. These may be based on prepared question sheets, on textbook readings or questions, or on library assignments. The teacher may permit flexibility in the basic notebook. He may prepare a list of possible assignments and permit pupils to choose from the list.

For the unit summary, the teacher may dictate an outline or provide one on duplicated sheets. For greater value, the pupils may develop their own outline, discussing their learnings, organizing them, and dictating the form in which the points are to appear. The final outline may be written on the blackboard for pupils to copy in their notebooks, or it may be duplicated for distribution. To aid in review a teacher may present a list of questions to be answered or he may assign certain questions at the end of textbook chapters. Pupils are expected to write the answers in their notebooks.

The amount of material to be included in the basic notebook must be decided upon by each individual teacher. It is a matter of personal viewpoint. However, it may be said that many teachers have a tendency to require too much, leaving little pupil time or enthusiasm for following up individual interests. Teachers whose pupils do much optional notebook work rarely make uniform notebook assignments more than once or twice a week.

Once assignments have been made, pupils should be held accountable for their completion. Because class time is provided, few pupils have difficulty finishing the assigned work but there are always some who cannot use their time efficiently. Occasional check-ups on these pupils keep them from falling so far behind that they develop a distaste for notebook work. It is also well to set aside a part of a period the day before a notebook is due to check required work against a list presented by the teacher. Pupils then use the remaining time to bring the required work to completion if necessary, or to do optional work if required work has been done.

Supplementing the basic notebook. The basic notebook, made up of a minimum number of required assignments as just described, is a framework upon which pupils may build as they wish. Many pupils find great satisfaction in notebook activities and display enthusiasm and initiative in their work. Other pupils develop little interest in their notebooks. Some have difficulty in completing minimum assignments. A teacher should recognize these differences in individuals and not expect high quality work from each. On the other hand he can always try to encourage increased efforts in hopes that his pupils will discover and take pride in unsuspected talents.

Optional work is stimulated by providing time early in each unit.

Each year, as Mr. Watson's seventh grade began the study of "Water In Our Lives," Mr. Watson set aside half of the fourth or fifth lesson for notebook work. He brought into the classroom a pile of popular magazines, scissors, and paste. He asked the pupils to find pictures of the uses of water to clip and put in their notebooks.

At the end of the period, after materials had been put away, Mr. Watson explained that pupils could look at home for more clippings to be added to the notebooks. He also mentioned that pupils could make drawings or paintings and asked for suggestions for subjects. Few pupils ever failed to respond to this approach. Many added dozens of clippings to their notebooks. Some copied diagrams from texts and encyclopedias. Others made colored drawings.

This same technique of starting all pupils on a specific activity may be used in other ways.

During a unit on astronomy, Mr. Watson asked his eighth grade pupils to make cartoons showing conditions encountered by the first men to land on the moon. Each pupil made at least one cartoon, but many made whole sections of cartoons and some used cartoons when doing notebook work for other units.

Color has strong appeal. Many pupils who take little interest in a black and white notebook become enthusiastic about the same type of work when color is added.

As his seventh grade pupils made their first notebook diagrams of the year, Mr. Watson would walk about the room giving praise and encouragement. Finally he would select one pupil and suggest that he use a red pencil to make arrows more prominent.

Once this diagram was completed, he would ask the pupil to display it to the class. Other pupils invariably wanted to use colored pencils too and from then on their notebooks became much more colorful.

Title pages permit pupils to exercise a certain amount of individuality.

Near the close of each unit, Miss Thompson gave her pupils time to prepare a title page for the notebook work on the unit. She never dictated the form of the page but she did suggest that the decorations be in keeping with the content of the unit.

Many novel and interesting motifs were worked out and displayed to the class. Sometimes pupils who had previously shown little interest in their notebooks became interested in adding more material to maintain the standard established.

Pupils are sometimes stimulated by seeing what other pupils have done.

At the end of each unit, Miss Harrington customarily chose the two best notebooks from each of her five sections. She put these on display and allowed pupils to look at them during class time. Thus the pupils who had made the notebooks received recognition and others benefited by the content and by the suggestions for material to be included.

Types of optional work that pupils may be encouraged to put in their notebooks include:

1. Decorated covers
2. Decorated title pages
3. Expansions of assigned work
4. Reports of optional experiments
5. Reports of optional field observations
6. Reports of problems worked out at home
7. Clippings of pictures and articles
8. Drawings and paintings
9. Cartoons
10. Original poems and stories
11. Clippings of poems and stories
12. Diagrams made from actual observations
13. Diagrams copied from books
14. Lists of applications or other items
15. Book and film reviews

Giving recognition for notebook work.   Mention has already been made of one teacher's method of recognizing superior notebook work by selecting and displaying the two best notebooks from each section. A number of other techniques may be used. The teacher may write favorable comments in the margins and commend pupils in private conversation. The teacher may call attention to excellent sections of notebooks during class time, reading selections or asking the pupils who prepared them to read selections. Materials that lend themselves to display may be made the subject of bulletin board exhibits. An unusual notebook may be partly separated and displayed in a show case.

There is a natural tendency to reward quantity instead of quality. A teacher should form the habit of looking for original work, for unusual activities, and for careful organization. Public commendation for these qualities encourages other pupils to follow the same pattern and to some extent explains to pupils who have spent hours gathering unrelated materials why they have not been selected for special attention.

Grades for notebooks represent part of the reward given for special effort. All notebooks should be graded. However, the teacher should remember that notebook work is not a goal of science education. Rather it is a means by which pupils can be helped to develop themselves. Some pupils benefit greatly from notebook work; others, little.

The basic notebook material may be graded in terms of completeness, neatness, and conformity to the pattern of organization. It cannot be graded on quality because this has been determined by the teacher. All pupils should receive a grade on this material. Optional material may well be graded separately. Or optional material may be used to increase the grade given for the basic notebook. Pupils should be given some understanding of the standards used in grading this material.

SCIENCE WORKBOOKS AND MANUALS

Workbooks are categorically condemned by many leaders in education, but sales continue to mount. Their popularity is certainly related less to high teaching value than to convenience. Nevertheless, blanket condemnation is not entirely deserved; workbooks do have certain assets upon which teachers can capitalize.

Workbooks vary greatly in content and organization. At one extreme are workbooks that reprint pages of associated textbooks, replacing key words with blanks that are to be filled in by pupils after reading their texts. These are the workbooks that have given the species a bad name. Their only function is to keep pupils busy; the harm they do in disgusting pupils with science cannot be estimated.

At the other extreme are workbooks that make provision for many different types of activities—forms for reporting data, diagrams to be labeled, blank spaces for sketches and clippings, suggestions for supplementary work, study guides for reading assignments, and self-testing devices. Sometimes in addition the teacher is provided with pads of tests, one per pupil, to be used in evaluating pupil achievement.

Workbooks of the latter type serve as a combined course of study, a study guide, and a record book. As a course of study it shows the pupil where he has been and where he is going; as a study guide it gives him detailed instructions for his work; as a record book it gives him a convenient depository for his findings.

Heavily burdened teachers find the better workbooks useful in conserving time and energy. They are freed from the preparation of study outlines, work sheets, and laboratory directions. They do not need to devise so many review and drill exercises. They find the standardized records easy to check. They are relieved of part of the burden of evaluation. The beginning teacher and the inadequately prepared teacher also find workbooks of value. They gain the security that comes from knowing exactly what to do next and from realizing that the pupils have been given adequate directions.

Laboratory manuals and workbooks may be useful in saving time for the teacher but they generally do not permit the pupils to formulate their own problems or encourage thinking.

Workbooks help pupils who are working under self-direction to study more effectively. Pupils who have missed time because of illness or from having left school prematurely can make up work without close supervision.

For all their advantages, the limitations of workbooks must not be forgotten. Workbooks are relatively inflexible; the content is highly organized and cannot be altered easily. There is little or no provision for the inclusion of new materials. Unused sections offend both the pupils and the parents who buy the books. Workbooks are directed toward uniform outcomes; if they dominate the program, pupils have little opportunity to develop special interests and talents. Most serious of all, workbooks deny pupils any participation in the planning process, any incentive to do independent work, any practice in formulating their own problems and any encouragement to do their own thinking.

It is far too easy for workbooks to dominate the program. The following lesson was observed during a search for master teachers under whom to place cadet teachers.

> *Mr. Andrews brought his general science class to order and directed them to open their workbooks to page 92. He asked the pupils to read in turn the answers to the questions that they were supposed to have done as a homework assignment. Upon the completion of this activity Mr. Andrews assigned pages 95 and 96. For the next twenty minutes he sat at his desk while the pupils looked up the answers to the questions on these pages, each of which was keyed to the textbook. The last ten minutes of the period was spent in checking the answers. The assignment was to work on another three pages of the workbook.*

There are situations in which the use of workbooks is justified, but they should always be used with care. If they come to dominate the program they operate contrary to the major objectives of science education. Teachers who feel they must use them should work toward the day when they are completely free of them.

SUGGESTED ACTIVITIES

1. Review several science textbooks, making note of the special features that are provided by each. Apply the Vogel spot check test to one of these.
2. Read a general science textbook completely. Apply one of the standard reading formulas to randomly selected portions of it to judge its reading level.
3. Prepare an assignment sheet to help retarded readers use their textbook more effectively.
4. Plan a fifteen-minute review based on the pictures in a textbook unit.
5. Review several science workbooks and decide what is the value of each and under what circumstances it can be used effectively.
6. Plan one unit of a basic notebook which would be required of each pupil in a class. Also list suggestions for optional materials pupils might include.

SUGGESTED READINGS

Barrilleaux, L. E., "Comparison of Textbooks and Multiple Library References: A Report on the Initial Phase of an Experimental Study," *School Science and Mathematics*, 63:245–9, March, 1963.

Lacey, Archie M., "*A Guide to Science Teaching in the Secondary Schools*," Wadsworth Publishing Company, Belmont, Calif., 1966.

Mallinson, G. "The Readability of High School Science Texts," *The Science Teacher*, 18:253–6, November, 1951.

Owen, A. M., "Selecting Science Textbooks," *The Science Teacher*, 29:20–23, November, 1962.

Pribnow, J. R., "Teaching Notetaking in Science and Mathematics Classes," *School Science and Mathematics*, 63:178–80, March, 1963.

"Textbooks on Science," N.Y. *Times Educational Supplement*, July 29, 1960.

Vogel, Louis F., "A Spot Check Evaluation Scale for High School Science Textbooks," *The Science Teacher*, 18:70–2, March, 1951.

Chapter 10

Recitation, Lecture, and

Discussion Techniques

A PRODIGIOUS NUMBER OF WORDS, BOTH ORAL AND WRITTEN, ARE USED DURing the course of a single lesson. Printed, the words would often fill a small book. Most of the words are used orally with some lessons based wholly or in large part upon classroom conversation. Speech is unquestionably the most extensively used of all teaching devices.

Perhaps because speech is such a natural process, teachers do not always give adequate thought to it when making their plans. All too often their lessons degenerate into rambling and uninspired discourses that hold the attention of but few pupils. It can be noted that most of the discipline problems of beginning teachers arise during such inadequately planned periods. Good planning is required for the use of language, just as for all other teaching aids. Used with purpose, language meets a number of needs in the classroom. The specific advantages of words must be understood and utilized properly. Their limitations must be realized and compensated for.

Other chapters of this book will also deal with the wise use of language—reading, pupil reports, and testing. This chapter will deal chiefly with the way a science teacher uses words in the classroom as part of his regular presentations.

TEACHER PRESENTATIONS

The Scoutmaster's Handbook of the Boy Scouts of America recommends that scoutmasters confine their remarks during scout meetings to a brief period called the "Scoutmaster's Three Minutes." This is sound advice for scoutmasters and is worthy of consideration by science teachers as well. Few individuals have the ability to hold an audience through the power of words alone. Not many science teachers can be included among the ranks of the fortunate. Strictly oral presentations in the classroom might well be limited to the "Science Teacher's Three Minutes."

Giving directions for classroom activities.   The quality of the instructions given for general class activities determines in part the effectiveness of the activities. Clear-cut and business-like instruction inspires respect. Knowing exactly what to do and what to look for, pupils are able to set to work immediately with assurance. Carelessly presented directions, on the other hand, tend to result in confusion. Pupils fumble, look about to see what others are doing, distract each other with whispers, annoy the teacher with questions, and use their uncertainties as an excuse for dallying. Serious discipline problems sometimes arise.

Mr. Langerford, student teacher in the seventh grade, directed his pupils to read pages 67 and 68 in the textbook. A few pupils began reading immediately. Most of the others had forgotten the assignment by the time they had located their books. These last began asking the page numbers of each other, at first in whispers, then in undertones. At the same time several hands were up. Mr. Langerford began answering the questions one by one.

"What is it, Martha?"

"Did you say page 67 or 68?"

"Both pages, Martha. What do you want, Tom?"

"What pages did you say, Mr. Langerford?"

"Pages 67 and 68, both. Yes, George."

"What pages are we supposed to read?"

Mr. Langerford's voice became tinged with irritation. "I just told you three times. Don't you ever listen? Pages 67 and 68!"

George's face reddened and several pupils tittered. Joe, whose book was open, closed it conspicuously and asked in an innocent tone but with a smirk on his face, "What pages did you say, Mr. Langerford?"

Experienced teachers avoid these situations. One teacher might direct his pupils to take out their textbooks, and only after the books were ready would he give the page assignment. Another might write the page numbers on the blackboard and then make the assignment, referring to these numbers as he does so.

Strictly oral directions are satisfactory only for the simplest of activities. Few people can keep in mind a lengthy set of directions after one hearing. Pupils need specific help in visualizing the procedures they are to follow—printed directions, diagrams, charts, and other types of visual aids.

When two or more steps are involved, procedures may be written on the blackboard or printed on sheets to be given to each pupil. The directions may be drawn up by the teacher alone or they may be prepared by the pupils.

> A senior science class decided that each member should have practice in removing stains from clothing. First they listed the common types of stains. Then they divided into committees, each of which would investigate one type of stain, prepare directions for its removal, and set up an experiment in which the others could participate. Two girls volunteered to type up the directions for duplication.

Visual aids are always useful for giving directions. A map helps pupils locate an item to be studied or defines the area in which a field study is to be confined. A diagram illustrates an electrical circuit to be wired. A photograph or slide shows what the final product of a construction activity should look like.

The best visual aids are the actual materials that are to be used in the activity itself.

> Mr. Ries provided his biology pupils with printed sheets that gave directions for pressing and mounting the plants they were to collect for study. Then he gave a demonstration, following the steps printed on the sheets and using plants which he had collected, to illustrate some of the problems the pupils might encounter.

The lecture method. Lectures seem to have certain immediate advantages. A large amount of material can be covered in a single class period. Time needed for troublesome laboratory and field activities is reduced. Fewer books and other teaching materials must be provided.

The advantages seem so obvious that lecturing has always had strong influence on teaching method. The extreme is reached in those university courses that are based entirely upon the lecture method. All that students need do is listen quietly, take notes, and assimilate the information that the instructor has gathered so diligently and organized so logically.

Unfortunately, the learning process is not so simple. The "pouring in" method is educationally unsound and cannot be recommended for the secondary school. Adolescents are too restless, too preoccupied with immediate problems, and too concerned with recognition by their fellows for purely passive learning. They are handicapped by the limitations of oral communication—inadequate vocabularies and insufficient experience backgrounds. They need meaningful experiences, active procedures, and self-identification with each new situation.

Teachers should limit themselves to brief presentations, such as a short description of a process, a statement of fact, a narration of personal experience.

> *Mr. Bradshaw, who had been stationed on a Caribbean island as a meteorologist during his military service, was finding weather a difficult subject to teach to a class of eighth graders. Pupils had little enthusiasm for the topic. Then one day Mr. Bradshaw happened to say, "Once I saw what a hurricane can do. I was on an island in the Caribbean—" Almost immediately the class attitude reversed itself.*

Thus Mr. Bradshaw discovered by accident the most valuable function of the oral presentation—the development of a vicarious experience. Mr. Bradshaw's pupils were able to share with him in imagination his experiences with a hurricane. They then had a background that enabled them to communicate with him. A teacher will find that his most effective oral presentations deal with his own experiences. He is able to supply the detail that makes the images vivid in the minds of his listeners.

Any oral presentation is effective only to the degree with which satisfactory images are evoked. That is why slides, exhibits, and demonstration materials are so helpful to a speaker. They help to make up for the limitations of words. Teachers should use them extensively during any of their oral presentations.

Guest speakers. Guest speakers contribute new points of view to the science program. They can answer questions with the authority of their experiences. They can supply details that are unavailable from the usual classroom resources. Potential guest speakers exist everywhere. It is only necessary that an individual have had experiences in some field of science to be able to make contributions. A school janitor can talk about the school heating system. A nurse can describe aseptic procedures in a hospital. A parent can talk about his experiences flying an airplane. A pupil from another room can talk about model airplane engines.

It must be remembered that individuals vary greatly in their ability to interest the adolescent audience. The most interesting speakers usually tell about their own experiences. It is sometimes desirable to encourage all speakers to do so.

> Mr. Pierce, the fire marshal, had obviously prepared diligently for his talk on fire prevention to the combined eighth grades of the local junior high school. But the mass of statistics he was presenting interested his audience very little. The pupils were becoming increasingly restless and were almost at the stage of rudeness.
>
> The principal, Mr. Bowan, sharing the platform with Mr. Pierce, recognized the nature of the problem. At the first opportunity, when Mr. Pierce had turned to him at the end of making a point, he gestured with his hand to arrest Mr. Pierce's attention.
>
> "Mr. Pierce," he said, "I'd like to know about some of the dangerous conditions you have seen as you make your inspections. I think these boys and girls would like to know about them too."
>
> The question launched Mr. Pierce upon a description of some of the places he had visited and some of the fires he had investigated. His audience became alert at once. At the end of his talk a number of the pupils asked questions and some stayed to talk with him after the class bell rang.

Whenever possible guest speakers should be encouraged to supplement their talks with slides, exhibits and demonstration materials. In some instances it is wise to take the class to the speaker rather than the reverse, if by so doing the speaker will have better facilities for illustrating the points he intends to make.

> Mr. Morris had asked Mr. Detling to speak to his physics class about making a reflecting telescope, for Mr. Detling had made his own telescopes. After thinking the matter over he asked Mr. Detling if it might not be better to take the class to Mr. Detling's home where the pupils could see the materials which were used. Mr. Detling agreed and was able to give both the practice and the theory of telescope making.

When extending an invitation to a guest speaker it is usually wise to make a specific request unless the speaker is known to be interesting to adolescent audiences. He may be asked to describe his experiences in a particular situation or to explain the operation of some well known device. He may also be asked to limit his talk to fifteen minutes to provide time for questions. Inexperienced speakers are usually grateful for such guidance.

QUESTION-ANSWER TECHNIQUES

Teachers use oral questions much more than they probably realize. It is not unusual for a teacher to spend more than half a period in interrogation. Certainly questioning has a place in the science program but it is doubtful whether the allocation of so much time to one type of activity can be justified. Teachers should give serious consideration to the amount and type of questioning they use.

Some functions of oral questioning. Oral questioning helps establish something of the experience backgrounds of the pupils and is especially useful at the beginning of each new topic. "Who has traveled in an airplane?" "Who has watched a pilot control an airplane?" "Who has seen an airplane take off?" "Who has seen an airplane land?"

Such questions represent a form of pretesting and will be referred to again in Chapter 11. The answers suggest the extent of the foundation upon which teachers can build. If this information is especially critical, it may be well to phrase each question in both the positive and negative sense in order to determine which pupils lack experiences as well as those who have had them: "Who has watched a pilot control an airplane?" "Who has never had a chance to see a pilot control an airplane?"

Oral questioning can be used to help pupils recall past experiences that may be utilized during the progress of a unit.

Mr. Bernstein held up a fifteen-ampere fuse and asked his seventh grade, "Does anyone know what this is?"

Several hands went up. "It's a fuse," said one boy.

"That's right," said Mr. Bernstein. "How many of you have heard of electric fuses before?"

All hands were raised.

"How many of you have seen electric fuses in your home?"

About half the hands went up. Three pupils described where electric fuses were located in their homes.

"Who knows what they do?"

Several pupils were eager to talk. One girl told of the occasion she plugged in an electric toaster and caused a frightening spark and the extinguishing of the lights in the kitchen. Another told of the time all the lights in the lower rooms of the house were out until an electrician could come to replace the fuses.

Through his questioning Mr. Bernstein set the stage for a study of electric fuses. The pupils knew what a fuse looks like and they had some concept of its importance. Pupils who had seen fuses before or who had had experiences with them were now thinking in terms of these experiences. Others had gained vicarious experiences with fuses through the narrations of their classmates. They all sensed the desirability for knowing more about them.

Oral questions are valuable instruments for review and drill but care should be taken not to overuse them in this capacity. Too few pupils can participate actively, and too many pupils are forced to sit quietly by. After a few minutes of brisk questioning the activity should be ended in favor of a different one.

Oral questioning is not recommended for evaluation when the questioning is done in class. At best, each pupil can be asked only two or three questions. It is difficult to formulate a large number of questions of equal weight and some pupils may benefit from the responses of others. Injustices are almost certain to occur. However, when individual conferences are possible, oral questioning gives an excellent method for assessing pupil achievement. This method of evaluation will be discussed in the next chapter.

The fallacy of leading questions.   "Leading questions" are much used to guide what are called "discussions." Typically the teacher asks a question which sets the pupils guessing. If an answer acceptable to the teacher is suggested a new topic is introduced. If no acceptable answer is given, the teacher asks related questions the answers to which lead step by step to the answer of the first question.

Mr. Milo's plans called for a discussion of conditions on the moon.
Pupils had mentioned the lack of air, plants and water.
"Why do you suppose there's no water?" Mr. Milo asked.
Several moments of silence. Then a girl asked somewhat hesitatingly, "Is it because the sun is so hot it dries out the water?"
Mr. Milo's face became blank. "No," he said shortly. "Doesn't anyone else have an idea?"
The silence continued.
"Well," he asked, "what do you know about the size of the moon?"
"It's smaller than the earth," several pupils shouted.
"That's right. Now doesn't that help you?"
Silence resumed.
"Well, what keeps the water on the earth?"
A few moments more of silence broken at last by one of the boys, "I guess it doesn't have any other place to go."

"Of course it does!" Mr. Milo exclaimed impatiently. *"It could go off into space."* Then with a more hopeful expression, *"What keeps you on the earth?"*

"Gravity!" shouted several pupils in evident relief.

Mr. Milo's vigorous nod was accompanied by a pleased smile. *"Good! Now how about the water on the moon?"*

After a short silence one of the boys asked, *"Isn't there gravity on the moon, too?"*

"Yes, of course, but how does it compare with gravity on the earth?"

Silence.

"Think back. How about the size of the moon?"

Then a hand waved violently.

"Yes, Jim."

"There's less gravity on the moon. So the water flies off into space."

Mr. Milo beamed with pleasure. *"That's very good thinking, Jim."*

The above technique of teaching can be likened to such games as "beast, bird, or fish," or "Twenty Questions," except that it is not frankly labeled a guessing game. Indeed, because the questions of the teacher are finally answered, the pupils assume that they have been thinking and the teacher assumes that he has been teaching.

Formulating oral questions.   Simplicity and directness are essential qualities of oral questions. Pupils have no opportunity to puzzle out the meanings of awkward and complex questions as they might were they reading them. They must grasp them immediately or not at all.

The pupils must be familiar with all the words used. The presence of one strange word, such as *superfluous* or *excessive*, distracts them and they lose the sense of the remaining words. Science teachers are especially apt to forget the vocabulary limitations of boys and girls. Teachers are used to hearing and using words that are unfamiliar to the bulk of the population. Without thinking they often penalize a large number of their pupils by what is in effect excluding them from participation in the work of the class.

Commonplace words can often be substituted for unfamiliar words, sometimes to the general improvement of the question:

Original: "What happens to the superfluous water in a leaf?"

   Improved: "What happens to the unused water in a leaf?"

Original: "Why does a bottle of warm soda pop effervesce when opened?"

   Improved: "Why does a bottle of warm soda pop foam when it is opened?"

There are often good substitutes for technical words. Unless the technical word itself is considered important, it is usually well to make the substitution.

> *Original:* "As your epidermis is worn away, how is it replaced?"
> *Improved:* "As your outer layer of skin is worn away, how is it replaced?"
> *Original:* "In what direction is light refracted as it passes from air to water?"
> *Improved:* "In what direction is light bent as it passes from air to water?"

When a concept is being tested and the knowledge of a word is considered essential in answering the question, there are in effect two things being tested with the same question. The question may well be divided to test each idea separately.

> *Original:* "Where is the cambium layer in a tree trunk?"
> *Improved:* "Where is the growing region of a tree trunk?"
> "What is the growing region called?"
> *or*
> "What is the growing region of a tree trunk called?"
> "Where is the cambium layer in a tree trunk?"

Technical jargon should be avoided unless there is good reason for using it.

> *Original:* "How can we measure the pH of the soil?"
> *Improved:* "How can we determine the acidity of the soil?"

Questions with inverted structure and dangling clauses should be avoided in favor of direct questions.

> *Original:* "When more salt is added to a salt solution, what happens to the freezing temperature?"
> *Improved:* "What happens to the freezing temperature of a salt solution as more salt is added?"
> *Original:* "If an air mass passes across the Great Lakes, what are its characteristics in winter?"
> *Improved:* "What are the characteristics of an air mass that passes across the Great Lakes in winter?"

Hypothetical questions can become so involved as the teacher tries to think of every eventuality that few pupils can follow them. The more complex questions should be written out rather than given orally.

Example: "Suppose you owned a wood lot and you didn't cut any trees for fifty years and you didn't let cows graze in it, and there were no forest fires, what would the trees be like?"

Sometimes teachers think in terms of completion-type questions and use them in oral questioning. Pupils have considerable difficulty in visualizing the questions.

Original: "Pollen is borne on the what?"

Improved: "On what part of the flower is pollen borne?"

Original: "The best way to make wood catch fire rapidly is blank."

Improved: "What can you do to wood to make it catch fire rapidly?"

Original: "Quartz crystals are formed from the what dissolved in ground water?"

Improved: "What is there dissolved in ground water that crystallizes to make quartz?"

Questions that can be answered by yes or no, or by any other either-or combination, require little or no thinking. If the first guess is not correct the second must be correct. Such questions have little value.

Original: "Does a fish give off carbon dioxide?"

Improved: "What gas does a fish give off during respiration?"

Controlling question-answer situations.   Insistence upon a few minor formalities can do much to maintain order during question-answer sessions. Even experienced teachers who seem to permit the utmost freedom in their classrooms demand respect while they are asking questions and listening to answers. Beginning teachers, who may not recognize the importance of the formalities, sometimes let the situation deteriorate.

Pupils should learn that permission is needed for contributing an answer. Teachers should be consistent in acknowledging only those who request permission to speak. The usual signal asking permission to speak is the raised hand. Teachers should always give this signal preference. If one pupil raises his hand and a second gives an answer without permission, the former should be recognized and the latter should be ignored no matter whether his answer is wrong or right.

Several hands may be raised at the same time. Usually it is best to give the pupil whose hand went up first the privilege of answering, but the other pupils should be told why that particular selection was made. If two or more hands are raised simultaneously, one pupil may be selected arbitrarily with the others being acknowledged.

"I can see that both John and Mary are ready to answer my question.
"I'll let John answer this one."

In most classes there are a few pupils who tend to dominate question-answer sessions. They should not be ignored as long as they raise their hands because they are cooperating completely with the teacher. And yet a teacher usually wishes to bring other pupils into the picture. Tact is needed.

"John, I see that you know the answer to this question, too. Let's ask June to answer it and then you tell me if you agree with her."

To bring a nonparticipating pupil into the picture, the teacher may ask special questions that the pupil's background enables him to answer better than anyone else. This technique counteracts his feelings of isolation and helps him become a member of the group.

A question directed specifically to a pupil whose mind is obviously wandering will recall him to the activity at hand. This may prevent him from becoming engaged in some other activity that will disturb others in the class.

Incorrect answers should be treated with the same courtesy as correct answers. A teacher would be most unfair to condemn an answer arbitrarily merely because it was not what he expected. Perhaps the question was poorly stated and the pupil misinterpreted it. Or the pupil may have had true understanding but found oral expression of it difficult. Again, his answer might have been wholly or partially correct and the teacher might have been wrong. Sometimes there are actually two sets of correct answers possible. And even if the pupil is completely wrong there is no excuse for sarcasm, scolding, or contemptuous comments. Everyone makes errors and holds wrong viewpoints.

Chorus answers are undesirable. For one thing, if several pupils can shout an answer in unison with little reflection, the question is probably too simple to be worth asking. Secondly, acceptance of a chorus answer encourages habits of uncontrolled talking. Chorus answers can be discouraged by preceding each question with the name of the pupil who is to answer it. This notifies other pupils that a selection has been made. This technique need be used only if pupils are in the habit of making chorus answers.

Good questioning proceeds at a brisk pace. Active participation is limited to one pupil at a time; the others must sit quietly without much hope for expressing themselves. Should the questioning drag or the answers become involved, some pupils are certain to begin thinking of other things.

Questioning is more effective if the questions have been written out beforehand. More attention can be given to the construction of the questions and to the type of answers expected. Less class time is needed for the teacher to state the questions. Some teachers write their questions on three-by-five cards, one to a card, which may then be organized in any fashion and shuffled through quickly as needed.

Every possible means should be used to encourage maximum participation. Questions should be given in clear, firm tones even when directed to nearby pupils, in order that all pupils be able to follow the line of questioning. Answers from pupils in front seats, often inaudible at the rear, should be repeated by the teacher so that pupils everywhere in the room can understand. The teacher should keep his eyes upon the class as a whole in order to recognize pupils who wish to contribute and to be alert for signs of inattention. He should be very careful not to allow himself to be drawn into a special discussion with one or two pupils or to allow a few pupils to dominate the activity.

Question-answer sessions should be terminated before pupil attention begins to shift. This is a type of activity that does not hold the attention of all pupils for very long. By the end of ten minutes the minds of most of the pupils will have wandered at one time or another and the number not paying attention at any one time will be rapidly increasing. Soon the number participating is too small to justify the time being spent and the ones not participating have become so many as to represent potential disciplinary trouble.

CLASSROOM DISCUSSIONS

By definition a discussion is a talking over of subjects from various points of view. As such, discussions have some important functions in the science program. Unfortunately, teachers often apply the term "discussion" to almost any type of talking in the classroom—questioning, lecturing, stating procedures to be followed. They say. "We will now discuss," when they mean, "I am now going to lecture to you." They say, "Let's discuss how we will do the experiment," meaning, "I will now tell you precisely what to do." When they say, "Let's discuss our findings," they mean, "I will now tell you what conclusions to draw." The remark, "Let's discuss this new topic," often means, "I will now ask you some questions and you will try to guess the answers."

Because of the lack of definitive thinking about discussions, teachers may fail to think through the purposes of the various types of verbal activities. They fail to take full advantage of these verbal activities and instead employ a great deal of time in purposeless conversation.

In a true classroom discussion, all pupils are free to express their viewpoints. This implies that pupils must first have a background that provides them with viewpoints. They cannot discuss something about which they know nothing. Second, the definition implies that the teacher does not dictate or seek to influence the opinions of the pupils as he leads the discussion. If he does so, he is actually lecturing, no matter how well he disguises the act.

True classroom discussions, though limited in application, have an essential place among science teaching techniques. Free discussion is the most effective means for raising problems that challenge pupils. Free discussion is ideal for verbal summaries. It is the only means for bringing about teacher-pupil planning. It is essential for consideration of controversial issues.

Good classroom discussions are not at all easy to conduct. It requires great skill to keep attention centered upon one point, without discouraging those who make irrelevant remarks, permitting a few pupils to monopolize the conversation, or influencing opinion. Leading a profitable classroom discussion is the most difficult of all classroom techniques.

Initiating a unit with a discussion. Discussions are commonly used for the motivation of pupil activities. They are effective when they raise problems that the pupils believe to be worth solving.

"I know that several of you smoke," Mr. Thomas announced to his biology class. "And I know that more of you will be smoking in coming years. I am sure also that you have heard various arguments against smoking. Let's try to find out what's behind some of these arguments to see if there is any truth in them."

For the next several minutes the pupils volunteered such information and misinformation as they had picked up incidentally from readings and conversations. They soon concluded that none of them knew much about the subject.

"I'm going to read about smoking," said one girl. "Can you tell me where to look, Mr. Thomas?"

Mr. Thomas mentioned a few sources of information. Other pupils expressed an interest in further investigations. A girl whose father had given up smoking because of ulcers said she would ask the doctor what smoking did to her father. Her suggestion reminded pupils of this source of information.

The discussion ended in a planning session, with pupils volunteering to investigate various aspects of the problem both by reading and by interviews with parents, doctors, and insurance company representatives.

Mr. Thomas made an excellent choice of a topic for discussion by adolescents. Many adolescents are faced with the immediate problem of whether to smoke or not to smoke. Most of them resent being told that they must not smoke but they are generally grateful for an opportunity to consider the several aspects of the question. The topic, as introduced by Mr. Thomas, was one for which the pupils had sufficient background to make true discussion possible and one about which some of them had well-formed opinions. On the other hand the pupils recognized their lack of positive information, and they engaged in sufficient controversy to feel a sincere desire to investigate further.

Controversial issues such as smoking generally make good topics for problem-setting discussion periods. Matters of current interest can also be used to initiate this type of discussion. Teachers may set up exciting demonstrations or display unusual materials to initiate problem-setting discussions.

> Mrs. Harvey brought to school a large paper wasps' nest which she had found in the country during the weekend. A few of the pupils had seen such nests before and recognized it as a wasps' nest—though some of them insisted it was a bees' nest. Mrs. Harvey gave each pupil a piece of the covering and asked for a description of it. The pupils described it as paper-like and proposed several possible origins. Then Mrs. Harvey cut open the nest and displayed the interior. Some dead wasps found inside were put in a glass dish and passed around. The pupils discussed the possible function of the comb, proposing that it was used for honey even though none was found in the comb. The pupils then listed a number of questions about the nest and its makers that they would like to investigate.

Some teachers form the habit of beginning each new topic with a discussion. This is not wise. Pupils do not always have sufficient background or sufficient interest for a discussion to be profitable in the early stages of a study. There are other approaches to science that are generally more valuable. Initial discussions should be used sparingly and only when conditions are suitable.

Planning sessions.   When pupils are to plan their activities with a minimum of guidance by the teacher, they need opportunities to talk over procedures, make decisions, and allot responsibilities.

> The city was suffering from a serious water shortage. Eighth grade pupils had heard so much about the problem, at home and in the newspapers, that they showed a strong interest as soon as Mrs. Evans mentioned the topic. Nevertheless they had few concrete ideas about

the causes for the shortage and knew little about either their own water supply system or the nature of water storage in general.

Mrs. Evans suggested that the pupils list the questions they would like to answer. She then suggested a general reading assignment in the textbook; the reading broadened the scope of the pupils' thinking and resulted in the addition of more questions to the list.

The pupils began making suggestions of things to do. Some suggested making a map showing the watershed, the storage reservoirs, and the aqueducts taking water to the city. Pupils suggested asking the local newspaper for rainfall records. They suggested making a bulletin board display of pictures of the water system of the city. They suggested experiments and demonstrations taken from the textbook readings, and studies of the amounts of water needed for washing dishes, for taking baths, and for flushing toilets. Mrs. Evans suggested measuring the water lost through a dripping faucet.

Thus the suggestions accumulated, some of them giving rise to new questions to be answered. Finally, the pupils portioned out the tasks, each individual volunteering to work alone or with one or two others on a special project.

The teacher who uses this technique for planning must be willing to permit his pupils to follow up their own suggestions. He may have plans of his own and he may make suggestions to amplify or round out the ideas of the pupils, but if he initiates the discussion fully determined that the pupils will adopt the plans he has in mind, he is wasting time and energy in a hypocritical attempt to be "democratic."

Discussions of results. Group discussions of the significance of data can be among the most worthwhile activities of the science program. The pupils have gained comparable experience backgrounds through their field or laboratory work and are now able to communicate effectively with each other. They are able to bring their collective judgment to bear on the problems, thinking through the issues, studying exceptions and discrepancies, and qualifying the conclusions they make. Often they find so many weaknesses in their data that they are desirous of repeating their observations under more carefully controlled conditions.

During a laboratory exercise, ninth grade pupils had tested the forces needed to draw loaded toy trucks up sloping boards. They had concluded that less force was needed to draw the trucks up the boards than to lift them directly.

After doing some reading, however, they discovered that the mechanical advantages which they had determined did not agree with those the textbook obtained. Friction was obviously the causative factor and the pupils wanted to use the low friction metal rollers described in the text. After the pupils had used these rollers they were more satisfied with their results.

The accumulated data now led to a consideration of efficiency and new problems arose. Efficiency seemed to increase as the slope increased. New experiments were planned to test this, using various devices, metal rollers, toy trucks, blocks of wood, and roller skates.

Discussion of the results obtained in the first experiments gave these pupils an understanding of some of the factors that affected their data. They were then able to devise methods for refining their experiment. Even had they been unable to incorporate the refinements, they would have understood the need for qualifications of their conclusions.

It is through discussion of results that pupils best see the workings of the scientific method. Complex directions for highly refined experiments are apt to be followed in cookbook fashion with little appreciation for the refinements involved. But simple experiments with their obvious limitations enable pupils to put the scientific spirit in action.

Discussions for summary and review. Generally teachers conduct reviews and oral summaries by question-answer techniques, because they prefer that the learnings be organized according to certain established patterns. If, however, a teacher is willing to let pupils develop their own form of organization on occasion, he may provide short periods of free discussion for this purpose.

Pupils are usually capable of dealing with limited amounts of information, especially if these have been recently covered by class work. They may not have the maturity to conduct major summaries and reviews without aid. Therefore, during a major review, a teacher may provide an overall pattern to guide the work and permit the pupils to deal with the segments of the outline as they wish.

Mrs. Lowell occasionally employs what she calls "buzz sessions" for review purposes. She provides a list of topics making up the unit to be reviewed. The pupils work in groups of three or four, each group selecting a topic. In their "buzz sessions" the pupils decide what they have learned about the topic. Later, they report to the class and stand ready to answer questions.

Techniques for leading discussions. During a classroom discussion the teacher serves as moderator. In brief his duties are as follows:

1. To keep the discussion moving
2. To keep the discussion pertinent to the topic under consideration

3. To encourage all pupils to participate
4. To keep some pupils from dominating the conversation
5. To acknowledge all contributions
6. To reject irrelevant comments without giving offense
7. To summarize frequently and keep the picture clear
8. To end the discussion when interest begins to wane

A discussion leader must be able to handle many different types of situations with tact and diplomacy. When several pupils wish to speak at once, it is his task to select one without discouraging the others. He must be able to listen to rambling and irrelevant discourses with patience, end them as promptly as possible without discourtesy, and then steer attention back into proper channels.

The nature of the topic has much to do with the success or failure of a discussion. Some topics lend themselves to discussion, others do not. First of all, the topic must be one about which the pupils have some knowledge. Only thus is it possible for them to do more than speculate idly. Controversial issues on which the pupils take stands often make good topics for discussions. These issues may deal with matters of current interest such as the fluoridation of drinking water. They may deal with such perennial arguments as the harm in drinking coffee. They may deal with conflicting laboratory data.

Topics that deal with indisputable facts do not lend themselves to discussion unless the pupils are uncertain about these facts. It would not be possible, for instance, for pupils to discuss the properties of air if each knew about these properties. The only verbal activity they could engage in would be to review the properties.

Physical conditions influence the effectiveness of discussions. Pupils should be able to hear and see each other. The most effective set-up is a circular arrangement of chairs. If seats are fixed, the teacher must take pains to repeat the statements of pupils in front seats for the benefit of pupils in the rear of the room. Otherwise the latter lose the direction of the conversation.

A discussion leader is frequently faced with the problem of seemingly irrelevant, sometimes facetious, remarks. He will find it good policy to treat all remarks as though they were serious in intention. A teacher cannot follow the workings of every pupil's mind. Perhaps a point raised in discussion has set a pupil thinking along a channel not anticipated by the teacher. This pupil may then blurt out a statement that to others seems irrelevant, often ridiculously so. Simple courtesy demands that this pupil be given a word of recognition and perhaps a brief explanation of why his point does not fit the present discussion. If the pupil is serious, he will understand and not be hurt. If he meant to be facetious, he gains little satisfaction from his effort.

During discussions, pupils are apt to ask many questions, both relevant and irrelevant. By tradition a teacher feels obligated to answer as many of these as he can. Perhaps this tradition dates back to the time when there were few books and the teacher had to act as an authority.

Actually, the practice of trying to answer all questions is educationally unsound. Few teachers have the background to answer carefully and accurately the majority of questions asked. More important, the answering of a question tends to bring to an end the intellectual activity that initiated the question. If a pupil asks, "Will this piece of pumice float?" and is told "Yes," there is nothing more for him to do. He may even forget the information in a short time. But if he is told, "Why don't you try it and find out?" he is at the beginning of a real learning situation.

Relevant questions can be used to set the stage for problems to be solved by the class, by groups, and by individuals. They should be welcomed. Irrelevant questions may be more troublesome. Sometimes the interested pupil may be detached from the group to work on the answer to the question. More often, the teacher must explain why his question cannot be dealt with at that time and, if possible, arrange for the pupil to follow up his interest later. Much depends upon the nature of the question, and much depends upon the teacher's ability to see potentialities in the question.

The effectiveness of class discussion generally drops off sharply after several minutes. Pupils have difficulty maintaining a high level of attention during discussion activities. Only one pupil can participate actively at a time; the others must sit quietly. At the very best, were the pupils to speak in turn for but ten seconds each, five minutes would elapse between turns. Pupils would need unusual stimulation to keep their attention centered upon a topic for this long a time.

What happens in practice is that a few pupils dominate the discussion and the others contribute little. Some of the latter listen idly, some day-dream, some read or write surreptitiously, some whisper to each other, and the more active of them move about uncomfortably. If the discussion continues too long, some of the latter may become disturbing influences.

> Mr. Turin, a student teacher, tried to conduct a discussion of safe driving practices for the last twenty-five minutes of the class period. For fifteen minutes the discussion seemed to proceed smoothly, but actually only six pupils contributed significantly. A few others occasionally raised their hand. One girl read a novel; a boy read a comic book. One boy worked on an English report. The others wriggled about, looked out the window, whispered, and gave but fleeting attention to the topic under discussion.

Ten minutes before the end of the period two girls began to giggle. A boy shouted "Quiet!" in mock authoritative tones. The girls stopped momentarily but soon resumed. Class attention was now distracted and confusion grew. Two boys talked audibly. A boy punched another boy and the latter yelped. A girl pretended to slap a boy's face for some derogatory comment.

Mr. Turin finally shouted for order. In the momentary silence he scolded the class and voiced threats about detention room. Noticing the boy reading the comic book he confiscated the book and put it in his desk.

The last few minutes of the period were completely disorganized. Pupils moved about and talked aloud at will. Scuffling broke out a couple of times. Some of the pupils walked about the room. The boy who had lost his comic book muttered continuous threats in an undertone and added to the din by deliberately dropping a book, scraping his chair about, and slamming books into his desk.

Blame cannot be attached to the pupils for Mr. Turin's trouble. They had cooperated for fifteen minutes, at least to the extent of keeping quiet. The fault lay with Mr. Turin, who had extended the conversation longer than was profitable. He attempted to keep pupil attention by scoldings and threats and minor punishments that served only to antagonize the pupils. They took their revenge in a multitude of petty but annoying ways.

A discussion leader must give as much attention to the pupils who do not participate as to those who do. He must try to draw all pupils into the discussion. When he begins to fail, he should bring the discussion to a close.

Pupil-led discussions. All that has been said about teacher-led discussions applies equally to pupil-led discussions. Such problems as suitability of topic, participation, and duration of the discussion are of the same importance. In addition, a pupil leader has a special handicap because he lacks authority. In class discussions, his fellows may not be inclined to cooperate with him even when the teacher is present. They may speak without being recognized. They may interject frivolous comments.

When attempting pupil-led discussions for the first time, it is well to search out the best natural leader, one who has the respect of his fellows, who is articulate, and who will accept the responsibility seriously. Once a successful pattern for behavior has been established, other pupils may be employed as leaders; but if the wrong choice is made the first time, it may be very difficult for later discussions to succeed.

Most successful pupil-led discussions center about experiences that are fresh in the pupils' minds. Many teachers employ them only for summary and review. However, there are situations in which pupil-led discussions are effective for planning attacks on problems, particularly problems that are an outgrowth of previous work.

> Mr. Wharton had been assigned a small physics class of sixteen serious-minded pupils. He was able to give them many responsibilities he might not have given to a more typical class. One day, after the close of a unit on light, he passed out duplicate copies of an instruction booklet for a well-known make of camera. When the pupils had skimmed through the booklet he announced:
>
> "I'm going to let you organize this next unit on photography your-selves. Jack, will you be the group leader and run a planning session to decide what you are going to do?"
>
> Under Jack's leadership the puils formulated a number of problems to work on—the meaning of depth of focus, focal lengths of lenses, nature of camera lenses, significance of the F-openings, color rendition, and light intensity factors. They divided into groups and began working on the topics, devising experiments to help with their under-standings.

Small group discussions are often more successful than class discussions. There are more opportunities for pupils to participate, and fewer personality clashes. In general the incentive for attention-getting acts is less. However, a teacher cannot keep in touch with the decisions of the pupils and must assign all responsibilities to the group leaders.

A description of Mrs. Lowell's "buzz sessions" as used for review has already been given. Some teachers may employ small group discussions for project planning.

> Mr. Scardamaglia's eighth grade science class planned to set up a weather station using homemade instruments. The pupils divided themselves into small groups, each of which chose a specific instru-ment to build. Mr. Scardamaglia allotted fifteen minutes of the period for planning sessions. He did not appoint leaders but allowed the groups to appoint their own leaders.

Small discussion groups may be detached from the main body of the class to plan special projects or to organize their findings.

> Several pupils in Mrs. Lowell's eighth grade science class expressed an interest in the outer atmosphere. Mrs. Lowell suggested that they do some outside reading on the topic. On the following day, four pupils reported that they had begun such readings.
>
> Mrs. Lowell accepted this effort as an indication of true interest and appointed the four as a special committee to work on the topic. The

pupils worked at the rear of the room for about half the period, doing additional reading and organizing their findings. On the following day they were given time to prepare a final report. The final copy of their report was duplicated and given to the other pupils of the class.

SUGGESTED ACTIVITIES

1. Write out directions that might be given orally for (1) a reading assignment in a textbook, (2) a simple laboratory exercise, (3) a notebook exercise, and (4) getting ready for a test.
2. Prepare a brief account of one of your own experiences that you think might help pupils understand a specific scientific principle.
3. Write out a set of questions you might use in guiding a discussion of the results of a field observation or a laboratory exercise.
4. Observe a science teacher leading a class discussion. What percentage of the class participates in the discussion? What percentage dominates the discussion? What percentage pays little or no attention to the discussion?
5. List ten topics that you think would lend themselves well to general class discussion.
6. Plan a seminar on one phase of modern genetics with you acting as moderator.

SUGGESTED READINGS

Davis, H. S., "Illuminate the Lecture," *Educational Screen and Audiovisual Guide*, 44:20–21, 1965.

DeMent, J., "Ultramacro and Ultramicro Science Terms," *Journal of Chemical Education*, 39:587–588, 1962.

"English for Science Pupils," N. Y. *Times Educational Supplement*, February 3, 1961.

Holley, D. L., "Individual Study of Language Problems," *The Science Teacher*, December, 1960.

Muller, R. L., "Student Response in the Lecture Instruction," *Audio-Visual Instruction*, 11:94–95, 1966.

Nations Schools, "Taped Lectures Reduce Need for Substitute Teachers" 79:73, 1967.

Phillips, C. A., "Written Recitation in Teaching Science," *The Catholic School Journal*, 63:68–69, 1963.

Verner, C. and G. Dickinson, "The Lecture, An Analysis and Review of Research," *Adult Education*, 17:85–89, 1967.

Chapter 11

Tests and Testing

TAKING A TEST CAN BE AN EXCITING EXPERIENCE, ONE TO WHICH PUPILS LOOK forward with enthusiasm. A good test provides stimulation and a challenge to the imagination. Unfortunately, teachers do not always know how to make their tests an integral part of their teaching. They use tests for a single function—the determination of grades. Tests thus become whips held over the heads of pupils to induce them to further efforts. Small wonder that many pupils look upon tests with dread.

THE USES OF TESTS

Tests may be used throughout a unit—at the beginning, at the end, and in between—each time with different purposes in mind. Sometimes a single test may serve two or more purposes. Tests should usually be used as part of the teaching process. Only occasionally are they needed for determining grades and never should test scores be used as the only measures of success in a course.

Pretesting. A pretest attempts to discover the status of pupils at the beginning of a unit in order that the teacher may know where teaching should begin. Perhaps he wishes to know something of the experience background of his pupils; informal questioning—"Who has seen an electromagnetic crane?" or "Who has been to Gilbert Lake State Park?"—may serve his needs.

A teacher may wish to test the information background of his pupils. His questions should be formulated with care; wording and phrasing are important. They should not be vocabulary tests but tests of understandings. In formal pretesting, short-answer questions permit the coverage of the widest range of information in a limited time. Of the short-answer type, true-false questions require the least time for construction, administration, and checking.

Formal pretests need careful construction. There is always danger that they will be lengthy, academic, and discouraging. It is wise to include a generous selection of easily answered questions so that pupils may find satisfaction in their achievements. Wording and phrasing are especially important at the beginning of a unit, for the pupils have not developed a common vocabulary; pupils may have an understanding or an experience but may not be able to identify it if questions employ technical terms. Generally, pretests should not occupy more than fifteen or twenty minutes for completion, lest an unfavorable attitude towards the subject be developed.

A spiral organization of test items may be helpful. The first and simplest questions make a hasty sweep of the area being previewed, the second set of questions covers much the same ground but in greater detail. A third set, if used, may test finer details and be much more difficult. With this organization, the discourgement factor has less influence.

Below is an example of a true-false pretest used in a ninth grade science class to open a unit on the senses. Notice the spiral organization of items, beginning with matters commonly observed by everyone and ending with information generally acquired only from books or from school situations:

Answer the following questions with "true" or "false."
1. Most knowledge is gained through the eyes.
2. People have either brown eyes or blue eyes.
3. There is one eyelid for each eye.
4. Tears wash dirt from the eyes.
5. Only one eye at a time is used when looking at a nearby object.
6. Sunglasses reduce the amount of light entering the eye.

7. Objects can be seen more clearly by day than by night.
8. The eyelids stay open for only a few seconds at a time.
9. There are always tears in the eyes.
10. Eyeglasses make objects look larger.
11. Colors of objects can be determined by starlight.
12. A person can see clearly all objects in front of him without moving his eyes.
13. Eyeglasses help a person see objects that are far away more clearly.
14. The black spot in the center of the eye becomes smaller in the dark.
15. Both eyes always move in the same direction when they turn.
16. The use of two eyes at once helps a person judge distance.
17. Light enters the eye through the black spot in the center.
18. There is a lens in the eye.
19. The black spot in the center of the eye is called the pupil.
20. The colored part of the eye is called the iris.

It is sometimes interesting to repeat a pretest at the end of a unit. This gives the teacher an opportunity to compare scores for determining progress. However, it must be remembered that a pretest should be constructed in terms of the vocabulary, knowledge, and interests of the pupils at the beginning of a unit. A final test does not usually make a good pretest, and a pretest rarely makes a good final test.

Tests for motivation. By accident or design many tests contain controversial questions which give rise to interesting problems. These problems may be used to initiate new lines of investigation.

A biology test contained the following item:
"Life processes in the animal embryo begin with _____"
Several pupils wrote in the word "birth" and during class consideration of this item argued heatedly in its favor. A number of pupils evidenced incomplete knowledge of prebirth conditions.
The pupils accepted the teacher's suggestion that they plan a series of investigations about the development of the human embryo. They proposed the following questions:
1. Can an embryo move? If so, when does it begin to move?
2. Does an embryo breathe? If so, how does it breathe?
3. Does an embryo's heart beat? If so, when does it begin?
4. Can an embryo die?
5. Does an embryo have to digest food?
6. Can an embryo feel? Does it think?

During their investigation the pupils referred to a number of books. Some asked questions of their mothers. Three girls interviewed a doctor. Two interviewed a nurse.

To utilize controversial questions, the teacher should ask pupils to look over their papers immediately after answering them. Then pupils are better able to recall the thinking that led them to their decisions.

Pretests may be designed expressly for initiating discussions. Such tests may include questions about common superstitions, or about matters of importance to the community, or about other controversial issues. For example:

True or false?

Hot water will freeze before cold water.

Sewage in the river improves fishing.

Fluoridation of drinking water is advisable.

It is not necessary that there be final answers to the questions on such a pretest. Sometimes answers can be obtained by experiment or field observations. In other instances, evidence supporting different points of view may be collected.

Pages 360–361 show a complete pretest used in an eighth grade class to initiate discussions about earth changes. A similar test may be constructed to arouse speculation about the topographic features around any school.

Motivating pretests, like other types of pretests, should be short. The terms used should be familiar to the pupils. The material dealt with should lie within the experience backgrounds of the pupils.

Some pupils are stimulated by progress tests. Such tests should be given frequently and regularly. Pupils may score their own papers and keep their own records. The preparation of a battery of progress tests is useful for individualized study units; pupils take the tests when they feel ready and score themselves. Self-scoring tests should have simple questions that have positive answers so that pupils do not need to refer constantly to the teacher for decisions about doubtful answers.

Tests for review and drill. This use of tests needs little explanation. In a series of tests it is commonplace to include review questions as well as questions on current material. Important questions may be repeated a number of times. Sometimes a test is made up entirely of review questions.

Review and drill tests may be written or oral. Short oral tests are excellent review instruments but, because only a few pupils can participate at one time, interest is apt to lag after a few minutes of questioning. Oral review tests should be conducted briskly and with little discussion of answers. It is well to write out the questions beforehand to insure simplicity and directness.

Tests designed solely for review and drill need not be graded by the teacher, but written papers may be collected for further analysis. It is usually wise to direct pupils to check their own answers so that they recognize their own mistakes and clear up misunderstandings. Usually checking is done as a uniform class activity, but pupils may be asked to check their papers and correct any mistakes as an out-of-class assignment.

Testing pupil achievement.   Great weight is often attached to the scores pupils make on their tests. Test scores usually determine a pupil's status in school and often decide his future. Obviously the tests used should be constructed with the greatest of care. "Trick" questions and unfamiliar test items are unjust. A fair test deals only with material familiar to pupils and, if it is a verbal test, it uses only language the pupils understand. A teacher must be sure that he is testing truly important outcomes. He must be sure that he is not ignoring important achievements because of the limitations of his test instruments.

A PRETEST USED TO INTRODUCE AN EIGHTH GRADE UNIT ON EARTH CHANGES IN AN ITHACA, N.Y., SCHOOL*

Which of the following statements do you believe to be the most probable? Which do you consider impossible? Mark those you think probable with a plus sign. Mark those you do not believe with a minus sign.

1. Cascadilla gorge
    _____ has always been as deep as it is now.
    _____ is being dug deeper every year.
    _____ was once a much smaller gorge.
    _____ was dug out by a glacier.
2. Enfield Glen
    _____ was changed by the last flood.
    _____ is cut from rocks that once were mud and sand.
    _____ would be deeper if the banks were made of clay.
3. Cayuga Lake
    _____ is filling up.
    _____ may someday disappear.
    _____ was here at the beginning of the world.
    _____ is a dammed-up river valley.
4. Ithaca is built
    _____ upon soil that came from nearby hills.
    _____ on soil that came from Canada.
    _____ on a delta.
    _____ on soil carried in by man.
5. The airport is built
    _____ upon a natural plain.
    _____ upon a swamp.
    _____ upon part of Cayuga Lake.
    _____ upon soil brought in by man.

* Thurber, W. A., "A Challenging Pretest," *Science Education*, vol. 24, no. 4, 1940, pp. 220–221.

6. The site of the Cornell campus
   _____ was once beneath the sea.
   _____ was once covered by ice and snow all year round.
   _____ has moved up and down in the past.
7. The salt mines
   _____ contain salt hidden there by early man.
   _____ are connected with the salt water of the sea.
   _____ contain salt from a dried-up lake.
8. The cement plant was built at Portland Point because
   _____ there is plenty of water.
   _____ there is salt.
   _____ there is limestone.
   _____ there is a view.

Teachers are constantly encountering the limitations of their tests. A boy may be able to show with a carburetor in his hands all the important parts, describe their operation, and demonstrate adjustments. Asked to write down his knowledge he may fail completely. He may not even be able to explain a diagram of a carburetor.

Undeserved comparisons are often made because tests are not wisely chosen. One boy may be able to set up electric circuits but be unable to discuss electrons. Another boy may talk glibly about electrons but not know how to wire a doorbell circuit. But the first boy is certainly as accomplished as the second.

Verbal tests contain certain variables that must not be ignored in constructing tests for evaluation. (1) A teacher may not express precisely what he wishes to find out from the pupil. (2) The pupil may not interpret the question correctly. (3) The pupil may not express his knowledge adequately. (4) Finally, the teacher may misinterpret the pupil's answer. It is thus possible for a pupil to fail a test while possessing the essential information.

Verbal tests are best adapted to measuring factual information that has been learned through verbalization. When pupils gain information through direct experiences, as is the case in so much of the science program, they should be tested with a nonverbal test, or else they should be helped to verbalize their understandings adequately before being tested.

To use verbal tests justly, pupils should be given ample practice with questions identical with or closely similar to those with which they will be tested. Frequent review and drill tests provide this practice. Pupils should know precisely the range of content a test is to cover and the areas of major emphasis on the test should have received major emphasis during class time. It is most unfair to include material that has been touched on briefly or not at all during class work.

Frequent evaluation tests give a more accurate picture of achievement than do a few major tests. Four or five short tests cover the same material as a long test without allowing the influence of fatigue, sickness, and emotional tension to become so important.

Using tests to evaluate teaching effectiveness.   Test results give a clue to the effectiveness of some of the procedures used by a teacher. Many variables must be taken into consideration but generally a set of high scoring papers indicates success in teaching the material included in the test, and a set of low scoring papers indicates failure in teaching.

When individual test items are analyzed, specific strengths and weaknesses may be pointed out. Again the several possible factors must be considered. High success for a certain item may indicate good teaching or it may indicate knowledge acquired from previous experiences. Low success may indicate poor teaching or faulty test construction. A later section will give detailed help in analyzing test scores.

Teachers should be conservative in claiming success for their teaching procedures on the basis of test scores alone. It is possible for pupils to have high test averages and yet end the school year with little satisfaction and even with distaste for science. Overemphasis on memorization of facts for the purpose of passing verbal tests tends to remove a science course into an abstract realm where pupils see little value to what they are doing. On the other hand, even if pupils have worked hard on special projects and can present many tangible evidences of success, general failure on verbal tests represents a serious problem. With the weight attached to the results of verbal testing, pupils cannot afford to fail their tests. And their failure to pass tests usually does represent a teacher's failure to help them verbalize their learnings.

Teachers are sometimes tempted to excuse themselves from the responsibility for a number of low test scores as long as a few pupils do very well. Careful study of the pupils is apt to show that the few who succeeded had acquired their knowledge in previous years or had superior backgrounds that enabled them to learn despite poor teaching. Apparent laziness and incompetence on the part of the others might have disappeared with a different teaching approach.

TYPES OF TEST ITEMS
AND THEIR SPECIAL PROPERTIES

Some type of test may be devised for almost any purpose. Some of the types are as interesting to do as puzzles and are used as such in picture magazines and popularized science books. The variety of test items is sufficient to keep the testing program interesting.

Test items may be divided into three categories—purely verbal tests, tests that involve pictures and diagrams, and tests that make use of actual materials. Each type has its own values and each has serious limitations. The last named type most closely approaches reality and can measure learnings that verbal and picture tests cannot evaluate at all. However, these tests generally are difficult to set up and administer. Verbal tests depend upon the interpretation of words. Pupils who lack fluency with words are penalized by them. However, when verbalization is considered an important outcome, these tests are valuable. Picture tests represent something of a compromise between verbal tests and tests based on actual materials. They are several steps removed from reality, but they do reduce some of the emphasis put on words in the purely verbal tests.

Performance tests. Performance tests measure a pupil's ability to carry out certain operations in science. The needed materials are placed before the pupil together with a statement of the problem to be solved. The pupil is expected to solve the problem and demonstrate the end result. He may or may not be expected to explain the reasons for his operations. He may be scored on the end product only, or on each step, or on his explanations, or on all three.

Performance tests come closer to measuring certain desirable outcomes of the science program than do most other tests. Unfortunately, not much experimentation with this type of test has been carried out and only a limited number of satisfactory problems have been developed. Most of these are in the area of electric circuits.

> *Example 1.* A pupil is given a length of glass tubing, a gas burner, and a match. He is told to make a right angle bend in the tubing.
>
> *Example 2.* A pupil is given a miniature electric lamp, a dry cell, and a knife switch. A card with the materials reads, "Connect these so that the lamp lights when the switch is closed."

Advantages. Little or no verbalization is required. Manipulative ability is tested. Understandings that are difficult to verbalize are tested. Pupils who do poorly on verbal tests may receive recognition for their achievements.

Disadvantages. This type of test is difficult to administer to large groups. If duplicate sets of equipment are used, a large amount of materials is needed. Otherwise, cumbersome rotation systems must be used so that each pupil gets a turn.

Identification tests. This type of test measures a pupil's ability to carry out identification procedures. He is given one or more unknown specimens and the materials he will need to test their properties. He is scored on the accuracy of his identification.

Example 1. A pupil is given ten unfamiliar mineral specimens, with equipment for determining such properties as hardness and streak. He is asked to give the names of the specimens.

Example 2. A pupil is given five bottles of solutions and litmus paper. He is asked to determine which solutions are acid, which are neutral, and which are alkaline.

Example 3. A pupil is given four unfamiliar leaves and a key to leaf identification. He is asked to use the key to determine the names of the leaves.

Advantages. As with performance tests, pupils are working with actual materials. The test measures their true understandings of procedures. Verbalization has little place in the test.

Disadvantages. As with performance tests, adequate materials must be provided. To be fair, the specimens must be unfamiliar to all pupils; this may be difficult to arrange.

Recognition tests.   In this type of test, familiar materials are presented to the pupils who are then to give the proper name of each specimen. Usually the specimens are numbered so that the pupil may write the name of the specimen opposite the corresponding number. Sometimes responses are oral.

Example 1. Twelve different flowers are placed in glass jars to which numbered labels are glued. The jars are placed in order on the laboratory tables. Pupils number their answer sheets from one to twelve and move in turn from specimen to specimen, writing down the name of each.

Example 2. Twenty-four trays, each containing identical sets of ten numbered rock specimens, are given to the pupils. The pupils write down the names of the specimens.

Example 3. Ten large mounted birds are held up one at a time before the class. The pupils write down the names of the birds in the order they are presented.

Example 4. Ten different insects are mounted in glass topped boxes, one to a box, and the boxes are given numbers. The boxes are passed about the class and the pupils are expected to write down the name of the order to which each specimen belongs.

Advantages. This type of test measures a pupil's ability to recognize and name actual materials. It is far superior to any purely verbal tests designed for the same purpose.

Disadvantages. The naming of specimens is a minor goal of science but is given great weight by this type of test. These tests have some of the administrative problems that handicap all tests using science materials— difficulty in providing adequate materials, storage of materials, noise and confusion during the taking of the test.

Name association test. A recognition test may be simplified by giving the pupils lists of names of the specimens to be presented. The pupils write the number of each specimen opposite the proper name. There may be more names than specimens, as in matching questions.

The association of names and specimens may be considered sufficient. If recall of names is desired, this type of test may be used as a teaching test to give early practice in naming of specimens. It may be followed by the recall type of recognition test described above. Advantages and disadvantages for this form are about the same as for the standard recognition test.

Modified recognition test. The following is an excellent test to determine what pupils know about science materials. Specimens are presented with questions about the characteristics of the specimens. Identification may be requested, but sometimes the questions are formulated so that naming is not essential.

> *Example 1.* A tray contains a fossil trilobite and a card with the question, "Is this group of animals common, rare, or extinct today?" The tray is passed from pupil to pupil for examination.
>
> *Example 2.* A specimen of hard maple lumber has tacked to it a card with the question, "Is this wood used most commonly for furniture, for paper pulp, or for framing houses?" The specimen is passed about the class.
>
> *Example 3.* A microscope shows a single stomata in a bit of leaf epidermis. Beside the microscope is a card with the question, "Of what use is this structure to a plant?" Pupils take turns looking through the microscope.

Advantages. Here is a test that emphasizes knowledge of characteristics and uses more than identification of specimens. It eliminates much of the dependence on words and pictures and diagrams that are typical of most test questions. The material covered can be truly practical. Pupils like this type of test. It is useful for self-evaluation. The specimens may be kept in a drawer or box for pupils to use when they have completed certain assignments. A few specimens may be put on a side table for pupils to use as they wish.

Disadvantages. The test is apt to be difficult unless familiar materials are used. If the answer depends upon identification as well as upon knowledge of the characteristics, a pupil may fail to answer it correctly for either of two reasons—inability to identify the specimen or lack of information about it. The administrative problems involved are the same as those for recognition tests.

Picture tests. Pupils may be given pictures with accompanying questions. These pictures may be clippings from magazines and old texts. The teacher whose hobby is photography may take pictures of local features, especially those seen on field trips, and prepare enlargements for testing purposes.

Pictures may be stapled in filing folders together with a set of questions to be answered. Then the folders may be passed from pupil to pupil. Duplicate folders reduce the time needed for taking the test. After the test, the folders may be stored in a locked filing case for use in succeeding years.

Example 1. A picture of an elm tree without leaves is pasted to a card. A question on the card reads, "What is the name of this tree?"

Example 2. A photograph of a transformer station is stapled to the left side of a filing folder. Letters identify some of the structures. On the right side is stapled a typewritten sheet bearing the following: "We visited this transformer station last week. What is the voltage of the electricity at A? What is C called?" Similar questions follow.

Example 3. A clipping from a magazine shows a steep hillside, and a valley with streams and lakes. Several features are identified with letters written with colored ink for contrast. Question sheets contain blanks for the answers and such questions as the following: "At which place will stream erosion be most rapid?" "Where will sediments be deposited?" "Where would you expect to find the clearest running water?"

Advantages. This type of test has some of the advantages of tests using real specimens, especially when the pictures deal with features seen by pupils in their class work. It is an excellent way to measure information gained during field trips. The test materials are more easily stored than are actual specimens.

Disadvantages. A major weakness of the test is the limitation of any pictures. Pupils must interpret two-dimensional images into three dimensions. The pictures must be very good if grades are to be recorded.

Diagram and model tests.   A model may be displayed in front of the class, or a diagram may be provided on a chart, the blackboard, or on duplicated sheets. Letters or numbers identify various structures. Duplicated question sheets may be provided or the teacher may point to certain structures in turn while asking about each.

Example 1. The teacher displays the enlarged model of an eye often seen in classrooms. He dissects the model and holds up several parts in succession. Pupils are asked to write down the name of each part.

Example 2. A chart shows a diagram of the human digestive system. Pupils are given sheets with the names of the organs. They are asked to write by each name the number that identifies the corresponding structure on the chart.

Example 3. Pupils are given sheets on which the diagram of a lift pump is printed. The valves are identified with letters. Beside the diagram is the question, "On the upstroke of the piston, which valve is open and which valve is closed?"

Advantages. Sometimes specimens and pictures are not available, or a knowledge of internal structure is to be tested. Then diagrams serve a purpose. They are better than strictly verbal tests when questions cannot be formulated clearly in words.

Disadvantages. Models and diagrams are far removed from reality. They are apt to be very difficult to interpret, especially for pupils who lack the ability to think in the abstract. Pupils should be thoroughly familiar with each model or diagram before it is used for testing purposes.

Drawing tests. Pupils may be asked to make drawings of some object or device they have studied during class work. Labels and explanations may be required in addition.

> *Example 1.* Make a drawing of a spider, showing the major parts of the body and where the legs, palpi, and spinerets are attached.
>
> *Example 2.* Make a diagram of the apparatus used to prepare sodium hydroxide from table salt. Label the parts.
>
> *Example 3.* Make a cross-sectional diagram of an electric light bulb. Show with a heavy line the path of the current through the bulb.

Advantages. This type of test measures a pupil's ability to visualize things studied in the science program. Some pupils are better able to express themselves by drawing than by writing.

Disadvantages. Some pupils cannot make an acceptable drawing even when they can visualize an object. Such a test item should be given as a choice so that these last pupils may choose some other form of expression. Generally, drawings require a disproportionate amount of testing time for completion.

Completion drawings. Pupils are given a drawing that is incomplete and they are asked to add the proper lines to complete the drawing.

> *Example 1.* An electric bell, a push button, and a dry cell are pictured on the question sheet. Accompanying directions read, "Draw lines to represent the wires needed for making the bell ring when the button is pushed."
>
> *Example 2.* The question sheet shows an outline drawing of a goldfish without fins. The directions read, "On this diagram of a fish draw the missing fins."

Advantages. This type of test requires less skill than a standard drawing test. Time needed for completion is short. The answers are usually simple to correct.

Disadvantages. Pupils may misinterpret the diagrams provided for them. Pupils need practice with completing the same types of drawings.

Essay questions.   These well-known questions require a pupil to describe in words, usually organized in paragraph form but sometimes in outline form, his knowledge on specific topics. Sometimes the points he is to cover are outlined for him, sometimes he must anticipate what the teacher expects him to cover.

> *Example 1*. Explain how a submarine is made to rise or sink.
>
> *Example 2*. Describe the life cycle of the American toad, indicating where each stage is spent and the seasons when important changes occur.
>
> *Example 3*. With the aid of diagrams explain why you can hear an echo.

Advantages. This type of test shows what goes on in a pupil's mind more clearly than other types of purely verbal tests. It indicates how orderly his thinking is and how good his grasp of fundamentals. Essay test items should be included in most tests.

Disadvantages. Some pupils cannot express themselves well in written language and are penalized unduly. They may be discouraged if faced with too many essay questions. Though essay questions are easy to formulate, they are burdensome to grade and few can be used in any one test without imposing a hardship.

Short explanation questions.   This type of question is but a shortened version of a standard essay question, the subject being limited so that the answer may be given in a single sentence.

> *Example 1*. Explain with one sentence the following statements: (1) The lowest string of a violin has a larger diameter than the highest string. (2) A trombone player lengthens his horn to play a low note.

Advantages. This type of question tests a pupil's understandings in the same fashion as an essay question but is more economical of time for both the pupil and the teacher. By using several of these instead of a single essay question, a greater coverage of material is possible.

Disadvantages. Some pupils cannot express themselves well even with single sentences and many have difficulty in writing concisely enough to give an answer in so limited a fashion.

Completion statements.   Pupils are given a set of statements that lack a word or phrase for meaning. The pupil is supposed to add a word or phrase in the blanks provided, either within the sentence or at the side.

Example 1. Fill in the blank in each of the following with the proper word:
(1) An explosive gas that is lighter than air is _____.
(2) The product resulting from the combustion of sulfur and oxygen is _____.
Example 2. Write in the space in the left-hand margin the word that best completes the following sentences:
_____ (1) The part of the automobile engine where air and gasoline vapor are mixed is the __(1)__.

Advantages. These tests measure how well pupils can recall words or phrases, and when recall is important they make an excellent testing device, easy to take and relatively easy to score. Wide coverage is possible in a short time.

Disadvantages. The test does not measure understandings, only recall of words. It cannot be scored mechanically; the teacher must be alert for the possible significance of each separate answer.

Multiple choice. A multiple choice test is somewhat like a completion test in that statements are not completed. Several possible suggestions are given and the pupil is to choose one or more from them. It stresses recognition rather than recall.

Example 1. Underline the word that best completes each of the following statements:
(1) The alloy of copper and tin is called (solder, zinc, bronze, brass).
Example 2. Write in the spaces at the left the number of the word that best completes each of the following:
_____ 1. The portion of the sun's spectrum that causes sunburn is (1) infrared (2) yellow (3) ultraviolet (4) Hertzian (5) orange.
Example 3. Underline the words that may be used to complete the following statements correctly. More than one word may be suitable.
1. Air is (colorless, elastic, weightless).
2. One of the gases in the atmosphere is (argon, nitrogen, oxygen, carbon dioxide).

Advantages. Multiple choice items can be answered and scored rapidly. A wide range of subject matter can be tested in a short time. The questions are fairly easy to write. By using four or five alternates in each question, the effect of guessing is relatively unimportant. These tests are excellent for all purposes—motivation, review, and evaluation.

Disadvantages. These questions measure only on the recognition level. Because the scoring is mechanical, there is danger that the problems of the pupils will be overlooked.

Correction tests.   Pupils are given sentences or paragraphs with a number of italicized words which reduce the meaning of the statements to absurdity. Pupils are to replace the italicized words with others which make the statements intelligent.

> *Example 1.* Change the italicized words in the following paragraph so that the paragraph has meaning:
>
> Tom went down to the *garden* to go fishing. The trout were swimming about with their *hands* and *feet* looking for *chickadees* and other insects. Tom baited his hook with a *carrot* and tried to catch one of the trout.

Advantages. This type of test is a welcome variant to standard tests and pupils like its absurdities. It measures recall in the fashion of completion tests.

Disadvantages. This type of exercise has the same disadvantages as completion tests with the added problem that the wrong words may distract the thinking of the pupils. Perhaps it should not be used for determining grades.

Matching exercises.   The question sheets for this type of test list two parallel columns of words or phrases. Often there are more items in one column than in the other. Pupils are asked to pair the words in the two columns and indicate their decisions by writing letters or numbers in appropriate blanks.

> *Example 1.* Choose from the list at the right the word that seems most closely related to each of the words in the left-hand column. Write the numbers of the words in the corresponding blanks.
>
> _____ refraction   1. mirror
> _____ light source   2. lens
> _____ absorption   3. incandescent wire
> _____ reflection   4. black cloth
> _____ light transmission   5. vacuum
>   6. night
>
> *Example 2.* Below are some scientific principles, each of which has been given a letter. At the left are some devices that operate because of these principles. Write the letter given to a principle in the blank by the device that operates on this principle. You may use each more than once.
>
> _____ thermostat   A. Cold air is heavier than hot air.
> _____ thermometer   B. Most liquids expand when heated.
> _____ hot air furnace   C. Different metals expand at different
>   rates when heated.

Advantages. This type of test is quickly answered if the number of items is limited to ten or so. The answers are quickly checked. The range of material tested may be broad. Guessing is reduced, especially if one column contains more items than the other.

Disadvantages. Too many items become confusing. There is always a strong possibility that two or more assiciations can be made for any item; mechanical scoring does not reveal the thinking of the pupil. Pupils should be given opportunities to explain their choices.

Grouping tests. This type of test requires pupils to recognize several terms that are associated with each other. In a list of several items the pupils are to select those that are related in some way and to discard those that are not.

Example 1. Below are sets of five terms, only four of which are related in some way. Cross out the word that does not seem to belong with the others:

cow duck horse rabbit cat
oriole robin chickadee tanager bat.

Example 2. Below are sets of five terms and a suggestion for the way four of the terms are related. Cross out the term that does not belong with the others:

hygrometer, barometer, anemometer, ammeter, thermometer (weather instruments)
hurricane, cyclone, typhoon, monsoon, isobar (type of wind).

Advantages. This is an interesting type of test and it stimulates discussion. It tests knowledge of groupings.

Disadvantages. Alternative groupings may suggest themselves to pupils unless suggestions are given.

Arrangement exercises. The pupils are given a list of terms that are to be arranged in some specified order.

Example 1. Following are the names of the planets. List these in order of their distance from the sun, beginning with the nearest:

Mars	Earth	Uranus
Pluto	Saturn	Jupiter
Mercury	Neptune	Venus

Example 2. Below are the names of the processes used in preparing a photographic print. List these in the order in which they occur:

fixing	washing	stop bath
exposure	development	drying

Example 3. Below are drawings of the four stages of the housefly. Put a number 1 by the first stage, a 2 by the second stage, and so on.

Advantages. This type tests knowledge of sequence and order. It is good for review and for starting discussions.

Disadvantages. It is difficult to give partial credit in scoring this test. Probably it should not be used in determining grades.

True-false items. In this familiar type of test, pupils are given a number of statements which they are to judge for accuracy. They may accept a statement or refuse to accept it, signifying their decisions with *true* or *false*, *yes* or *no*, or a plus or minus sign. Sometimes a pupil is permitted to qualify his answer with a sentence telling why he cannot answer either way.

> *Example 1.* Write the word *true* or *false* in the blanks at the left of each statement:
>
> ——————— 1. White pines have five needles in each cluster.
>
> *Example 2.* Circle the letter T at the left if you believe a statement to be true. Circle the letter F if you believe it to be false.
>
> T   F   1. A ship will sink deeper as it passes from the Hudson River into the Atlantic Ocean.
>
> *Example 3.* In the space at the left of each statement, make a plus sign if you believe the statement to be true. Make a minus sign if you believe it to be false. If you do not believe the statement can be called either *true* or *false*, make a zero in the blank and explain your reason below.
>
> ——————— 1. Ice must change to water before it can change to a vapor.

Advantages. A great number of items can be answered in a short time, making broad coverage possible. The answers can also be checked rapidly, particularly with the use of a key. This type of test is good for initiating discussions and makes a good pretest.

Disadvantages. It is very difficult to write items that are strictly true or false without qualifying them in such a way that pupils can guess what is expected of them. Much of the material which lends itself to this type of testing is relatively unimportant in the science program. If pupils guess the answers, they have a one to one chance of selecting the right answer. Mechanical grading makes it impossible to know why a pupil made his choice. True-false items are not well suited for determining grades.

Modified true-false items. True-false tests may be modified to reduce the guessing prevalent in standard true-false tests and to encourage a higher degree of thinking. The statements made are the same but pupils are to rewrite false statements so that they are true. Usually some clue as to the desired change must be given.

Example 1. If you judge the statements below to be true, write *true* in the spaces at the left. If you judge them to be false, re-write them so that they are true.

_____ 1. Chlorine added to drinking water removes dissolved minerals.

Example 2. Below are some statements, some of which are true and some of which are false. If you believe a statement is false, change the italicized word so that the statement is true.

_____ 1. Butterflies have *four* wings.

_____ 2. Houseflies have *four* wings.

Advantages. This modification of a true-false test is useful in stimulating discussion.

Disadvantages. The time needed for checking the answers is increased and it is difficult for pupils to score them. It is also difficult to assign credits for giving grades.

Sometimes—always—never items. This type of test is much like a true-false test with a third alternative offered.

Example 1. If you believe one of the statements below to be always true, circle the letter A at its left. If you believe it is never true, circle the letter N. If you believe that it may sometimes be true, circle the letter S.

A   S   N   1. A magnet has two poles.

A   S   N   2. An electric current sets up a magnetic field.

A   S   N   3. Like magnetic poles attract each other.

Advantages. The addition of the third alternative reduces the chances for guessing to one in three. The test is speedily answered and scored. The questions may stimulate a good deal of discussion while being scored.

Disadvantages. When writing the items it is difficult to avoid giving clues to the answers expected. The fairly high chances for guessing correctly reduce the value of these items for giving grades.

TEST CONSTRUCTION

Test construction is the most critical phase of the testing program. A number of factors must be considered: the function of the test, the type of learning to be tested, the way the test is to be administered, and the way it is to be scored. A number of decisions must be reached before actual writing begins.

Techniques for testing easily verbalized factual information are highly developed; these may be used with assurance. Performance tests for determining degrees of manipulative skills are also reliable. Less can be said for the procedures that have been developed for measuring the broad outcomes of science—the skills used in applying principles to new situations and the ability to think critically, and to discriminate. Statistical analysis of the results from these last tests shows that unwanted factors often enter and invalidate the results.

The problem is that these broad outcomes are not verbal; they determine courses of action and the only real way to measure them is to see how an individual reacts in a specific situation. He must not even know that he is being tested, because that knowledge will condition his behavior.

Verbal tests designed to measure broad outcomes commonly describe hypothetical situations and ask pupils to make decisions or describe courses of action they might follow. Pupils are conscious of being tested, of course; they may take added time for reflection, they may be influenced by the wording of the question or a list of alternatives from which to choose, and their answers may be completely unrealistic.

The verbal factor enters immediately. A special premium is given for ability to visualize from the printed page and to express thoughts in writing. The final score on the test reflects reading and writing ability in an undetermined amount. Another factor, insight, enters this type of testing. Pupils with insight can make proper choices with a minimum of background. Thus a test may measure intelligence as well as achievement and the final score is affected by both.

It is recommended here that beginning teachers be cautious about using tests of broad outcomes in the determination of grades lest injustices occur. However, this statement should not blind teachers to the high value of these tests in promoting discussions and stimulating special problems.

Preliminary decisions. The type of test item used in measuring factual information will be determined by the level of learning expected. It would be unfair to ask questions that demand mastery when the topic tested was treated casually in the classroom. Essay questions are best for determining mastery. Completion items may be used for the recall level. Various association exercises may be used for the recognition level.

The range of the sampling desired influences the choice of test items. Little sampling is possible with essay questions or other questions that require a relatively long time for completion. Short-answer test items permit broad coverage in the time allotted.

Problems of scoring must be considered. If a teacher must give long tests to a large number of pupils he should use test items that are scored quickly. If pupils are to score the tests only items that call for positive answers should be employed so that the teacher need not determine the validity of the many alternative answers that may be given.

For major tests it is usually wise to include several different types of test items. Variety makes taking a test more pleasurable and reduces the fatigue factor in both taking and scoring. Variety also permits the display of a greater variety of pupil talents; in a series of short tests this objective can be met by using a different type of item for each test.

When tests are to be used for grading, items that permit simple scoring are preferred. Test items that require weighted scores for different types of answers, such as modified true-false, or correction factors to compensate for guessing, are too cumbersome to be practical.

Writing test items. The best questions are always simple and direct. Each additional adjective, adverb, and qualifying clause increases the complexity of a question and augments the possibilities for misinterpretation. Words should be those commonly used in the classroom; the mere introduction of a new word in a lesson does not justify its use in a test unless it was used again and again so as to become part of the pupils' vocabulary. There is always danger that verbal tests may become little more than vocabulary tests. Questions should be written to measure understandings rather than the ability to use words.

Precision of writing is essential. Essay questions are particularly apt to be vague. Instead of asking pupils to describe the life history of the honey bee, the question should specify precisely what is wanted:

> *Describe the life history of the honey bee, telling what stages it passes through, where the eggs are laid, how the young are cared for, and how the queen differs from the other females in the colony.*

Short answer questions that allow but one correct answer need especially precise writing. It is not uncommon to find two or more of the choices correct even though only one is accepted. In a matching exercise, the word "inorganic" in the right-hand column could be matched correctly with nine of the ten words in the left-hand column. A multiple choice item on a final examination read:

> *Water in the atmosphere exists as a* (1) *solid* (2) *liquid* (3) *gas.*

Completion questions are especially difficult to write because even slightly different interpretations of the questions may bring to mind a wide range of answers. The following question illustrates the point:

Green plants produce their own _____.

A pupil who thinks in terms of photosynthesis may write "food," "sugar," "carbohydrates," or some equivalent word. All would be correct. A pupil who thinks along a different channel might answer "chlorophyl," "cellulose," "leaves," or even "oxygen." These answers are not all equally valid, but they do not represent errors of thinking and should be accepted because the question itself is at fault. The above question should be rewritten to help pupils understand more precisely what answer is desired of them:

Green plants can produce their own food only in parts that contain _____.

Broad generalizations are particularly difficult to test. Frequently even the test maker does not have sufficient background to recognize the limitations of a generalization. The following item has been encountered several times:

Magnets have (1) one pole (2) two poles (3) three poles (4) four poles.

Undoubtedly, the test makers have expected the second choice to be the only correct choice. They have not realized that magnets with more than two poles do exist. They would not have fallen into error, however, had they written the question so that it dealt with a specific case:

Our bar magnets have (1) one pole (2) two poles (3) three poles (4) four poles.

Weaknesses of the types just illustrated are not serious in tests used for motivation, review, drill, and the like. Indeed the variations in answers can give rise to very interesting discussions and additional study. But it is most unfair to include such questions in tests which are used for determining grades.

TESTING PROCEDURES

Administering tests.   Generally the most favorable time to give a test is at the beginning of the period. During the interval between classes the pupils have had opportunities to move about and relax. They are in the best condition to sit in quiet concentration for a few minutes. If the test is given later in the period, it may be wise to let the pupils stand, stretch, and otherwise release physical tensions. If the test is given at the end of the period, it should be timed carefully so that all pupils complete it before the class bell rings.

It is difficult for pupils to sit quietly and concentrate when they are excited about athletic contests, social events, and holidays. Tests used at these times should be short. The scores may not be valid and should rarely be used in determining final grades.

Physical conditions under which tests are to be taken deserve consideration. Lighting should be adequate and shades should be drawn if sunlight falls on the pupils' work. The temperature should be comfortable and the air fresh. It is sometimes desirable to ventilate a room thoroughly before a test, this being preferable to trying to adjust windows during the test.

The manner in which a test is introduced may greatly influence the attitude of the pupils. An efficient, business-like manner, with directions given crisply and clearly, makes the test seem important. A calm, unhurried attitude relaxes the pupils without minimizing the importance of the task.

The shortest possible interval between the announcement of a test and the beginning of work helps keep the attention of the pupils centered on the task. Pupils should clear their desks and have their pencils ready. If duplicated question sheets are used, these should be divided and passed back by rows. If the questions have been written on the blackboard, these may have been covered by charts which are quickly removed. As soon as each pupil is ready, directions for answering the test should be given tersely but adequately.

Interruptions should be kept at a minimum. Errors in the question sheets may be discovered by reading the test in advance of the class period; corrections may be dictated at the same time directions are given. Pupils who are puzzled by illegibility, unfamiliar words, and possible multiple interpretations may be helped in individual consultation rather than by loud-voiced questions that distract others.

Cheating is much more prevalent than many teachers realize and is a serious problem. It is unfair to those who do not cheat. Those who cheat deprive themselves of a chance to recognize their own strengths and weaknesses. It contributes to the moral degeneration of young people.

Cheating can be reduced by improving the emotional atmosphere of the classroom. Tensions tend to build up when a great deal depends upon the outcome of a test. Pupils cheat to protect themselves against the penalties that may result from failure. The use of frequent practice tests gives pupils a feeling of competence. Determination of grades by the use of many measures, including many tests, reduces the importance of any one test.

Cheating can be discouraged by establishing conditions that make it difficult. Opportunities for cheating are minimized if the pupils are well separated from one another and if their desks are cleared of books and papers. For major tests, it may be desirable to prepare for alternate rows two forms of a test, possibly with the same questions but in scrambled order.

Cheating is reduced if the teacher is obviously alert to the problem. He should move quietly about the rear of the room, watching the pupils casually. If he reads at his desk, or writes on the blackboard, or leaves the room, he is encouraging his pupils to cheat.

The conclusion of a short test does not usually present any serious problems because most pupils complete their work within a minute or two of each other. The variation in working time is greater for long tests and activities must be provided for those who complete their task first. These pupils may begin work on assignments, or do independent reading, or work on individual projects. Directions for beginning general assignments may be given at the time directions for the tests are given. Specific assignments may be given as each pupil turns in his test paper.

Checking and scoring tests.   Pupils gain the greatest benefits from testing when they check their answers immediately after taking a test. At that time they can best recall the thinking that led them to make certain decisions. Whenever possible, pupils should be allowed to score their own tests, either as a group, with the teacher serving as the authority, or as an individual assignment, with texts and notebooks serving as authorities.

From the administrative standpoint the best types of tests for pupil-scoring are those which call for single, positive answers, such as multiple-choice items and matching exercises. If a test permits alternative answers, as in the case of most completion questions and essay questions, the teacher is forced to judge each answer that differs from the one he dictates. This is time consuming and quickly becomes boring to a large number of the pupils.

Teachers should plan to score all tests used for determining grades. Grades become permanent records as to the successes and failures of pupils. Pupils cannot be trusted with this important aspect of teaching. They are not experienced in objective evaluation and they lack sufficient background to recognize exceptions and fine distinctions. And some are tempted to cheat because of a feeling of insecurity.

The task of scoring a large number of test papers can be most burdensome. Teachers should be alert for ways of simplifying the task. Often a few minutes spent in properly organizing a set of test questions can save an hour or more of scoring time.

Essay questions are especially fatiguing to look over. A teacher's objectivity deteriorates after reading through several dozens of answers. To reduce the fatigue factor it is wise to include single essay questions along with short-answer questions in a number of tests rather than to construct a few tests of essay questions only.

To improve objectivity in scoring essay questions, it is helpful to prepare a check-list of points expected in the discussion. A teacher should use a check list with discretion, however, remembering that pupils may not think of all the points that a teacher would desire even though they could discuss them adequately had these points been brought to their attention.

Short answer tests can be scored quickly through the use of keys. The process is simplified if the pupils are asked to write their answers in blanks along the left-hand margin of the question sheet. A matching exercise and the key used to score it is shown below.

A KEY USED FOR RAPID GRADING OF A MATCHING EXERCISE

Key	Answers		Matching exercise
2	4	bituminous coal	1. abrasives
3	10	chalcopyrite	2. coke
6	6	galena	3. copper
1	1	garnet	4. gasoline
7	7	gypsum	5. iron
8	8	limestone	6. lead
5	5	magnetite	7. plaster of Paris
4	4	petroleum	8. Portland cement
9	11	pitchblende	9. radium
11	9	sphalerite	10. sulfur
			11. zinc

Another method which reduces the time for scoring is the use of a key placed over the answer sheet in such a fashion that correct answers can be observed through holes in the key. A set of numbers or letters is provided for each question on the sheet. The pupils are directed to block out the symbol which corresponds to the correct choice given in the question. The key is made by cutting out the correct symbols in an extra question sheet. Figure 21 shows part of an answer sheet and key used in this fashion.

A device useful for rapid scoring of multiple-choice items is the arrangement of the correct answers in an easily memorized sequence such as 3, 2, 4, 1, 3, 2, 4, 1, and so on. Or the sequence may shift regularly—1, 2, 3, 4, 2, 2, 3, 4, 3, 2, 3, 4, and so on. The answers for the test given on page 383 are arranged in this fashion.

The dangers of mechanical grading must be emphasized. The individual and his ways of thinking are completely ignored. Proper analysis of tests, as described in the next section, will help identify exceptional ways of thinking and weaknesses of testing procedures.

No set rule determines the amount of credit to be allotted to correct answers to the different types of questions. Teachers must rely upon their own judgment. Generally, more credit is allotted to those questions that require the higher degree of thinking. Thus a multiple-choice item might be given one credit, a completion question might be given two credits, a one-sentence answer five credits, and a one-paragraph answer ten credits.

When true-false and other either-or questions are used, the guessing factor should be considered. Theoretically, a pupil can achieve about half credit without even reading the questions and any knowledge, however slight, should raise him above this level. Obviously a correct choice should not be given the same relative weight as a multiple-choice item, for instance. Factors can be applied to reduce the weight of these items, but these are complex; it is simpler not to include such questions on tests used for final grades.

Teachers customarily assign credits in ten's to simplify the calculation of test grades in percentages. This is not necessary or always desirable. A test might be made up as follows:

12 multiple choice items at 1 credit each	12
4 completion items at 2 credits each	8
1 one-sentence answer question at 5 credits	5
Total	25

The final percentage grade may be calculated by multiplying the point score by four. Thus, a paper with twenty points credit would be given a grade of 80 percent.

Some teachers prefer to use letter grades, especially for essay questions. It is then necessary to convert number grades gained on short-answer tests. One method commonly used to do this is to give an A for grades between 90 percent and 100 percent inclusive, a B for grades between 80 percent and 89 percent inclusive, and so on.

Some teachers prefer to record point scores rather than percent or letter grades. This procedure has the advantage of permitting the use of

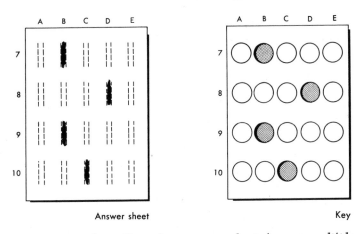

Figure 21. *A portion of an answer sheet from a multiple choice test, correctly answered, and its key. The key is prepared by cutting out the correct choices from a blank test paper. When the key is placed over the answer sheet, a pupil's correct answers show through the holes in the key.*

tests of different lengths without providing factors to insure proper relative weights. However, pupils may not understand the significance of a point score, and it may be wise to convert these to percentages on the papers before returning them.

The effort to be objective in grading is apt to result in some overly rigid practices. There are, however, several ways to provide flexibility without being influenced appreciably by prejudice. One may give pupils a choice of several questions, say ten out of twelve questions. This procedure assumes that none of the material of the test is essential and that pupils should be credited for mastering any substantial portion of it.

A test may also be graded on the basis of fewer questions than are actually asked. For instance, a test may be made up of 44 items but the grade would be calculated on the basis of 40 questions. This practice presupposes that it is natural and not serious for pupils to make some mistakes.

Some teachers like to add bonus questions for pupils to answer if they have time and inclination. Credits earned from the bonus questions are added to the basic score. This procedure awards pupils for additional effort in the course. Teachers may also give as bonus points more credit than is generally assigned to a question when the answer is unusually good. This practice rewards pupils for extra insight.

Some of the above methods make possible percentage scores over a hundred. When point scores are used, this is immaterial. Special explanations might be in order should outsiders investigate the grading system.

Analyzing test results.   After a test has been scored it is usually worthwhile to spend a few minutes in analysis of the results. An analysis may reveal deficiences in teaching and faulty test constructions that would go unsuspected otherwise. Sometimes one discovers that pupils are penalized for the faults of the teacher.

Short answer tests are easy to analyze. A test given to twenty-eight ninth grade pupils is shown on page 383. The grades attained by the pupils tell little save that about half the class did rather poorly. There is no clue as to whether the fault lies with the pupils, the teacher, or the test. An analysis may help identify the difficulties.

The first step is to total the number of correct answers for each item. These are written in the blanks on an unused paper as shown in the sample. Immediately it can be seen that items 1, 2, 4, 7, and 8 gave little difficulty to any pupils. Quick review of the questions shows that the material is not simple and the alternate choices are not ridiculous. It may be assumed that the material tested by these items is well taught.

The other items, particularly number 9, are unsatisfactory and need further investigation. The papers are now sorted into two equal piles with the higher scores in one pile and the lower scores in the other. The distribution of correct answers in each pile is now determined for each item. The information is then entered on the test sheet.

In the case of item 3, twelve of the high scoring pupils gave correct answers, but only two of the low scoring pupils were able to do so. Random guessing might account for the latter two. Most likely this is a difficult question, as examination of the wording reveals. It is difficult for many pupils to believe that carbon, which they know as a black solid, can exist in the air. The distribution of their choices shows that they selected soil or fertilizer as the logical source for a black solid. It is probable that this information was treated on an abstract plane and only certain pupils could grasp the concept. The fault lies almost certainly in the teaching.

Thirteen of the high scoring pupils answered 5 correctly. No pupils selected the rose as a choice, a fact that indicates some understanding of the nature of the rose plant. Wrong choices were distributed between mosses and ferns and probably some pupils guessed mushrooms correctly. The pupils seem to have little understanding of these three plants. They need extensive experiences with them.

Assuming some guessed item 11 correctly, almost half the class had little knowledge of the structure of cactuses. Probably this subject was touched upon in class without the use of specific examples so that only pupils with good experience backgrounds or the ability to visualize from words grasped the desired concept.

The answers for item 10 show about the same distribution as those for item 5. It is surprising that more pupils did not answer this one correctly. Some of them must have been confused by the question or by something said in class. Perhaps the correct alternative looked too simple when compared with the last two. Many pupils who do not feel secure in academic work do not trust their own knowledge in tests.

Item 6 would be a confusing question if class discussion had centered about trees, because certainly a large amount of a tree's food is converted to wood and cellulose. Perhaps that is what happened in this case. Again the distribution of scores indicates that it was a difficult question.

A NINTH GRADE SCIENCE TEST AND DATA
USED TO ANALYZE IT*

Name____ *28 pupils*____   Score_____

Choose the word or phrase you think best completes the following sentences. Write the number of the word or phrase in the blanks at the left.

28   1. Plants that make their own food must contain   (1) acids   (2) bases   (3) peptones   (4) chlorophyl.

26   2. Energy needed by green plants for food manufacture comes from   (1) light   (2) fats   (3) fuel   (4) air.

14   3. The carbon needed for the sugar produced by plants comes
12-2   from   (1) water   (2) the soil   (3) the air   (4) fertilizer.
                 2   5   14   7

28   4. During food manufacture, a plant gives off   (1) proteins   (2) oxygen   (3) carbon dioxide   (4) alcohol.

21   5. An example of a plant that cannot make its own food is the   (1)
13-8   rose   (2) moss   (3) mushroom   (4) fern.
                0   4   21   3

12   6. Much of the food produced in a green plant is stored as   (1)
8-4   starch   (2) wood   (3) cellulose   (4) vitamins.
           12   6   10   0

26   7. Trees manufacture most of their food in their   (1) roots   (2) stems   (3) leaves   (4) bark.

27   8. The manufacture of food by green plants is called   (1) osmosis   (2) photosynthesis   (3) chloroplasts   (4) solution.

8   9. Hydrogen needed by plants for the manufacture of food comes
4-4   from   (1) the soil   (2) water   (3) air   (4) acids.
             5   8   12   3

* The significance of the italic numbers is given in the text.

18
——
12-6

10. Food manufactured by plants is used chiefly for   (1) growth
                                                                                              18

(2) keeping warm   (3) enriching the soil   (4) inorganic com-
                  1   5   4

pounds.

16
——
11-5

11. Most cactus plants manufacture food in their   (1) roots   (2)
                                                                                         0

leaves   (3) stems   (4) flowers.
   12   16   0

20
——
8-12

12. Parasitic plants get their food from   (1) the soil   (2) other plants
                                                              2   20

(3) animals   (4) the air.
       6   0

Distribution of Grades:

100 — 1	67 — 9
92 — 3	58 — 4
83 — 3	50 — 1
75 — 7	

Item 9 shows such a low total that the correct answers could be attributed to random guessing. It seems likely that this topic received no attention in class work, perhaps because of an oversight. Like item 3, it is difficult, and pupils need many concrete experiences to make the concept meaningful.

The distribution of scores for item 12 opposes the pattern shown for most of the other items. In this instance more of the low ranking pupils answered the question correctly than did the high ranking pupils. The effect of random guessing cannot be ignored, but it seems likely that the test item itself is at fault. Critical inspection of the alternate choices reveals that the third alternative is correct. Perhaps some of the higher ranking pupils had information that led them to make this choice.

In summary, the analysis shows that about 40 percent of the material covered by the test was well taught. Of the remainder, most had been well taught on an abstract level but about half the pupils needed more concrete experiences—experiments, demonstrations, and the like. One topic seemed to have been ignored during classwork. One test item was faulty and should have been discarded when the teacher calculated scores.

Similar analyses may be carried out for all test results. When working with essay tests and performance tests, it is necessary to break down each question into its component parts to calculate the distribution of correct answers. One must not expect to understand all the situations revealed by an analysis, but the analysis will point out many things that normally go unsuspected.

STANDARDIZED ACHIEVEMENT TESTS

Inevitably, during the testing program, the question arises, "How does this group of pupils compare with pupils elsewhere?" To make comparisons many tests have been constructed for use on a system-wide, a county-wide, or a state-wide basis.[1]

Such tests constructed by amateurs are apt to be unfair to pupils because of mechanical faults—poorly worded questions, "tricky" alternatives in multiple choice items, and the like—faults that can be discovered only by expensive statistical analysis. In consequence, there has been a demand for tests constructed by commercial testing bureaus which have the facilities for proper analysis. These tests are standardized for nation-wide usage and supposedly represent the best in test making.

Standardized tests have been constructed for each of the major subject matter areas. For science, there are batteries of tests to measure general achievement in science as well as tests for the special branches. There are also tests that are claimed to measure scientific aptitude.

Uses of standardized tests. Standardized achievement tests are best adapted for diagnostic purposes. In the science program they may be used as follows:

[1] Tests have been prepared by the various National Curriculum Study Groups for their courses of study. Biological Science Curriculum Study Test Material: A set of four quarterly tests has been prepared for each of the three versions of the BSCS material. These tests are available from the respective publishers of each version.
1. BSCS High School Biology (green version), Rand McNally and Company, P.O. Box 7600, Chicago.
2. Biological Science: Molecules to Men (blue version), Houghton Mifflin Co., 2 Park Street, Boston.
3. Biological Science: An Inquiring Into Life (yellow version), Harcourt, Brace and World, Inc., 757 Third Ave., New York.
4. A final comprehensive examination for BSCS, which is the same for all three versions, can be obtained from The Psychological Corporation, 304 East 45 Street, New York, N.Y.
Chemical Education Material Study: A set of five achievement tests covering the material of this approach has been prepared by CHEMS. In addition, a two-part first semester examination and a two-part final examination have been prepared. All test items are multiple choice in design. Tests are available for purchase from W. H. Freeman and Company, 660 Market Street, San Francisco.
Education Development Center, Inc. (PSSC): A set of ten multiple-choice tests has been prepared by the Educational Testing Service of Princeton, New Jersey. Tests numbered five and ten are comprehensive in nature and are designed for use at mid-year and at the conclusion of the PSSC course.
Chemical Bond Approach: As with the PSSC testing program the Educational Testing Service of Princeton has produced in conjunction with the CBA testing committee a set of multiple-choice tests for use with CBA materials. A comprehensive final examination is also available.

1. *To determine the achievement level of individual pupils.* This information is helpful in assigning a pupil to a grade or section, and to determine his fitness for an advanced course.

2. *To determine a pupil's areas of strengths and weaknesses.* A battery of achievement tests reveals the areas in which a pupil has achieved more or less than that which is normal for others of his age and grade. The information helps in guiding him into special fields or in planning remedial work.

3. *To determine a pupil's progress.* Two forms of the same test, given a few months apart, indicate growth during the interval. Abnormal growth, whether unusually rapid or slow, draws attention to his need for special consideration.

4. *To determine the relative standing of a class as a whole.* This information helps in program building. A class that scores much higher than the national norm can probably do more advanced work than a class at or below the norm.

5. *To determine areas of strength and weakness for a class.* During the planning of a balanced program it is helpful to know which areas need special emphasis.

6. *To determine class progress.* Progress as measured by achievement tests is one measure of the effectiveness of the teaching procedures being used.

Limitations of standardized tests.   Scores attained on standardized tests should not be used as sole determiners in making up final grades; it may be that they should not enter into the grading process at all save to reveal pupils who are being penalized unfairly by the testing techniques used. Standardized tests cannot fit the local curriculum. They cannot measure most of the desirable outcomes of a program.

Standardized tests are sometimes misused. Too much is expected of them. Their misuse can be traced to the fallacious assumption that there is a certain body of information that pupils should acquire by regular yearly increments. This presupposes that there is a universal curriculum, which is contrary to present-day educational philosophy.

> Teachers and administrators sometimes make the mistake of assuming that the total effectiveness of the learning situation can be measured by standardization tests. If this kind of thinking prevails, the results of the achievement test become identified as the main objective. Instead of a curriculum being a growing thing, changing from time to time to meet the needs of students and the community and responding to the individual talents of the members of the teaching staff, it becomes stereotyped and even sterile. The chief end of teaching, under such circumstances, is the

preparation of students to pass the achievement test. Thus teachers are prevented from attempting to make any improvements in the curriculum, because they are afraid that any deviation, no matter how slight or how desirable, may result in students making lower marks on the examination.[2]

The weaknesses of standardized tests do not make them useless; they only limit their usefulness. Standardized tests are among the many educational tools needed to insure maximum benefit for the boys and girls in our schools.

List of standardized tests. The list of standardized tests compiled by Lacey[3] is of interest to the science teacher.

1. *The Iowa Placement Examinations in Chemistry and Physics.*
   (Aptitude tests designed to predict success in first-year college chemistry and physics.) Bureau of Educational Research and Services, State University of Iowa, Iowa City, Iowa.

2. *The Engineering and Physical Science Aptitude Tests.*
   (Aptitude tests designed for similar purpose as the one above.) Psychological Corporation, New York, New York.

3. *Cooperative Science Test for Grades 7, 8, 9.*
   (Designed for measuring achievement in science.) Educational Testing Service, Princeton, New Jersey.

4. *Cooperative General Science Test.*
   (Designed for measuring achievement in high school science.) Educational Testing Service, Princeton, New Jersey.

5. *The Read General Science Test.*
   (Also designed to measure achievement in high school science.) Harcourt, Brace & World, Inc., New York, New York.

6. *Nelson Biology Test.*
   (Designed to measure achievement in high school biology.) Harcourt, Brace & World, Inc., New York, New York.

7. *The Cooperative Biology Test.*
   (For measuring achievement in biology.) Educational Testing Service, Princeton, New Jersey.

8. *The Anderson Chemistry Test.*
   (For measuring achievement in Chemistry 1.) Harcourt, Brace & World, Inc., New York, New York.

[2] Lindgren, H. C., *Educational Psychology in the Classroom*, Wiley, New York, 1956.
[3] Lacey, Archie L., *Guide to Science Teaching in Secondary School*, Wadsworth Publishing Co., Belmont, California, 1966.

9. *The Dunning Physics Test.*
   (Illustrates use of multiple-choice and multiple-option to measure outcomes of instruction in physics.) Harcourt, Brace & World, Inc., New York, New York.

10. *The Cooperative Physics Test.*
    (For measuring achievement in physics.) Educational Testing Service, Princeton, New Jersey.

11. *The Cooperative Chemistry Test.*
    (For measuring achievement in chemistry.) Educational Testing Service, Princeton, New Jersey.

The reader who is interested in the very latest information on tests for measuring aptitude and achievement in science should write to the Educational Testing Service, Princeton, New Jersey, for their latest descriptive materials. Such descriptions and representative samples are available free of charge.

Directory of standardized tests.   Below is a directory of sources of testing materials which are of interest to the science teacher.

1. Educational Testing Service, 20 Nassau Street, Princeton, New Jersey.

2. Psychological Corporation, 304 East 45th St., New York, New York. 10017

3. Harcourt, Brace & World, Inc., 750 Third Avenue, New York, New York.

4. The American Chemical Society, 1155 Sixteenth Street, N.W., Washington, D.C.

5. Bureau of Educational Research and Service, State University of Iowa, Iowa City, Iowa.

6. California Test Bureau, 5916 Hollywood Boulevard, Los Angeles, California.

7. The National Science Teachers Association, 1201 Sixteenth Street, N.W., Washington, D.C.

8. Bureau of Publications, Teachers College, Columbia University, New York, New York.

9. Educational Test Bureau, Educational Publishers, Inc., 720 Washington Avenue, S.E., Minneapolis, Minnesota.

10. Houghton Mifflin Company, 2 Park Street, Boston, Massachusetts.

11. Public School Publishing Company, 204 West Mulberry Street, Bloomington, Illinois.

12. Science Research Associates, Inc., 57 West Grand Avenue, Chicago, Illinois.
13. Stanford University Press, Stanford, California.

MEASURING PROGRESS TOWARD BROAD GOALS[4]

For many years, progressive science teachers have desired tests that demand more than a simple recall of facts. Unfortunately, techniques for writing the desired test items have not been as highly developed as those used for testing factual information.

In 1958–59, the Bureau of Examinations and Testing of the New York State Education Department planned a massive attack on the problem, channeling efforts towards the preparation of Regents Biology Examinations. Committees were appointed, consultants were employed, and at one time, over fifty experienced teachers were under contract to provide test items.

Of the several thousand test items submitted, only a tiny fraction were found suitable for inclusion in Regents examinations. Many were discarded immediately because they were based on factual information rather than on thinking skills. The remainder were submitted to a large sample of high school age youngsters, and the results were analyzed. Most of the items so tested were found to be invalid. Of the remaining few, many were too difficult for present use but may be suitable for use later as high school teachers realize what is being demanded of their pupils.

From the results of the above study, the Bureau issued a tentative guide for the preparation of biology test items. The following paragraphs from the introduction of the guide indicate the philosophy of the Bureau and the guiding committee.

> Probably the greatest challenge will be presented by efforts to test various skills and attitudes, partly because there are fewer precedents in this field of testing than in the testing of facts and partly because there are many influences at work to bring about outcomes which are contrary to the avowed goals of science education. The pressure to include ever more and more facts is, perhaps, one of the most serious of these influences. Teachers who submit to the pressure present pupils with masses of information without showing how the information is obtained. They expect pupils to

[4] Hedges, William D. *Testing and Evaluation in the Sciences*, Wadsworth Publishing Co., Belmont, 1966. This excellent paperback publication presents many examples of test items based on the categories of Bloom's taxonomy (cognitive domain). Topics included are measuring the ability to analyze relationships, analysis of organizational principles, and abstract relations.

verbalize generalizations without an adequate understanding and appreciation of the facts upon which the generalizations are based or the limitations
of the generalizations.

Direct experience type activities suffer severely from pressures to include
more subject matter. Field work is abandoned early. True experimentation
is found too time-consuming. In its place, demonstrations, films, pictures,
and laboratory exercises of the verification type are used to defend the
statements of teacher and text. There is little time for discussion of results,
for consideration of the relative weights of evidence and of the validity of
conclusions, and for an analysis of hypotheses and theories.

In consequence, test makers are faced with the problem of giving recognition to pupils who, by themselves or through the efforts of superior
teachers, develop important attitudes and skills, without penalizing those
pupils whose teachers have not upgraded instruction beyond conventional
levels.

Probably for a few years, questions dealing with attitudes and skills must be
rather simple, but there should be in each examination at least a few that
call for more of the type of thinking that is a goal of science education.
The inclusion of even a few of these will serve partly to recognize those
pupils who have achieved this goal. Possibly of greater importance, such
questions will serve to remind teachers that they must give as much attention to the way their pupils learn as to what they learn.[5]

One portion of the guide deals with testing abilities and skills. This
section is quoted here because the suggestions may be useful to teachers
who wish to construct tests which measure more than factual information.

A science program must be more than a presentation of facts which pupils
can temporarily memorize without engaging in high-level thinking. An
examination that is designed to recognize pupils who have done more than
dutifully master a set of facts must itself do more than concentrate upon
those facts.

The questions written for this area of the blueprint should test such abilities and skills as the following:

1. the scientific approach to problem solving, particularly the use of the
   experimental method

2. the recognition of cause-effect relationships

3. the evaluation of methods and data

4. the analysis and interpretation of data, including simple mathematical
   skills

5. the appropriate organization of data and suitable generalization there-
   from

6. the application of specific facts and general principles to common problems

---

[5] Division of Educational Testing, Bureau of Test Development, The New York State
Education Department, *Teacher's Guide for the Biology Regents Examination*, The
University of the State of New York, Albany, 1962.

7. the recognition of the various facets of scientific thinking

Some of these important abilities and skills are taken up under the following subheadings:

Techniques of Experimentation: Controlled experiments are the ultimate authority in scientific research. Pupils should have wide acquaintance with true experimental techniques. They should understand what is meant by the independent variable and the dependent variable. They should recognize controlled factors and know the significance of uncontrolled factors. They should have formed the habit of looking for uncontrolled factors in their own experiments and those of others. They should know how to draw conclusions with the possibilities of uncontrolled factors in mind.

For testing skills with experimental techniques, the standard situations described in laboratory manuals may not be particularly valuable. Pupils very often can easily memorize the procedures without understanding the significance of what they do. Better examples for test purposes can be found in reports of original research such as those given in *Science;* many of these experiments are simple, straightforward, and very interesting.

Illustrative Questions

Multiple Choice

1. It has been suggested that something in tomato juice prevents seeds from germinating while in the fruit. To test this, one might moisten 50 tomato seeds with tomato juice. For a control, he should
   (1) moisten 50 tomato seeds with water
   (2) moisten 50 seeds of another fruit with tomato juice
   (3) keep 50 tomato seeds in a cool, dry place
   (4) chemically analyze the juice of a tomato   1. _/_

2. A species of beetle is usually found feeding on the undersurface of leaves. An experiment was performed by inverting a plant and observing that the feeding beetles then preferred the side of the leaves which had become the top surface. From this observation, the most probable conclusion would be that these beetles normally feed on the undersurface of leaves because they

   (1) react negatively to sunlight
   (2) react positively to gravity
   (3) are safer from their natural enemies
   (4) prefer that surface for their food   2. _4_

Evaluation of Methods and Data: Some of a research scientist's highest level of thinking goes into the evaluation of experimental methods and the data obtained by these methods. The search for uncontrolled factors is especially critical.

Illustrative Questions

Multiple Choice

1. Pupils concluded that their bodies give off carbon dioxide after they had blown through limewater. However, one girl argued that since there is

carbon dioxide in the air they inhale, the experiment proves nothing. The girl's argument

(1) is unscientific
(2) is invalid because there is too little carbon dioxide in the atmosphere to be considered
(3) shows that the pupils needed a control to check the effect of inhaled carbon dioxide on limewater
(4) ignores the reaction of isotopes of carbon dioxide produced during respiration   1. _3_

Organization and Interpretation of Data: Successful manipulation of data depends upon a number of skills, including certain basic mathematical skills. Pupils should be sufficiently familiar with the metric system to visualize the units and to carry out computations within the system. However, they should not be expected to have memorized formidable conversion constants or to have mastered elaborate conversions from one system to another.

Pupils should be able to organize data in tables and graphs and should be able to interpret both of these forms. Among simple statistical procedures, they should be able to calculate percentages and averages.

Illustrative Questions

Multiple Choice

1. A count of the mustard plants in a field averaged 12 plants per square meter. This is about the same as saying that there were 12 plants in each
   (1) square yard
   (2) square foot
   (3) three square feet
   (4) six square yards   1. _1_

2. The body temperature of a living whale stranded on a Connecticut beach was found to be 33° centigrade. This is about the same as a Fahrenheit temperature of
   (1) 50°
   (2) 70°
   (3) 90°
   (4) 110°   2. _3_

3. If each pair of robins raises two broods of four nestlings each year, and yet the total robin population remains stable, the percentage of the robin population that must die each year is
   (1) 20%
   (2) 60%
   (3) 75%
   (4) 80%   3. _4_

4. *Temperature* (°C.)   *Oxygen Concentration (parts per million)*

Temperature (°C.)	Oxygen Concentration (parts per million)
0	14.7
15	10.3
30	8.3

The above table gives the amount of oxygen that may be dissolved in water at different temperatures. From the table you can deduce why

(1) warm water enters into chemical reactions more readily than cold water
(2) trout survive better in cold water than in warm water
(3) photosynthesis proceeds more rapidly in aquatic plants than in land plants
(4) the bottom of deep lakes is commonly lacking oxygen   4. _2_

5. The graph below shows the tiny changes that take place in the diameter of a pine tree from hour to hour.
On the basis of the graph, a reasonable hypothesis would be that
(1) the trunk expands when heated by sunlight
(2) the trunk expands during periods of transpiration
(3) there is a daily rhythm to the water pressure in the trunk
(4) the rate of growth of a tree is greatest during rainy seasons   5. _3_

Characteristics of Instruments: Through their laboratory work, pupils should have learned a good deal about commonplace instruments used in biological research. It is especially important that they know something of the limitations of these instruments and the effect of the limitations on the data collected.

Illustrative Questions

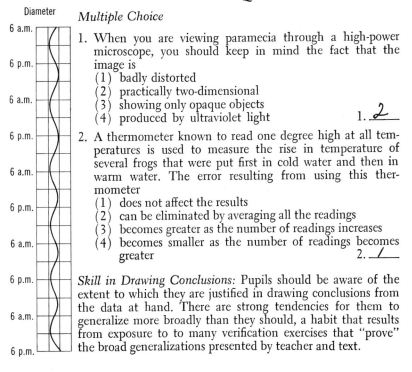

Multiple Choice

1. When you are viewing paramecia through a high-power microscope, you should keep in mind the fact that the image is
(1) badly distorted
(2) practically two-dimensional
(3) showing only opaque objects
(4) produced by ultraviolet light   1. _2_

2. A thermometer known to read one degree high at all temperatures is used to measure the rise in temperature of several frogs that were put first in cold water and then in warm water. The error resulting from using this thermometer
(1) does not affect the results
(2) can be eliminated by averaging all the readings
(3) becomes greater as the number of readings increases
(4) becomes smaller as the number of readings becomes greater   2. _1_

Skill in Drawing Conclusions: Pupils should be aware of the extent to which they are justified in drawing conclusions from the data at hand. There are strong tendencies for them to generalize more broadly than they should, a habit that results from exposure to to many verification exercises that "prove" the broad generalizations presented by teacher and text.

Illustrative Questions

Multiple Choice

1. Forty young rats were fed on milk, bread, and a concentrate of all known
vitamins. Forty other rats had the same diet except that water replaced
the milk. The rats receiving the milk gained weight 10% faster than
the others. This seems to show that
   (1) milk is an essential food
   (2) young rats need milk for proper growth
   (3) milk contains nutrients not classed as vitamins
   (4) milk contains all the known vitamins   1. *3*

2. Two petri dishes of a nutrient jelly are inoculated with a species of
bacteria. One dish is placed in sunlight on a warm window sill; the
other is placed in a dark refrigerator. The bacteria in the refrigerator
grew slowly; the ones in sunlight did not grow at all. From these data
a scientist would decide that
   (1) sunlight is harmful to bacteria
   (2) this species of bacteria grows best in a cool, dark place
   (3) bacteria grow better in the dark than in the light
   (4) he does not have enough evidence for a conclusion   2. *4*

Identification of Patterns of Scientific Thinking: Young people can cope
with the barrage of ideas coming at them from every side only if they can
identify the type of thinking involved in each. They should be able to
separate facts from generalizations, to differentiate between idle speculations and well-founded hypotheses, to identify direct evidence and circumstantial evidence. They should be able to judge when someone is "jumping
to conclusions," reasoning from analogy, or employing circular reasoning.
They should know the difference between inductive and deductive reasoning. They should know the relative value of untested hypotheses, theories
supported by indirect evidence, and theories supported by direct evidence.
Questions testing such skills will vary greatly both in form and content.
Suggestions can be found in scientific articles both in those of a general
nature in which theories are discussed and in reports of original research.
Newspaper articles provide another source of questions for testing pupils'
ability to get to the heart of an argument. Discussions of fallacies, abandoned theories, and unqualified generalizations may also be used.

Illustrative Questions

Multiple Choice

1. A few kinds of animals, such as the duckbill (platypus), lay eggs. This
shows that
   (1) mammals and birds are closely related
   (2) certain mammals have degenerated to lower forms
   (3) evolution has taken place among mammals
   (4) it is difficult to generalize about animals   1. *4*

2. Insects have a number of sense organs, but zoologists usually refuse to
identify positively the type of senses involved in each except for the
eyes. This type of thinking is an example of

(1) generalizing upon insufficient evidence
(2) withholding judgment
(3) being critical of authority
(4) inductive reasoning   2. _2_

SUGGESTED ACTIVITIES

1. Make up several samples of different kinds of test items. Submit these to your science methods class for criticism.
2. Study the test items given in a textbook or other publication, examining them for possible weaknesses that might confuse pupils.
3. Obtain a set of answer papers from a science teacher, and analyze the scores to look for weaknesses in test construction.
4. Prepare a pencil-and-paper test for a science class, administer it, and analyze the results.
5. Set up a test that uses actual materials, and administer it to a science class.
6. Examine standardized tests in science or the science section of general achievement tests. Try to determine how well the tests meet their objective.
7. Start a test item file.

SUGGESTED READINGS

Ahmann, J. Stanley, *Testing Student Achievement and Aptitudes*, The City of Applied Research in Education, Inc. (The Library of Education), Washington, D.C., 1962.

Brandwein, Paul F., Fletcher G. Watson, and Paul E. Blackwood, *Teaching in High School Science: A Book of Methods*, Harcourt, Brace & World, New York, 1958.

College Entrance Examination Board, *Science: A Description of College Board Tests in Biology, Chemistry, and Physics*, Educational Testing Service, Princeton, N. J., 1954.

Cronbach, L. J., *Essentials of Psychological Testing*, 2nd edition, Harper, New York, 1960.

Dressel, Paul L., and Clarence R. Nelson, *Questions and Problems in Science*, Test Item Folio I, Educational Testing Service, Princeton, N.J., 1956.

Faunce, R. C., and C. L. Munshaw, *Teaching and Learning in Secondary Schools*, Wadsworth Publishing Company, Belmont, Calif., 1964, Chapter 13.

Gerberich, J. Raymond, Harry A. Green, and A. N. Jorgensen, *Measurement and Evaluation in the Modern School*, David McKay Company, New York, 1962, Chapter 18.

Hedges, William D., *Testing and Evaluation for the Sciences*, Wadsworth Publishing Company, Belmont, Calif., 1966.

Hoffman, B., "Toward Less Emphasis on Multiple Choice Tests," *Teachers College Record*, vol. 64, December, 1962, pp. 183–189.

Link, F. R., "Approach to a more adequate System of Evaluation in Science," *The Science Teacher*, 34:20–22, February, 1967.

Montag, B. J., "Testing," *American Biology Teacher*, 26:589–591, 1964.

National Society for the Study of Education, "The Measurement of Understanding," *Forty-fifth Yearbook*, Part I, University of Chicago Press, Chicago, 1946, Chapter 6.

National Society for the Study of Education, "Science Education in American Schools", *Forty-Sixth Yearbook*, Part I, University of Chicago Press, Chicago, 1947, Chapters 6, 8 and 15.

Richardson, John S., *Science Teaching in Secondary Schools*, Prentice-Hall, Englewood Cliffs, N.J., 1957, Chapter 7.

Schwartz, G., "How to Score Teacher Made Tests," *Industrial Arts and Vocational Education*, December, 1962. Vol. 51, p. 23–24.

Smith, Herbert A., and K. E. Anderson, "Science," *Encyclopedia of Educational Research*, 3rd edition, Macmillan and Co., New York, 1960, pp. 1216–1232.

Thomas, R. Murray, *Judging Student Progress*, Longmans, Green and Co., New York, 1960.

Travers, R. M. W., *How to Make Achievement Tests*, Odyssey Press, New York, 1950.

Chapter 12

Unit Planning

UNIT ORGANIZATION BECAME AN IMPORTANT FACTOR IN EDUCATIONAL PRAC-
tice early in this century. Previously, the educational scene was dominated
by the "recitation method" with its daily ground-to-be-covered procedures.
Unit organization seemed a possible antidote for the abuses of the daily
recitation. It was designed to make more use of positive motivation and
to give greater attention to individual differences.

Superficially, units in the science program have always appeared to be
little more than blocks of subject matter. In consequence many teachers
have the wrong impression of what a teaching unit involves, and they fail
to take full advantage of its characteristics. A true teaching unit is as
concerned with the means of presentation as with the subject matter. In
other words, a teaching unit is composed of both method and content.

Unit organization makes two types of contributions to the educational
process. First, it breaks up the year's work into sections small enough so
that pupils can grasp the scope of any one of them during a brief overview.
Most pupils work better on a series of short tasks than on a few large ones.
They can grasp better the purpose of what they are doing. They can
concentrate more intently for short periods and are spurred on by prospects

of early completion of each task. They are stimulated by their more frequent successes.

The second type of contribution of unit organization stems from procedures used in developing a unit. There is an introductory phase during which pupils are shown the purpose of what they will be doing and during which they are made ready for their tasks. This is followed by the presentation of new material. Finally, there is a concluding phase during which the material presented is made meaningful to the pupils.

Unit organization has had strong influence on modern teaching practice. At one time the use of teaching units was even called the "unit method," to distinguish it from the "recitation method," the "project method," and the "laboratory method." Today the distinction no longer exists and such techniques as recitation, project work, and laboratory work may be called for in a unit plan. But the basic structure of the unit still remains a prominent feature in the educational scene.

THE STRUCTURE OF A TEACHING UNIT

Teaching units are organized on the premise that in order to learn pupils need more than mere exposure to subject matter. Accordingly, a teaching unit is made up of introductory phases that prepare the pupils for the experiences that lie ahead of them; a main presentation provides the pupils with opportunities for meaningful experiences; and the concluding phases allow the pupils to organize and review the learnings they have acquired.

Thus a teaching unit has a structure of its own. It is neither a block of subject matter nor a series of independent lessons. Each lesson plays a role in the development of the unit. Under some circumstances a lesson may be part of the introductory phase or it may be devoted to the presentation of new experiences. Usually, however, a single lesson has more than one function, perhaps getting the pupils ready for a new experience, then presenting the experience, and finally helping the pupils assimilate the learnings. There is no stereotyped pattern for the development of a teaching unit; everything depends upon the nature of the subject matter, the background of the pupils, and the conditions under which the unit is taught.

The elements of a teaching unit.   The teaching unit as developed early in this century has the following elements:

1. Motivation
2. Overview
3. Inventory of background
4. Presentation of new experiences
5. Organization of learnings

6. Summarization
7. Drill
8. Review
9. Evaluation

It is important to realize that these elements of a teaching unit need not be used in the above order. Review and drill may be used throughout a unit, not just near the end. Sometimes an inventory of pupil backgrounds serves little purpose. Motivation may need attention several times.

The motivational phase.   Pupils need a purpose for what they do—not a purpose dictated by the teacher, but a purpose they themselves recognize. The motivational phase is designed to help pupils establish their own purposes for what they will be doing as the unit progresses.

The motivational aspect of planning is often misunderstood. Too often teachers act on the assumption that motivation can be applied from without. They set up their own purposes for the unit, usually without reference to the needs of pupils, and try either to force these purposes upon the pupils or to "sell" them to pupils with a variety of clever tricks and devices. A later section of this chapter will describe some specific techniques for handling the motivational period.

The overview.   An overview of a unit helps pupils see the scope of the material with which they will be dealing. They then can look ahead and plan their procedures accordingly. Obviously, the overview is of great importance in teacher-pupil planned units. The overview must be complete before plans can be made. However, the overview need not be made by the teacher; the pupils themselves can define the scope of their work and prepare the overview, not necessarily in the formal sense but perhaps as they are defining the problems they intend to solve.

In teacher-dominated units the complete overview need not be given at the beginning. It is often wise to break the presentations into segments and precede each with a correspondingly limited overview.

The inventory of experience backgrounds.   "Start with pupils where they are" is a precept of modern education. It is of special importance in science teaching because so many science understandings depend upon the experience backgrounds of the pupils.

An inventory of such experiences as are pertinent to a unit is useful in pointing out things that need not be repeated and that can be depended upon during discussions. It also shows lacks on the part of one or more pupils who will then need special attention.

The presentation of new experiences.   Everything in a teaching unit is centered about the presentation of new experiences. All else is either a preparation or a follow-up for this phase of the unit.

Experiences presented may be either direct or vicarious. In general, first-hand experiences are more profitable because they are so well remembered, because all pupils can benefit from them, and because the resulting learnings tend to be more accurate than those derived through some medium of communication. However, books, films, and other sources of vicarious experiences are valuable when pupils have backgrounds adequate for interpreting them.

In most units, a judicious balance between direct and vicarious experiences is desired. Direct experiences introduced early in a unit provide a background helpful in interpretation of vicarious experiences introduced later. Direct experiences also encourage all pupils to take an active part in the work of the unit and thus benefit by the early introduction of such experiences.

There is no fixed rule for the presentation of new experiences. Usually it is wise to present a few in each lesson rather than to concentrate a large number in a few lessons. A few lessons should be devoted to review or organization or some other type of activity.

The organizational phase.   Good teaching practice specifies that pupils should have opportunities to bring their learnings together in some form that shows relationships. Teachers commonly decide upon the pattern for such organization and they make sure that pupils recognize the pattern by providing study guides. Some teachers depend upon the organization given in the textbook.

However, in the teaching unit provision should be made for pupils to develop their own pattern of organization occasionally. This gives them a more active role in the process and is more effective in producing understandings. The pattern that results may not be conventional, but it will be meaningful to the pupils.

Organizational activities are commonly verbal. Most written reports are summaries. Oral summaries are frequently used, often to help in the preparation of written reports. However, organizational activities need not be verbal. Many projects are in effect nonverbal reports. Their preparation involves careful organization.

Summarization.   Summarization is an integral part of the learning process and is given an important place in the teaching unit. However, summarization is too often provided by the text and the teacher. Pupils should be given opportunities to carry out this activity for themselves.

Summarization is needed near the close of a unit to bring together all the learnings. Summarization is also desirable at intervals during the progress of a unit. Some teachers plan to end each day's lesson with some type of summarization activity.

Organization and summary commonly go hand in hand. As soon as a pattern of organization has been developed, learnings may be summarized according to this pattern. Sometimes from the summary a pattern of organization becomes evident.

Review and drill. If there is learning, there is certain to be forgetting. As soon as pupils cease to use the facts or skills they have learned, they begin to forget them. A review is in effect a reteaching; drill is intensive and prolonged review. Whenever learnings are considered important enough for pupils to remember, review and sometimes drill must be provided.

Reviews are commonly verbal but need not be so. There are more effective ways to recall learnings. A learning experience repeated, in shortened form or with sufficient variation to hold interest, makes one of the best forms of review. Exhibits of collections, posters, and the like may be effective reviews.

Evaluation. Evaluation in the teaching sense is self-evaluation, provided to help pupils discover what they have achieved and what they have failed to grasp. This type of evaluation should come well before the end of a unit so that pupils can understand the nature of their deficiencies and then attempt to remedy them.

Numerous short tests given throughout a unit help with self-evaluation. They also serve as review and drill when constructed with these functions in mind. It is usually good practice to give two or three short written tests a week.

Because verbal tests measure only limited outcomes, other forms of self-evaluation should also be provided. Whenever possible, performance tests should be used. Individual interviews, during which pupils demonstrate and explain, are especially effective. Self-checking devices are helpful. Electric question boards make self-evaluation seem like a game. Science crossword puzzles are often used for vocabulary testing. Picture quizzes and the like are effective.

The final test of a unit serves only to provide a grade and to help a teacher evaluate his own teaching effectiveness. It should be constructed with these purposes in mind.

SELECTING THE CONTENT FOR A UNIT

The success or failure of a unit is determined in large part by the nature of its content. Some material lends itself to good teaching practices; some does not. Criteria for a good unit are listed below:

1. It should be possible to base each unit upon many direct, individualized experience activities.
2. A unit should deal chiefly with work that has not been done before.
3. The range of materials included in a unit should be sufficiently wide to interest all pupils.
4. It should be possible for the more capable pupils to extend the unit beyond the limits suggested.
5. The unit should have many direct applications to the immediate lives of the pupils.
6. The unit should anticipate some of the future needs of pupils.
7. A unit should be part of a sequence that permits growth from year to year.[1]

The choice of subject may be dictated in part by the program outlined in a course of study or a textbook. However, all such programs can be modified to meet specific situations; even when the content is mandatory, the pattern for organization is not. The nature of a unit can therefore be dependent upon a number of important factors.

The need for limitation of content. All too often teachers plan units entitled "Electricity" and "Reproduction." These topics are far too broad to be given adequate treatment in single units. To attempt to use them encourages superficiality of thinking and may produce incorrect concepts because of over-simplification. Many pupils become confused and discouraged by the many subdivisions and possible ramifications.

More suitable units can be built around such limited topics as "Electricity in the home" and "Starting plants without seeds." Pupils are able to grasp the scope of these units in one brief overview. They can keep the major problems and methods of attack in mind throughout the unit. They have opportunities to discover the details upon which the more limited generalizations are based.

Following are some titles of successful units. The scope is self-evident from the titles.

[1] From *Science 7–8–9*, New York State Education Department, Albany, 1956.

1. How our homes are heated
2. Hard and soft water
3. Instruments of the school orchestra
4. How our bodies are controlled
5. Plainville's water supply
6. Developing new breeds of animals
7. Vacuum tubes and their uses
8. Plants in autumn
9. Weather instruments at the airport
10. Geology of Danby State Park

The importance of familiar materials.   Units based on familiar materials are generally more successful than units based on remote and strange materials. Pupils have an experience background on which new understandings can be built. They recognize the signficance of the problems that are raised. They appreciate better the references that are made during the progress of the unit and they understand better the applications that are made.

Whenever possible, a unit should be built around local features. A unit on the local water supply is generally better than a unit on water supplies in general. A unit on glaciers can have real significance in Tacoma, Washington, where the glaciers on Mt. Rainier can be seen each clear day, but a unit on limestone formation would be of more significance in Miami, Florida.

A unit based on local and familiar materials need not be confined to these narrow limits. As individual pupils demonstrate interest and adequate background for more extended coverage they may be given special assignments.

The need for suitable experiences.   Learning is not a "pouring in" process, but a gradual process that comes about as a result of experiences. Unit planning, therefore, is largely a matter of deciding upon suitable experiences that may be provided for pupils. The content of the unit should be determined in large part by the availability of suitable activities for providing the experiences needed.

The best topics for units permit a variety of field trips, experiments, demonstrations, and projects. All these experiences can then be amplified by available books, films, and slides. Topics that must depend upon lectures and textbook readings for basic understandings are not well suited for young people with limited experience backgrounds.

Consideration for general education objectives. The general education objectives of the science program, as distinct from subject matter objectives, are those that bring about desirable changes in the ways of thinking and acting of boys and girls. General objectives demand situations in which pupils have opportunities to grow. Teacher-pupil planning, small and large group problem-solving situations, pupil presentations of subject matter, and projects of all kinds are essential in working toward general objectives. Content should be chosen to permit the use of such activities.

WRITING UNIT PLANS

Following the determination of content and the writing of appropriate objectives comes the selection and organization of learning activities. The teacher who has a card file of suggestions for activities may now turn to it for help in this critical phase of planning.

Using a prepared form. A prepared form is an important time saver in any type of planning. Of various forms that have been developed only two are illustrated here. The first is relatively simple for beginning teachers to understand and prepare. The second has certain advantages of flexibility that make it of great service to experienced teachers.

The simpler of the two forms is shown on pages 406–407. The activities and their expected outcomes are arranged in parallel columns. In this form the activities are listed in the left-hand column and the outcomes in the right; a varient of this form reverses the two columns. The activities are listed in the sequence in which they are to be presented but minor modifications can be made as the unit progresses. This type of form makes no provision for the several phases of the teaching unit. A teacher must keep in mind as he plans his needs for organizational activities, review activities, and the like.

Certain cautions must be observed when using this form. The parallel arrangements encourages a tendency to write a single activity followed by a major outcome. This encourages superficiality and unwarranted generalization. The expected outcomes should be limited in scope and each should be attended by a sufficient number of learning experiences to insure understanding. Usually these activities should represent different approaches to the same point.

The major disadvantage of this form is its relative inflexibility. The schedule is determined in advance and the teacher is more or less committed to follow it. Any major alterations necessitate rewriting the entire plan. In consequence, unexpected events and new directions of interest cannot be utilized conveniently.

An entirely different form, shown on pages 408–409 is a plan for what is known as a resource unit. The plan does not specify what is to be done nor the order in which presentations are to be made. Instead it lists in rich variety activities that may be used as conditions dictate. It is not a teaching plan but a true resource to which teachers may refer during daily lesson planning.

The major advantage of the resource unit is its flexibility. The first lesson of a unit may reveal unexpected conditions. Pupils may have stronger or weaker backgrounds than anticipated. They may display unusual interests. They may have negative attitudes toward the subject chosen or the presentations used.

The resource unit does not commit a teacher to a predetermined organization. When planning the second lesson of a unit he may turn to the resource unit for suggestions that enable him to fit this plan to the interests and abilities displayed during the first lesson. The third lesson can be built in accordance with conditions discovered during the teaching of the second lesson. At any time the unit may be directed into a new channel if this seems advisable.

A minor advantage of the resource unit, but one not to be ignored, is its long useful life. Any plan that specifies procedures and schedules should be rewritten before each reuse to fit it to changed conditions. But revision of the resource unit is no more than the addition of new suggestions as these are encountered and the crossing out of suggestions found impractical. Rewriting is needed only when the plan becomes cluttered to the point of confusion.

For many beginning teachers the resource unit may be considered as too flexible. The daily plans can deviate too widely. The class may ramble. The unit may go on indefinitely. To use a resource unit wisely a teacher must have in mind at all times the general scope of his unit so that deviations do not go too far astray, so that important phases are not ignored, and so that the unit is brought to a close in a reasonable time.

The two forms shown on pages 406–409 may be duplicated on standard notebook paper and punched to fit two-ring or three-ring notebook covers. It is helpful to punch the sheets so that the pairs face each other and are both visible when the notebook is open. The reverse side of each sheet may be used for test questions.

Planning the motivational phase. The unit plan shown on pages 406–407 uses a simple trick to puzzle pupils, first as a demonstration to capture attention and then as a general activity to make sure each pupil recognizes his own strange limitation, and is puzzled by it. The inevitable "why" is raised and pupils have a purpose for studying nerve action as applied to this particular situation and later as applied to other equally interesting situations.

Ordinarily, motivation presents no problems. A number of topics are

TWO PAGES OF A UNIT PLAN IN GENERAL BIOLOGY*

UNIT 6   How our bodies are controlled

Date   February 6   Approximate Time   Three weeks

Principles toward which the unit is leading:
Many of our activities are controlled by our nervous systems

We can consciously control some acts; others we cannot control

Some of our actions are controlled in whole or in part by internal
secretions

Activity	Expected outcome
1. Demonstration: Difficulty of catching dollar bill dropped between fingers	Awaken interest in mechanics of body
2. Class experiment: Pupils working in pairs repeat above with strips of paper	
3. Trace path of nervous impulse on chart of nervous system	Understanding of paths of impulses
4. Pupils make similar chart for notebooks	
5. Demonstration: Class in circle, each pupil touches pupil ahead as soon as he feels touch. Time elapsed divided by number of pupils gives reaction time	Understanding of reaction time and its importance
6. Discussion: Reaction time in sports and in driving autos and planes	
7. Special project: Make a reaction timer and test others	
8. Special project: Work out time and distance needed to stop cars at different speeds	
9. Demonstration: Electric stimulus of nerve in freshly dissected frog leg	Recognition of similarity between nervous impulse and electric current
10. Experiment: Pupils test own reactions to electric stimulus	

* Other pages of the plan list additional activities and possible outcomes. The last page also includes test items.

Activity	Expected outcome
11. Special project: Read in physiology book about nature of nervous impulse	
12. Special project: Test earthworms for reaction to electricity	
13. Class experiment with knee-jerk reflex, eyelid reflex, iris reflex, balancing reflex	Understanding of paths involved in certain special cases
14. Assigned reading: Pages 102–113 in textbook	
15. Home problems: Test dogs for vibrassa-eyelid reflex and for scratching reflex. Test baby for grasping reflex	
16. Film: "The Nervous System" (EBF)	Summarize and organize understandings and lead into study of nerve centers
17. Chart of brain	Location of important centers
18. Assigned reading: Pages 113–131 of textbook	
19. Special projects: Make chart of human brain and of other animals for comparison. Dissect out brain of cat or rabbit. Compare brain capacity of different animals using sand in school collection of skulls. Read about experiments on the brain. Read about brain surgery	
20. Class experiment: Pupils practice with mirror writing	Understand how motor skills are learned
21. Home project: Continue practice with mirror writing, keeping records of time and results	
22. Discussion: Development of motor skills such as piano playing, auto driving, and so on	

RESOURCE UNIT PLAN

Title   Static electricity   Time   allotted   2 weeks

Principles toward which the unit is leading	Bodies may be given electrical charges
	There are two types of charges
	Charging bodies gives them energy
	Bodies attract or repel each other depending on charges
	A spark is caused when charges jump through the air

Former experiences common to all pupils	Sparks caused by scuffing feet on a rug
	Sparks when combing hair or petting cats
	Shock when leaving automobile
	Static on radio
	Lightning

Firsthand experiences Experiments	Rub different objects and test for charges
	Rub paper with different fabrics and put on wall
	Dancing paper dolls; action of paper fringe
	Floating bathtub toy; attraction of ping pong ball
	Behavior of two charged balloons, strips of paper, pith balls, fringed paper, pivoted rubber rods
	Reaction of unlike charged bodies—pivoted rubber and glass rods, charged bottle and balloons, charged pith balls and charged rods, etc.
	Production of sparks by brushing paper, balloons, etc.
	Lighting of fluorescent and neon lamps by charges
	Discharging sparks near a radio to make static
	Use home-made electrophorus and charge metal cans

Demonstrations	Golf leaf electroscope
	Static electricity machine
	Leyden jar
Field trips	To transformer station to see lightning arrestors
Home problems	Test various plastics for charges
	Brush hair or pet cats in dark
	Produce sparks near A.M., F.M. radios and television

Reference books	Text: pages 136 to 182
	Morgan: *Things a Boy Can Do with Electricity*
	Zim: *Lightning and Thunder*
Films, slides pictures	Thunder and lightning
	Folder of clippings of pictures of lightning
	Make charts showing distribution of charges on materials used in experiments

Summarization activities	Make chart showing how lightning is produced
	Make a model showing how lightning rods operate
	Make model or chart showing safety in thunderstorm

of such great importance to pupils that a mere reference to one of them is sufficient to set the stage. The pupils are already conscious of problems. Sometimes they raise the issues themselves and a teacher needs only to capitalize upon them.

A new airbase had been established near the community and the sky was crisscrossed by jet vapor trails.

"Can we study about jet planes, Miss Dobson?" asked a boy in her eighth grade science class.

"Why, I guess so. What would you like to find out about them?" And thus a new unit was initiated.

Adolescents usually show immediate interest in problems that deal with their own bodies, with automobiles and other devices they consider important, with matters of local controversy, and with sensational events. However, much depends upon the backgrounds of the pupils. A topic of high interest to one group may be of little interest to another group. A teacher must know his pupils well to anticipate the topics that are of immediate importance to them.

Pupils often have had experiences which they have recognized as important but about which they have done little thinking. The teacher needs only to help them formulate some problems to awaken their interest.

Another round of polio shots had provided the pupils with some freshly tender places.

"What happens inside you when you have a polio shot?" the biology teacher asked her class.

The pupils were obviously surprised that this aspect of inoculation had not occurred to them. They had been content to accept the statement that the inoculations reduced their chances of contracting polio.

While the pupils were still speculating their teacher continued, "And what happens inside you when you are vaccinated?"

The pupils caught the trend of the teacher's thinking and began listing the other types of injections that they had received or had heard about. They were fully ready to begin a study of immunity.

Sometimes a brief argument in which the pupils have opportunities to espouse one cause or another serves to initiate thinking and establish an interest in the content of a unit.

Upon the complaint of a private conservation group, a local farmer was arrested for shooting a number of hawks. He had pridefully displayed the hawks on his main entrance gate and there was no question of his guilt. But though his fine was light his indignation was high, and many of his neighbors in that rural community sympathized with him. The teacher had only to mention the incident in his general science class to start an argument. Out of the argument grew a study of wildlife conservation.

It is not necessary to provide for the motivation of the complete unit during the introductory phase. Sometimes it is better to arouse interest in one limited topic out of which will grow interest in the remainder of the unit.

> Mr. Leland gave each pupil in his chemistry class a new nail and a test tube of copper sulfate solution. He directed the pupils to dip the nail in the solution and examine it. The pupils were immediately interested in finding out why the nail became copper colored. After they had found an answer to this specific question they wanted to know whether they could produce similar effects with other combinations and they were ready for a more formal study of displacement.

The motivational phase of a unit should be kept short. Teachers commonly defeat their own purpose by employing lengthy discussions and question-and-answer periods in an attempt to persuade their pupils that the unit to be studied will be interesting and meaningful. A properly selected topic should appeal to the pupils a few minutes after it has been introduced. If it does not, the fault probably lies in the selection of the topic or in the method of presentation; increased time for "motivation" will only intensify the pupils' boredom.

The overview. An overview is, as the name implies, a general survey of the content of a unit. Under no circumstances should it be so lengthy and so detailed that pupils are dismayed at the prospect of what lies ahead of them. Brief, but exciting glimpses of some of the high points are all that is desirable.

> "We are going to study a unit on lenses," Mr. Davidson announced.
> "How would you like to find out how a slide projector works? And a camera?"
> "Oh! May we take pictures?"
> "Of course. If you have your own camera maybe we can help you find out how to take good pictures with it."
> "Good! I'll bring mine."
> "So will I."
> "What else are we going to study?"
> "We will find out how magnifying glasses work. And microscopes. And telescopes. Maybe we can even make some telescopes."
> "Oh! This is going to be fun!"
> "I'm sure it will be, Janet. Let's start right away by looking at these lenses."

Should pupils have an insufficient background, a complete overview at the beginning of a unit might be meaningless. It may be better in such a case to begin work on a minor problem out of which pupils develop experiences suitable for appreciating an overview of the major body of the unit.

> Mr. Pettingill opened a unit on stream erosion with a field trip to a nearby stream to study the way running water erodes stream banks at a curve. The pupils made sketches of their observations.
>
> Back in the classroom the pupils speculated about the differences between the inside and outside banks. Mr. Pettingill directed the pupils to their textbooks for authoritative answers to their questions.
>
> The following day pupils came to class with additional questions about other aspects of stream erosion they had discovered in their textbooks. Mr. Pettingill helped them itemize and organize these questions on the blackboard. The resulting list served as an overview for the material that would be studied in the unit.

Whenever pupils help outline the scope of a unit in the above fashion the function of the overview is successful.

Preparing to inventory the experience backgrounds of pupils.

> "How many of you have seen kittens being born? Calves? Puppies? How many of you have seen chickens hatching? How many have watched frog eggs develop?"
>
> These were the questions Mr. Brown asked of his biology class at the beginning of a unit on reproduction. From the answers he knew fairly well what the background of his pupils might be and where he would need to start in developing his unit.

Often all that a teacher needs to find out from his pupils are the answers to a few questions. Sometimes a brief discussion of an introductory demonstration or topic of immediate interest reveals the extent of the knowledge of pupils. A teacher must be cautious in drawing conclusions, however, because a few vociferous youngsters often give the erroneous impression that an entire group has certain experiences or understandings.

Written preview tests may be used occasionally, providing these are interesting. Long, detailed preview tests may discourage pupils who do not feel secure in the science program.

Many experiences can be taken for granted. By the time boys and girls enter the secondary school they have shared such common experiences as lighting matches, operating electric switches, and boiling water. In a rural community all pupils will have seen seeds being planted and fertilizer spread on fields. In a coastal community they will have noticed the changes in tides and the appearance of a ship as it approaches over the horizon.

In addition to out-of-school experiences pupils will have shared a number of classroom experiences, especially in systems that use a uniform science program. In some schools a seventh grade teacher can be certain that all of his pupils will have at some time connected electric lamps and dry cells during their years in the elementary school. Sometimes a chemistry teacher may be certain that his pupils watched a demonstration of electroplating in the ninth grade.

The preparation of an inventory can be of much help during planning in eliminating needless repetition of experiences and establishing a foundation upon which to build. The resource form shown on pages 408–409 has a section on which this inventory may be made.

Planning first-hand experiences. A teacher's primary concern in planning a science unit is the collection of an adequate number of suggestions for field work and for classroom experiments. If enough of these suggestions can be provided the unit will probably be successful. It is relatively easy to select needed demonstrations and to find books, films, and pictures to amplify the unit.

Special attention should be given to the possibilities for individual experimentation. These are much more numerous than one may suspect, if one is thinking in terms of traditional college laboratory exercises. Popularized science books are filled with countless suggestions for experiments that require only simple materials and easy techniques.

Demonstrations have a place in the science program but they have serious limitations that make them inferior to individualized experiments and field work. They should be used when the latter are impractical.

Field work, which provides some of the most valuable of teaching situations, is apt to be neglected unless during planning there are deliberate efforts to search for specific possibilities. Traditional science teaching, particularly in the physical sciences, has so neglected field work that possibilities do not suggest themselves and must be searched for. Nonetheless, it is difficult to conceive of a unit which permits no field work because of the nature of its content.

Homework is usually thought of in terms of reading and the preparation of reports or other written papers. Homework in terms of first-hand experiences has never been given much recognition. Nevertheless, there are endless things pupils can do outside school hours to amplify their first-hand experience backgrounds. Each unit plan should contain numbers of suggestions for these activities to be assigned either as required or as permissive work. The resource unit plan form shown on pages 408–409 has a special section for writing these suggestions.

Using books and other instructional aids.   Books and other instructional aids provide many learnings that cannot be gained through first-hand experience in the usual school situation. Through exposure to films, film-strips, slides, models, and overhead transparencies, the student can become acquainted with such things as nuclear fusion, ecology of a swamp, structure and function of the circulatory system, pharmaceutical chemistry, and the production of electricity. These sources of vicarious experience should be used freely, but always with consideration of their limitations.

Books requiring different levels of reading ability should be listed in the unit plan. These may include books written for young children and books written for college students, since the range in reading levels of high school pupils is great.

First attention should be given to the books kept in the science class-room. These are always available and are therefore most useful. A brief survey of the school library and the community libraries will give the names of books pupils can borrow. If there is space, the titles of suitable books that are not available may be listed to serve as suggestions when library requests are presented.

Instructional aids available in the school collection should be listed. Rental films may be listed if there are opportunities to obtain them. Free and inexpensive materials loaned by various agencies should be listed so that they may be ordered.

Instructional aids should only be used if they provide an effective method for teaching the concepts of a selected unit. The materials should give a clear, succinct presentation of these concepts. The vocabulary used and the nature of the concept should be within the grasp of the students in the class. Special attention should be given to materials used by pupils who do not read well or who have limited experiential background.

Providing summarization activities.   Pupils need opportunities to bring together their learnings, organize them, and view them as part of a com-plete picture. Various types of projects serve excellently for this purpose. Among the projects that may be used are charts, models, collections, ex-hibits, and paintings. Dramatization can play an important role with plays, assembly programs, radio presentations, and mock television programs. Notebook and scrapbook exercises are helpful. The results of class work may be written up for the school and local newspapers.

A wide range of activities is desirable. There should be suggestions to suit different interests and different talents. There should be activities that can be carried out by the class working as a whole, by small groups working independently, and by individuals.

Suggestions for project work may be difficult to classify. Many projects require collecting information as well as organizing it. It matters little where these suggestions are placed in the final plan, as long as the potentialities of each are fully utilized.

To culminate a unit on electricity a physics class prepared an exhibit depicting some of the major developments in the history of that area of science. On a table were displayed miniature models of some of the devices that brought about early discoveries or made these discoveries useful. Behind the tables a frieze gave names, dates, places, and pictures to supplement the exhibits.

Summarization is usually thought of as conducted by the teacher. This need not be so. Pupils often are able to summarize their learnings with a little help from the teacher.

Near the close of a seventh grade unit on the uses of water, Mrs. Blair divided her class into six groups, each of which was directed to prepare a summary of the work done in one of the major areas of the unit— water power, drinking water, water for recreation, and so on.

The pupils met, used their notebooks and textbooks for reference, and prepared summary outlines. The class then reconvened, the summaries were discussed briefly, and given to Mrs. Blair. She had the summaries duplicated so that each pupil could have a copy.

Planning for review and drill. Needs for review and drill cannot well be determined in advance. Pupils may grasp desired content quickly, or they may be very slow. The best form of review and drill is reteaching. From the list of suggestions for demonstrations and experiments may be selected some that were unused earlier in the unit; when presented they review learnings often in a very interesting way.

The pupils in Mr. Jordan's physics class had constructed step-down transformers by winding coils of wire on large nails. Though these transformers were inefficient they could be used to make flashlight lamps glow.

A few days later Mr. Jordan placed a socket containing a flashlight lamp on his demonstration table. Immediately it began to glow.

The pupils were mystified at first but after noting that the lamp glowed only when placed in one spot on the desk, they recalled their laboratory work and solved the puzzle. Taped to the bottom of the socket was an inconspicuous coil of wire. Underneath the table top was another coil connected to a source of A.C. current.

Preparing for evaluation.   Excellent test items may suggest themselves during the preparation of a resource unit. If these questions are written out immediately they will be available at any time during the teaching of the unit. If they are not written out, they may be forgotten or recalled with difficulty.

If the resource unit form described in the previous section is used, the test items may be written on the reverse of the second sheet. Additional pages may be added if needed. Amendments and additions may be added at any time.

It is convenient to have a selection of test items immediately available whenever a test is to be constructed. Sometimes one is in a hurry and sometimes one is tired. It is much easier to select suitable items for a test than it is to formulate them.

Greater justice is done to pupils when test items are written out before the unit is taught. The items may be written with greater care, or, if not, there is an opportunity to revise them. Special words used in the questions are introduced carefully and drilled upon. And the test items are written with the over-all view of the unit in mind.

SPECIAL UNITS FOR SPECIAL PURPOSES

During the past half century, several unusual and interesting teaching procedures were proposed, tried out, and abandoned. Each type had certain strengths but each also had its weaknesses. Too much was expected of it, and when it failed, it was discarded completely. Nevertheless, these procedures have important values when used with care and understanding. Each type appeals to different personalities. Each changes the emphasis in a program, adds variety, and broadens the appeal of the science program to young people.

The major weakness of most of these special teaching procedures was their inflexibility. Once embarked upon, a set of plans had to be continued through to the end or abandoned entirely. There was little or no opportunity to adjust the plans as new conditions arose.

When using these special procedures in the science program it is important to remember this inflexibility. The units should be kept short and limited in scope. No matter how strongly the procedures may appeal to an adult, there is no guarantee that a group of adolescents will be challenged by them for more than a few days at a time.

Contract units.   During the 1920's there were several experiments with completely individualized instruction. Generally, all these plans established subject matter goals and then set the pupils working toward these goals as rapidly as each could progress. These plans emphasized subject matter achievement almost to the exclusion of everything else. They succeeded best with those pupils who enjoy working alone on academic tasks. Other pupils did not fare so well.

One of the individualized programs became rather famous as the so-called "contract plan." Each pupil was given a list of a set of tasks. He could "contract" to do a minimum number of these tasks for a satisfactory but minimum grade. Or he could contract to do a greater number of tasks for a higher grade.

The contract plan appeals to certain pupils and it is a welcome change from conventional procedures. A short contract unit often gives excellent results.

Miss Birdsall was doing her cadet teaching in a system that allowed her to experiment with almost any procedure she wished. One day, her supervisor stopped to see the principal of the school.

"What kind of a girl did you send me anyway?" the principal asked bluntly.

Fearing that Miss Birdsall had committed some serious faux pas, the supervisor asked what she had done.

"She's not in any trouble," the principal explained. "But when I came home the other night at eleven o'clock my son was still working on his science. The next night he worked until after ten. Ordinarily, he never does any kind of homework unless I make him. So I asked him what he was doing. He told me he was trying to finish his science contract. I thought contracts went out years ago."

A contract unit used for science should be short, perhaps five or six days at the maximum. It should be based on activities that pupils can carry out successfully by themselves, at home, during study periods, and in the library. Book research, simple home experiments, and field work lend themselves best to the contract plan. Pages 418–421 show the outlines of two different types of contract units—one for a PSSC course and the other for a general science course.

A CONTRACT UNIT IN PSSC PHYSICS*

Kinematics

The following activities, laboratory experiences and assignments comprise the total program of this unit. The items which must be completed for the student to be eligible for the indicated grade are given in the accompanying table. Answers to the questions in the text will be posted at the appropriate time. A seminar will follow the program. During the seminar, difficulties experienced in the program may be resolved.

The time allotted for completion of this unit is two weeks.

SCHEDULE			
Item		Item	
1		8	
2		9	
3		10	
4		11	
5		12	
6		13	
7		14	

GRADING		
Items to be completed to be eligible for the indicated grade		
for minimum credit	additional work required for:	
	B	A
1	2	10
4		
5	3	12
6		
7	9	
8		
11		

Tutorial conferences may be arranged as required.

As each part of the program is completed, place a check mark in the space provided on the schedule. This will serve as a progress record and will be used by the teacher in grading your work. All written work must be submitted along with the laboratory notebook upon the completion of the program or the expiration of the allotted time.

* Adapted from a unit prepared by Mr. Olcott Gardner, Science Teacher, Jamesville DeWitt High School, DeWitt, New York, 1967.

SCHEDULE
CONTRACT UNIT

Kinematics

Item	Process	Description
1.	Organize	Obtain materials for the unit and receive preliminary instructions for commencing your study of kinematics.
2.	Explore	Techniques of measuring short time intervals. Laboratory experience #II–1.
3.	Investigate	Motion, speed, and acceleration. Laboratory experience #II–2.
4.	Discuss	The derivation and application of motion relationships in seminar.
5.	Read	PSSC Physics—Chapter 5, # 1.
6.	Do	For Home, Desk, and Laboratory Problems—Chapter 5, #1, 2, 4, 5, and worksheet #1.
7.	Explore	Displacement situations—Worksheet #2—Using a pendulum.
8.	Observe	Lecture on the calculus of limits.
9.	Read	Chapter 5—Complete the balance of the chapter in the text.
10.	Do	PSSC Physics—Home, Desk, and Laboratory Problems, Chapter 5, #8, 9, 12, 14, 15, 18, 20.
11.	Evaluate	Evaluate your progress with the questions provided. After the test items have been graded, review any concepts which were not fully understood. Correct all items missed and turn in your corrections. If a tutorial session is needed make an appointment within one week of the completion of this step of the program.
12.	Research	Worksheet #3—A research problem dealing with acceleration.

A CONTRACT UNIT*

Common solutions

Read through the following items and check those that you would like to do. Then decide what grade you would like to contract for. Grades will be given as follows:

D—The starred items plus one more from each group
C—The starred items plus two more from each group
B—The starred items plus three more from each group
A—The starred items plus four more from each group

Discuss your choice with your teacher and then sign your name in the proper place on the other side of this sheet.

* Prepare a title page for the section on solutions in your notebook.
* Introduce your unit with a description of what a solution is.
* Write an article telling why solutions are important to us.

Group one

* Learn how to use filter paper to filter liquids. Make a diagram for your notebook. Filter the mixture of muddy water and ink your teacher will give you. Describe your results.

1. By experiment discover ten substances that dissolve rapidly in water and ten substances that dissolve slowly or not at all.
2. Filter tea, coffee, milk, cocoa, and six other common liquids. Describe what happens in each case.
3. Write an article on the nature of ocean water. Illustrate it with a graph showing the composition of ocean water.
4. Explain what "hard" water is and how it becomes hard.
5. Make up an experiment to show whether heat affects the rate with which something dissolves. Write up the experiment.
6. Find out how food becomes dissolved in our bloodstream.
7. Experiment to find out whether salt dissolved in water changes the boiling temperature of the water.
8. Set up an experiment to show how minerals get into plant roots.
9. Show that substances dissolved in water may change the density of the water.

Group two

* Evaporate the water from a solution of common table salt. Describe in your notebook what happens.

1. Write an illustrated account of the way sugar is prepared from sugar cane or sugar beets.
2. Find out how much mineral is dissolved in a gallon of tap water by evaporating the water.
3. Explain why rain water is "soft."
4. Tell how table salt mined from the earth can be purified.

* For a general science course.

5. Talk with a plumber about the problems caused by hard water in hot water systems. Write up your interview.
6. Prepare some distilled water and write up the process in your notebook. List some uses of distilled water.
7. Read about the playa lakes of the Great Basin west of the Rocky Mountains. Tell how they are formed and what happens in them.
8. Tell how early settlers prepared potassium hyroxide (lye).

Group three

* Read about crystals and the way they are formed. Write up your findings in your notebook. Draw some crystal forms.

1. Make some sugar or copper sulfate crystals.
2. Tell how stalagmites and stalactites are formed.
3. Make a "crystal garden."
4. Carve from soap or a potato the shapes of some natural crystals such as quartz.
5. Show how to "frost" glass with epsom salt.
6. Tell how crystals are used in industry.
7. Make a collection of sedimentary rocks made of materials cemented together by chemicals crystallized from water.
8. Make some candied orange peel.
9. Tell how petrified wood is formed.

This work is to be done at the end of the fifth period after the contract is signed. Extension will be granted in case of sickness. Extra credit will be given for superior work and additional work.

_____   _____
        (Date)   (Pupil's signature)

_____   _____
(Grade contracted for)   (Teacher's signature)

Following a review of test papers that culminated the preceding unit, Mr. Axtell initiated a discussion of the meaning of a contract. He referred to contracts used in the construction of a school or office building. The pupils knew that a construction company can contract to build either a large building or a small building, and that the remuneration varies in each case. Mr. Axtell told about the time clause, which sets the limits within which a job must be completed and which penalizes a builder who does not complete his work on time. He also mentioned the possibilities for bonuses if construction is finished early or if superior work is done.

Mr. Axtell proposed that contracts be used in the study of the next unit. The pupils were excited about the prospect and looked over the sheets of possible activities eagerly. Mr. Axtell directed the pupils to read each item carefully and check the ones each thought he would like to do. On the basis of the check marks each pupil determined the contract he would sign for. Mr. Axtell advised each pupil personally if there seemed any question about how much to contract for. Not many pupils aimed too high and none underrated his ability.

For the first two days all work was done individually in class time. On the third day, Mr. Axtell presented a demonstration near the end of the period. On the fourth day, he used part of the period for a discussion of results and a report of some special projects. On the fifth day he gave a culminating test during the last half of the period.

Most of the pupils completed their contracts on time. A few completed them before hand and were encouraged to do additional tasks for bonus points. A few pupils did not finish on time and had to stay in detention room to make up their work.

Teacher-pupil planned units. It is highly desirable to have pupils participate in the planning of science work. They understand much better the purpose of what they are doing and they benefit in many ways from the experience with cooperative planning.

It must never be forgotten, however, that pupils are not trained in educational psychology nor in the special methods of science teaching. They cannot be expected to do planning that is equivalent to what a teacher can do. They will neglect areas and procedures of which they know nothing. They may select problems that are too big for solution. And they will greatly overestimate their attention span.

The teacher must give constant attention to the planning process. It is usually well for him to plan beforehand in complete detail the unit suggested to the pupils. He is thus able to use his plans as a starting point and as a reserve of constructive suggestions should the pupils' imaginations fail.

Limited topics are best for teacher-pupil planned units. Pupils grasp better the overall development of the unit. Mistakes in estimating pupil interest and attention span are less damaging. It is also well to choose subjects that can be treated through conventional methods. Pupils understand how to obtain information from books, but they may have difficulty in setting up original experiments and in doing field research.

The original Morrisonian Unit of the 1920's, although teacher-dominated, can be adapted excellently to teacher-pupil planning. The Morrisonian Unit was divided into five steps:

1. Exploration (determination of pupil background)
2. Presentation (overview of the unit)
3. Assimilation (collection of information)
4. Organization (development of understandings)
5. Recitation (verbalization of understandings and applications)

The same five steps are desirable in the teacher-pupil planned unit but the emphasis is shifted to include increased opportunities for pupil initiative. The first step of the planning process may be given over to a free discussion of a problem set up by the teacher. This introductory problem must be selected with considerable care in order that the pupils will accept it as their own. It must appeal to their imaginations, lie within their experience background, and lead naturally into a number of subproblems which the pupils can recognize without help.

The second step, which usually intergrades with the first, is the planning period proper, during which the pupils define precisely the problems and the procedures they expect to use in their solution. As planning proceeds, the pupils gain an overview of the unit, just as the beginning discussion reveals their experience background.

The third step, like that in the original Morrisonian Unit, is one in which pupils gather information. This they may do by experimentation, by field work, and by reference to books. The fourth, or organizational step, is similar to the original plan but is modified to the extent that pupils organize their information for presentation to each other rather than in a form dictated by the teacher. The fifth period of the teacher-pupil planned unit is similar to the original recitation period except that its purpose is the sharing of experiences, rather than evaluation. Pupils should use demonstrations and exhibits of their work more than strictly verbal reports.

Some of the more exciting teacher-pupil planned units have dealt with such subjects as "What makes us tick?"—a unit on human behavior. Pupils are greatly interested in themselves and how they look to others. They attack such units vigorously. However, much skill is needed to keep these units within bounds. Without careful guidance, class time is spent in wild speculations, in reading sensational literature, and in discussions of morbid aspects of the subjects.

Teacher-pupil planned units need not differ radically from other units in a science program. Perhaps for the first few attempts at this teaching it is wise to be somewhat conventional. Later, as pupils demonstrate their readiness to accept responsibilities, they may be given greater independence.

Mr. Dewey's first experience with a teacher-pupil planned unit thoroughly convinced him of its feasibility. He chose the unit "Iron and Steel," because he anticipated his chemistry classes doing profitable library research. He was pleasurably surprised to discover that his pupils were able to plan activities other than book work and to make suggestions that had not occurred to him.

The initial discussion centered upon the relative values of different metals, the pupils thinking at first in terms of the rare metals but quickly realizing that in terms of utility steel surpasses them all. The discussion quickly raised some questions that were puzzling the pupils —"What is the difference between iron and steel?" "Why is steel better than aluminum for airplane engines?" and "Why doesn't stainless steel rust?"

The pupils seemed genuinely interested in these questions and Mr. Dewey suggested that they list all questions that they would like answered.

Some of the pupils wanted to attack these problems immediately but the majority proposed a more systematic and comprehensive approach. As a result, problems of a more general nature were set up. It was at this time that Mr. Dewey gave his first concrete help, chiefly in wording problems succinctly and in proposing aspects the pupils had not considered. Below are the problems that were finally established, as well as the preliminary problems:

Preliminary list of problems	Final list of problems
1. What is the difference between iron and steel?	1. How is iron produced from ore?
2. What is stainless steel?	2. How is steel made?
3. How strong is steel?	3. What are the properties of steel?
4. Why can steel be picked up by a magnet?	4. How may the properties of steel be changed?
5. Why is steel needed for airplane engines?	5. How is steel shaped into different objects?
6. How does a steel-cutting torch work?	6. What are the advantages of alloy steels?
7. How are steel parts welded together?	7. How can iron rust be prevented?
8. What makes a knife blade lose its temper?	8. What are some general and specific uses of steel?
9. Why can't you paint over iron rust?	

The pupils worked by committees, one to each problem, with the intention of reporting back to the class on their findings. To make their reports interesting, they planned to use models, charts, collections, and other visual aids. For a total of five days the committees worked for the major part of the regular class periods on their problems and sometimes met outside school hours. Once each day, however, the class met as a whole to report progress and difficulties. On the fourth day, Mr. Dewey led a discussion of the general principles of presentations. The pupils had many excellent ideas about the ways these could be made.

Presentations began the sixth day. One group had a model of a blast furnace and samples of ores, coke, and limestone to illustrate its report. Another group had charts of open hearth furnaces and Bessemer converters. One group had obtained help from a physics teacher in setting up a demonstration of the reaction of steel to different stresses.

Still another prepared an experiment on the tempering of steel, in which the others could participate.

Presentations took up the better part of three class periods. When the pupils were through, Mr. Dewey proposed that the presentation materials be made into an exhibit for display cases in the main foyer. Another period was used for preparation of the exhibit.

At the end of the unit, Mr. Dewey asked for an evaluation of the method used. All the pupils agreed that it was very effective. One girl exclaimed, "I never learned so much before in my life!" The culminating test of the unit bore out her claim.

Project units. The "project plan" was another of the experiments in individualized instruction that orginated during the early years of the twentieth century. It was suggested first by the success of what were called "job assignments" in vocational agriculture, but came eventually to center more about academic problems rather than about such practical things as raising ten chickens and forty tomato plants.

Much of the good of the project plan can be incorporated into the science program. Science lends itself to the same types of practical projects as those used in vocational agriculture. A later chapter will deal with the nature and value of science projects. This section will deal with building units around the projects.

One type of project unit requires that pupils work alone on individual projects. The pupils have identical assignments such as: "Make a booklet of leaf prints." Or a list of possible activities may be presented so that pupils have a choice of the things to do. The following list was posted on a bulletin board to guide pupils in selecting a project for a seventh grade unit on common animals:

1. Catch a caterpillar and keep it alive in a cage, giving it proper food.
2. Start an ant colony.
3. Make an aquarium with some minnows in it.
4. Collect twenty insects, kill them and mount them properly.
5. Keep some earthworms in a box of soil.
6. Make a census of the birds living in your block.
7. Keep some water insects in an aquarium.
8. Make an aquarium for a pond snail.
9. Keep a land snail in a terrarium.
10. Keep grasshoppers in a cage.
11. Keep a tadpole in an aquarium.
12. Make a suitable habitat for a frog.
13. Keep a toad in a terrarium.

The more the science teacher can individualize his program, the more he can do for his pupils. As pupils follow up their special interests, they discover their strengths and weaknesses, develop their particular talents, and learn the satisfaction that can come through achievement.

During the development of this unit pupils first made tentative choices of the projects they would work on and began reading about the animals to be studied. Each then planned the materials he would need. The better part of the next two periods was spent in setting up cages and making collecting equipment. The class then took a field trip to a nearby undeveloped park area where most of the animals were available. Parts of two following periods were spent in establishing the animals in the cages or aquariums and in reporting on activities. Although a new unit was started after the sixth day, the pupils kept their animals for about two weeks longer.

The teacher of the class discussed above used an interesting technique with his project units. While one section carried on a project unit, his other sections had a different type of unit. Through such rotation, he provided more working space for his pupils than he could do if all sections carried out projects at the same time.

Project work by small groups is popular with pupils who like to work together. As with previous examples, the projects may be assigned or choice may be permitted. Groups may be of uniform size or they may vary with the nature of the project.

> Mr. Scarry used a project unit for an eighth grade study of astronomy. He suggested a number of possible projects and permitted pupils to suggest others. He did not specify the number of pupils who might work in a group but he controlled the maximum number of pupils who could work on any one project. Some of the projects chosen by the pupils were: charts of the solar system, a model of the moon, constellation viewers, and telescopes made from mailing tubes and lenses.
>
> Mr. Scarry initiated the unit with a discussion of possible projects and ways to carry them out. This was followed by organization into groups and group planning meetings. Pupils were expected to collect needed materials within a certain time, until which time Mr. Scarry conducted an introductory study of astronomy. When everyone was ready, Mr. Scarry gave the class three periods for group work. At the end of the unit pupils displayed their projects to the others and discussions followed.

A teacher may also develop a unit in which the entire class works on one project. A teacher of earth science may suggest that the class set up a weather bureau making all the apparatus—hygrometers, rain gauges, and so on. Or a class may prepare a map showing all the trees in a park. Assembly programs, radio programs, and special exhibits make interesting project units for an entire class.

> In the Cherry Valley Central School, New York, pupils with good academic records were permitted to substitute earth science for the

usual ninth grade general science course. The resulting class was made up of highly enthusiastic and capable pupils.

Early in the course the pupils became proficient in the use of contour maps. One year a pupil suggested that the class make a relief model of the area surrounding the community and thus a project unit was initiated.

The initial planning stages showed the need for a careful survey of the area. To obtain expert help with this phase, the class asked a civil engineer to explain the nature of a survey and the operation of the instruments used. Following his talk and demonstration, several boys made levels, plane tables, and other equipment in the school shop.

The engineer volunteered to help the class during the first day of the survey and supplemented the improvised equipment with his own instruments. The pupils demonstrated such a sense of responsibility that he left his instruments with them for the balance of the survey.

The survey required several periods even when supplemented by the out-of-school efforts of several of the pupils. But finally the data were complete and the pupils had a contour map from which the model could be constructed.

Before making the model the pupils had to investigate the media to be used. Committees were appointed to ask about and read about papier mâché and plaster of Paris. Experiments with these media were undertaken. Procedures for building up the contours were devised. Finally model making began.

Each class member was busy on some phase of the work. Some made molds, some mixed plaster. Some prepared trees from rubber sponges and houses from bits of wood. As work progressed the accuracy of the model was constantly checked against the data available.

Though five weeks were needed for the completion of the unit everyone agreed that the result was well worth the time. The model was attractive with its bright paints and its miniature trees, buildings, and bridges. It was informative because of its wealth of detail. Parents brought the project to the attention of the town officials who provided for the display of the model in a public place. Everyone, it seemed, was happy with the results.

TEAM TEACHING

Team teaching involves a group of teachers who are jointly responsible for the planning and instruction of a course. The group of teachers may be as few as two or as many as five or six depending upon the nature and objectives of the course, the size of the class, and the facilities to be used. The teachers of the team cooperatively develop a series of units of instruction and share in teaching, evaluation, and course improvement.

The North Babylon High School, North Babylon, New York, has used the team teaching technique in various courses. The description prepared by Carl Smith,[2] Co-ordinator of Science, North Babylon Schools, shows what was involved in planning the program and gives the details of the course in biology:

> It was decided to take 100 tenth grade academic students and place them in four special experimental classes of 25 students in each of four academic areas. All other academic students were taught in conventional classes. The experimental group which I will call the Ax group was made as heterogeneous as possible.
>
> Scheduling the classes was done by the administration. In order to have all four classes meet at the same time for large group instruction (groups of 100) and still be able to have small group instruction (groups of 12 to 15) it was decided that two subject areas should work together. Mathematics and Science were scheduled for the third and fourth periods of the day. Two classes would meet for biology during the third period and two classes the fourth period. Those classes that had biology the third period would take mathematics the fourth period and those that had biology the fourth period would take mathematics the third period. This arrangement would permit combining four classes for large group instruction in biology during the fourth period while the four classes would have mathematics the third period.
>
> The teachers' schedules were arranged so that two teachers would be free while two teachers would be teaching either the third or fourth period.
>
> The schedule has permitted the teams to operate in the following manner: On days that small group instruction is beneficial, the biology classes are broken down into groups of 12 to 15 for discussion. The two teachers who are free during the third and fourth periods become discussion leaders. Two extra periods are provided for all teachers working in a team.
>
> The coordinators of the various subject areas have assumed responsibility as team leaders. Their job is to coordinate the activities of the team. The team as a whole plans lectures, discusses which teachers are best suited to lecture, plans small group instruction, plans library work, works out daily programs, and works out long-range plans. A student teacher has been working with the team. His duties are to aid in preparation of visual aids, laboratory work, etc. He sits in on all discussion and helps plan activities. He will give at least two lectures to the large group.
>
> *Team Teaching in Biology:* The group in biology is a very compatible one. There is at least one meeting a week in which problems, lectures, examinations, visual aids, and students are discussed.

[2] Smith, Carl, "Impressions on Team Teaching," *The Science Teachers Bulletin*, vol. 27, no. 2, pp. 30–34, Fall, 1962.

Each of the members of the biology team has a specific assignment that is his throughout the year. One teacher prepares all the examinations given to the students in the four Ax classes. The examinations, however, are submitted to the team for approval before they are given to the students.

A second teacher prepares all laboratory experiments, both materials and dittoed sheets for the four classes. A third teacher prepares all visual aids materials for use with the overhead projector that is used during large group instruction. These responsibilities are apart from the normal responsibilities assumed when these teachers are assigned a lecture or when they have small groups with which to work.

The Lecture: Preceding the commencing of a unit of work in biology there is a discussion among the teachers in the teams as to the areas to be covered in that unit. Assignments for specific lectures are given at this time. On the day of a lecture (large group instruction) the four Ax classes meet in a lecture hall that seats 150 students. There is an overhead projector and screen set up at the front of the hall.

The teacher lecturing prepares an outline of the material to be covered in the lecture which is given to the students, and a complete copy of the lecture is given to each of the four teachers.

A second teacher sits in on the lecture for attendance purposes. The other two teachers in the team are free to work on responsibilities they have in regard to their lectures, examination, visual aids, or laboratory.

The main purpose of the lecture is to be able to teach a lesson once to four classes instead of four times. Lectures are better prepared than conventional lessons because more time is spent in research, preparation of visual aids, etc. The lecture prepares the student for discussion periods that follow on the day immediately following the lecture.

The Small Discussion Group: The small discussion group is centered around the material covered in a lecture. This type of classroom setup enables the students to participate more in the activities of the class. It is more educationally sound to have a group of 12 to 15 in a class than to have 25 to 30.

The regular class of 25 is split into two groups during a particular biology period. One teacher who is free that period assumes the responsibility for one small group, and the regular teacher assumes responsibility for the second group. The students know and are familiar with all the teachers since all the teachers lecture to them.

The reactions of the teachers and pupils to this program are very favorable. The teachers believe that instruction has been improved tenfold by using the technique. The work load of teachers is decreased so that more time can be devoted to preparation of lectures, materials, and laboratory, permitting better instruction. The teachers of the team get a chance to exchange ideas where this was not possible in a conventional teaching situation. The students have expressed their desire to take chemistry in a team teaching situation. The general feeling of the students is, "I am working much harder but learning much more."

Even though the reactions to team teaching have been favorable, certain precautions must be considered before embarking on such a program. There are questions such as, "What will this program do to improve the existing situation? If team teaching is used who will be on the team? What is the advantage of having more than one teacher involved in the course? What are the advantages of this program over the usual course? What facilities can be used if the course involves 50 or more students?" These questions and many more should be asked before an attempt is made. Team teaching should not be employed just to say, "We are using the team teaching technique in our schools."

The success of a team teaching program depends on the teachers involved in the team. The ability and personality of a teacher should be considered seriously before placing him on the team. Some teachers present material better than others; some are more effective in the laboratory; while others may prepare visual aids, construct tests, and administer the course.

Many of the teachers who have utilized team teaching have based their programs upon the lecture method with discussion groups and laboratories being used to reinforce lecture material. These teachers have neglected the type of laboratory programs which emphasize discovery. This weakness is not inherent in team teaching. Team teaching can and should emphasize discovery in science thus working toward the broad goals of science education.

SUGGESTED ACTIVITIES

1. Plan a teaching unit similar to the sample given on page 406. Make certain that you include activities that can be used to provide for each of the elements of a science unit described on page 399.
2. Plan a resource unit. Set up the first lesson plan to be used with this unit.
3. Assume that you have just completed a unit, "The Circulation of the Blood." What are some charts and models that your pupils can make to help them summarize and organize what they have learned?
4. You are about to teach a unit on rocks in a seventh grade general science class. List the motivation factors that you might be able to utilize to stimulate pupil interest in this unit.
5. Design a contract unit for chemistry, physics, or biology, utilizing your own format.
6. Design a contract unit from ESCP materials using the format on page 418.
7. Compare your local or state syllabus with one of the national study group programs such as BSCS, PSSC. Determine philosophies of approaches, activities, etc.

SUGGESTED READINGS

Baynham, Dorsey, "Schools of Future in Operation," *Phi Delta Kappan* 42:350–354, 1961.

Beggs, David W., III, *Team Teaching, Bold New Venture*, Unified College Press, Indianapolis, 1964.

Biological Science: An Inquiry into Life (BSCS—yellow version), Harcourt, Brace & World, New York, 1963.

Biological Science: Molecules to Man (BSCS—blue version), Houghton Mifflin Co., Boston, 1963.

Chemical Education Material Study, *Chemistry, An Experimental Science*, Freeman Press, San Francisco, 1963.

Colyer, L. M., "Principle-Unit-Project Method of Teaching Science," *Science Education*, 46:460–468, December, 1962.

Dushman, S., "Science in the Curriculum," *Science Teacher*, 28:19+, March, 1961.

High School Biology (BSCS—green version), Rand McNally & Co., Chicago, 1963.

Harnack, R. S., "Teacher Decision Making and Computer-based Resource Units," *Audiovisual Instruction*, 12:32–35, 1967.

Henry, G. H., "Unit Method: the New Logic Meets the Old," *English Journal*, 56:401–406, 1967.

Lambert, Phillip, "Team Teaching for Today's World," *Teachers College Record*, 64:480–486, 1963.

McCafferty, R. C., and G. R. Easterberg, "Understanding Heredity," (Unit Plan), *School Science and Mathematics*, 67:60–87, 1967.

Mersand, J., "How to Teach by the Unit Method," *High Points*, 47:37–43, 1965.

Michael, Lloyd S., "New Directions in Quality Education in Secondary Schools," *Bulletin of the National Association of Secondary School Principals*, 47:36–63, 1963.

Physical Sciences Study Committee, *Physics*, D. C. Heath Co., Boston, 1965.

Shaplin, Judson T., and Henry F. Olds (eds.), *Team Teaching*, Harper, New York, 1964.

Strickland, Ruth G., *How to Build a Unit of Work*, U. S. Government Printing Office, Washington, D. C., 1946.

Sund, R. B., and L. W. Trowbridge, *Teaching Science by Inquiry*, Charles E. Merrill Books, Columbus, Ohio, 1967.

Chapter **13**

Planning Science Lessons

Monday morning Miss Johnson met her general science classes with only the vaguest of plans in mind. Things went badly from the start. The pupils were restless and little interested in the material she was trying to present. The dismissal bell had a welcome sound.

"My!" sighed an exhausted Miss Johnson as she walked from the building with another teacher. "Pupils just can't settle down on Monday, can they?"

Miss Johnson spent half an hour or so Monday evening writing plans for the next day's lessons. Tuesday morning she went to school a little earlier than usual to prepare materials called for by her plans. As she gathered equipment for experiments and as she set up demonstrations, she found herself beginning to look forward to her classes.

Teaching was much more enjoyable all day Tuesday. The atmosphere was relaxed and everyone seemed to be having fun. Goals were attained smoothly. Time passed swiftly. Miss Johnson ended the day tired but with the contentment that comes with a job well done.

Careful daily lesson planning is the key to successful teaching. Regularly looking ahead permits a teacher to anticipate pupil reactions, to prepare adequately to utilize these reactions, and to avoid foreseeable difficulties. Lack of planning encourages fumbling and indecision, with accompanying disciplinary problems.

A teacher without plans ends his day tired from his efforts to keep classes running smoothly and discouraged with his lack of success. A teacher with good plans is also tired, but his tiredness is tempered with satisfaction and with anticipation for the next day's work.

THE INFLUENCE OF PLANS ON PUPIL BEHAVIOR

Attention is a form of pupil behavior that can be observed readily. Since attention is essential for learning, even though it may not insure learning, and since it can be measured more conveniently than interest and achievement, it makes a good criterion for judging the effectiveness of lesson plans. Other criteria must be applied as well but none show up the strengths and weaknesses of teaching procedures so effectively as observation of pupil reactions to material presented.

Analyzing the performance of lesson plans.   On the following pages four science lessons are analyzed in terms of pupil attention. The data were collected by a single observer sitting at the rear of the classrooms. At one-minute intervals he recorded the number of pupils who seemed to be concentrating upon the lesson. He also made note of the type of classroom activities being carried out during the lesson.

Later, the percentage of pupils showing attention was calculated for each interval, using the total enrollment of the class as a base. These percentages were plotted against time as shown in Figure 22.

The resulting curve in each case indicates general shifts of class attention but tells nothing of individual pupil behavior. Should two points on the curve show ninety percent attention there is nothing to tell whether the same or a different group of pupils were giving attention at each time.

The areas above and below the curve have interesting significance. The area under the curve represents in pupil-minutes the portion of the period during which desired learnings may take place. The area above the curve represents in pupil-minutes the portion of the period during which desired learnings undoubtedly do not take place.

Analysis of a tightly planned lesson. The lesson analyzed in Figure 22 was taught by a cadet teacher who won high praise from his sponsor

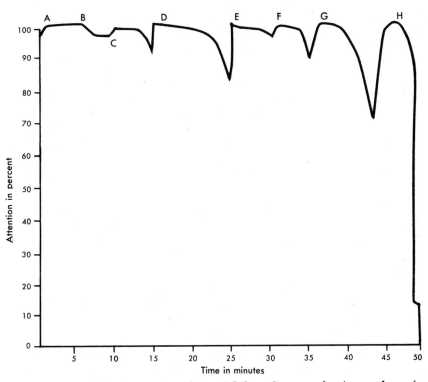

Figure 22. *Attention curve of an eighth-grade general science class of twenty-six pupils during a well-planned demonstration-discussion lesson.*

teacher for his excellent class control. Analysis of this lesson, typical of others he taught, gives the reasons for his success.

The subject of the lesson was boiling water. During preceding lessons the pupils had studied other properties of water. At point A on Figure 22 the teacher announced that two pupils would perform a demonstration they had prepared beforehand. The pupils heated a stoppered flask containing a little water and made the cork pop out. On request they repeated the demonstration. Then they explained the cause.

At B the teacher resumed charge of the class and reviewed the steps and outcome of the demonstration. During his review he asked what steam looks like. Several arguments started at C and continued to D. To settle the dispute the teacher placed a flask of hot water over a gas flame at D. While the pupils were waiting for the water to boil and produce steam he directed them to make diagrams of the apparatus in their notebooks. As soon as steam issued from a tube coming from the flask he sent pupils in groups of three to look at the steam. By the time the diagrams were completed all of the pupils had seen the steam and noted its appearance.

At *E* the teacher interrupted work long enough to help the pupils summarize their observations and label their diagrams correctly. He allowed a few more minutes for completing the diagrams at *F*.

At G he asked if any pupils knew the temperature of boiling water. Several pupils suggested 212° and two suggested 100°. To obtain an authoritative answer the teacher directed two pupils to put a thermometer in the flask of hot water and heat it again.

Attention wandered a little while the pupils were waiting for the water to boil but returned again at *H* as soon as the boys began to read the thermometer. During the last five minutes the teacher asked the pupils to summarize their learnings in their notebooks. Most pupils completed the assignment quickly and sat waiting for the end of the period.

This was a tightly planned lesson and was admirably taught. There was no confusion and little noise. Rarely was the attention of more than two or three pupils diverted from the subject at one time. The weakest point in terms of attention was the interval during which pupils waited for the water to boil the second time.

The lesson was rather formal and did not provide many opportunities for individual initiative or for independence of thinking. However, it was well suited for a beginning teacher who did not feel in complete control of the classroom situation.

Analysis of a lesson based on project work. The lesson in Figure 23 was taught by a master teacher of several years' experience. His pupils were making dioramas representing various types of environments, working in groups of two or three. Planning and preparatory work had been done in previous periods.

The pupils came to order quickly at A but the teacher was interrupted by a messenger from the school principal. At B the teacher announced that the class would resume work on the dioramas. For the next several minutes all pupils were busy getting out their materials and beginning work. The teacher moved from group to group answering questions, finding needed materials and helping with techniques. For several minutes at a time he gave full attention to one or another of the groups.

At C there were definite signs of slackening interest. Increasingly the pupils began to move about the room and talk with each other. It was difficult to determine how much of this talk concerned the projects. Nonetheless, work on the projects continued satisfactorily.

At D there was a rapid decline in attention. Two pupils left the room for drinks. Three boys left their own groups and distracted other pupils. Two of the boys scuffled with each other but stopped when the teacher looked their way. About fifteen minutes before the end of the period, at E, one group of pupils began to put away its materials. Other groups followed

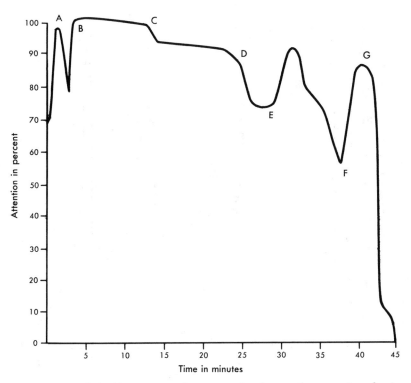

Figure 23. *Attention curve of a general science class composed of twenty-eight seventh-grade pupils during a period given over to project work.*

suit and within seven or eight minutes almost half the class had nothing to do.

The teacher, who was busy with one group, had failed to notice what was happening. When he did at *F*, he announced loudly that the period was far from over and that the pupils should keep on working. Most of the pupils resumed work, but five minutes before the bell rang interest began dropping rapidly again. By the end of the period all but one group had put away its materials and sat waiting for the dismissal bell.

In spite of a few weaknesses this was a successful lesson. Any observer would have been impressed with the enthusiasm and energy of the pupils as they worked on their projects. Progress was notable. The teacher was not upset by the numerous small shifts in attention. He expected this. Only when he discovered some of the groups ending work prematurely did he exert his authority.

In criticism one might say that the one type of activity was extended for too long a time for some of the pupils, although about half the class

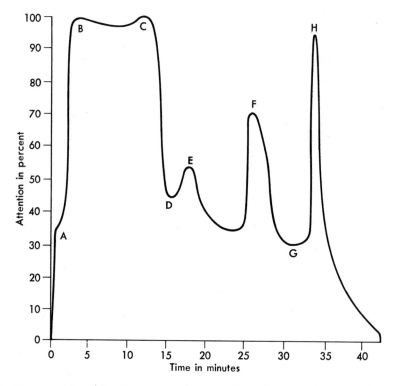

Figure 24. *Attention curve of a seventh-grade general science class of thirty-three pupils studying uses of compressed air by demonstration-discussion procedures that were carelessly planned.*

maintained high interest almost to the end. There should have been some provision for those pupils whose interest waned the most rapidly.

Analysis of an improperly planned lesson. The lesson analyzed in Figure 24 was taught by a cadet teacher who had little control of his pupils and who did not recognize that his difficulties stemmed from careless planning. The lesson dealt with uses of compressed air. In previous lessons the pupils had studied the common properties of air, including its elasticity.

The class was slow in coming to order. The teacher spoke sharply to the class as a whole and to individuals without effect (A). When he produced a blowtorch, however, attention became universal and remained high while he pumped up the torch and lighted it.

At C the teacher began making a diagram of the blowtorch on the blackboard, turning his back on the pupils without giving them directions for anything to do. A few pupils copied the diagram in their notebooks but the majority did not feel obligated to do so. The teacher ignored the increasing disturbance during the three minutes he took to make the diagram.

At *D* the teacher attempted a discussion of the diagram but received little cooperation. He turned to the discussion of other uses of compressed air with no better success. Noise steadily increased. At *F* he shouted for order. At *H* he clapped his hands. Neither act had more than momentary effect.

During the last part of the period most of the pupils talked to each other. Some shouted across the room. A few of the boys in rear seats tussled openly. Five minutes before the end of the period all the pupils had books closed and were watching the clock. Several of the boys sat poised ready to jump just as the bell rang.

This particular cadet teacher had been having trouble with discipline during previous lessons. This was reflected in his difficulty in getting the class to come to order at the beginning of the period. Much of his difficulty could be traced to inadequate planning. For this lesson, his plans consisted of a sheet of paper headed "Uses of Compressed Air," followed by a list of examples. He had carried out his planning so far as to borrow a blowtorch.

His demonstration captured and held attention immediately. Had he followed this with other worthwhile activities, his lesson would have been successful. Instead he turned his back on his pupils for three minutes, leaving them with nothing to do. Only a few pupils had sufficiently good work habits to copy the drawing. The other pupils seized the opportunity to talk loudly and scuffle. The teacher was unable to recapture attention through discussion and he had no alternatives planned in case discussion failed. Therefore he was helpless and his pupils took advantage of him.

His errors were several. He did not plan in terms of what the pupils would be doing. He thought only in terms of learnings. He depended too much upon discussion without having sufficient skill to lead a discussion. He tried to prolong a discussion activity over too long a period. He made no provisions for the pupils while he was drawing the diagram. He had no extra activities planned to be used if his other procedures failed.

Analysis of an inadequately planned lesson. Figure 25 analyzes a lesson taught by a teacher with over twenty years' experience, who was being severely criticized by her principal for the quality of her work. The subject of the lesson was convection in air. Topics covered previously could not be determined by the observer.

The class came to order and the subject of the lesson was announced (A). The teacher conducted a short discussion of the way rooms become heated when steam radiators are used. Few pupils participated actively but most of them seemed to be giving attention. One boy, however, read comic books throughout the period.

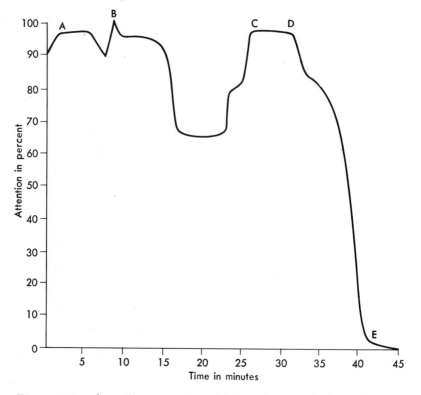

Figure 25. *Attention curve of an eighth-grade general science class of thirty-five pupils during a demonstration-discussion lesson for which planning was inadequate.*

At *B* the teacher picked up a convection box and explained its use. Interest was high while she set up the demonstration but dropped quickly because only the pupils in the front rows could see the smoke in the box. The teacher asked two pupils to describe what they saw.

At *C* the teacher directed the pupils to make drawings of the convection demonstration for their notebooks. All but the one boy with the comic books participated. Several pupils moved freely about the room during this interval, sharpening pencils, going out to get drinks and looking at each other's work. There was little noise and no confusion. At *D* pupils began finishing the assignment. The teacher had nothing planned for the remainder of the period. Five minutes before the end of the period all had finished and sat patiently watching the clock.

The faults of this lesson could have been corrected easily. Her plans were inadequate. She did not have enough material to fill the period. She thought not in terms of pupil growth but only in terms of subject matter.

She had given no attention to the visibility of her demonstration. A few more minutes spent in planning and a little more in preparing materials and her lesson would have been completely successful.

Anticipating pupil behavior. Lesson planning is made much more effective by looking ahead to the possible reactions of pupils in each new situation. Analysis of a large number of lessons has produced several generalizations that can be used as guides in anticipating pupil behavior. These generalizations are listed below:

1. Class attention is gained quickly by introducing a new activity.
2. The longer an activity is continued the more rapidly the attention level declines.
3. Activities vary in their ability to hold attention.
4. A change to an activity distinctly different from its predecessor raises the level of attention.
5. It is impossible to predict accurately how long class attention can be maintained by any one activity.
6. The attention level drops quickly when pupils have nothing specific to do.

Through the proper application of these generalizations it is possible to plan a lesson that maintains a high level of attention throughout a period. Such a plan reduces and may eliminate many of the problems of classroom control. It must be remembered, however, that control is not the only objective and that consideration must be given to other factors as well as to attention.

THE ACTIVITY APPROACH TO LESSON PLANNING

Could a lesson be no more than a list of topics to be covered, planning would be simple indeed. But boys and girls are not passive receptacles into which information can be poured. They are active human beings and their learning processes are active. Lesson plans must include what pupils are going to do in order to learn, as well as what they are expected to learn.

The importance of activities in learning. Learning requires action on the part of the learner. Even when a pupil is listening to a lecture, reading a book, or viewing a film, his mind must be accepting new impressions and relating these to other experiences if he is to learn. Most science learnings require physical participation as well. First-hand experiences depend upon the use of all the senses; many important learnings depend upon manipulation in order that touch and the muscular senses be brought into action.

Activities have another role that is not fully appreciated. Associations do not occur spontaneously; incentives are needed. Occasionally pupils make associations with the deliberate intent of learning—perhaps they wish high grades or perhaps they wish to escape punishment—but usually they prefer to spend their energies in ways that promise more profit in terms of their immediate needs.

Properly selected activities provide the incentive that adolescents need to learn what teachers consider important. The pupils make the associations, not for the sake of learning, but because they need the associations to carry out the activities which seem important to them.

Types and functions of learning activities.   Many classroom activities— reading, viewing films, writing reports, taking tests—are primarily intellectual. Field work, laboratory work, and many projects require a large amount of physical participation as well. The former type, which some teachers label "passive learning activities," are satisfactory for presenting vicarious experiences and may be used in summarization, organization, and review exercises. The latter type are essential for first-hand experiences and may also be used for some types of summaries, organization activities, and review exercises.

Some classroom activities are solitary in nature; these permit pupils to learn at their respective rates and in their respective ways. Other activities are social in nature; these take advantage of the gregarious instincts of adolescents and at the same time help prepare pupils for working together in adult life.

Some activities hold pupils to closely supervised patterns of action. When employing such activities the teacher has opportunities to direct learning along desirable channels. Other activities give the pupils more or less responsibility for their own actions. These last activities give practice in planning, in setting and working toward objectives, and in self-control.

Activities differ greatly in their ability to capture and hold attention. Spectacular demonstrations gain every eye immediately. Good films enthrall pupils for half an hour at a time. On the other extreme, there are reading exercises that interest pupils for a few minutes only and writing assignments that appeal to none.

Activities vary in the amount of initiative and independence of thinking they encourage. A dictated notebook exercise requires little mental activity but sometimes has value in providing each pupil with presumably essential information. Completely different are true experiments which many involve high-level thinking.

Activities and the selection of subject matter.   Many science topics are a pleasure to teach because so many appropriate activities may be utilized. Static electricity, for instance, provides many excellent lessons for general science because there are dozens of simple experiments, demonstrations without end, projects of all degrees of complexity, good films, and a great range of related readings.

Certain science topics may be ill-suited for specific teaching situations because so few appropriate activities may be employed. The study of genetics, as one example, does not fit well into most general science programs. Genuine experimentation is rarely possible. Illustrative materials are lacking or few in number. Emphasis must be placed upon lectures, readings, charts, and pictures—sources of information which few youngsters are prepared to interpret adequately.

Lesson planning includes a consideration of the teachability of the topics proposed for treatment. Certain topics for which few useful activities are available are judged unsuitable at the very beginning and are replaced by others which can be taught more satisfactorily.

The need for balance in utilizing activities.   Every activity is apt to have a different impact on pupils. Some pupils may benefit greatly from a specific activity; other pupils may find the same activity meaningless. When several types of activities are used chances that each pupil will find something of value are increased. Learnings are usually increased through the use of several types of activities applied to one topic. Several experiences tend to reinforce a specific learning. In addition, the strengths of one activity help to compensate for the weaknesses of another.

Overemphasis on one type of activity may deny pupils important benefits. Too much socialized work is apt to discourage independent work. Too much individualized instruction and solitary activity keeps pupils from gaining practice in working together. An excessive quantity of reading takes the emphasis from first-hand experiences, while too much manipulative work minimizes the value of books.

Classroom activities and classroom control.   Activities planned for a lesson may have several functions. Each is chosen in terms of some limited subject matter objective. Each usually is directed toward some broad, general education goal. Each may also, by its interaction with other activities, play a part in classroom control.

Below is a brief lesson plan that was developed with the problem of control in mind. It provides a variety of activities and occasional opportunities to use the larger muscles:

Topic—Electromagnets

10:00–10:10:   Ten-question written quiz on properties of permanent magnets.

10:10–10:15:   Pupils exchange papers and correct answers.

10:15–10:25:   John and Herbert demonstrate the electromagnet they have built.

10:25–10:40:   Pupils work in pairs making and testing an electromagnet. John and Herbert assist where needed.

10:40–10:50:   Class discussion of results. Begin plans for discovering uses of electromagnets and making an exhibit of ways they are used.

The introductory activity puts an abrupt end to the freedom enjoyed during the changes of classes. During this solitary activity the pupils are held by the challenge of the test questions. Following this short period of intense concentration pupils are given an opportunity to relax and move about a bit as they check their test papers. The next activity, which has high interest through the use of student demonstrators, welds the pupils into a single group. A comparatively long interval follows during which the pupils, acting in small groups, have opportunities to manipulate, to move about, and to let their interests diverge into different channels. The last activity brings the pupils back to act as a single group, restricting movement but encouraging controlled talking and free range of imagination.

Consideration for the specific qualities of science activities in the fashion described does much to eliminate discipline problems. Three or four completely different activities in one lesson provide welcome variety. Proper alternation of the several types ends rigidly controlled situations before pupils rebel, and puts an end to periods of freedom before they develop into license and anarchy. Classroom control problems almost always can be traced to over-long use of one activity, or to an uninterrupted sequence of activities that hold pupils under tight control for long periods.

Choice of activities for the insecure teacher.   A beginning teacher or a teacher faced with a new group of pupils finds it wise to employ only activities that present few control problems. He may prefer to choose for his first few lessons only activities that require little special motivation such as those listed in the left-hand column of Table 12. Even the experienced teacher finds these activities useful on those difficult days that precede vacations or athletic events.

Gradually, the teacher may work toward inclusion of activities listed in the right-hand column. The first written reports may be short—a few sentences in length—and supplemented by diagrams and clippings. The first field problems may be limited in scope until pupils discover the

Activities that need little motivation	Activities that need strong motivation
Watching films and filmstrips	Preparing written reports
Watching demonstrations	Constructing elaborate models
Taking short field trips	Doing extended field work
Taking short tests	Taking long tests
Doing simple experiments	Doing mathematical exercises
Preparing simple demonstrations	Looking up answers to questions in textbooks and workbooks
Constructing charts and models within abilities of pupils	Doing extensive library research

Table 12. *Some common activities classified according to the amount of motivation pupils need in order to engage in them freely.*

challenge of these problems. Library research problems may be permissive in nature so as to appeal to pupils with adequate reading ability. As a teacher becomes better acquainted with his pupils and knows their special interests and abilities, he may broaden the scope of these activities, sometimes requiring all pupils to engage in them, at other times making them permissive only.

The insecure teacher may also find it wise to alternate with intervals of tight control only such activities as are listed in the center column of Table 13. The activities listed in the right-hand column require consider-

Activities that hold pupils to the same task with little freedom	Activities that hold pupils to the same task but permit some freedom	Activities that permit pupils to work on different tasks with considerable freedom
Taking tests	Watching demonstrations	Preparing demonstrations
Filling in blanks on worksheets	Doing laboratory exercises from direction sheets	Preparing charts
Reading in textbooks	Taking short field trips	Constructing original models
Writing up reports of demonstrations	Constructing models from kits	Doing library research
Making diagrams of apparatus	Examining specimens	Solving problems by experiment
Solving mathematical exercises	Studying prepared slides with a microscope	Doing field work
Looking up answers to sets of questions	Checking test papers and homework	Preparing reports of independent research
Watching films and slides		Setting up exhibits
		Producing plays and assembly programs

Table 13. *Some common science activities classified by the amount of freedom they permit pupils.*

able skill to handle properly. They also require pupils who are accustomed to taking responsibilities for their own actions. Both teachers and pupils need to work gradually toward full utilization of these valuable activities.

MAKING A LESSON PLAN

It is important that daily lesson planning be reduced to the utmost simplicity. Science teachers are busy people. They usually have full schedules and additional responsibilities as well. They need all the time they can find for the preparation of materials, for working with especially interested pupils, and for keeping abreast of new ideas in science teaching. The time spent in actually writing plans should be kept as short as possible.

When to write a plan.   The most advantageous time to plan a lesson is immediately after the preceding lesson. The extent and direction of the material covered is fresh in mind. The interests of the pupils have been revealed. Past mistakes are still vivid.

Good lesson plans can rarely be made several days in advance. No one knows how far a class may go in a single lesson or in what directions their interests will lead the work. To try to hold a class to a precise amount of material each day stifles enthusiasm and initiative.

For the same reason a teacher should not try to make a single plan serve for several different sections, except perhaps on the first day of work. The nature of each section is different, not only because there are different pupils but because the pupils have different effects upon each other. But even though different sections need different plans these plans are only adaptations of a basic plan and materials prepared for one class can be used sooner or later for other classes.

The value of a schedule.   The several activities used during the progress of a science lesson interact with each other, one activity being affected by those that have gone before and in its turn affecting those that come afterwards. Thus the order in which activities are introduced becomes important and the time allotted to each needs serious consideration.

A schedule for the activities enables the teacher to see at a glance how the final balance is working out. It shows whether one activity is being planned for too long a time to hold the attention of pupils. It shows whether there is adequate provision for the various talents and interests within a group. It shows whether the various types of activities are being alternated in the most advantageous fashion.

A schedule once prepared need not be considered as inflexible. Often an activity awakens more interest than was anticipated; the time allotted for it may well be extended. Sometimes an activity has little appeal; it is usually better to pass to another activity than to hold the pupils to something for which they see no purpose. Sometimes pupils themselves propose an activity that promises to be more profitable than those scheduled; plans may then be abandoned or modified as needed.

A form for lesson plans. A good lesson plan form is a real time saver. It reduces the amount of writing needed. It establishes patterns for procedures. It is a reminder of items that might be forgotten otherwise. The lesson plan form shown in page 448 is adapted from a form used by Dr. Philip G. Johnson of Cornell University. It is remarkably simple and very easy to fill in, but it provides for all the major features essential in a good plan.

The heading serves to identify the plan. It stipulates the topic to be dealt with and provides for a listing of goals. The main body of the plan is a schedule of the activities to be employed; both the order of the activities and the time considered appropriate for each are given. Space is left at the end of the schedule for the assignment. This does not imply that the assignment is to be given last. It is a device for directing attention to this important item.

Two boxes at the bottom of the sheet complete the form. One box is provided for a list of references—books, films, pictures—called for by the plans. The other box is provided for a list of materials required by the demonstrations and experiments planned. These lists are highly useful when the teacher is assembling his teaching aids in advance of the lesson.

This lesson plan form is duplicated on notebook paper punched to fit a standard looseleaf notebook. The reverse side of the sheets is large enough for the listing of questions that may be asked orally or written on the blackboard.

Establishing objectives for a science lesson. Only specific subject matter goals need be listed in a lesson plan. Sometimes these goals are best stated in terms of behavioral objectives. Major subject matter goals are listed in the unit plan and these influence both the composition of the lesson and the direction it takes. General education goals are kept in mind at all times.

Subject matter goals suitable for a single lesson are necessarily limited, otherwise they cannot be attained within the allotted time. Providing major objectives are not forgotten, limited goals are desirable; they center attention upon a narrow area, make possible several different approaches, and encourage thorough treatment.

DAILY LESSON PLAN

Class   Chemistry, Section 3   Date 11/6

Unit   Acids and Bases   Topic   Acids in Foods

Specific Objectives   to review tests for acids

to test common foods for acidity

to discover importance of acids in foods

Time	Activity		
10:05–10:10	Return quiz papers		
10:10–10:20	Review tests for acidity with demonstrations		
10:20–10:40	In teams of two, pupils test foods given them		
10:40–10:45	Summary of results		
10:45–10:55	Assignment—optional reports		

1) Production of vinegar
2) Pickle making
3) Vinegar and taste
4) Kinds of vinegar
5) Vinegar as a preservative
6) Chemical reactions during making of vinegar
7) Test for citric acid
8) The citrus fruits
9) The uses of citrus fruits
10) Vitamin C and citrus fruits
11) Nature of vitamin C
12) pH of various citrus fruits
13) Variation in pH of oranges
14) Cause of sour milk
15) pH of buttermilk
16) Production of cheese
17) Production of butter
18) Sour cream cake
19) Making cream of tomato soup
20) pH of tomatoes
21) Making of sauerkraut

Assignment

Materials			References
Litmus paper	Tomato	Apple	
Phenolphthalein	Sweet milk	Pear	
Methyl orange	Sour milk	Pineapple	
Vinegar	Buttermilk	Grapes	
Orange	Tea	Cereal	
Lemon	Coffee	Cabbage	
Grapefruit	Cocoa	Sauerkraut	
	Peas		

Subject matter goals for a lesson may be written as learnings. These are specific enough to be attainable within a period. Principles may be listed instead but these tend to be broad in scope and may lead to superficiality.

Organizing a lesson.   Each lesson is constructed to fit a particular situation; there is no pattern that should be followed. True, within a series of lessons provision must be made for the introduction of new material, for summaries, for the organization of learnings, and for any needed review and drill. But no single lesson need contain each of these teaching elements; in general it will contain only two or three of them.

It is good practice to open many lessons with some activity that reviews work of preceding days. One may use for this purpose a short written test, a brief period of oral questioning, slides, or a film that fits the need. One may also repeat a demonstration or ask pupils to repeat some presentation. A daily review is not necessary. Usually project work provides its own review.

Many teachers like to end a lesson with a verbal summary, either written or oral or both. The verbal summary sends pupils from the classroom with a knowledge that certain topics have been covered during the period. Verbal summaries are not always the most effective summaries and should not become a fixed part of each lesson plan.

New material is introduced in most lessons but not all, some lessons being devoted to organization of learnings, to summaries, to review, and to testing. New material can be presented through either direct or vicarious experiences or both. The former usually have the greater impact but the latter are effective when pupils have a background adequate for interpreting them.

When possible, it is well to use several approaches with both direct and vicarious experiences included. If direct experiences are given first they help broaden the background that pupils need for interpreting the latter. The interactions of several approaches help compensate for the weaknesses of any one approach and reinforce the learnings that are developed.

Pupils need time to assimilate and apply new material. Presentations should be broken frequently by activities that help pupils summarize and organize their learnings. It is never wise to present adolescents with large masses of new material at one time.

The number of activities selected for a period must vary with conditions. As a general rule three or four completely different activities provide needed variety and take care of different learning requirements. A few activities such as project work can hold pupil attention for twenty minutes or longer; most have a holding power of less than fifteen minutes. It is rarely wise to build a lesson plan about a single activity. With pupils who do not respond readily to classroom situations, lesson plans may call for five activities.

Certain activities fulfill two or more functions at once and reduce the number of activities that need be planned. Most projects, for instance, involve all the learning elements. As pupils work, they need new material which they gather for themselves from various sources. As they plan, which of course they do continually, they organize this material in usable form. The project serves as a summary of their learnings, and when the pupils return to it on later days, it reviews their learnings also.

The desirability for over-planning.   In departmentalized schools pupils are allotted to teachers for definite lengths of time. If pupils complete their work sooner than expected, or if they lose interest in it, the teacher is not free to dismiss them or to turn to another subject. He must keep them until the end of the period.

Even the most experienced teacher cannot estimate accurately the length of time pupils will spend on an activity. They may want more than the estimated time, especially if the work is interesting. But if they have had identical work in previous grades, or if they are completely uninterested in the topic, they cannot be held to an activity as long as was estimated.

It is not uncommon to find that a lesson has moved more quickly than anticipated and that all the suggestions in the plan have been exhausted several minutes before the end of the period. There then comes an interval that is demoralizing to the pupils and discouraging to the teacher.

Though it is possible for a teacher to extemporize in such a predicament, it is far better to anticipate the possibility and over-plan each lesson, adding to the original schedule one or two additional activities. The time spent in planning the activities and preparing any needed materials is not wasted because if unused one day, they may be included in the following day's plans.

Importance of the transition intervals.   During a well-organized lesson the progression from one activity to the next is made so smoothly a casual observer may notice nothing remarkable. The pupils end one activity and begin a new one with little hesitation and confusion. However, such smooth transitions are the result of careful planning, they rarely happen by chance.

The importance of transitions is more readily understood by analyzing difficulties that arise because this aspect of planning was neglected.

Mr. Caywood's plans called for the pupils to make "saxophones" from soda straws. The pupils entered the activity with enthusiasm and soon had a wide variety of noise makers.

The plans then called for a discussion of the relation of pitch to length of air column. But when Mr. Caywood tried to initiate the discussion his voice was drowned out by various squeakings and tootlings. Only by shouting and by making a few threats did he obtain sufficient quiet for the discussion.

The reaction of Mr. Caywood's pupils was perfectly normal. They had made their saxophones and they wanted to use them. They felt little incentive to lay them aside in order to engage in a discussion. Mr. Caywood had given no consideration to the means by which he was to end one activity and begin the next. He had visualized the two separate activities either of which would be perfectly satisfactory alone but which conflicted when placed in the order he used them.

Had Mr. Caywood anticipated the problem he could have planned an adequate transition with little effort. He might have arranged to collect the straws before beginning the discussion. Or he might have used a more tightly controlled activity to follow the making of the saxophones.

Beginning teachers must be especially concerned about transitions because they have few resources on which to draw when problems begin to arise. Experienced teachers have usually learned by trial and error the procedures that succeed and those that fail. For all this, it is not uncommon to see an experienced teacher ungracefully shouting at his pupils when a little forethought would have kept things going smoothly.

An unfortunate consequence of the failure to consider transitions is an increased dependence upon formal methods of teaching. A teacher may believe fully in the advantages of the free and informal classroom, and he may prepare plans and materials diligently. But when he finds himself with serious discipline problems, he mistakingly places the blame on the activities that give pupils freedom. He is apt to abandon all such activities and turn completely to formal teaching procedures.

If pupils can be brought into the planning process the problems of transitions are reduced. Pupils know exactly what they will be doing and they turn from one activity to the next with little direction from the teacher.

The transition from a tightly controlled activity to a freer one causes little difficulty. The pupils are already quiet and listen to directions calmly. The reverse process, changing from a free activity to a tightly controlled one, is more troublesome. The pupils are busy at their different tasks, or they have ended them and are busy with activities not called for in the plans. They are usually talking and there is a high noise level in the room. A teacher has difficulty projecting his voice above the hubbub.

Several techniques may be used for making this kind of transition. One common procedure is to give directions for the second activity when giving directions for the first. For instance, pupils about to carry out a laboratory exercise may be told that they are to return to their seats as soon as they have finished in order to make diagrams of the apparatus used.

Another technique is to end an activity with another that introduces itself. The projection of the first slide of a set, or the blinking of the room lights in announcement of a film indicates that a new activity is about to start. Similarly, a teacher may hold up a sheaf of test papers or worksheets, thus announcing something new to do, and the pupils receive the papers as they come to their seats. A somewhat similar technique calls for the teacher to write on the blackboard the directions for the new activity. Pupils who first notice the writing of the directions begin the new activity and the others soon follow suit.

An activity may be ended by sending pupils around the room to collect tools, materials, and waste. This signals the end of the activity and removes the causes for distraction. The technique is not always successful, because pupils sometimes argue about giving up the things they are working with.

A difficult transitional period occurs at the end of long tests, long reading assignments, and long writing assignments. Some pupils are certain to complete their tasks ahead of others. By keeping such tasks short, the time spread is reduced. When a wide spread is anticipated, the pupils who finish first can be given interesting things to do. They usually like to put away materials, take care of plants and animals, and arrange the bulletin board. Some prefer to work on their own special projects or read special books.

A transition that causes annoyance for many teachers is the one at the beginning of the period. Pupils enter the room talking loudly about their own affairs, teasing each other, and sometimes scuffling. They may not cease these activities the instant the bell rings.

It is often well to begin classes with a tightly controlled activity such as a test, a worksheet to be filled out, or a sheet of printed directions. Discussions and directions given orally should rarely be used. Films, slides, and interesting demonstrations may serve to initiate a period when pupils are accustomed to settling down to work quickly.

The ending of a period may be as difficult as the beginning but teachers are apt to ignore the problem. Nonetheless it is a sign of poor planning when pupils stack their books several minutes before the end of the period, sit watching the clock, and jump the instant the bell rings. Plans should provide sufficient interesting activities to keep pupils busy until there is a signal to prepare for dismissal.

Planning assignments.   The most valuable assignments are those in which boys and girls carry on at home science activities that seem important to them and that contribute to their general growth. Obviously, this type of assignment varies from pupil to pupil. One individual may benefit most by reading a specialized science book. Another may benefit most by working with his father on a model of a derrick. A third may benefit most by studying an ant hill.

Too frequently assignments require work of a stereotyped and unpleasant nature for which the pupils can see little purpose. Indeed, many assignments seem to be little more than "busy work" selected without thought of possible value to the pupils.

Commonly the assignment is a hurried order given as the dismissal bell rings, "Read pages 74 through 82 in your textbook." The purpose of such an assignment is not obvious. Is it made to give the pupils practice in reading? Are they only to acquaint themselves with the contents of the pages? Are they expected to master all the information on the pages?

Another common assignment of doubtful value is the order to write out the answers to the questions at the end of the chapter. Again the purpose of the assignment cannot be determined by either the pupils or an observer. Certainly boys and girls with high academic ability do not benefit from writing out the answers to such questions and it is an insult to ask them to do so. And pupils with very low academic ability cannot succeed at this type of work, so they do not benefit either.

Assignments used by master teachers provide flexibility for pupils of different interests and talents. Often these assignments are voluntary in nature. One pupil may choose to report on the content of certain pages in a supplementary textbook. Another may wish to look in reference books for answers to questions raised by the class. A third may volunteer to ask a specialist for information. A fourth may wish to try an experiment at home. Commonly pupils work together on such assignments.

A type of assignment that is little used but that has much promise calls for a repetition or a continuation of work done in class.

Mr. Cole's eighth grade science class was about to study photography. Mr. Cole brought in photographic papers and the chemicals needed for developing them. The pupils mixed the solutions, darkened the room, and established a routine for the operations.

Each pupil placed some object, such as a paper clip or a leaf or a cutout of opaque paper, on a sheet of photographic paper and exposed it to sunlight for a few seconds. The pupils then took turns developing the silhouettes they had produced.

At the end of the period Mr. Cole explained where the pupils could buy paper and chemicals and how they could improvise materials to repeat the process at home. The next day all pupils, working either alone or with a friend, had repeated the experience, and some had tried to make prints from photographic negatives.

Many other possible classroom activities use materials easily procured by pupils and are challenging enough to start the pupils working at home. Mr. Cole's record of one hundred percent participation will not generally be obtained, twenty-five percent should be considered high, but this is work done because the pupils want to do it, work for which they have given up television, movies, and other activities.

Whenever any assignment is made, whether it be required or voluntary, the pupils should understand exactly what is expected of them. If information is wanted, pupils should know precisely what they are to discover and why the assignment is important. If models are to be made or if experiments are to be tried out, pupils should have in mind exactly what they are to attempt. The assignments need not have been dictated by the teacher; they may have originated through group planning, but always they should be carefully defined. An assignment worth making is worth making painstakingly.

Using a lesson plan.   A lesson plan is a guide but never a mandate. Its purpose is to give direction to the work of the pupils and to give the teacher a sense of security. But it should be altered if unexpected conditions arise.

Perhaps the pupils find one activity suggested by the plan so interesting that they wish to continue it. If the teacher feels that the additional time would be well spent he may allow the activity to run over the scheduled time and even to the end of the period. The displaced activities may then be worked into the next day's plans.

The pupils may show an interest that makes an activity assigned to the end of the plan more suitable for earlier presentation. A teacher should feel free to make the change. Spontaneous interest makes any activity more meaningful.

Sometimes pupils indicate an interest that suggests activities not written into the plan. Again the teacher should feel free to abandon his plan and utilize the new activities if this seems advantageous. Should the new avenue of work turn out to be less profitable than expected, he may return to his plan for the remainder of the period.

ANALYSES OF SOME SAMPLE LESSON PLANS

It may be helpful to examine a few lesson plans to see how the activities have been selected and organized. Some of these plans are for rather formal situations, some are for very free situations, and some are for situations in which a transition occurs from formal to moderately free conditions.

A lesson plan for an earth science class is shown on page 456. The period opens with a report from two pupils who have kept a record of cloud formations since the last class period. This is followed by an interval during which the pupils, working alone, bring their individual weather records up to date. The teacher does not supervise the pupils during this activity; they are free to consult the weather instruments and each other's records. The two pupils who will later put on a demonstration use this time to make final preparations.

The principal topic of the lesson is now introduced, previous work having been part of routine procedures. Two boys demonstrate the formation of fog, this activity bringing the class back together again as a single group.

Next comes a brief summary of pupil experiences with fogs, this discussion being led by the teacher. After a few contributions by the pupils the teacher makes a pertinent assignment—to read about the various types of fogs. It is assumed that he makes the assignment specific, perhaps in terms of the fogs described by the pupils. He also uses the opportunity to choose the cloud observers for the next twenty-four hours and to ask for volunteers to prepare another demonstration.

The pupils now begin working in pairs to familiarize themselves with dew point apparatus, the concepts thus developed being helpful in their reading about fogs. As pupils finish their work with the dew point apparatus they return to their seats and begin calculations that strengthen their concepts of dew point. If any time remains they begin their reading assignment.

An overview of the unit shows that the teacher has planned to dominate the room only during transitions and for the short discussion period. At all other times he is either at the rear of the room or moving about giving individual help and encouragement. He could even step from the room for several minutes without changing the program.

This lesson has considerable variation in the types of activities, and the types vary among large group, small group, and individual activities. No single activity is carried on for a long time, but the period is not "choppy" because all the activities in the last part of the period are closely related.

Transitions are well taken care of; the two that might give difficulty—leading from the individual work on weather charts and leading from the group work with dew point apparatus—have been anticipated. To care for the first, the plan utilizes curiosity in a demonstration presented by fellow pupils, and the second is cared for by the individualized work that is to be done as soon as the group work is finished.

DAILY LESSON PLAN

Class   Earth science, Section I   Date   10/3

Unit   Precipitation   Topic   Formation of fog

Specific Objectives   to show relation of temperature and dew point

to show causes of fog

to become acquainted with various types of fog

Time	Activity
9:15–9:20	Cloud observers report on clouds of last 24 hours
9:20–9:25	Bring individual weather charts up-to-date
9:25–9:35	Demonstration (Jack and Don) of fog formation
9:35–9:40	Summary of experiences with fogs
	Assignment
9:40–9:55	Become familiar with dew point apparatus in pairs
	Use textbook
9:55–10:05	Practice determining relative humidity from dew point data
Additional	Begin assignment

	Read about types of fog
Assignment	Volunteers prepare demonstration on condensation nuclei
	New cloud observers appointed

Materials	References
12 dew point apparatus	Pictures of fog for bulletin board
12 thermometers	Mimeograph sheets of dew point tables
6 bottles of ether	

The lesson is rigidly planned with few opportunities for the pupils to exercise initiative. It is the type of lesson that is effective in almost any situation in which the teacher has reasonable control of the pupils. It is suitable for lessons early in the year before a teacher has become well acquainted with his group. It does not, however, represent the ideal lesson toward which a teacher should be working.

On page 448 is a lesson plan for a chemistry class studying acids. At the beginning of the period, probably as the pupils are settling down, a set of quiz papers is given back. Presumably there is some discussion of answers, but the time allotted is short. Perhaps the answers were discussed immediately after the test was taken.

The principal work of the period begins with a review of tests for acids, with pupils demonstrating the techniques as they recall them. The information so reviewed is then applied immediately to tests of common foods by the pupils working in pairs. Upon completion of the tests, the pupils summarize their findings in their notebooks.

The period ends with an assignment of project work. A number of topics are listed and probably some pupils will suggest others. Some of the topics call for book research, some for experimental research, some for models or charts. Pupils may work alone or in pairs on the project of their choice.

Excepting the return of the quiz papers, activities change from large group to small group to individual, and back to large group again. The transition from small group work is taken care of by directing the pupils to summarize their results in their notebooks as soon as they complete testing the foods.

The weakest point in the lesson is the assignment. If the pupils do not work as rapidly as anticipated there will be no time for the assignment, or the assignment will be made hurriedly. Also, because the pupils will be completing work on their notebooks at various times, it will be difficult to bring them all together for the assignment. It might be better to suggest that the pupils continue testing foods at home and delay the assignment of projects until the next lesson.

This particular lesson does not permit much opportunity for pupil initiative and independence of thinking. The assignment, however, leads to lessons that allow pupils to work on material of their own choosing and that gives them considerable latitude in their procedures.

The biology lesson plan on page 458 begins with reports by committee chairmen of decisions made near the close of the previous period. After the reports, the committees meet again to plan their approach to certain experiments. Recorders list the materials needed, and chairmen ask for volunteers to work after school assembling materials.

Committee work is interrupted by a film introduced without previous discussion. After the film the pupils recall various types of plant responses pictured in the film. If any time remains, the pupils begin the preparation of a summary sheet for their learnings in their individual notebooks. The assignment is suggestive, not required, and made at the end of the discussion period.

The activities in this lesson vary from large group work, to small group work and to individual work, to large group work, and if there is time, to individual work again. The teacher dominates the room for a few minutes during the discussion. The only difficult transition, at the end of the committee work, is provided for by beginning the film without discussion. A certain amount of pupil initiative is encouraged by the committees and the voluntary assignments. The film, however, greatly shortens the time when the pupils must be responsible for their own behavior.

The lesson plan for a physics class, page 459, illustrates the use of the

DAILY LESSON PLAN

Class   Biology, Section 2   Date   5/2

Unit   Behavior   Topic   Responses of plants

Specific Objectives   to begin group experiments on plant behavior

to become acquainted with some general responses of plants

Time	Activities
1:50–1:55	Group chairman report on experiments each group has chosen
1:55–2:05	Planning sessions to determine materials needed by each group Recorders compile lists Request for volunteers to stay after school to collect materials
2:05–2:25	View film "Germination of Seeds"
2:25–2:35	Summarize plant responses, shown in film Discuss time-lapse photography if needed
Additional	Prepare summary sheet of plant responses for notebooks

	Volunteers stay to assemble materials for experiment
Assignment	(optional) Begin experiment or field observations of plant responses

Materials	References
	Film—"Germination of Seeds"

problem approach during most of a period but with sufficient variation of activity to keep the pupils busy. The teacher presents the problem, "Will any kind of light make the radiometer turn?" The pupils are then asked to suggest different light sources that may be tested. In his plan the teacher has listed several possibilities to help in assembling sufficient materials for the experiments.

The pupils are then directed to divide themselves in groups of two or three members each, depending upon the number of suggestions to be

DAILY LESSON PLAN

Class   Physics   Date   3/16

Unit   Radiant energy   Topic   Infrared radiation

Specific Objectives   to discover radiation beyond the red end of spectrum

to discover some of the properties of infrared rays

Time	Activities
10:30–10:40	Demonstration of radiometer in sunlight
	Speculate on types of light that operate radiometer
	Plan experiments to test kinds of light
	Possible suggestions:
	Fluorescent lamp Incandescent lamp
	Gas burner Neon lamp
	Flashlight Argon lamp
	Arc lamp Gas mantle lamp
	Burning wood Electric hot plate
10:40–11:00	Groups of two or three test possibilities
11:00–11:10	Summary of results and discuss
11:10–11:20	Teacher demonstration of effects of various filters on behavior of radiometer. Introduce "infrared." Assignment
Additional	Groups begin planning experiments using filters

Assignment	Read about the nature of infrared
	(optional) Plan demonstrations of effects of infrared radiation

Materials		References
Radiometers	Argon lamp	
Lamp cords	Gas burner	
Fluorescent	Gas mantle	
lamp	burner	
Incandescent	Electric hot	
bulb	plate	
Flashlight	Set of filters	
Neon lamp bulb		

tested. During the next few minutes they assemble and put in operation the various light sources. They then test the effect of the different light sources on the radiometers.

When the tests are completed the pupils reconvene to summarize their discoveries. More questions may arise from the experiments and be discussed. If there is time, the teacher will demonstrate the effects of some of the light filters on sunlight to show that different rays exist. The pupils are now ready to recognize that the rays which turn the radiometer form a limited portion of the spectrum. Their reading will strengthen this concept. Optional assignments permit pupils to explore further the nature of infrared.

The activities change from large group to small group and back to large group. Physical activity is permitted in the middle and major portion of the period. The teacher dominates as a moderator during the two discussion periods and as a demonstrator during the last activity. He might minimize his role still further by using pupil secretaries to keep records on the blackboard and by using pupils as helpers with the demonstrations.

Control problems might arise during the small group experiments as certain groups finish ahead of others or as some groups wait their turn for the use of the radiometers. However, pupils in physics classes are usually interested enough to watch the work of other groups.

The optional assignment is of the type that appeals to physics students. Several pupils might volunteer to present demonstrations. They would be aided by references to books which contain suggestions for such activities.

SUGGESTED ACTIVITIES

1. Observe a science lesson. Spot check the attention of the pupils at regular intervals. (This is best accomplished by several observers, each of whom studies a section of the class.) Plot the results as shown in Figure 22. Analyze the lesson to determine which situations produce a high percentage of attention and which situations permit attention to lapse.

2. Observe a science lesson by an experienced teacher and note how he makes a transition from one activity to the next. Note also how he opens and closes his lesson. Which techniques are effective in terms of classroom control, and which could be improved?

3. Make a lesson plan that calls for three or more activities. Provide proper transition from one activity to the next so that classroom control is maintained.

4. Plan a lesson that is based on a full-period field trip. Give proper attention to such factors as attention, assignments, and the like. If necessary, reread pertinent sections of the chapter on field experiences.

SUGGESTED READINGS

Brandwein, Paul F., F. G. Watson, and Paul E. Blackwood, *Teaching High School Science, A Book of Methods,* Harcourt, Brace & World, New York, 1958, pp. 126–145.

Coombs, J. R., "The Logic of Teaching," *High School Journal*, 50:30–34, 1966.

Guthrie, J. T., "Expository Instruction Versus a Discovery Method," *Journal of Educational Psychology*, 158:45–49, 1967.

Lacey, Archie L., *Guide to Science Teaching*, Wadsworth Publishing Company, Belmont, Calif., 1966, pp. 90–97.

Mersand, J., "How to Plan a Lesson," *High Points*, 47:5–26, 1965.

Mickelson, J. M., "Evolving Concept of General Method," *Theory Into Practice*, 5:81–86, 1966.

Richardson, John S., *Science Teaching in Secondary Schools*, Prentice-Hall, Englewood Cliffs, N. J., 1957, Chapter eight.

Salling, A., "Structure and Style of Teaching," *Journal of Secondary Education*, 42:66–76, 1967.

Sund, R. B., and L. W. Trowbridge, *Teaching Science by Inquiry*, Charles Merrill Books, Columbus, Ohio, 1967, Chapter five.

Chapter 14

Standards, Evaluation,

and Grading

"THIS COURSE IS THE HARDEST ONE I EVER TOOK BUT I LIKE IT." "I ONLY GOT a C but it's my own fault; I should have worked harder." "He's strict but he's a wonderful teacher." "It's a good course. You have to work hard but you learn a lot." Frequently heard comments such as these indicate that pupils like courses for which they have respect. They do not object to hard work providing they know they have chances for success. It is when they recognize that their chances for success are slim or nonexistent that they shun difficult courses.

Science teachers are faced with the problem of setting standards that make their courses challenging without automatically failing large numbers of pupils. This country cannot afford a highly selective process that frightens all but a few from work in scientific fields. Neither can it afford mass education processes that hold all pupils to mediocre standards. A weak compromise has no place. Schools need standards that are broadly conceived and applicable to the great range of pupils in the schools.

462

STANDARDS IN COMMON USE

For a number of years secondary school teachers have been at the focal point of much sharp criticism. They have been accused of lowering their standards and at the same time they have been accused of not attracting enough young people into scientific occupations. Many of the criticisms are not based upon sound evidence. They are based upon opinions and upon vague recollections of conditions that existed twenty or more years ago. Actually, the record of science teachers has been good, though not as good as could be wished. A larger percentage of each age group is electing science courses today than ever before. Each generation of young people is better informed about science than the one before it. If the quality of exhibits in science fairs is a valid indication, the achievements of the best of today's product will equal if not surpass those of yesterday's best.

Many of the criticisms have been inevitable and are the result of changing conditions. A few decades ago secondary schools were concerned chiefly with preparation for college. Today, secondary schools recognize an obligation to the large numbers of pupils who will not attend college. The change in emphasis, as might be expected, is lamented by college professors.

In addition, colleges today use a much broader base for determining admission qualifications than was used a few decades ago. As a result, college professors must work with a less homogeneous student body than they are accustomed to. They mistakenly attribute the change to the preparation their students have received in secondary schools.

A third factor that has resulted in criticism specifically directed at science teachers has entered the picture because of the expanding nature of the science field. In physics, for instance, time that could once be given to the solution of problems in mechanics must now be shared with a study of nuclear energy; the topic of internal combustion engines, once limited to gasoline engines, must now include diesel engines, gas turbines, jet engines, and rockets. In consequence, pupils in physics today have a less intensive training but a broader one.

Among the more justifiable complaints are those that concern the neglect of highly gifted pupils. As teachers have found themselves faced with pupils of increasing diversity in ability, they have allowed themselves to concentrate upon the pupils who presented the greatest problems. Pupils who could do the required work satisfactorily have received little attention.

Maximum standards. The work of secondary school pupils is usually judged by a narrow set of academic standards of the type that may be called "maximum" standards. These standards are set above the ability levels of all but the most able pupils and in consequence most pupils fall short of these standards. However, because teachers do not expect these standards to be attained, they accept as satisfactory a little less than the maximum.

Maximum standards operate successfully in relatively homogeneous groups. By accepting as satisfactory those achievements that represent 60 or 70 percent of the maximum, teachers make it possible for all pupils in the group to succeed. Slight differences in ability can be compensated for by extra effort and all pupils are in competition with each other.

However, as the ability range widens, maximum standards become less workable. In a group having a normal distribution of academic abilities, as represented by IQ's ranging from 80 to 130, as much as half the group fails automatically if the maximum standards are based on the ability of the most able pupils. There is then no incentive for large numbers of pupils. Competition is limited to the few most able individuals.

The strict application of maximum standards to heterogeneous groups has resulted in so many failures that science teachers have attempted compromises which have not been satisfactory. They have tried lowering the level of the maximum enough to permit most pupils to succeed. The results have been unfortunate. The more able pupils are now without challenge; they can attain success without effort. They feel contempt for their courses and find no satisfaction in their high grades.

As another compromise, teachers have attempted to apply the normal distribution curve to the grades they give, thus insuring fixed percentages of high, low, and medium grades. Some injustices have been eliminated, automatic failure for one, but new injustices have been introduced. No matter how hard a group works, or how little it does, the same number of pupils pass and fail.

"Marking on a curve," as it is called, is not sound statistically or in principle. The curve of normal distribution has statistical reliability only when applied to groups of several hundreds; its application to groups of thirty is ridiculous. Such marking eliminates in effect all standards; pupils have no definite objectives to work toward and no feeling of accomplishment; teachers have nothing by which to judge the effectiveness of their teaching and no incentive to make superior presentations.

Minimum standards. In some types of training, the standards that are set call for the complete attainment of all objectives. Since these objectives must lie within the ability range of all individuals concerned, the standards are of a minimum nature. Minimum standards are utilized in adult driver education courses; a student must become proficient in each qualification to pass; his achievement is not satisfactory if he applies the brakes properly only sixty percent of the time; he cannot offset a lack of knowledge of traffic laws by superior performance at the wheel.

Minimum standards deny success to no one except the lazy, the indifferent, and the truly incompetent. They provide definite objectives toward which to work and from which a sense of accomplishment can be attained. Minimum standards put no ceiling on the work of superior individuals, but they do fail to give these last proper guidance in their work above the minimum.

Minimum standards could be used more extensively in the science program. Some kinds of knowledge and skill, particularly in the areas of health and safety, may be considered essential. These could be used in setting up minimum requirements that must be mastered for success.

Multiple standards.   Teachers of vocational subjects often set up several sets of standards to operate in parallel, thus enabling a pupil's strengths to compensate for his weaknesses. A teacher of typing, for instance, has standards to judge proficiency with the typewriter, skills with handbooks and dictionaries, usage of grammar and punctuation, spelling ability, and ability to organize typed material. A teacher of vocational agriculture has standards to judge knowledge of theories and practices, skills with tools and equipment, ability to keep records, and success with project work.

Multiple standards are used to a limited extent in the academic phases of the science program but they could be applied much more broadly and much more extensively. Science is as broad a field as the vocational subjects, and there should be a place in it for a great range of abilities and talents. There should be standards to judge the acquisition of facts, ability to communicate science understandings, skills with science equipment, abilities to keep records and use handbooks and tables, and success with projects.

MAINTAINING STANDARDS

As has been shown, the problem of setting standards is particularly difficult for heterogeneous groups. As long as groups are relatively homogeneous, traditional maximum standards operate satisfactorily. It is for such subjects as general science, which take in all pupils, that new solutions are needed.

Using composite standards for heterogeneous groups.   If science classes could be kept small and class loads light, the use of multiple standards would give an excellent solution to the problem of standards. Each pupil could develop his special talents to the utmost and at the same time be credited for his successes. He would be able to explore his interests and abilities and emerge with an honest appraisal of himself, neither deflated for having failed to meet a narrow set of standards, nor inflated for having found success under ridiculously low standards.

With multiple standards, the lowering of standards to reduce failures would not be necessary. Pupils who could not succeed in one way could find success in another. All standards could be kept high. Unfortunately, multiple standards require a free program and close supervision. Each pupil must be judged separately and on his own merits. With typical classes, science teachers do not have the time to use multiple standards exclusively.

Some of the advantages of multiple standards can be retained by using composites of two or more types of standards.

> For many years Mr. Langer has utilized a composite of minimum standards and multiple standards in his general science classes. For each unit he lists a number of requirements which each pupil must fulfill completely. These requirements include facts to be learned, experiments to be carried out, reports to be written, and home assignments to be completed. Mr. Langer accepts no substitutes and does not deviate from the standards he sets for these requirements.
>
> As soon as a pupil completes a minimum requirement, Mr. Langer encourages him to undertake additional assignments. Mr. Langer provides lists of suggestions from which pupils may choose. He also encourages his pupils to make their own suggestions, although he retains the power of veto. Mr. Langer gives full credit for all additional work and sets no limits to the amount that may be done.

Composite standards of the type used by Mr. Langer are both just and practical. The minimum requirements need but little supervision, leaving the teacher free to give individual help and encouragement as pupils complete their tasks. Classroom techniques need but little alteration save that more time is given for independent and small group work than is customary in the conventional program. A large share of the additional work is done outside school hours and requires little class time. Finally, the pupils recognize the basis for their grades and approve of it.

Setting minimum standards for heterogeneous groups.   Minimum standards represent the very least that can be accepted as satisfactory. To be applicable, minimum standards should be within the abilities of all pupils.

To be practical they should apply quickly and readily. To be useful, they should apply to the type of work that challenges pupils.

Minimum standards fall generally into two categories. Some are satisfied by the mere completion of a task, as when a teacher requires each pupil to carry out a specified laboratory exercise. Others can be satisfied only by the display of some degree of proficiency, as when a teacher requires a legible and well-organized report of an experiment.

The second category of standards is concerned with knowledge and skills and is generally considered as more appropriate for the science program. However, the first category has usefulness in setting up minimum standards. After all, merely doing things can have value; laboratory exercises can be challenging even though required; making diagrams can allow self-expression even though based on a chart; tables can be filled in with interesting data even though data are taken from assigned readings.

Minimum standards applied to the acquisition of facts and understandings should be selected with the three levels of learning in mind—*mastery*, *recall*, and *recognition*. Pupils should be expected to master only such material as is important enough to justify the special time and effort involved. Other material should be dealt with on the lower levels and judged appropriately.

A number of sources are helpful in setting minimum standards for factual learnings. Textbooks and courses of study list information commonly considered important. Tests represent another source of ideas. However, since these sources do not apply closely to any one situation, the teacher should consider them as suggestive only.

Under a strict interpretation of minimum standards each pupil should gain all required learnings to do satisfactory work; he should attain a perfect score on each test measuring minimum essentials. In practice, insistence upon perfect test scores is not realistic; scores a little short of perfection may be accepted.

Textbooks, courses of study, and laboratory manuals provide help in determining uniform assignments. Every effort should be used to keep these assignments from being routine and boring; challenging problems should be used whenever possible.

For those assignments that need only to be done to represent satisfactory work, there is no problem of setting standards: checkmarks on a checklist show whether or not pupils have met the minimum standards. If skills are to be developed, however, criteria for judging them should be set up ahead of time and announced to the pupils so that they have opportunities to practice these skills. Likewise, when reports and papers are to be prepared, pupils should be told frequently what is expected of them so that they may have the points in mind as they work.

Helping pupils attain minimum standards.   Once a requirement has been announced it is imperative that all pupils be held to the requirement lest they lose respect for both course and teacher. Threats and punishments, however, are poor stimuli; pupils respond better to encouragement, to help, and especially to success.

Frequent small tests used for review and drill are of great help in bringing all pupils up to the same level of knowledge.

> Mr. Baker gave a ten-question review test dealing with cell structure. He made note of the most frequently missed questions and included these in a test a few days later. As the year progressed he occasionally included one or more of these same questions in tests until he was certain that all pupils could answer them.

The practice of repeating questions until all pupils have learned them is useful for teachers who are preparing pupils for the New York State Regents examinations and other standardized examinations. Teachers have found that by using two or three short tests weekly they ensure success on the examinations and have the remainder of their class time for working toward broader goals.

It is well to allot a certain amount of class time for the beginning phases of all uniform assignments. During this time the teacher is free to move from pupil to pupil, interpreting directions, clearing up misunderstandings, and indicating the standards he expects the pupils to meet. Should it be necessary for the pupils to complete their assignments out of class, they work with more assurance for having had supervision at the beginning.

Class time may be allotted for make-up sessions to bring all pupils up to the same level of achievement.

> Halfway through the general science period Miss Lobdell made an announcement.
>
> "Tomorrow," she said, "I will collect your notebooks and look over the section on weather prediction. Let's take some time now to see if you have all your required work."
>
> As soon as the notebooks were opened she continued, "First you should have a title page. We worked on that last week. Next you should have a table of contents. I will give you time to make that later this period."
>
> Miss Lobdell continued to specify precisely the titles and order of the pages she had required the pupils to make in their notebooks. She also suggested the most suitable locations for the various types of optional work many of the pupils had done.

"And now," Miss Lobdell concluded, "you may use the remainder of the period to prepare the table of contents and complete any unfinished work. Some of you may find it necessary to do some work at home tonight."

Pupils who have lost time because of sickness should be given special opportunities to make up their work. When possible this work should be done under supervision, perhaps during a free period, or during the class period while others are doing optional work. Often other pupils are qualified to help a classmate set up experiments or review for a test.

In any group there are apt to be pupils who do not do the work expected of them, usually because of lack of interest. Though the teacher should always try to use positive motivation there are times when these pupils must be compelled to do their work.

Compulsory make-up sessions are generally necessary, preferably at times inconvenient to the pupils. School policy varies as to when make-up sessions may be held but usually some provision is made for them. Teachers should treat make-up sessions as devices to help pupils pass their courses rather than as punishment. Threats to "keep pupils after school" do not frighten many pupils and may but make them more stubborn. Much more effective is a polite request to appear at a certain time for help in catching up with the others in the class.

During a make-up session pupils usually need a brief review of the requirements. They may have forgotten the assignment even if they were listening when it was made. They need the same help in beginning their work as they would have needed in class time.

Encouraging work beyond the minimum.   After pupils have met the minimum standards that have been set for the class as a whole, any further work they may do should be of a permissive nature. This does not mean that pupils may work or not as they please, but that they may choose the nature of the assignments they undertake. Thus opportunity is provided for them to follow up special interests.

Uniform standards cannot be applied easily to permissive work; each case must be judged on its own merits rather than by comparison with what other pupils do. Rating is best done on a positive basis with pupils receiving credit for their achievements without penalty for weaknesses.

Special achievements fall in the following categories:

1. *Superior work on required assignments.* For example, all pupils have been asked to study vegetative reproduction using textbooks, films, and experiments, reporting their findings in their notebooks. One girl illustrated her report with clippings, colored drawings, and diagrams giving more than fifty different examples of this type of reproduction.

2. *Investigation in depth of a required topic.* For example, all pupils were directed to make a study of the operation of a standard automobile engine, learning the function and operation of the major parts. One boy became interested in the fuel injection system of his father's automobile and studied it thoroughly. He read advertising literature, talked with mechanics, and studied the maintenance manual used in garages for the repair of this type of engine. He described his findings to the class, illustrating his talk with a chart borrowed from a sales agency.

3. *Acceptable work on a permissive assignment.* A chemistry teacher listed a number of demonstration experiments in the field of electrochemistry. He asked each pupil to choose one demonstration-experiment from the list, or to suggest another, and to work up the demonstration for presentation to the class. Each pupil received a grade for his efforts.

4. *Voluntary work on suggested projects.* During a study of tone quality a physics teacher called attention to the difference in quality of the several reed instruments and suggested that some pupil might be interested in comparing the structure of these instruments. One girl, who played the clarinet in the high school band, volunteered to undertake this study.

5. *Voluntary services.* For example, a general science teacher took a photograph of a class project. Two pupils volunteered to prepare enough enlargements so that each pupil in the class could have a print.

6. *Independent work on teacher-approved projects.* A pupil read of a way to make rayon fibers from filter paper using only simple apparatus. He asked his chemistry teacher if he could undertake this project. The teacher not only gave permission but also allowed him to begin the project during the regular class period.

7. *Completely independent work.* An eighth grade girl had learned to make blueprints of leaves in a summer camp. She continued work on her collection during the summer and into the fall. When her science teacher heard of her work he asked her to exhibit her collection and describe her procedures.

8. *Shared experiences.* A seventh grade boy watching television saw an experiment with magnets and iron filings in water. He tried the experiment at home and asked his science teacher if he could show the experiment to the class.

9. *Shared materials.* While on a trip into nearby mountains a boy collected several "books" of mica. He gave several sheets to each pupil in his class so that the structure could be examined closely.

Teachers must expect to provide time and facilities for permissive work just as they provide time and facilities for uniform assignments. During part of a period pupils may be working toward minimum objectives; during the remainder of the period they may be working on permissive assignments. Some homework assignments may be directed toward meeting minimum objectives; others may be completely permissive in nature.

All pupils should be expected to do some work beyond the minimum. Even seriously handicapped pupils who find minimum requirements too much for them can do additional work, usually of a nonacademic nature. In many cases teachers may find it necessary to provide suggestions and even specific directions.

Pupils need special recognition for all work they do above the minimum. Grades are inadequate measures at best and difficult to explain to pupils. Merited praise from the teacher and opportunities to display achievements to other pupils are usually sufficient. Superior work can be acknowledged through special displays, radio and newspaper publicity, and competition in science fairs.

Evaluating work beyond the minimum. All permissive work should be given credit toward the final grades of pupils. However, because uniform standards cannot be applied, a teacher must judge each item separately. If he evaluates only on a positive basis, giving credit for accomplishments, it is not likely that he will be unfair to individual pupils.

Learnings above the minimum requirements can be measured in part by suitably designed tests. One form of test is constructed with two parts, the first measuring mastery of the minimum requirements and the second part, which allows choice of questions to be answered, measuring learnings above the minimum. A variant on this form of test uses bonus questions which a pupil may choose to answer if he thinks that he can earn extra credit.

Tests may be constructed with a broad range of questions so that pupils who have explored special fields may find material they have studied. With such a test a satisfactory grade may be represented by a score of fifty or sixty percent of the total. Greater achievement is represented by higher scores.

Pupils may volunteer to take tests for extra credit. These may be tests constructed by the teacher; but because teacher time is limited, tests found in textbooks, workbooks, and review books are more often used. Pupils preparing for college board examinations or other standardized tests may concentrate on this type of test.

Extra notebook work should be judged by several standards operating in parallel. Points that should be considered are: thoroughness, organization, accuracy, handwriting, spelling, grammar, care with diagrams and labels, wise use of illustrative materials. Some teachers insist that all additional work be pertinent to the topics studied in class; other teachers encourage pupils to include material on current events, special investigations, and matters of special interest to the pupils.

Library research projects may be rated upon the number of sources used, the thoroughness of investigation, the organization of data, the treatment of conflicting points of view, and the quality of the summaries. Written reports may also be rated upon handwriting, spelling, grammar, and documentation.

Experimental research problems should be rated in terms of originality, statement of problem, thoroughness in collecting data, organization and summarization of data, and carefulness in reporting findings. Special attention should be given to the conclusions drawn and the attempts to substantiate the conclusions through further investigation.

Demonstrations presented by pupils may be rated according to the amount of preparation involved, the presentation of the problem, the organization of the data collected, and the conclusions drawn.

Construction projects may or may not involve original planning; some projects represent no more than the assembly of commercial kits, others represent the step-by-step following of prepared plans, still others represent complete planning on the part of the pupils. Some projects are preceded by extensive research; this research adds to knowledge and deserves recognition. Teachers should remember that large spectacular projects may not represent as much investigation, experimentation, and problem solving as smaller, less conspicuous efforts. Additional points to consider are the skills with tools and materials, attention to details, and ingenuity displayed.

Teachers should not forget to give credit for the many lesser contributions of pupils, care of classroom plants and animals, voluntary distribution and collection of materials, help with cleaning glassware and organizing apparatus, and assistance with bulletin boards. Pupils who serve with distinction as group leaders, secretaries, or in other capacities deserve recognition also.

The problem of grading for "effort" always arises. Should pupils receive extra credit for sheer volume of their work even though the quality seems low? The criterion to be used in evaluation is the benefit to the pupil. Many activities represent important learning situations even though tangible results are difficult to demonstrate. A teacher will not perpetrate many injustices if he errs on the side of generosity.

Another problem that arises in evaluation is the basing of credit on ability. Should a pupil of high ability receive as much credit for a piece of work as a less able classmate who does work of the same caliber? Ability is hard to measure and attempts to do so add another variable to the already confusing problem of evaluation. However, at times a teacher may be justified in giving one pupil unusual credit for a mediocre accomplishment while refusing another pupil credit for an equally mediocre accomplishment. The effect upon the pupils involved is the most important consideration; the teacher must be careful not to seem unjust in his judgment.

MAKING GRADES CONSISTENT WITH STANDARDS

The determination of grades is a serious responsibility. Grades, once entered in the records, have great impact on the lives of pupils. They represent success or failure with all the attendant emotions. They are used to compare one pupil with another. They are used to determine readiness for promotion and graduation and fitness for college or other advanced training. They are taken into account in awarding scholarships and in deciding upon employment. It is unfortunate that so much weight is given to grades because there are no truly objective measuring devices that can be used in determining them. Grading must be largely subjective in nature.

The more factors that a teacher can take into consideration in grading the less likely it is that he will commit injustices. Grades based on tests alone, for instance, do not give as good a picture of achievement as grades based on reports, research, projects, and tests.

Types of achievement.   Certain types of achievements can be evaluated with some degree of assurance. These achievements fall in the following categories:

1. *Learnings that can be measured by tests.* These include word meanings, statements of principles, recognition of applications, and solution of verbal problems. Learnings that are difficult to measure include understandings of complex situations, understandings that do not lend themselves to verbalization, appreciations, and attitudes.

2. *Skills that can be demonstrated quickly.* These include skills with reading, with mathematical processes, with the use of books, tools, and equipment. Difficult to measure are such skills as problem solving skills.

3. *Completion of assigned tasks that are simple in nature.* It is relatively easy to check off tasks such as laboratory exercises, mathematical exercises, and workbook activities as soon as they are completed.

4. *Certain aspects of permissive work.* Reports and projects carried out by pupils under the supervision of the teacher can be evaluated in terms of the end products and in terms of such procedures as are observed. It is difficult to determine many of the major benefits to the pupils.

5. *Tangible results of independent work.* The end products of independent research and of independent project work can be evaluated. Unless part or all of the work has been done in the classroom the procedures cannot be evaluated. The major benefits to the pupils cannot be evaluated.

Keeping records of achievements.   Full records are essential for arriving at grades. It is difficult to remember the nature and extent of each pupil's achievements, especially in the case of pupils who work quietly and without spectaclar results.

Record forms should permit notations as to the different types of achievements pupils may have. A portion of a record book adapted for science records is shown on page 475. There are four major headings:

1. *Quizzes and unit tests.* Several spaces are reserved for the scores of short tests. A few spaces are reserved for the scores of longer tests and unit tests.

2. *Assigned work.* This section is treated as a check list except that grades are given for work which surpasses the minimum.

3. *Permissive work.* In this section are entered the grades given for optional assignments carried out as part of regular class work.

4. *Voluntary work.* In this section are recorded the grades given for work that pupils undertake spontaneously and do largely on their own time. There may be no entries in this section for some pupils and only a few for others.

A record book is convenient to carry about and store. The records are compact and easily examined. However, there is not enough space to specify the nature of the achievements indicated in points 3 and 4 above. In consequence a busy teacher has difficulty in calling to mind precisely what each pupil has done; he is handicapped in arriving at final grades.

On page 476 is a sheet from a standard 8½″ by 11″ notebook in which one teacher keeps his records of the voluntary work done by his pupils. This form, which the teacher makes in quantity with a duplicator, has spaces large enough for brief notations of each activity carried out. When determining grades he skims over the sheets to refresh his memory.

Some teachers prefer to keep their records on filing cards despite the problems of carrying and storing cards. The front of a card is used for test grades and notes on other achievements. The reverse is used for notes on conferences and for observations of behavior.

Assigning grades. When records are kept in the above fashion, final grades are determined by combining all the results of a pupil's work. Test grades are averaged, with long tests being given more weight than short tests. For example, if a test that ends a unit is three times as long as a typical quiz, the score on that test is tripled before averaging it with the others.

Grades for required work and for permissive work are then averaged, proper weight being given according to the nature of the difficulties involved in each assignment. These results are combined with the test average to give a tentative final grade.

Credit given for voluntary work may be determined in a number of ways. Some teachers include the grades in with the permissive assignments.

A TEACHER'S RECORD BOOK

Name	Quizzes							Unit test	Assignments			Permissive			Voluntary		Average
Alton, Patrick	9	8	9	7	6	8	8	78	✓	✓	A	B	B	C	B		
Carra, Richard	7	8	a	7	8	8	8	75	✓	B	✓	C	C	C			
Cockfield, Nancy	10	9	10	10	10	10	10	95	A	A+	A+	A	A+	A	A+	A	
Coulter, Roxanne	8	8	7	a	a	7	3	82	B	✓	B	A	B	A			
Crosby, Ralph	4	6	3	6	6	3	6	40	✓	✓	✓	D	D	O			
Davis, Edna	7	9	7	7	7	6	6	80	✓	✓	✓	A	A	A	C	C	
Dodge, Robert	10	10	10	8	8	10	10	100	A	B	B	B	B	A			
Enell, Carl	6	7	7	10	6	6	6	45	✓	✓	B	C	A	C	C		
Griffen, Faith	7	4	8	6	6	7	7	63	✓	✓	✓	D	D	A			
Harris, Robert	9	8	7	9	9	4	4	85	A	✓	A	E	D	D			
Ikeda, Vivian	8	8	8	9	8	9	9	94	✓	B	✓	A	B	A			
Jackson, David	6	3	6	6	2	a	a	48	✓	✓	✓	C	D	C	C	C	
Jorden, Christine	10	7	10	8	9	10	10	95	✓	✓	✓	D	B	D			
Lawrence, Joanne	5	6	5	8	6	7	7	64	✓	✓	✓	D	D	D	A+		
Lindop, Kathryn	0	8	7	9	7	7	7	81	B	✓	B	C	C	B	C		
Mason, Donald	a	a	a	a	9	9	9	95	a	✓	a	a	C	C	B		
Miller, Jane	7	8	8	4	8	8	8	82	✓	✓	✓	B	B	C	C	C	
Miller, June	9	8	7	9	8	7	7	88	✓	✓	✓	B	B	B	C	C	
Monahan, Michael	8	9	10	10	6	4	4	51	✓	✓	✓	A	C	D			
Motley, Louise	10	7	6	8	10	9	9	98	B	A	✓	A	C	A			

475

									Names
									Book report
									Article report
									T. V. science
									Radio science program
									Interview
									Watched or worked with scientist
									Radio-T. V. broadcast
									Class report
									Class demonstration
									Exhibit
									Bulletin board
									Project
									Research
									Wrote news article
									Field trip
									Other

A TEACHER'S RECORD OF VOLUNTARY WORK

(Courtesy of Walter DeNeef, Dryden Central School, Dryden, N.Y.)

Other teachers work out a system for raising the final grade a certain number of points for each voluntary activity, the amount of increase depending upon the grades earned in each case.

It is sometimes convenient to use numerical grades for tests and letter grades for other achievements. A conversion table is then needed. Each teacher should construct his own to fit his method of scoring. A conversion table that is commonly used is shown below:

Score in percent	Letter grade	Significance of grade
90 to 100	A to A—	Superior
80 to 89	B to B—	Good
70 to 79	C to C—	Fair
60 to 69	D to D—	Satisfactory
Below 60	E	Unsatisfactory

The method of amalgamating grades in determining final grades helps to reduce some of the injustices that are bound to result when test grades alone are used. With this process the highest grades are reserved for the pupils who excel in tests and who exert themselves to do superior work. Pupils who pass tests easily are not penalized for failing to work but they are denied superior grades unless they do more than the minimum. Pupils who have special aptitudes but lack all around excellence can earn high grades by exploiting their special talents. Pupils who lack academic ability and find tests difficult can still earn satisfactory grades by sufficient hard work. Only pupils who lack ability and refuse to try are certain of failure.

SUGGESTED ACTIVITIES

1. Make up a set of minimum requirements for a unit in general science, assuming a heterogeneous group of students. Be sure that the requirements are realistic—that the learnings justify the time needed for mastery, that each requirement lies within the abilities of each pupil, and that there are not more requirements than can be attained within the time allotted for the unit.

2. Write out suggestions for activities in which pupils might engage after they have completed the minimum requirements for the unit just mentioned. Try to find suggestions to meet a wide variety of interests and abilities.

3. Work out final grades for the pupils whose test and project grades are given on page 475. Compare your grades with those worked out by other prospective teachers. Defend your basis for grading.

SUGGESTED READINGS

Brandwein, P. F., *et al.*, *Teaching High School Science: A Book of Methods*, Harcourt, Brace and Co., New York, 1958, Chapters 19 and 20.

Buros, Oscar K. (ed.), *The Fifth Mental Measurements Yearbook*, Gryphon Press, Highland Park, N. J., 1959, pp. 799–831.

Cline, V. B., *et al.*, "Factor Analysis of Self-Ratings, Teacher Ratings and Indexes of Achievement in High School Science," *Journal of Education Research*, 58:10–15, 1964.

Cronbach, L. J., *Essentials of Psychological Testing*, 2nd edition, Harper, New York, 1960.

Dutton, W. H., and L. Stephens, "Measuring Attitudes Toward Science," *School Science and Mathematics*, 63:43–49, 1963.

Faunce, R. C., and C. L. Munshaw, *Teaching and Learning in Secondary Schools*, Wadsworth Publishing Company, Belmont, Calif., 1964, Chapter 13.

Gerberich, J. Raymond, Harry A. Green, and A. N. Jorgensen, *Measurement and Evaluation in the Modern School*, David McKay Company, New York, 1962, Chapter 18.

Heil, Louis M., *et al.*, "The Measurement of Understanding in Science," *The Measurement of Understanding, Forty-fifth Yearbook*, National Society for the Study of Education, Part I, University of Chicago Press, Chicago, 1946, Chapter 6.

Neissen, A. M., "Marking on a Curve," *School Science and Mathematics*, 46:155–158, 1946.

Reilly, J. J., "Evaluating Critical Thinking in Science," *Science Teacher*, 28:34–35, 1961.

Reiner, W. B., "Evaluation and Testing in Science Education," *Education*, 80:28–31, 1959.

Smith, H. A., "Appraisal and Projection in Science Education: Some Meditations," *American Biology Teacher*, 28:797–803, 1966.

Weaver, Edward K., "Evaluation of Student Achievement in Science," *Science Education*, 32:81–87, 1948.

Chapter **15**

Providing for the

Exceptional Pupil

THE GREATEST CHALLENGE IN EDUCATION TODAY IS THE DEVELOPMENT OF means whereby each young person can progress at his maximum rate as far as he is able to go. Completely individualized instruction is too expensive. Mass instruction techniques, though providing equal schooling opportunities, are unjust to pupils who should progress more rapidly or more slowly or in other directions. The European system of isolating young people in rigid groupings is not compatible with American democracy. Acceleration and retardation by grades brings in many social adjustment problems.

Within the science program, educational opportunities can be equalized by various forms of grouping and by limited individualization of instruction, both of which can be applied within moderate sized heterogeneous classes. When facilities permit, small groups of especially talented youngsters may be isolated temporarily in classes geared for their particular abilities.

IDENTIFYING ABILITIES AND INTERESTS

Pupils can be provided for only when the teacher knows them as individuals—their interests, personality traits, abilities, background, and specific needs. Obviously, no teacher can come to know his pupils that well unless he is fortunate enough to teach in a small school system where he works with the same individuals year after year. He must usually depend upon other sources of information.

Counseling records. Records of each pupil are usually kept in the guidance office of a school. If there is no guidance office these records will be found in the administrative offices. Among the records of each student are the results of standardized tests, the courses taken, and the grades achieved. Of special value are the results of group intelligence and group achievement tests. In a recent study,[1] designed to identify gifted pupils, group intelligence test scores proved to be the most effective single screening method. Approximately 92 percent of the gifted students in the study were located on the basis of these scores alone.[2] The second best single method was found to be results of group achievement tests. Scores from any standardized reading, mathematics, or science tests may also prove to be useful. Grades give a measure of a pupil's performance in school and a clue to his reaction to academic work.

The data in the guidance office are more useful in locating problems than in finding answers. The records show which pupils should be doing better work, but tell neither why they do not nor how to help them. Low intelligence test scores do not explain low grades; they point only to a common factor causing both.

The personal data questionnaire. Many teachers prepare a questionnaire which they ask pupils to fill out the first day of school. The information on interests and backgrounds is of value in making plans to utilize special interests and experiences. A personal data card used by the science teachers in one school system is shown on page 481. This particular card also provides space for other data—standardized test results, grades, and records of special activities.

[1] Gallagher, James J. (ed.), *Teaching Gifted Students: A Book of Readings*, Allyn & Bacon, Boston, 1966, p. 39.

[2] The I.Q. cut-off point was 115 on the Otis Quick Scoring Mental Ability Test.

PERSONAL DATA CARD

(Last name)	(First name)	(Section)	(Homeroom)

(Street address)

M.A. _____

R.L. _____

(City)

A.G. _____

_____

(Birthday)	(Age)

(Father's name)	(Occupation)

(Mother's name)	(Occupation)

If you have lived in other cities or states, tell where.

Give the names of some of the places to which you have traveled.

What kinds of work have you done for pay?

What are some of your hobbies?

To what organizations do you belong? What offices have you held? What is your rank (in Scouts, Civil Air Patrol, etc.)?

What kinds of movies, radio programs and television programs do you like best?

What kinds of reading do you like best?

What is the name of a book you have read recently?

What magazines do you take at home and read regularly?

Personal contacts.   Most of a teacher's acquaintance with his pupils comes as he works with them in the classroom. With mass instruction techniques only the extremes stand out—the enthusiastic and the actively noncooperative. The more that a teacher can individualize his instruction the better he comes to know the pupils as individuals and the better he can meet their special needs.

Closer acquaintance is gained during such out-of-class work that the pupils might engage in—science projects, science clubs, and other activities in which the science teacher may have a part. In activities out of school, such as scouting, the teacher comes to know his pupils as they really are, away from the artificial environment of the classroom. To help themselves identify their pupils better, many teachers keep brief notes on special characteristics. These may be kept in a card file, on the personal data questionnaire, or in a notebook.

Conferences with other teachers. Any teacher who has had previous contacts with a pupil has important information about him—his special abilities, his interests, and his background. Unfortunately this information cannot be passed along as readily as are his grades.

In large systems, a science teacher cannot interview all the former teachers of each of his pupils, but he can contact them about special problem cases. Information gained must be interpreted with caution because teachers, being human, develop prejudices and may do injustice to certain pupils.

EMPLOYING GROUPING IN THE SCIENCE PROGRAM

Grouping is not new in the science program. For many years science teachers have divided their classes into teams of two or three for laboratory work. However, such grouping has been employed more often in the interests of convenience than with the full potentialities of grouping in mind.

Contributions of grouping. Grouping, when properly employed, produces a number of beneficial outcomes:

1. Allows full participation by the individual.
2. Gives maximum direct experience with materials.
3. Provides for wide range of interests.
4. Provides for wide range of talents.
5. Permits close matching of assignments to abilities.
6. Takes advantages of adolescents' desire to work together.
7. Gives shy and retiring pupils increased security.
8. Gives practice in democratic processes.
9. Helps pupils explore their leadership potentials.
10. Provides a change from standard classroom techniques.
11. Helps teachers become better acquainted with individuals.
12. Helps teachers find time for special help for individuals.

Not all of the above benefits will be operative at the same time. However, the teacher can usually plan for several of them in any one grouping situation.

Some considerations in setting up groups. A little knowledge of the general nature of preadolescents and adolescents helps the teacher organize his groups wisely. Preadolescent boys, for instance, usually object to being paired with girls. Many adolescents rebel when required to work with someone they consider unacceptable; the problem of the reject must be given careful forethought.

Two or three persistent troublemakers, taking advantage of the relative freedom of group work, can upset an entire class. Teachers are apt to separate these individuals, a technique which is successful as long as each is accepted by the group to which he is assigned and finds worthwhile things to do. Commonly, however, these individuals are ignored by their teammates and gradually drift back together again.

Sometimes it is well to put these individuals, who are generally of the same age, mental ability, and interests, into one group to work on a problem equated to their special interests and abilities. They often do better together than when forced to work with pupils who have been more successful in school than themselves.

> Mr. Woodhull, a cadet teacher, had been warned not to group Chuck and George together. But he forgot the warning and allowed them to team up in constructing a telegraph set. To everyone's surprise, the boys worked with all seriousness and were heard to complain when other groups became a bit frivolous.

To care for the reject, the teacher should try to find one or more secure individuals who are willing to choose him as a member of a group. Sometimes a private conference beforehand, with the problem presented honestly to them, is sufficient to gain their cooperation.

Good leaders are needed for groupings of three or more. Haphazard assignment of leadership responsibilities may give difficulty, especially if a "clown" or a "slave" is put in charge of a group; many pupils will refuse to work under unacceptable individuals and many pupils will not know how to accept leadership responsibilities.

Attention must be given to providing each member of a group with worthwhile things to do. If an experiment can keep but three pupils busy at the same time, the group should contain no more than three members. If there are only two books available for a reading project a teacher is inviting trouble if he assigns more than two pupils to the group.

Most groups of three or more require some help with organization.

Adolescent leaders have not had enough experience to recognize the importance of assigning suitable responsibilities to each member of their respective groups. They tend to do too much themselves and they fail to share the problems of planning. A teacher must expect to give help with assigning responsibilities, especially if assignments are at all complex.

A teacher should not be discouraged if grouping procedures do not come up to his expectations. He is dealing with individuals who have minds of their own; no group activities will go exactly as the teacher has planned. In addition, secondary school pupils are just learning group processes; in many systems they have been given no practice within curricular boundaries. Failures are inevitable. But failures should not end grouping; the pupils probably need more experiences in simpler situations. Refusal to grant them these experiences will delay their growth.

Using detached groups.   The practice of detaching a small group of pupils from the remainder of a class to undertake special work has much to recommend it. The pupils selected usually have high interest in the problems. They work with enthusiasm. They need little supervision.

Gifted pupils benefit especially by detached grouping. They accomplish regular class assignments in a fraction of the time needed by their classmates. They need additional problems to challenge them while the remainder of the class is catching up.

Interestingly enough, retarded pupils also benefit from detached grouping. In such group work they find problems that enable them to use any special skills, usually manipulative in nature, that they might possess. The teacher must recognize, however, that work on such problems does not help retarded pupils pass pencil-and-paper tests to which they might be held; they will need special help if they are required to pass these tests.

Detached grouping always has permissive aspects. Perhaps a teacher calls for volunteers to undertake a special project.

> "I would like to have some models of synclines and anticlines like those shown in the textbook," the earth science teacher announced. "Would anyone like to try making them?"
>
> Two hands were waved vigorously. The teacher made an assignment to busy the other pupils while he met with the two volunteers to plan their course of action.

Once pupils are accustomed to the practice of detached grouping they commonly propose their own problems on which to work.

> The biology teacher was approached by three classmates during the interval between classes. "Miss Pfitzer," said the spokesman for the

group, "Suzanne, Betty, and I are interested in the experiment you told about yesterday—the one where you put hormones on slips to make the roots come out faster. Do you suppose we could do that?"

The teacher may also appoint a committee to undertake a special task which seems of value to the individuals.

Mr. Cummings ended a discussion on skin diving by making an assignment to the boy who had shown the most interest. "Chester," he said, "will you choose a couple of your friends to find out more about the effects of pressure on divers? You can work at the back of the room and we will listen to your report tomorrow."

It is possible to detach more than one group at a time. However, problems of supervision increase rapidly as the number of detached groups increases. If a teacher must conduct regular classwork and at the same time give help to two or more groups working on entirely different topics, he may find the situation difficult.

Simple pairings. For many types of laboratory and field experiences grouping by pairs is effective. Individual participation is insured in such small groups and organizational problems are minor or lacking. Commonly classes are divided into teams of two for work on uniform assignments. There are advantages to having pupils work on the same problems: materials can be prepared easily and supervision is relatively simple.

It is also possible for each pair of pupils to work on different problems. This makes it possible to equate the assignments to the abilities and interests of the pupils. The usual technique for making the assignments is to prepare a list of suitable problems from which each pair chooses the one it wishes to work on. The teacher may also permit pupils to propose related problems in place of those on the list. The major disadvantage of using different assignments lies in the difficulty of preparing materials for so many situations. Some topics lend themselves more satisfactorily to this technique than do others.

Mr. Morrone's eighth grade science classes were studying solutions. At the beginning of the period, Mr. Morrone demonstrated the use of a filter in distinguishing solutions from suspensions. He uncovered a large assortment of samples on his front table and asked the pupils to choose partners and test two or three of the samples for solubility.

In this case, Mr. Morrone gave his pupils the privilege of choosing their own partners. Many teachers prefer to make pairings on an arbitrary basis to control the nature of the groups. At times this latter practice is justified, but the pupils are denied opportunities for taking responsibilities for their own behavior.

When pupils are allowed to choose their own partners, a certain amount of noise and confusion must be expected. This can be kept within an interval of short duration by proper planning. If the pupils understand clearly the problems they will undertake and the procedures they will use, most of them will go to work as soon as they have chosen their partners. The teacher should keep himself free of other responsibilities during this interval to give attention to any pupils who do not tackle their problems immediately.

Because pupils work at different rates, there should be some provision for groups that complete their assignments early. Additional investigations may have been proposed during the planning process. Or the teacher may make suggestions to individual groups as each completes its task. It is also possible to provide in advance individual reading or notebook assignments to be worked on as soon as the group assignments are fulfilled.

Groupings of three or more pupils.   Within the larger groups the social structure is much more realistic than in groups of two. The impact of different personalities is stronger. There is more give-and-take and more compromise. Special talents can be given more adequate recognition. Leadership calls for more than mere aggressiveness; leaders must have tact, diplomacy, and consideration for others.

Subject matter learnings may be more uniform when pupils work alone or in pairs, but individuals in larger groups may learn more thoroughly, especially the leaders who must interpret the problems to their groups. Interest is often high because of the variety grouping techniques give to the program.

However, as pointed out previously, larger groupings demand special planning. Leaders must be selected with care. Worthwhile responsibilities must be available for each member, and leaders need help in assigning responsibilities.

Mr. Watson, a student teacher, planned germination experiments for group work. He arbitrarily divided the class into five groups of six pupils each, gave them the needed materials and told them to go to work.

The responsibilities involved divided themselves naturally into three parts. Three pupils in each group assumed these responsibilities but no one tried to find suitable occupations for the remaining members. Some of the unoccupied pupils watched passively, some discussed matters of personal interest with each other, and three of the older boys became disturbing influences.

Mr. Watson could have avoided this problem in one of two ways. He could have provided more materials and set up ten groups of pupils instead of five. Or he could have retained groupings of six and given help in organizing the activities of each group.

The amount of organizational help groups need depends upon the nature of the problems undertaken. With simple activities, pupils readily set up their own groups, choose leaders, and plan their courses of action.

> After a marine-life collecting trip, Miss Harrington asked her pupils to divide themselves into groups and take care of the specimens, one group cleaning up the gastropod shells, another group pressing algae, a third group putting coelenterates in preservative, and so on.

For more complex problems, attention must be given to the selection of group personnel and the allocation of responsibilities. Each group must have a leader with whom other group members will cooperate. If special skills are called for, the teacher must use his influence to see that each group includes pupils having these special skills.

A teacher may find it wise to select leaders in advance for problems that are unusually complex and when much depends upon the activities of the leaders. The teacher may also give leaders detailed suggestions for group organization.

> Mr. Wilson announced that for an experiment with vacuum tubes the pupils would work in groups of threes, one varying the grid voltage, the second noting the plate current, and the third keeping records. He selected six pupils to serve as leaders and asked them to choose the other members of their respective groups and assign the responsibilities.

Sometimes a teacher may find it wise to meet with the group leaders beforehand to work out the membership of the groups.

> Mr. Kane planned six different tropism experiments to be carried out by an equal number of groups. He chose six pupils of demonstrated leadership ability and conferred with them while the remainder of the class worked on a special assignment.

> Mr. Kane outlined the experiments and the methods of attack. He suggested a pattern for group organization, proposing that each group have a chairman, a secretary for taking notes, an artist for making diagrams, an experimenter to do the manipulative work and an experimenter's helper to assist him. The leaders accepted his suggestions and after discussing the qualifications needed for each job, set up the group membership so that these qualifications were provided for.

Because many secondary school pupils have had little experience with grouping procedures, the beginning teacher is advised to move slowly in utilizing groupings of three or more. He may start with simple pairings and with detached groupings and as experience grows he may add the third member to the groups, giving detailed help in organization. Gradually, as pupils develop suitable skills, they may be given additional responsibilities. The ultimate will be reached when they suggest their own problems, organize themselves into groups, and plan their own methods of attack.

HELPING PUPILS WORK ALONE

Most adolescents are highly gregarious and find security only in the company of their fellows. And yet they need opportunities to explore their capacities to work alone; some of them may find their greatest challenge in completely independent work. The science program should be organized to include short periods of independent work with plentiful options for pupils to continue working alone in follow-up activities. In addition, the teacher should constantly extend invitations for pupils to undertake projects that are not related directly to classwork.

Gifted pupils often prefer to work alone on their own investigations. They can work at their own pace on the topics which interest them most.

Individualizing classroom instruction. The vision of a group of pupils working independently, each beginning at the point to which he had already progressed and continuing as rapidly and as far as his abilities permit, is one that has long intrigued educators. Continued experimentation, however, has not produced techniques that continue to be used on a large scale in American schools.

Truly individualized instruction can be successful only when personal tutoring is possible, and with individuals who have strong incentives for learning as well as knowledge of how to obtain information. These are conditions rarely encountered in public secondary schools. Many compromises are necessary.

Easily supervised activities based on reading and writing lend themselves well to individualized instruction. Science notebooks provide excellent independent learning situations.

> Mr. Shaver's earth science class was made up of ninth grade pupils of exceptionally high ability, all excused from the standard general science course to enter this small, select section. Mr. Shaver provided duplicate assignment sheets listing fifteen questions on astronomy. The first of these called for little more than recall of learnings in previous grades. The problems became increasingly complex and the last few called for extensive library research. The pupils undertook the assignment with high zest, doing much work outside school hours. Most of them completed all fifteen tasks although this was not required; all pupils did the major part of the tasks.

This type of work appealed strongly to this special group of adolescents. It would not have equal success with unselected groups including pupils who do not find reading sufficiently rewarding. Variety is needed for most pupils—experiments, project work, field trips, as well as reading and making reports.

> Mrs. Abernathy duplicated a set of questions for her pupils to answer, listing suitable references, and announced that as soon as the pupils had completed this assignment they could read further on any topics that interested them, or try out experiments described in the reading, or undertake special projects associated with the unit.
>
> One boy, an avid reader, was able to answer the questions without reference to books. Most of the pupils completed the work within half a period. A few needed a longer time.

Mrs. Abernathy's technique contains some of the elements of completely individualized instruction and yet is practical within the usual classroom situation. First of all, there is consideration for the backgrounds of the pupils—further reading is not required if pupils already know the answers. There is freedom to work at different rates. There is incentive to work at the maximum rate—at least for those pupils who are challenged by the optional tasks. And there is provision for pupils to go farther than the minimum.

A practical feature of this technique should be noted. Mrs. Abernathy started all pupils at work on identical tasks making up a minimum assignment which required little supervision. Thus she was free to give special help to any who might need it. And as pupils began to complete the assignment, usually at different times, she was still free to help them get started on new tasks.

Programed materials provide excellent opportunities for individualized classroom instruction. They permit students to explore more advanced materials, to study specific concepts in depth, and to learn at their own individual rate.

> Mr. Szabo presented a well-planned lesson on chemical bonding and then proceeded to assign readings from a programed textbook. All students were asked to complete the basic material on chemical bonding before the next scheduled test period. Students who wanted to explore the subject in greater depth were referred to supplementary programed texts.
>
> When the pupils started their work, Mr. Szabo was available to help the students with their individual learning problems. Most of the students progressed rapidly. The slow learners were permitted to take the materials home and thus kept abreast of their peers. Students of superior ability gained a deep understanding of the topic by utilizing the supplementary materials.

When teachers used programed materials they find that their role changes from that of a disseminator of information to that of a highly individualized tutor who can effectively deal with each student's learning problems. Provision can be made for students of all mental abilities in the same classroom situation.

Ideally, individualized instruction in science should make provisions for laboratory and field work. Practically, because of size of classes and problems of supervision, more compromises are necessary. Sometimes small group laboratory exercises can be blended with individualized instruction of other types.

> Mr. Marsted asked his physics pupils to complete two laboratory exercises dealing with the measurement of voltage and current. These

were to be followed by assigned readings and mathematical exercises. After the minimum requirements were completed, pupils could undertake additional laboratory work or reference work. Pupils were asked to work in pairs for the first two exercises but to work alone thereafter.

As essential feature of all individualized instruction is frequent testing. Pupils must know how well they are progressing. The teacher must know when additional work is needed and when pupils are ready to undertake new tasks. Because pupils are in different stages of progress, testing must be done on an individual basis. Tests must therefore be easy to administer and simple to evaluate.

Self-administered and self-evaluated progress tests are distinctly advantageous. Pupils like performance tests and identification tests of this type. When pencil-and-paper tests are used, the questions should be of the type that permit only one correct answer lest the pupils find it necessary to turn to the teacher frequently for help in scoring.

It is well to provide two or three forms of the same test. A pupil who fails the first test, does additional work and returns for retesting, can be given the second form. This reduces the "carry over" effect when the same form is used twice.

When the teacher wishes to test progress himself, he should use tests that can be scored quickly. If the work of the pupil is in tangible form a single glance is sufficient; one look at a simple electric circuit or a bend in glass tubing tells how well a pupil has done. Skills in reading weather maps, contour maps, and the like can be determined quickly.

Mr. Puzilla wrote on his own copy of a contour map the height of certain hills and the distances between certain points. In testing a pupil's ability to read a topographic map, Mr. Puzilla was able to check answers quickly.

Pencil-and-paper tests are apt to require more time for scoring and the teacher is apt to be interrupted frequently in the process. If he confines his test to diagrams or to easily memorized sequences of numbers, he can limit scoring to a quick scanning and reduce the necessary time to a few seconds. (See Chapter 11 for quick scoring techniques.)

Oral testing is the preferred method for determining progress because this allows the teacher to analyze the pupils' strengths and weaknesses in order to suggest remedial procedures. Oral questioning introduces some problems of time and privacy. The time element can often be reduced by asking first a few sampling questions and exploring only the areas in which deficiencies seem to be revealed by the answers.

Mrs. Wilbur tested each pupil's knowledge of anatomy by pointing to organs in a dissected cat with the expectation that the pupil could give the names and functions of those organs. She discovered that the pupil who could give correct answers to the first three or four questions usually did as well on additional questions of the same difficulty. She developed the practice of limiting her oral tests to four questions except for pupils who revealed deficiencies; these latter pupils were tested more thoroughly.

Encouraging independent work.   Pupils who have the ability to do independent work usually grasp the basic material of a course in a fraction of the time needed by their fellows; they can work on special assignments while their fellows are catching up with them. Even when they lose out on some of the planned learnings of a course, the material they do learn is usually of equal value. It is difficult to imagine that any pupil is harmed by being allowed to follow up some special interest in science.[3]

A teacher must not expect pupils to undertake independent work spontaneously. Few pupils are accustomed to so much freedom. They do not have the background to recognize challenging problems. They need much help in defining problems, in planning methods of attack, and in overcoming unexpected difficulties. A teacher will find that for weeks at a time no pupils will be working on independent projects and he will rarely find more than a small percentage of his classes so engaged at any one time.

The teacher must expect to provide most of the ideas for independent work. Many suggestions will arise from regular class work.

During an eighth grade unit on gardening, discussion turned to the hardiness of various garden plants. Julie volunteered to do some reading on the topic and report to the class.

The next day Julie was most enthusiastic about a book which gave the probable geographic origins of plants and used it as a basis for her report. The science teacher recognized Julie's enthusiasm and suggested that she make a map of the world on which she could paste pictures of garden plants in the countries of their respective origins.

A teacher may select a pupil to do independent work basing his selection on the pupil's demonstrated abilities and interests. The pupil is usually pleased at being thus singled out, and he may be attracted by the thoughts of substituting one form of work for another. He may also be stimulated by the prospects of entering his project in a science fair. Thus a

[3] It might be noted here that no science program is complete; it can only sample the most important topics. The most difficult decision in planning a program is deciding which topics to sample and where gaps must be left because of time limitations.

Pupils with high interest and aptitude can carry out projects of amazing complexity. This girl has produced her own influenza vaccine and tested its effectiveness on mice. Below are the first and last paragraphs of her report:

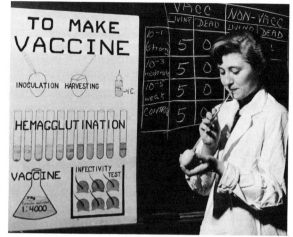

Figure 26.   *For my experiment, I wanted to find whether I could successfully vaccinate mice against a strain of mouse influenza that would kill any mouse that was not immunized or vaccinated. I worked with a mouse-chick adapted virus, PR_8, which was isolated in Puerto Rico. To grow enough virus to work with, I took a stock culture of PR_8 virus, made a 1:10 dilution of virus and salt solution (1 c.c. virus and 9 c.c. salt). This I inoculated into 50 ten-day-old chick embryos. These were refrigerated for one day to kill the embryo and chill its fluids. I then harvested the virus, cutting the top off each egg and drawing off the virus-infected allantoic fluid.*

Figure 27.   *My first group of mice, both vaccinated and nonvaccinated, received a very strong dilution of virus, 10^{-1}, or a ratio of 1:10. The second group of mice, both vaccinated and non-vaccinated, received a dilution of virus of moderate strength, 10^{-3}, or a ratio of 1:1,000. The third group of mice received a weak solution of virus, 10^{-5}, or a ratio of 1:100,000, and the fourth group of mice received no virus. . . . My chart shows the results after the mice had had the virus five days: mice with their tails up represent live mice; mice with their tails down are dead.*

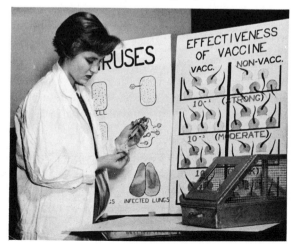

pupil who normally would not think of deviating from regular class assignments is encouraged to follow up special interests.

> Godfrey was a capable student but had far more enthusiasm for the physical sciences than for the biology course he needed for a science sequence. The biology teacher recognized Godfrey's problem and was sympathetic with him.
>
> "Godfrey," he said one day, sitting down beside him, "I've just found this plan for a reaction timer. It measures the time a person needs after seeing a red light before he can put on the brakes. Do you think you could make it?"

A permissive atmosphere in the classroom helps encourage pupils to suggest their own problems.

> Mr. Thompson makes many of his assignments in the following manner: "For tomorrow I want you to do any one of the jobs listed on this sheet. If you can think of something else you would rather work on see me and we will talk it over."

A teacher must make an early decision about the amount of class time that a pupil may use for his special work. Usually it is well for all pupils to participate in field work and laboratory activities, and to view the same films and demonstrations. A pupil should be able to get started on his task during the remaining portions of several successive periods. If his interest is high enough he will put in much additional work outside of class. There will be exceptions; unusually talented pupils working on projects of high caliber may be given more time; pupils with unfavorable home conditions may need additional time to make adequate progress.

A teacher must also decide which requirements will be relaxed to permit independent work. Pupils of high intellectual capacity usually pass the same tests as their classmates without difficulty. There is little value in their engaging in activities which are designed to reinforce learnings; work on practice exercises and written reports can well be excused. For grading purposes, substitutions may be made; a report of a project may be used in place of one or more experiment reports and a grade may be given for the tangible accomplishments of the project in place of grades for regular assignments.

Comparable decisions in the case of the pupil who does not do so well on tests and other academic requirements are more difficult to make. The teacher may determine which segments of the planned material are of vital importance to the pupil and set these as minimum requirements that must be met; above this minimum the pupil may substitute his project work for activities required of the others. Or the teacher may decide that the outcomes of the independent work are of equal value to those resulting from the planned program and permit complete substituion.

PROVIDING FOR EXCEPTIONAL PUPILS
IN HETEROGENEOUS GROUPS

Among the pupils in any one school a few are certain to deviate widely from the norm in one or more respects. Some may be academically brilliant. Some may be seriously retarded readers. Some may be social rejects. Some may be serious disciplinary problems.

With normal distribution the teacher rarely encounters over one or two such exceptional pupils in any one class. The problem of providing for them is not troublesome if classroom procedures are flexible and the teacher is alert to his opportunities.

The brilliant pupil in the heterogeneous group. Special pains must be taken to make sure that the brilliant pupil is not ignored. It is far too easy to hold him to the same assignments and to the same standards as his classmates, assuming that because he attains high grades nothing more need be done for him.

It is a mistake to believe that brilliant pupils must be held back by being in the company of less gifted pupils. Pupils are held back, not by their classmates, but by stereotyped and inflexible classroom procedures.

The program for the brilliant pupil should be a judicious blend of regular class work and special assignments. He should work with his classmates on the introductory phases of each unit, he should participate in all field work, and in much of the group work. But while other pupils are doing individual work—reading, reviewing and writing—he should be engaged in activities that are suited to his superior abilities.

Usually the brilliant pupil is easily encouraged to do special work. He is curious; he grasps problems readily; he has a superior background. During regular classwork, as questions arise, he may be assigned the task of investigating some of these. Although other pupils will undertake special problems, his will be more complex. The brilliant pupil may be detached with one or two others for special group work. His partners need not be of equal ability; each can make contributions.

The greatest help that may be given the brilliant pupil is the opportunity to do original research. He usually cares little for stereotyped exercises; he prefers to investigate problems that have unfamiliar outcomes.

His research may begin as an outgrowth of regular classwork but he should be encouraged to continue it both in and out of school. Many of these pupils will willingly work evening after evening if the teacher will stay with them and give a little help.[4]

The brilliant pupil can also be given special responsibilities in the classroom. He may prepare and present demonstrations. He may help supervise certain types of laboratory work. If he has leadership ability, he may take charge of groups working on special projects such as assembly programs. Working with other capable youngsters, he may keep laboratory equipment in order and take charge of the classroom library. These opportunities will help him develop broadly as well as specifically.

Retarded readers in heterogeneous groups.   Seriously retarded readers who do not suffer from a lack of mental ability benefit from all phases of the science program except those that directly involve reading or are based upon a background provided by reading. These pupils profit almost as much as their fellows when working with materials and when using audiovisual aids. They are handicapped chiefly by a reduced experience background and a feeling of inferiority in academic matters.

These pupils find meaningful a science program based chiefly upon direct experiences, such as field work, and supplemented by such audiovisual aids as films, slides, and pictures. To profit fully, these pupils must feel that what they are doing is worthwhile and that they have important abilities. They need the confidence that comes with success.

Individual and small group activities provide many opportunities for retarded readers to excel. They can set up electric circuits, make models, perform experiments, put on demonstrations, and prepare visual aids. In addition, they may display leadership ability, artistic talents, and dexterity with tools to a degree that makes them outstanding among their fellows.

Retarded readers need not be denied opportunities to read. They must be expected to undertake reading assignments along with their classmates. However, assignments should be flexible to allow these handicapped pupils to find the required information in books suited to their degree of skill. When textbook assignments are made, retarded readers may be given study guides to help them locate specific items of information.

[4] The Gifted Student Committee of the Biological Sciences Curriculum Study has compiled a list of unsolved problems in biology which have been submitted by research biologists. These have been published under the title, *Biological Investigations for Secondary School Students* and are available from the Biological Sciences Study Committee, Boulder, Colorado. Background material, a suggested approach, and a selected bibliography are provided with each problem.

The Chemical Bond Approach Committee has produced suggestions for individualized research. These are extensions to the regular laboratory work. The Physical Sciences Study Committee has developed a sequence of advanced topics that may be interspersed with the materials outlined in the basic PSSC text.

Few retarded readers are able to write well and most of them dislike writing. These pupils may be permitted to substitute diagrams, drawings, and clippings for written assignments with the understanding that labels and captions are to be carefully prepared. They may maintain science notebooks on the same basis.

The retarded reader can be helped to keep up with his classmates in nearly all respects except in passing pencil-and-paper tests. Here he is at a distinct disadvantage. He has difficulty interpreting questions and writing answers. In addition, much of the material tested by this means is derived from reading. Though he is better able to handle short-answer tests than essay and completion tests, it would not be fair to his classmates to use such tests exclusively. This is one of the situations in which the retarded reader must recognize and accept his limitations.

Providing for the dullard.   The term "dullard" is reserved here for the pupil who is truly lacking in native ability. There are fewer dullards in the usual teaching situation than might be supposed from hearing teachers talk, because retarded readers and other handicapped pupils are often classed thus unjustly.

The true dullard is, as the name implies, "dull."[5] He has few strong interests. He makes few contributions to the work of the class. He is usually over-age and therefore often oversized for his group; however he may be poorly developed and poorly coordinated. He makes few friends, but he sometimes forms strong attachments for others. He is apt to be the butt of his classmates' jokes. He may not take offense if he does not understand that he is being ridiculed, but if plagued sufficiently he may fly into a blind rage.

The dullard is not usually a discipline problem except when other pupils deliberately incite him to get him in trouble. Generally he responds well to praise and is eager to do whatever is asked of him. But he needs sympathy and understanding. There is no purpose in holding him to conventional standards; he can see the same demonstrations, watch the same films and listen to the same discussions as his classmates without gaining more than indistinct impressions and unconnected ideas.

However, he is still a human being. He has intelligence and can learn facts about familiar situations and he can develop certain skills. He lacks mostly the ability to transfer learnings from one situation to another. As much as possible his work should be directed toward achievements that will help him in everyday living—safety habits, the wise use of household devices, care of plants and animals.

[5] The dullard cannot be distinguished by IQ alone, although some people try to make this simple distinction. He is identified by a number of characteristics discussed above. It should be noted too that some pupils with low IQ's are not dullards, but secure low IQ scores because of emotional or other problems.

The dullard should be expected to do work along with his classmates, but the nature of his assignments may be changed. He can do manipulative work, but he will need help in organizing it. The problems with which he is faced should be one-step problems carefully chosen for their simplicity. Oral directions are needed because he cannot interpret written materials.

> *During a study of plant reproduction, Mrs. Clay asked Tom, a dullard, to make a chart of different kinds of fruit. She provided him with seed catalogs, scissors, paste and a sheet of card. She helped him print a title. She asked him to cut out pictures of things he knew had seeds inside. Tom worked diligently on his project, not only in class but during a study period. The final chart was colorful and appropriate to the subject being studied.*

The dullard is happy to accept certain kinds of simple classroom responsibilities. He attends these duties faithfully, often arriving at school early and leaving late.

THE SCIENCE PROGRAM
FOR HOMOGENEOUS GROUPING

Schools that practice "homogeneous grouping" bring together in each section pupils with approximately the same academic ability as measured by intelligence scores and school success. For the median sections the science teacher has no special problems, but for the extremes he is faced with real challenges.

Science for high-level sections.   In the top one or two sections are concentrated the best students in a school. If there are any geniuses, these will be included. Most of the pupils, however, will be in the "superior" category. Some may even be of little more than average ability, but they have sufficient drive to rate well academically. In other words, despite the term "homogeneous" the top sections may show a considerable range of ability.

These sections can be a pleasure to work with. The pupils have adjusted well to secondary school conditions. They all read well and have satisfactory mathematical skills and insight. They usually have rich experience backgrounds. Their interests tend to be academic in nature.

Nevertheless, many teachers who ask for an assignment to these sections fail completely to provide a suitable program. They make one of two mistakes. Either they try to speed up the rate of instruction—covering more ground in the time allotted, or they provide more of the same program used for other pupils—more readings, more mathematical exercises, more written assignments.

The program for superior students should be planned with the overall development of these young people in mind. They do not benefit by being crammed with more information and by perfecting minor skills. They need opportunities to explore their abilities and interests, to discover the satisfaction of research, and to become leaders.

A program for superior students makes extensive use of laboratory experiences. The mere fact that they can read well should not diminish the emphasis upon situations in which pupils must think for themselves. Time for additional laboratory work can be taken from that allotted for the review and drill activities provided for less able students. The laboratory work should be largely of the research type; superior students do not need as much practice with laboratory skills as other pupils, and they find little challenge in exercises the results of which are known beforehand.

Superior students benefit greatly from field experiences. They can comprehend industrial processes, research laboratory activities, and ecological relationships, and they have the ability to do the follow-up reading necessary.

Superior students should not be denied opportunities to work with tools and other materials. These media are as essential for their education as for that of the less gifted. Indeed, superior students can surpass other pupils in such work because they can depend upon their reading for new techniques and processes.

Films and other visual aids have an important place in their program, but these must be chosen with the nature of the pupils in mind. Many visual aids now on the market would be no more than a waste of their time. The best materials will awaken new interests, define problems, and aid in the solution of problems appropriate for the achievement level of the pupils.

The program for superior students may be highly individualized with pupils spending much time on special research projects. These projects should not be primarily reading projects but should deal chiefly with laboratory and field problems.

These pupils are capable of participation in the planning process. Some teachers do little more than outline the basic program at the beginning of the year. The pupils are brought into all unit planning and determine much of what is undertaken each day. Under these teachers the science classes bear more than a superficial resemblance to a science club.

Science for low-level sections.   In these sections are grouped all the truly unfortunate youngsters in a school—unfortunate in their endowments and unfortunate in having to be in these sections. There may be a few dullards. There will be pupils lacking in academic skills. There will be pupils handicapped by underprivileged backgrounds. There may be pupils held back by physical illness or personality deviations or pupils who are emotionally unstable because of family strife. Some may be incorrigible delinquents. The pupils range greatly in age; sometimes seventh grade pupils are eighteen years old. Physically many of them are men and women. With a sprinkling of younger pupils in each section problems arise.

Pupils in a low-level section benefit little from a standard program that is merely diluted "down to their level." They need a program that is planned specifically in terms of their maturity level, their lack of academic skills, their approaching entry into the adult world, and their feelings of inadequacy.

The school administration should feel responsible for providing the facilities needed for suitable instruction for these unfortunate youngsters. Classes must be kept small; the activities best suited to them, including construction, simple experiments, and other manipulative activities, are difficult to supervise. The classroom for these sections should be well stocked with tools, raw materials, simple science equipment, and art supplies. There must be ample workspace on tables and work benches. The library for this classroom needs a wide variety of books—not childish books, but books that are profusely illustrated and simply written.

The subject matter of the program should deal largely with concrete things with which the pupils are acquainted. They benefit little from the study of abstractions. They should learn about the repair of electrical equipment, the operation of automobiles and the wise choice of clothes rather than about the principles of heat transmission and cell division.

Visual aids that concentrate on practical applications are desirable. Those that deal with generalizations may mean little. Though the visual aids may be simple in their presentations they must not be childish lest they antagonize young people who consider themselves adults.

Pupils in low-level sections benefit greatly from project work. They can make models, dioramas, and charts. They need opportunities to display these and receive recognition for their efforts. The subjects for these projects should be practical problems rather than attempts to illustrate scientific principles.

By keeping notebooks these pupils can gain some experience in writing. Most of the material, however, should be in the form of drawings, pictures, and clippings, all suitably labeled and supplemented with brief captions. For written material that the teacher considers important a technique may be borrowed from the early grades. The pupils talk over what is to be said and dictate it to the teacher who writes it on the chalkboard. The pupils then copy it in their notebooks. Thus it becomes their written work, but they are not penalized by inadequacies of spelling and rules of punctuation.

Book research should be limited to the search for specifics such as the names of foods containing Vitamin C and the names of plants that live well in north-facing windows. The pupils may look for recipes, for lists of materials needed for projects, and for directions for building things.

They need special help for any reading assignments. Usually guide sheets telling them exactly what to look for and often telling them where to find the information are most useful.

Tests, of course, should involve a minimum of reading and writing. Performance and identification tests should be used whenever possible. Matching tests and multiple-choice tests, with plenty of practice, may be used for measuring understandings that can be verbalized.

Teaching the unsuccessful learner.   Unfortunately, dullards and under-achieving students of average and above average ability are often placed in classes that do not make provision for their specific needs. Classes composed of these "unwanted" students are often rotated within the staff of the science department. Consequently, no single teacher becomes acquainted with the problems of these students. In many school systems these classes are assigned to new teachers who have neither the training, nor the experience necessary to make adequate provision for these students.

Teachers who work with unsuccessful learners should be especially trained to handle the problems involved in teaching these students. Most teachers have neither the interest, nor the patience and time required to deal with this type of pupil. The Special Materials Committee of the BSCS is convinced that the unsuccessful learners deserve teachers who[6]

1. consider the teaching of unsuccessful learners important

2. have some competency for teaching unsuccessful learners

3. understand the importance of laboratory experience for unsuccessful learners

4. have little doubt that these youngsters can learn and appreciate the concepts of modern science courses

5. have a good background in the principles of the science courses which they teach.

[6] Biological Sciences Curriculum Study, "The Special Student and BSCS Biology Special Materials," BSCS Newsletter, 24:27, 1965.

SETTING UP SPECIAL PROGRAMS
FOR PUPILS TALENTED IN SCIENCE

If maximum help is to be given to pupils with high scientific aptitudes, a special program must be provided. The program used for high-level sections under homogeneous grouping is not sufficient because in these sections are many pupils with little interest in science as a career or even as an avocation. The special program can be much narrower and far more intensive.

The values of the special programs have been amply demonstrated in several schools. The caliber of the instruction can be kept high; pupils can be challenged with high level problems; the teacher can spend more time on positive guidance and less on awakening interests and reinforcing learnings; and the pupils tend to stimulate each other.

Certain administrative problems are involved, however. The special sections must be kept small if adequate supervision is to be provided. This means that additional room space and teacher time must be found, not an easy task in some crowded and overloaded systems. It also means complexity in scheduling, especially if the pupils are not to be kept together for other classes. These problems are not enough to outweigh the values of special science programs but they must be taken into consideration.

Identifying the gifted in science. Truly gifted students are marked by more than the ability to attain good grades in a standard program. Many pupils without special talent attain good grades through hard work and perseverance. The truly gifted have a number of other characteristics that must be looked for.

Various testing devices may be used to identify gifted students. Group intelligence tests provide a good standard. Gifted students make up 5 percent of the population[7] and are generally considered to have an I.Q. above 115. Verbal comprehension tests tell how well a pupil can read; gifted students are generally excellent readers. Abstract reasoning tests indicate the power to interpret diagrams; tests of mechanical relationships and of spatial visualization deal with other important aspects of giftedness.

The above tests are not designed to isolate students with high talent in science, but taken as a whole they suggest capacity for science. They may be supplemented by special science aptitude tests. No one test should be depended upon to identify the gifted in science.

[7] Hildreth, Gertrude H., *Introduction to the Gifted*, McGraw-Hill Book Co., New York, 1966, p. 25.

Subjective evaluation will also play a part in the detection of the talented in science. The following characteristics have been suggested for guiding observations:

1. *Extraordinary memory.* Most gifted students display a prodigious memory. A high school student recently displayed his mental ability by playing a game of chess completely by memory. He made all his moves and kept track of his opponent's moves without having any opportunity to see the chessboard.

2. *Intellectual curiosity.* This trait is often indicated by a persistence in asking questions and an eagerness to investigate marginal content, which usually challenges only those who are intellectually mature.

3. *Ability to do abstract reasoning.* This may be revealed by unusual insight into probable discrepancies and by skill in formulating hypotheses from new data.

4. *Ability to apply knowledge to other situations.* A student who selects formulas and principles appropriate to a new situation and evaluates the results is exhibiting such ability.

5. *Persistence in worthwhile behavior.* This characteristic is common to leaders in science. It is reported that Edison worked continuously for 72 hours while working on the wax record. After he was 80 years of age he began the study of botany. He tested thousands of plants for rubber in the remaining four years of his life. A scientist does not give up easily. This type of perseverance should not be confused with aimless plodding.

6. *Command of language.* Gifted students generally exhibit a larger vocabulary, better use of words, more fluent speech, and better facility in writing than their peers.

Another way to identify gifted science students is to investigate their science interests. Brandwein[8] suggests the following list of interests as a guide:

1. Participating in science club activities.

2. Using leisure time for science hobbies.

3. Reading scientific literature beyond the demands of school assignments.

4. Participating in science fairs and other contests.

5. Volunteering to undertake special science reports or projects in connection with class work.

6. Attending meetings of junior and adult science societies in community.

7. Visiting scientific institutions such as museums, botanic and zoological gardens, industrial plants, and research laboratories.

[8] Brandwein, Paul, *et al.,* "Teaching High School Biology," *A Guide to Working with Potential Biologists,* BSCS Bulletin No. 2, Boulder, Colorado, 1962.

8. Using parents' allowance and gift money for the purchase of scientific materials and books.

9. Exploring and collecting objects of biological, geological, or ecological interest.

10. Indicating aspirations and setting goals toward a career in science.

Selecting pupils for the special program.   Before any selection can be made, the numbers to be admitted to the program must be determined. Too many pupils make supervision difficult; too few may make a program impractical from an administrative point of view. The ideal number for one person to handle is about twelve. A few more or less make no special hardships. Too few can be disadvantageous in developing an *esprit de corps* and in providing the stimulation that comes from within the group. It is better to accept some who are not of the highest capacity if they will work well with the others.

Because the final selection will probably come from among the honor students, records of grades make a good point of departure. The intelligence test scores and reading test scores of these honor students may then be checked for indications of high general intelligence. On the basis of these three characteristics—grades, particularly in mathematics and science, IQ's, and reading levels—a reasonable sized group may be chosen for further analysis.

Not all of the pupils thus selected will care to enter a special program in mathematics and science. The labor of investigation can be reduced by asking an expression of interest at this time, usually after a personal interview and with time for conferring with parents. However, if the effects of disappointing a large number of pupils is feared, this step may be deferred until later.

The final selection should be made on the basis of specialized tests, conferences with other teachers who know the pupils, and personal interviews.

In large systems there may be enough pupils of extremely high ability to fill a special section. In smaller systems there may be no more than one or two pupils of such high caliber. This should not be a deterrent to setting up a special section—pupils of moderately high ability benefit from the experience of working up to capacity.

In Milwaukee[9] in co-operation with the University of Wisconsin research services, a program has been developed for students of superior ability. Admission to the program is on the basis of intelligence test data, school achievement, teacher nomination, and parental consent. Provisions

[9] Hildreth, *op. cit.*, p. 308.

include special classes in three centers, part-time classes for the students in their respective schools, and enrichment in regular classes.

Universal standards for admission to special programs cannot be established since the proportion of gifted students will vary from school to school and city to city. A school located near a large university may have little difficulty in filling a special class for gifted students; a school located in an impoverished area of a large city may have difficulty in locating more than a few students of superior ability.

Organizing course content. Commonly special sections deal with materials comparable to that which the pupils would normally study under the standard program. Thus in the year when pupils would usually elect biology, the content of the special program is biological in nature, but enriched and intensified.

For ninth grade pupils, earth science is sometimes substituted for general science. The reason for this is primarily psychological; talented pupils could gain as much by an enriched course in general science.

Courses for talented pupils should be organized to permit pupils to explore deeply. If too much is crowded into the program, the material will be only superficially covered, and the classes will be turned into "cram sessions."

Field and laboratory experiences should be utilized almost to the exclusion of other approaches because in these situations pupils find problems that demand the fullest exercise of their special abilities. Any pupils can memorize information presented by the teacher, by books, and by visual aids, but only unusual pupils can carry on what is the equivalent of true scientific research.

Students in the special program should carry on individual projects that involve original research insofar as possible. Many classes may be in the nature of seminars, in which pupils present their problems and criticize each other's conclusions. The research need not be original insofar as the field of science is concerned but should represent original thinking on the part of the pupils. Sometimes they may verify results others have obtained; sometimes they may apply previous findings to new situations. The projects may involve the construction of apparatus which, though modeled after existing apparatus, will include original features to fit special needs or situations.

Advanced courses. There has been a tendency to accelerate the science gifted by giving them biology or earth science in the ninth grade, chemistry in the tenth grade and physics in the eleventh. The senior year is left open so that the student can take an advanced placement course or an advanced science course which has been developed by the science teacher.

The advanced placement course is neither an enriched high school course nor a watered-down college course. It is rather a sophisticated college level course recommended for high school seniors who have the academic ability to handle the material. Advanced placement programs are offered in many high schools. The courses offered through this program are often accepted by colleges as an equivalent freshman course.[10]

Many teachers and school systems have produced their own advanced science courses. An example of such a course offered by Mr. Richard Kelly, science teacher, Guilderland Central School[11] is described here:

Advanced biology in the school is an elective course for the gifted student who is desirous of receiving advanced training in various aspects of animal biology. The class meets five days per week with a two- to three-hour laboratory scheduled one day per week.

The year course is divided into three major segments. The first segment is a rapid review of the animal kingdom with lectures on taxonomy and the reasons for studying this important area. Laboratories on biostatistics and malarial parasites are included as introductory material. Lectures are given on the taxonomy of the chordates with detailed study of the borderline forms being stressed. Detailed dissection of the bullfrog and the cat follow with the learning of the vertebrate body plan. Lectures on the major body systems such as integumentary, skeletal, circulatory, endocrine, etc., coincide with the laboratory work. Keeping of good laboratory records and laboratory diagrams is emphasized. The students are given practical experience through examinations on the representative organisms.

The second semester of the course consists of microanatomy with emphasis placed upon the student learning the technique of obtaining, preparing, embedding, sectioning, and staining of various animal tissues. Experience with the microscope and microtome is provided. Each student also prepares an illustrated lecture on one tissue of his choice which is presented to the class. This includes the preparation by the student of his tissue and photomicrographs of it. Experience with reference material is provided. The last phase of the course is spent on radiation biology with a basic treatment of the physics of radiation. Detailed study of the effects of X-radiation are made using the white rats as an experimental animal. Use is made of the count rate meter and tracers. Beneficial uses of radiation are also studied.

Since the class enrollment in advanced biology is limited, preference is given to seniors who meet the qualifications. Juniors who have had biology and are taking chemistry are also eligible. More successful completion of the basic biology course is also required. The course is designed for those students contemplating a career in the biological sciences, particularly in the fields of nursing or premedicine.

[10] The Advanced Placement Program is described in Chapter 3, pp. 113–114.

[11] Communication from Richard Kelly, Guilderland Central School, Guilderland Center, N.Y., July, 1963.

Extracurricular programs for the gifted.   A number of special programs have been developed by high schools and colleges for the academically talented student. The programs are sometimes supported by an outside agency. Some high schools have instituted special summer or school year programs which are course oriented. Other programs may involve a seminar experience or research. Colleges and universities have set up programs which give students challenging academic experiences during a summer or during the school year. These college programs offer course work or research or both.

Seminar programs have been established by local science teachers, industrial groups, and scientific societies. These seminars are usually held either in the evenings or on Saturdays during the school year.[12]

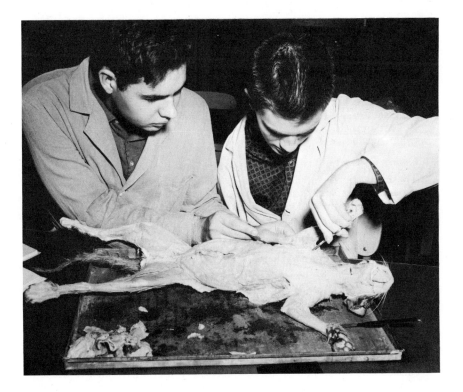

Some high schools are offering advanced biology courses for the science talented.   These courses emphasize the laboratory as the place where information is uncovered rather than covered.

[12] A description of a science seminar conducted by a science teacher is found in Chapter 3.

In Westfield, New Jersey, the senior high school has Saturday classes in advanced science, physics, and mechanics taught by instructors from neighboring New Jersey college. Bennett College has established a Saturday school for gifted high school students with a grant from the Carnegie Corporation.[13]

Programs in science and mathematics offered by colleges and universities and research institutions are often supported by outside agencies such as the National Science Foundation.[14] These programs are available during the summer or the school year to talented students. The purpose of these National Science Foundation programs is to provide talented pupils with an academic experience on the college level. Some of these programs are course oriented and others stress research. An example of such a program offered at Syracuse University is given below:[15]

General Program Outline

Talented high school students who are interested in the biological sciences are selected as participants. These students are boarded at the university for a period of six weeks; all the usual student facilities are available to them. The class meets from 9 A.M. until 5 P.M. daily for five days a week. Financial support for many of the programs has been obtained partly from such sources as the National Science Foundation and partly from the student himself. The student's community should be encouraged to contribute whenever possible.

Course Content

The ideal course should cover a broad range of zoological topics—with emphasis upon laboratory experiences in each field. A schedule of events which should prove effective may include the following:

(1) A lecture and discussion conducted by the course instructor from 9 to 10:30 A.M. daily, Monday through Friday. Fundamental concepts and recent achievements in the various fields should be stressed. Although narrow specialization is to be avoided, the teacher should devote adequate time to teaching his own speciality. Aside from the educational value, this is an important factor in establishing good rapport with the students.

(2) For the first few weeks, the 11 to 12 A.M. interval is devoted to "guest lecturers" who present a seminar on their own research and field of interest. These are a valuable supplement to the regular presentation. These guests range from terminal year graduate students to prominent professors. The former enables the student to identify himself with the speakers to a considerable extent and brings the practicality of doing research to the level of the student. The exposure to prominent biologists provides substantial motivation.

[13] Hildreth, *op. cit.*, p. 366.

[14] For further information, write to the Program Director, Special Projects in Science Education, National Science Foundation, Washington, D.C.

[15] Druger, Marvin, "A Proposed Model for a Summer Course in Zoology for Gifted High School Students," *Science Education*, 46:447–451, 1962.

During these first few weeks, the students prepare their own seminar on a topic of interest to them. These topics are decided upon in consultation with the instructor, and cover material which is not to be discussed by the instructor as a regular part of the course. Thus the student not only has the experience of presenting a scientific discussion to a peer group, but he also is helping to broaden the scope of the course content. Our student seminars covered a wide range of topics including migration in birds, communication in bees, radar in bats, industrial melanism, biological clocks, sickle cell anemia, theories of amoeboid motion, ATP in muscle contraction, the general adaptation syndrome, hereditary diseases, temperature regulation in reptiles, slime molds, drug resistance in bacteria, transduction, and the evolution of the horse.

These seminars are approximately one-half hour in length, and are generally followed by a lively discussion. In our course, the students also prepared a paper on the subject of their seminar, thus obtaining experience in scientific writing. Seminars were usually conducted on Monday, Wednesday, and Friday, while this time on Tuesday and Thursday was devoted to instruction in use of the library and how to write a scientific paper. One method used here was to have the students write critiques of published scientific papers which were then discussed.

Student seminars were one of the most successful aspects of our course. Bright students usually seek an audience, and have a great deal to say.

(3) Lunchtime is from 12 noon until 1 P.M. The instructor should have lunch with different groups of students, as this is an excellent time to get to know the students well and develop good rapport.

(4) Laboratory sessions are conducted daily from 1 P.M. until 5 P.M. The exercises must be selected carefully and should include at least one illustrative exercise in major fields of zoology such as cytology, protozoology, genetics, embryology, physiology, microbiology, comparative anatomy, and ecology. It is a good idea to consult with researchers in each field and, if possible, enlist their aid in planning and carrying out the best possible exercises. Emphasis should be placed upon living organisms and experiment-type exercises, although one or two dissections are to be included.

(5) Students should be encouraged to do some minor project on their own. Since this project must be completed within a six-week period, it is most expedient for the instructor to suggest a number of research possibilities. These should not be forced upon all the students, but should be available for those who seem capable of handling a project in addition to the regular course content. These projects should be consonant with the abilities of the individual student and may include such items as: learning a technique (i.e. Drosophila salivary gland chromosome preparations, paper chromatography, etc.); doing an unusual dissection; simple behavioral experiments on various organisms; learning how to culture invertebrate animals; parasite studies; experiments on nerve-muscle physiology; and experiments on drug resistance in micro-organisms. The aim of this is to allow the student to work out a bit of research for himself, accumulate data, and if possible, present a brief oral summary of his work.

The first two mornings of our course were spent in discussing project possibilities, thus giving the students a survey of problems in many fields at the same time.

As part of the regular schedule of events, all students can be taught one or two specialized techniques. In our course, each student prepared a permanent slide, involving fixing and imbedding of tissue, use of the microtome, etc. This was done in small groups at odd intervals during the day. Also, each student made a Drosophila cross and analyzed the results. Other techniques may be substituted for these.

Again, I was amazed at the capacity of the students to carry out all of these activities—and well.

(6) A variety of examinations should be given regularly. These students enjoy being tested, but these tests must be ingenious and interesting, stressing general relationships and concepts. No emphasis should be placed on grades, and the point should be stressed that the exam is intended as a review and as a chance for the student to determine his own mastery of the material, by using it in a concise and thoughtful manner. Practical examinations are invaluable, since through them the student can be taught important relationships that he may have missed during the course. When properly done, these can be the most interesting and challenging type of exam for the student.

At the end of the course, the instructor should interview each student and discuss various highlights of the course, including practical material from the laboratory work.

Although a course grade that is meaningful to the academic world should be avoided, an intra-group numerical rating may be worthwhile. Also the instructor may do well to evaluate the student's work at the final interview and discuss future plans with him.

(7) The course should include as many special events as possible. The talents of specialists in various fields should be utilized whenever possible. We attempted to enlist the aid of persons in fields which were little known to the students. For example, demonstrations and discussions concerning electron microscopy, paleontology, field biology, basic research in medical and dental sciences to, and various subjects in, genetics and embryology were presented by qualified workers in these fields. These "special events" help to make the course a unique experience for the students, and also provide a change of pedagogical scenery.

Another way to enrich the program would be to exchange student speakers between simultaneous courses in botany and zoology. Occasional evening discussion groups may be conducted on an informal basis. A simple, but effective, way to change pace is to rearrange the lecture and laboratory schedule, and conduct an occasional class in the evening, giving the students the afternoon free.

Many colleges offer programs which are not supported by an outside agency. Among the most outstanding of these is the Governors School Program which is held at Salem College.[16] Each summer, talented students in the arts and sciences are invited to participate in the program.

[16] For further information write to Program Director, Governors School Program, Salem College, Winston Salem, N.C.

Regardless of the discipline in which the student is interested, he must take a philosophy course required of all participants. Each student also takes a second course which is in his own area of interest. Science students may take a high level laboratory course in physics, chemistry, biology, or mathematics.

Colleges also provide opportunities for talented students to work on research projects during the summer or academic year under the supervision of a college professor. This type of activity is offered on an individual basis and special arrangements can be made by the student or by the science teacher with the professor concerned.

Many commercial laboratories offer summer employment to talented students who wish to work with a scientist on a research project. It is necessary to contact these laboratories to determine whether opportunities of this kind are available.

SUGGESTED ACTIVITIES

1. For a unit in biology plan a list of activities that may be carried out by pupils working in small groups. These activities should provide for a wide range of interests and abilities.
2. Plan a unit in physics for a group of gifted pupils. Provide opportunity for the pupils to explore this unit in depth.
3. Plan a general science unit for a small class of retarded pupils. Provide opportunities for individual and group work suitable to these individuals.
4. Investigate the opportunities for enriching the science experiences of scientifically talented youngsters in a school in which you may be teaching.
5. Design an advanced placement program in chemistry.

SUGGESTED READINGS

Abramson, David A., *The Effect of Special Grouping of High Ability Students in High School upon Their Achievement in College*, No. 144, Bureau of Educational Research, Board of Education, City of New York, 1960.

Bareday, George Z., and Joseph A. Lauwerys (eds.), *The Gifted Child: The 1962 Yearbook of Education*, Harcourt, Brace and World, New York, 1962.

Brandwein, Paul F., *The Gifted Student as Future Scientist*, Harcourt, Brace & World, New York, 1955.

————, "Teaching High School Biology," *A Guide to Working with Potential Scientists*, BSCS Bulletin, No. 2, Boulder, Colo., 1962.

Collette, Alfred T., and John Burdick, "Secondary Science," *Curriculum Planning for the Gifted*, Louis Fliegler (ed.), Prentice-Hall, Englewood Cliffs, N. J., 1961.

Conant, James B., *The Identification and Education of the Academically Talented Student in the American Secondary School*, The Conference Report, February, 1958.

Flanagan, John C., et al., *The American High School Student*, Technical Report to the U. S. Office of Education, Cooperative Research Project No. 635, Pittsburgh: Project TALENT Office, University of Pittsburgh, 1964.

Flanagan, John C., and William W. Cooley, *Identification, Development and Utilization of Human Talents*, A Report of the Eleventh Grade Follow-Up Study, Prepared by the School of Education of Pittsburgh in cooperation with the Office of Education, U. S. Department of Health, Education, and Welfare, Pittsburgh, 1965.

Gallagher, James J. (ed.), *Teaching Gifted Students: A Book of Readings*, Allyn and Bacon, Boston, 1966.

Hildreth, Gertrude H., *Introduction to the Gifted*, McGraw-Hill Book Co., New York, 1966.

National Education Association, *Research on the Academically Talented Student*. A Report Prepared by the National Education Association Project on the Academically Talented Student, Washington, D. C., 1961.

Southern Regional Education Board, *The Gifted Student: A Manual for Program Improvement*, A Report to the Southern Regional Project for Education of the Gifted by the State Department of Education Representatives in the Project. Georgia: Southern Regional Education Board, 1962.

Taylor, Calvin W. (ed.), *Creativity: Progress and Potential*, McGraw-Hill Book Co., New York, 1964.

Waterman, A. T., "Science and Society: Integration through Education," *Teachers College Record*, 64:151–158, 1962.

Chapter 16

Improving

Communication Skills

COMMUNICATION IN SCIENCE SHOULD BE CONCISE AND OBJECTIVE. IT IS NOT an easy style to master. Professional writers spend hours on each short article they produce. Many prominent men employ specialists to prepare their speeches. And the articles of prominent scientists commonly require drastic editing before they can be published. Secondary school pupils are understandably lacking in skills with this type of self-expression. They have had little practice and little help.

The responsibility cannot be shifted to the English teachers. The English program has been allotted but a fraction of the time needed to produce accomplished writers and speakers. English teachers can do no more than lay the foundation upon which other teachers, including science teachers, can build.

Science teachers need not think of themselves as teachers of communication skills. They make their greatest contributions when they set up situations in which pupils actively desire to write or speak about their science experiences. In these situations pupils are stimulated to conscious efforts at self-improvement and they gain the practice that is so essential for increase in the powers of self-expression.

VOCABULARY DEVELOPMENT

Words are but symbols that have no meaning until the user is able to associate them with mental images and sensations. Vocabulary development consists of providing the proper associations, giving practice with these associations and reteaching after periods of forgetting.

Vocabulary development often includes provision for the experiences upon which associations are based. The person who has not seen cork may associate the word with the wrong substance or make no association whatever. This aspect of vocabulary development is of particular concern to the science teacher because so many words of science deal with things and conditions that pupils have never encountered previously.

To further complicate the process of vocabulary development there are, in effect, four different vocabularies that must be developed in parallel—a listening vocabulary, a speaking vocabulary, a reading vocabulary, and a writing vocabulary. The first two depend upon sound symbols, the last two upon visual symbols. There is a difference between hearing a sound and producing it. There is a difference between seeing a symbol and writing it. Hearing and seeing are passive; meanings are often suggested by context. Speaking and writing demand active recall and require a much higher level of previous learnings.

The vocabulary of science.   All special fields have their technical terms. Science, with its many subdivisions, has developed the most extensive specialized vocabulary of them all. But scientific words are not science in themselves. They are tools with which specialists communicate with one another. All understandings about commonplace phenomena can be expressed in commonplace terms.

Some of the words of science are so useful as to be worth teaching. "Distillation" is one of these; it is much more concise than any equivalent in basic English and has many applications in post-school situations. "Photosynthesis" is debatable; it has a precise meaning that is rarely appreciated even by science teachers themselves, but it is a useful term in science courses. "Polydactylism" has little value in a nonspecialized science course and none outside of school situations; it does not justify inclusion in the required vocabularies of young people.

Scientific jargon, which is useful to specialists trying to be concise, has little place in the secondary school program. It may be confusing. The teacher who uses "hot" instead of "radioactive" may give a totally wrong impression for the sake of saving four syllables. Nonspecialists are apt to use jargon because of its novelty rather than because a purpose is served.

Occasionally a difference exists between the scientific definition of a word and the common usage of the word. No better illustration is found than the word "steam." For centuries, steam has referred to the visible cloud above hot water. Physicists, however, upon learning about evaporation redefined the word to apply to invisible water vapor, a definition accepted by dictionaries.

Science teachers are apt to insist that pupils abandon the common association and adopt the scientific definition, and they become irritated when pupils do not do so. These teachers have not paused to consider the difficulties involved. Associations developed during early childhood are exceedingly tenacious. Second, in this case it is difficult for pupils to make the new association because an invisible substance is involved. Finally, as soon as pupils are outside the school, common usage tends to reestablish the old association.

Sometimes there is little value in making a struggle against common usage; the word "detergent" has gained such a specialized meaning that its dictionary meaning is all but forgotten. Sometimes a substitution is possible; "water vapor" serves equally well in place of "steam." Sometimes a teacher must give many experiences with "animals" so that pupils themselves broaden its meaning to include more than mammals.

A little common sense helps too. The perennial argument about "work" in physics classes can only antagonize pupils who know what makes them tired. It is easier and more accurate to qualify the word with "useful" or "accomplished" or some other descriptive adjective.

It is not to be expected that science teachers will agree upon the words to be introduced or ignored. It seems better, however, to be conservative, developing basic understandings rather than vocabulary. Too many words introduced too rapidly make science seem difficult and remote. But understandings make it possible for pupils to develop their vocabularies as they need new words.

Techniques for building vocabularies. A word worth introducing is worth introducing carefully. Once a teacher has decided that a term should be in the vocabulary of his pupils, he should make sure that it receives adequate attention.

Miss Hendrickson demonstrated to her biology classes the effects of squeezing ripe puff balls. She explained briefly that from each of the particles given off a new mushroom plant could develop. She then named these particles "spores" both orally and in writing on the blackboard.

Miss Hendrickson asked her pupils to examine some of the spores with a microscope and then read about the life histories of mushrooms in their textbooks. At the end of the period, following a brief discussion of the reading assignment, she described the techniques for making spore prints from gilled mushrooms. The class planned a trip to a nearby woodland park to gather some of these mushrooms.

The next day the pupils took their trip and brought their mushrooms back to school, placing the caps on white cards. A day later, spores falling from the "gills" had left prints on the cards. These were sprayed with artists' fixative and labeled appropriately.

Miss Hendrickson suggested that interested pupils could make additional spore prints, make drawings of mushroom plants, and read about the economic importance of mushrooms. Later she set the class at work on molds, raising some, noting the spores, and reading about life histories of molds.

Note the steps with which Miss Hendrickson fixed the word "spore" in the vocabularies of her pupils. First she provided a first-hand experience which probably served to recall similar experiences pupils had had previously. She gave the term orally and in writing. Examination through the microscope helped fix the association. Reading gave practice in associating the printed word with the actual spores.

Through the following days the pupils used the word frequently, hearing it, speaking it, reading it, and writing it on cards and diagrams. They had opportunities to relearn the word if they forgot it from one day to the next. Finally the word was given broader meaning by its application to molds, and learning continued.

Such elaborate procedures are needed only for such words as are important enough to be used frequently by all pupils. Other types of situations may be set up to encourage the learning of new words without insistence that these be memorized.

Miss Neilson's seventh grade pupils brought in caterpillars and kept them in cages with suitable food. Well-illustrated books at different reading levels were placed nearby. As soon as the caterpillars began to pupate the excited pupils began reading the books. They prepared charts and wrote reports of their observations. Soon they were using such technical terms as "pupa," "chrysalid," and "metamorphosis" without any direction from Miss Neilson.

Though first-hand experiences are best for ensuring proper associations, the previous experiences of pupils may also be used. The "teeter-totter" is familiar enough to all pupils to serve in the introduction of the word "fulcrum." However, it is difficult to be sure that all pupils have had certain experiences and even more difficult to ascertain whether the experiences have been meaningful. Past experiences should be relied upon only when necessary.

Photographs are useful in helping pupils recall past experiences. They also have limited usefulness when proper interpretations can be made from two-dimensional representations even though the material lies outside the pupils' past experiences. Diagrams and models may be used to reinforce associations but should not be depended upon to serve alone in vocabulary development.

Dictionaries and glossaries have but limited value in building a scientific vocabulary. Their definitions are given in words that may fail to produce a satisfactory image with which to make associations. These tools should be used to help pupils obtain a more precise definition of words that are already understood in part.

ORAL PRESENTATIONS

Though adolescents chatter freely, few of them speak well. Their discourses tend to ramble and are often pointless. Their limited vocabularies lack the words needed for the finer shades of meaning. Their self-consciousness hinders them when they face a group.

Science teachers can provide extensive practice in oral presentations. Talks may range in complexity from simple descriptions of observations to elaborate research reports. They may be spontaneous or carefully written out before hand. Conditions may range from talks to a few classmates to formal speeches before large audiences, including radio and television audiences.

Brief reports in the classroom.   Pupils often volunteer to make special investigations as part of their regular classwork. Reports of their investigations may be integrated into the daily lessons.

> Patrick volunteered to ask his father, a salesman for sound equipment, about the frequency ranges of various recording and play-back devices. Patrick's physics teacher, in his plans, allotted him five minutes following a demonstration of tape recorders, and provided a follow-up experiment on the range of human hearing.

Time at the beginning or end of periods may be set aside for special reports that are not pertinent to the regular work of the class.

> Susan had been studying the habits of morning glory blooms, tagging buds and keeping records of the times each opened and closed. When she was ready to make her report her science teacher set aside ten minutes at the beginning of the next science period for her presentation.

Some teachers set aside a regular time for reports of readings or incidental observations.

> It was Thursday morning, time for seventh grade field reports. Colin described a pair of mourning doves he had seen in a cemetery. Margaret displayed some flowers she had picked on the way to school—flowers the teacher identified as Robin's plantain and pussy-toes. George told about the trout he had caught over the weekend and volunteered to post a picture of trout on the bulletin board so others would know what they were like. Marvin told of the large bumblebee that had entered his bedroom and the teacher explained how queen bumblebees look for new nesting sites in the spring. No other pupils had reports and so regular classwork was resumed.

A touch of formality is beneficial in all short reports. Pupils should speak from the front of the room and should be ready to answer questions from other members of the class. Thus they gain from the experience of facing their audiences. This technique also reduces the idle chatter that would result if pupils were free to speak from their seats; they come to the front only if they have something they think important.

Pupils rarely have difficulty with short oral reports. They cannot stray far from the point. They are able to retain class attention for the few minutes during which they are speaking. Nonetheless, pupils should be encouraged to use visual materials as much as possible while reporting. Visual materials give the speaker a sense of confidence, they help him keep his talk centered on one point, and they assist in holding class attention.

> Jack illustrated his report on birdhouses with a sheet of cardboard in which he had made openings suitable for different types of birds. He also displayed a wren house and a bluebird house as two applications of desirable hole size.

Reports of major projects.   Pupils commonly put a great deal of time and effort into project work. They need recognition for their achievements. Teachers may help them prepare reports that will be well received by their audiences.

Visual materials should be considered essential in all major presentations. These may be exhibits of actual materials, charts, blackboard drawings, lantern slides, models, tables, graphs, and the like. Demonstrations that repeat processes employed are effective. There should be large printed labels so that the audience sees words as well as hears them.

> Elinor, an eighth grader, had made a study of dandelion greens. In a brief introduction to her report she explained how she had become interested in the project and what her problem had been. She followed this with a description of dandelion plants, using fresh specimens, mounted specimens, and a chart which she had prepared to illustrate her points.
>
> Elinor turned next to the procedures she had used in her research. She had interviewed a number of European-born housewives who gathered dandelion greens each spring. From them she had found how plants with mild flavor could be distinguished from plants with bitter flavor. She illustrated her findings with charts and dried specimens. She mentioned that she had collected both types and cooked them and that differences in flavor certainly existed.
>
> She then described the results of a field investigation in which she made a census of the two types in typical areas. She summed up her findings with bar graphs. She concluded that two distinct varieties of dandelions exist even though not recognized in the botany books she had read.

This report deserves special study as an example of the help that may be given other pupils. First, the subject was familiar to the listeners but a new and interesting aspect was being described. Elinor was talking from first-hand experiences; she was able to convey the spirit of the investigation and the picturesque details, and she talked with authority. Her charts and materials gave meaning to statements that were difficult to verbalize. Her graphs summed up her observations. Her specimens gave authenticity to her conclusions.

Pupils do not need to be highly articulate to present good reports. Usually, if a pupil is interested in his work, he can describe what he has done and what he has found out in adequate fashion. Should he have speech defects or should he suffer unduly from self-consciousness, the teacher may help him organize his presentation to put major reliance upon demonstrations and visual aids rather than upon words.

> Sixteen-year-old Antonio had displayed a high degree of skill in the construction of a kymograph. His science teacher persuaded him to enter the project in a science fair and demonstrate its action. Though Antonio was unskilled in oral presentations, and very self-conscious about his foreign language background, he memorized a short introduction that was sufficient to set the stage for his demonstration. He

followed the introduction with a deft dissection of a frog muscle which he subjected to a series of fatigue tests. Judges were much impressed with his techniques.

This report should be compared with one made by a boy with a serious stammer who tried to give a memorized talk on galaxies. It was a painful experience for everyone, the boy, the judges, and the audience. The boy may have been accomplished in this field, but no one could have been certain.

Some pupils prefer to investigate books and journals for information rather than do field or experimental research. They usually need guidance in the selection of suitable topics. Left to themselves, they are apt to choose such broad subjects as "jet planes" or "evolution." Their reports are made up of generalities and are rarely satisfactory. Much more suitable topics would be "Jet engine fuels" or "Development of common breeds of dogs." These topics permit the pupils to speak in specific terms and use more interesting visual materials.

Generally pupils should learn to speak from notes. This helps them develop a natural and relaxed manner of presentation. Exceptions may be granted to those pupils whose visual materials serve to give the talks direction. Memorized speeches are generally unsatisfactory; the pupils adopt an unnatural delivery and appear nervous lest they forget their lines. An oral reading of a written report is also to be discouraged though short passages may be read for special emphasis.

Book and film reviews.   Oral reviews of books and films, when well presented, encourage listeners to read the books and view the films. Pupils usually need help in preparing such reviews.

As in all other oral presentations, visual materials are helpful. A pupil presenting a review of *Twenty Thousand Leagues Under the Sea* might well prepare a chart of the Nautilus to explain its features. A pupil reviewing Teale's *North with the Spring* might prepare a map to locate the regions described by the author. A pupil reviewing Sweazey's *After Dinner Science* might demonstrate one of the experiments described.

Pupils need help in understanding that it is better to present a sample of a book in some detail than to describe the book superficially. A well selected sample shows the quality of a work and whets the appetite for more.

Julie, who liked to paint bird portraits, chose to review one of the biographies of Audubon. She concentrated upon what the book had to say about Audubon's painting techniques. She used some prints obtained from a calendar to illustrate these techniques. Then she read a brief section of the book to tell how Audubon obtained specimens for painting, and another section to tell how he supported himself while obtaining materials he needed to make his paintings accurate.

A teacher is justified in allowing pupils to use class time in preparing reviews. Pupils gain the impetus that they need to complete their reviews outside of school. In addition, the teacher is able to give suggestions about the organization of the review and the improvisation of visual materials.

Group presentations. Most adolescents feel more secure when giving talks as members of a group than when required to do so alone. They feel more at ease because audience attention is divided. They can accept responsibilities according to their knowledge of their strengths and weaknesses. Some self-conscious individuals will not volunteer to speak except in group presentations.

Four ninth grade boys gave a report on a balloon ascension into the stratosphere. The first boy outlined briefly some of the preliminaries of the ascent. The second boy prepared hydrogen, with which he filled a rubber balloon to show buoyancy; he explained the dangers of hydrogen and the advantages and disadvantages of helium used in the actual ascent. The third boy displayed a chart showing the expansion of a partially filled balloon as it ascends and demonstrated this expansion with a rubber balloon in an evacuated bell jar. The fourth boy described the gondola, using both a model and a chart to illustrate its major features. The first boy resumed the floor and described the flight itself together with some of the findings of the expedition.

Some teams of pupils have prepared such interesting talks that they have been in demand by service clubs and other organizations. This is truly a fine experience for the pupils concerned.

In addition to presentations of the type described, groups of pupils may conduct quiz programs based on popular radio and television programs. Sometimes a group serves as experts and tries to answer the questions that come from their audience. Sometimes they serve as judges of the answers given by their classmates to questions which they previously formulated. These activities add spice to reviews and drills as well as giving practice in speaking to the participants.

Science plays and assembly programs. Science plays can be rewarding to both audiences and participants. The plays need not be elaborate; those produced by a small group of pupils for their classmates can be little more than skits which utilize a minimum of properties and a maximum of imagination.

The chemistry class was working on individual and small group projects. Four pupils chose to dramatize Goodyear's discovery of the vulcanization of rubber. The first two scenes, or skits, humorously pictured the problems of wearing rain garments made of unvulcanized rubber. The garments were completely imaginary.

The next two scenes portrayed Goodyear's discouragement and final success. The last scene returned to the original theme with vulcanized rubber garments replacing those of unvulcanized rubber.

The production took about ten minutes. It was enthusiastically re-received by the other pupils who suggested that such dramatizations be used more often in the chemistry program.

Pupils like to use properties, scenery, costumes and special effects. These can be incorporated without making the production unnecessarily elaborate. A papier-mâché skull and a retort make a pupil an alchemist; a blow on a paper carton is an explosion; a red lamp produces fire light. Pupils display a good deal of ingenuity in improvising these properties.

More elaborate plays, which require extra time for preparation, may be produced for the benefit of pupils in other sections of the same course. If sufficiently interesting they may be used for an all-school assembly.

One ninth grade section wrote and produced a three-act play for an assembly program. Act One was set in a nineteenth-century home; two boys and two girls comment on the difficulties of life in the eighteenth century but are highly amused when one of the girls reads aloud some predictions for the twentieth century. Act Two was set in a modern home; two boys and two girls comment on the hardships of living in the nineteenth century but are amused at predictions for the twenty-first century. Act three was set in a home a century hence and two boys and two girls comment on the hardships of the twentieth century. The curtain fell just as one of the girls began to laugh at some predictions she was reading.

Short plays are best written by the pupils themselves with little help from the teacher. They can get basic facts from textbooks and encyclopedias, and use imagination to provide the incidents. They can also find a wealth of detail in biographical accounts, much of which is dramatic enough to be set directly in play form.

Occasionally science plays are published in education journals; titles may be found in the *Education Index. School Science and Mathematics* can furnish reprints of some of these.

The preparation of science programs for all-school assemblies provides unusual learning opportunities for pupils. The planning process, as ideas are proposed, discussed, and judged, is richly rewarding. Ingenuity is challenged during the preparation of properties, scenery, and special effects. Production and presentation provide experiences not afforded by regular classroom work. Some teachers feel justified in making the preparation of an assembly program the equivalent of a regular unit of study.

Programs made up of a number of short features—skits, talks, demonstrations, novelty acts, tableaux, and the like—are relatively simple to produce. Responsibilities can be apportioned among several groups of pupils to permit full participation. Two or more teachers can divide up the direction more easily.

The five biology sections of the Alexander Hamilton High School presented ten tableaux, or living pictures, called "Great Moments in Medicine." Among the scenes pictured were the first vaccination, the first use of antiseptic surgery, and the first use of an anesthetic. Narrators explained the importance of each scene.

A run-down sheet of the type shown below is helpful in planning and producing programs made up of many short features.

RUN-DOWN SHEET FOR ASSEMBLY PROGRAM ON AIRPLANE FLIGHT

Scene 1

1. Recording of flight sounds. Lights up. Curtain up.
2. Announcement of purpose of program.
3. Demonstrations of Bernoulli's principle—Shadow projection.
4. Demonstration of lifting effect on wing section.
5. Projection of slides showing pressure distribution on wings.
6. Flight of rubber-band powered model.
7. Curtain.

Scene II

1. Flight sounds. Lights up. Curtain up.
2. Demonstrations of rotational axes of airplane.
3. Demonstration of effects of wind on control surfaces of models.
4. Demonstration of large skeleton model showing how pilot moves control surfaces.
5. Demonstration in center of auditorium of flight of controllable model.
6. Curtain.

Scene III

1. Flight sounds. Curtain up. Back drops part.
2. Demonstration of action of "Link Trainer" model built by boys.
3. Recording "The Air Force Song." Final curtain.

The run-down sheet states the unifying theme and shows the sequence. It guides stage managers, electricians, property men, and the director or directors. It becomes the basis for the program given to the audience.

All programs should be planned with the nature of the adolescent audience in mind. Action should be fast paced; there should be no long lapses. Suspense is essential, with a gradual building up toward the final climax. Comic relief can be provided by inserting comedy scenes or by using a clown who stumbles around parodying serious members of the cast and getting in everyone's way except at critical moments.

Television and radio programs.   Much that has been said about assembly programs applies to television programs. Many of the same benefits to the participants can be expected, although television program directors do not usually permit pupils to make as many decisions as would be allowed in the production of programs for school audiences.

As with assembly programs, action should be rapid; at all times there should be something going on for the cameras to pick up. Emphasis should be put on spectacular demonstrations, the display of active animals, and the like; dialogue should be minimized. Humor is always an asset.

Television has certain advantages in the production of science programs. Through the medium of the long focus lens the audience can be brought close to demonstrations, a fact that permits the use of smaller materials than can be used in auditoriums where visibility is always a problem. A television program director can also send a camera man away from the studio to film special scenes that can be woven into the program; these are silent but can be given meaning by a narrator.

As with assembly programs, three or four short skits are easier to produce than one long feature, and they permit more pupils to participate both as actors and property men. A run-down sheet is helpful in holding the program together and may be required by the television program director.

Radio programs are relatively more difficult to produce effectively than television programs. Through words alone the audience must be given a picture of what is going on. This limits science programs to materials familiar to the audience. Reference to the sour taste of a lemon, the "lightness" of cork, and the feel of wool are immediately intelligible. But no amount of description can give a meaningful picture of a Bunsen burner or a Florence flask to the adult with no training in science.

The problem of identifying participants is equally difficult. Since voice quality is the only recognizable characteristic a few participants with unlike voices should be used; two boys and two girls make a good balance, with perhaps an adult voice added if necessary for the action. The audience can be helped in identification of voices by the frequent use of names as the participants address each other.

Though most of the action must be implied by the words of the participants, a narrator may be used to describe what is going on. His voice should be different and he should speak in a more deliberate fashion so that he is easily identified when he breaks into the program.

Pupils love sound effects, but these are not easy to build into the program. Many things do not sound on the air as they do in actuality. Commonly they must be identified for the listener, and timing is always important. If the program can be taped in advance, pupils will have opportunities to experiment and discard sound effects that are not suitable.

Participants in radio programs work from scripts that permit close control of the situation. However, there is danger that as pupils read these scripts naturalness will be lost. To avoid this it is well to give the participants only short sentences, phrases, and exclamations to read. Rarely should one person have a line of more than one short sentence. Sentences containing dependent clauses should be broken into two separate sentences and assigned to different individuals. Even poor readers, who benefit greatly from such experiences, can participate with this type of script. A portion of a science radio program script illustrating some of the points made above is shown below. Note the short direct sentences, each expressing a single idea, and note the distribution of the lines among the participants. These devices make reading easier, give an effect of spontaneity, and help maintain listener attention through constant change of voice and manner of delivery.

Teacher: You pick out something this time, Dixie. Shut your eyes and reach in the box.

Dixie (Short pause): Here!

Bill: It looks like a can.

Dave: I know what it is. It's a "come-back."

Bill: What's that?

Dave: You roll it along the floor. Pretty soon it stops and rolls right back to you.

Teacher: Show us, Dave.

Dave (Pause): All right. Now watch. See it rolls right back to me.

Bill: I see. That's why it's called a "come-back."

Dixie: What makes it work?

Teacher: I think I can show you. This end pulls off.

Karen: There's just a rubber band and something hanging on it.

Teacher: That's a weight hanging on the rubber band, Karen.

Bill: Let's see. When you roll it————.

Oh! I understand. When you roll it the rubber band twists up.

Teacher: Here, Bill. See if you can show us.

Bill: See, when I turn the can the weight winds up the rubber band.

Dave: Then the rubber band unwinds and makes the toy come back to us.

Teacher: We could say that energy is stored in the rubber band, couldn't we?

Dixie: Why, yes. That's where it is stored.

Karen: Where is it stored in the toy automobile?

Teacher: Did you ever see one taken apart?

Bill: Yes, I have. There's a spring in there.

Teacher: So the energy is stored in the spring.

Dave: There's a spring in the clock, too.

Some science radio programs may be of the panel type. These are useful in describing field work, visitations, and special events. An interviewer may ask questions of the panel or a moderator may direct the conversation. For this sort of program "skeleton" scripts may be sufficient. The following "skeleton" script was written for one of a series of radio programs reporting the field observations of a science class. The key words or phrases guide each participant but permit self-expression.

Mr. Baker: A week ago on this program we told about our first field trip at five below zero. We didn't do any better this time, did we, Miss Miller?

Anne: Colder.

Joe: About the same on the trip—colder night before.

Jack: More animal signs seen.

Terry: Have interest in tracks. What kinds?

Jack: Name four.

Anne: Name some more.

Terry: Bird tracks seen.

Joe: Surprised at blue heron.

Mr. Baker: Sees one or more tracks yearly. Not common.

MORE AND BETTER WRITING

Secondary school pupils are very reluctant to write, and they do so only when required or under duress. Few write for pleasure; however, skill in writing is too important to be ignored by science teachers. They share the obligation to help pupils develop this skill.

Encouraging pupils to write. By the time a pupil has reached the secondary school he has gained sufficient word power and writing skill to express himself on paper. He may, and probably does, write with a scrawl. He may misspell words. He may break rules of grammar or omit punctuation marks. But he can convey his thoughts to a reader.

The pupil can use writing for communication, although unconscious of certain refinements that make communication easier, but this represents lack of experience, not incompetence. He needs practice, not in the narrow sense of the term, but through purposeful writing experiences.

The briefer forms of communication, such as labels and captions, are apt to go unnoticed in the search for valuable writing experiences. Actually, brief communications give excellent practice with words and terse expressions. Best of all, pupils are able to judge the effectiveness of their own writing and make improvements when needed.

More extensive writing projects for the science program may be suggested in unlimited numbers, but pupils do not always undertake them willingly. For years they have been compelled to write and rewrite papers destined only for the ash can. They no longer feel pleasure in writing to express themselves. The science teacher must use special efforts to establish a strong sense of purpose in his pupils.

Pupils usually see the advantage of supplementing an exhibit with a short paragraph or so. When they have exerted themselves in independent research—field work, original experimentation, and the like—they recognize the need for reports. They like the prestige that comes with preparing notes for publication. They can be challenged by such group projects as play writing.

The teacher can give a great deal of help in organization. One long report may be broken into several minor projects, each of which can be undertaken separately and polished as needed. Sometimes an outline is needed. Usually suggestions for the use of visual aids are required.

The teacher must develop a constructive attitude when evaluating the written work of his pupils. He should train himself to look beyond the mere mechanics of spelling, punctuation, and grammar, remembering that what is said is the important thing. He should note efforts to organize, to select descriptive words, to provide emphasis. Whenever he can, he should give praise for a picturesque phrase, a lucid sentence, and a well-constructed paragraph.

Discovery and correction of minor errors can often be left to the pupils themselves when they have a purpose for providing fault-free written materials. An elementary teacher describes a technique that could be used equally well in the secondary school:

My fifth grade had set up and labeled the exhibits for a science show to which parents were invited. The pupils agreed that the labels should not be misspelled or have other serious mistakes. So they chose three committees, one to check spelling, one to criticize sentences and word usage, and a third to judge neatness. These committees were harsher than I would have been but their decisions were accepted by their classmates. It was a valuable experience for everyone.

The use of editorial committees as just described can solve many problems for the teacher. Committees may check entries in science shows. They may check the work of bulletin board committees. Materials produced for duplication—committee reports, summaries, pupil-planned demonstrations, and the like—should be edited. And any articles submitted for publication in the school or local newspapers need careful editing. Pupils learn to be critical. They get in some interesting arguments and they learn to appeal to proper authorities—dictionaries, grammars, and secretaries' handbooks.

Minor writing experiences.   The preparation of labels for exhibits gives practice with spelling, printing, and organization of words. Often the work demands reference to a dictionary for help with spelling.

Pupils quickly see the advantage of supplementing a title with a brief but informative phrase or sentence. The writing of a caption requires considerable skill but a pupil undertakes it willingly because it is short. Some labels use common words but often the labels become quite technical as pupils do advanced reading about their interests.

Labels for nature trails may be much the same as those just described, but when they call attention to items more or less removed from the labels, as when dealing with a bird nest high in a tree, they involve special problems of writing. Again, because the captions are brief, pupils attack the task readily and do surprisingly well.

Labels that are used with working models may tell the viewer how to operate the model. These labels give pupils excellent practice in writing directions. A label attached to an exhibit of fluorescent materials inclosed in a box is shown below:

FLUORESCENCE

The things in this box will glow when they are in ultraviolet light.

1. Look in the peephole.
2. Press Button A to see them by regular light.
3. Press Button B to see them by ultraviolet light.

George Warner

Complex exhibits may require a number of separate labels which together represent an elaborate piece of writing but which, because they are separated, give pupils little trouble.

Chart making provides the same type of writing experiences as are provided by label making. A number of pupils find chart making a real challenge. They accept without question the need for appropriate headings and descriptive comments.

Pupils often become discouraged when they discover errors of spelling or produce poorly drawn letters on charts that have taken much time and energy to produce. They may abandon their projects even though nearly completed. If they are advised to make all captions on separate cards which can be attached to the charts with rubber cement, they can easily replace those on which there are errors or unsightly printing.

Bulletin board displays are much more effective when pictures and diagrams are attended by descriptive captions. There should be a single unifying title for the entire exhibit, captions for each picture or diagram, and perhaps a paragraph or two of additional information.

Among the standing committees in Mrs. Bull's chemistry sections were bulletin board committees responsible for preparing two displays each term. One committee chose to show the products derived from corn. The pictures for the display were clipped from advertisements in magazines. Labels from containers of corn products were also used. The pictures were arranged about a picture of an ear of corn and connected to it with lengths of ribbon. Labels told briefly how each product is prepared and used. In some instances the chemical processes were described.

Pupils gain valuable writing experiences by serving as class or group secretaries. When lists of words and tables of figures are to be made, it is well for the secretary to keep records on the chalkboard so that all pupils may participate in the organization of the material, in any corrections that are needed, and in the analysis of the data. Afterwards the data may be copied off by either the secretary or all the pupils. When no extensive writing is called for, pupils who are not normally inclined to write often volunteer to be secretaries.

During a demonstration experiment on the burning of a candle under various conditions, it became desirable to record the data in some convenient form. A girl volunteered to be the secretary. The pupils suggested a two-column arrangement and dictated the headings for the columns. They then told the secretary how to enter the data already collected, criticizing her spelling when she made some mistakes. Then as more data were collected, they told her where entries should be made.

Sometimes a teacher may choose to provide in advance a form for the secretaries to fill in. This procedure can be justified in many cases. It does, however, deny the pupils opportunities to participate in deciding the form of organization, an important part of the writing process.

Elementary school pupils sometimes keep a class notebook or a class scrapbook. Generally, one pupil is responsible for the organization of the book, although sometimes a committee is assigned the task. All pupils contribute pictures, clippings, diagrams, paintings, and written accounts. Secondary teachers might find this device a useful one to use at times.

Another technique observed in a sixth grade classroom might have value in secondary school science classes.

> Miss Dixon's sixth grade kept a nature diary and Anne was the recorder. As pupils reported their observations of things they had seen outdoors, Anne collected the reports, edited them, and typed them for the diary. The diary contained over one-hundred pages by the end of the year, with each pupil having contributed several items, mostly short paragraphs but a few running more than a half-page in length.

This nature diary gave all pupils writing experience and gave Anne considerable editorial experience. The technique should have value in the secondary school if it can be adapted to the increased maturity of the pupils.

The school newspaper may feature a science column if the idea is proposed to the editors. In one school there are class reporters who collect items of interest from the pupils, usually about special projects and sometimes about unusual observations. The reporters may edit the accounts written by the other pupils or they may write the accounts themselves. Teachers must constantly remind both the reporters and the other pupils if the column is to flourish.

Major writing projects.   Comparatively few pupils volunteer to undertake tasks that they know will demand extensive writing. This is partly because of reluctance to begin something they believe will be unrewarding and partly because of a feeling of incompetence in writing skills. However, when pupils become engrossed in special activities, they need only moderate encouragement to write about what they have seen and done.

Among the easier reports to organize and prepare are those based on anecdotal records. Anecdotes tend to organize themselves chronologically. As soon as one anecdote is written it may be laid aside and another started. There is no necessity for transition and development. One anecdote may be revised without affecting the others.

> Seventh grade Millicent watched a robin building a nest outside her bedroom window. Each day she wrote up her observations, describing

the activities of the robin and the changes in the nest. Her final report needed only an introductory paragraph to be an excellent piece of writing.

Similar to anecdotal records, in that they are composed of several discrete items, are reports that describe a number of separate but related objects, situations, or events. An organization based upon position may be used.

For a biology project, Jennifer made a study of a blueberry bog on her parents' property. She explored the bog carefully, collecting specimens and taking pictures. She incorporated her observations in a report that was illustrated with photographs and dried specimens. The report was organized in three main sections, each dealing with one of the divisions of the bog—the open portion, bushy section, and the wooded section. She added an introductory section locating the bog and indicating her interest in it. She wrote a final section giving her conclusions about the future of the bog.

Directions for carrying out processes are relatively simple to write, based as they are on step-by-step procedures that provide their own organization and that need only a brief introductory statement to be effective writing.

Ollie and Harry were as nearly incompetent academically as two boys can be in the ninth grade. But they were interested in automobiles. One day their science teacher asked them if they could change tires. Both could.

"Now look," their teacher told them, "you fellows go take off a tire and put it back on. As you do it, write out each step. Then come back and I'll let you tell the rest of the class just what you did. I want all of them to know how, so that someday when they drive their own cars they will know what to do."

The next day Ollie and Harry brought in the directions. They had been so ashamed of their crude handwriting that they had borrowed a typewriter to make a more legible copy. They were very proud of their contributions to the class.

A teacher may ask certain pupils to find experiments for their classmates, summarize the procedures, and prepare duplicated copies. The pupils then take charge of the class and supervise the laboratory work for which they have written directions.

A diagram sometimes aids pupils in organizing their reports by suggesting the nature and order of the topics to be taken up. A radio circuit diagram, for instance, gives a beginning and an ending point and includes the important intermediate steps. A flow diagram, such as that shown in Figure 18, page 243, is useful in writing about a manufacturing process; it suggests that the general nature of the successive processes should be described first, then each process may be described in detail. Sometimes a map helps in the organization of a report.

> James became interested in the reasons why the small river near his home veered sharply from one valley wall to the other. From a map he noticed that each sharp bend occurred opposite the mouth of a tributary valley. Field work and continued map study convinced him that alluvial fans deposited by tributary streams forced the main stream to the opposite sides of the valley.
>
> His teacher encouraged him to write up his study as a special report for earth science. First he drew up a map of a ten-mile section of the valley and plotted the alluvial fans as he had found them through his field work. For his report, after an introductory section, he described each fan in detail and the nature of the associated bend in the main stream. A final section gave his conclusions.

Science writing may go beyond reports of project work. Play writing may become a major project for a number of pupils, as in this incident described by one teacher:

> Our play writing project was one of those pupil suggestions which just grows once it gets started. In a class committee meeting someone said, "Why can't we review our work by writing a play?" So they began. Someone else suggested that they write a challenge to the other science classes to compete with them and that the best play would be given over the public address system. Not everyone responded, for play writing is not the easiest type of project. In each class the finished plays were read and the two best plays selected by student vote. This resulted in six possible choices.
>
> One of the class presidents asked the dramatics teacher to select the winning play. She selected two, one for its interesting style and the other for its content. The result was that both girls rewrote their plays, one for greater interest and the other for more content, and both playlets were used in a freshman assembly.[1]

Science fiction appeals to many boys who are avid readers of this type of literature. Some boys who never volunteer for any other type of writing will try their hands at short, pseudo-scientific stories.

[1] Harrison, Florence, "Science Projects for Girls," *School Science and Mathematics,* 13:605–608, 1943.

The writing of poetry appeals to a different type of pupil. Science themes suitable for poems are limitless. Sometimes pupils need a little help with this means of self-expression.

Mr. Willis used a few minutes of class time to explain to his earth science pupils the nature of a couplet. Then he suggested that each pupil try to write a couplet about a fossil trilobite found on a field trip.

Some pupils can be stimulated to write essays. Controversial topics such as "The importance of vivisection" appeal. Descriptive essays such as "The earth as seen from its satellite" may be in accord with specific interests. If sufficiently challenged, pupils will do an enormous amount of work in research and writing.

Throughout the year the science teacher may drop suggestions for stories, poems and short essays that would be appropriate for the subject under study. Always he must try to provide recognition commensurate with the efforts and achievements of the pupils who accept the challenge.

SUGGESTED ACTIVITIES

1. Select at random ten definitions from the glossary of a science textbook. Analyze each from the standpoint of the experience background pupils would need for correct interpretation. In instances where pupils lack the proper background, plan the necessary procedures by which the words could be introduced to the pupils.
2. Read a science book that could be used for supplementary reading. Present an oral review of the book to the methods class, using visual aids of the type that a secondary school pupil might use.
3. List various techniques that can be used to build the pupils' scientific vocabularies.
4. Select an eighth grade general science unit. Plan writing experiences suitable for a class of pupils with a wide range of academic ability.
5. Divide the methods class into several groups and have each write and produce a science skit.

SUGGESTED READINGS

Alatis, J. E., "Our own Language Barrier," *American Education*, 1:12–13, 1964.
Bennett, C., "Toward an Active Vocabulary for Science," *Science Education*, 49:269, 1965.

Brestow, W. H., "Communications in Curriculum," *Education Leadership*, 23:143, 1965.

Burns, P., "Means of Developing Vocabularies," *Education*, 85:533–538, 1965.

Lockwood J. B., "Research on Problems in Reading Science," *School Science and Mathematics*, 59:551–556, 1959.

Peoples, J. A., "Relationship of Teacher Communications to Principal Behavior," *Journal of Experimental Education*, 32:407–411, 1964.

Thompson, J. J., "New Method of Teaching Science," *Science Education*, 48:390–392, 1964.

Veatch, J., and G. Hayes, "Individualizing Instruction," *NEA Journal*, 55:38, 1966.

West, N. E., "Vocabulary: Basic Factor for Understanding Science," *The Science Teacher*, 27:15+ December, 1960.

Chapter 17

Science Projects

After the class consented that our group would be permitted to work on machines, which we were plugging for, we then decided among ourselves who was to work individually on inclined planes, pulleys, or levers. We then went to the library to get some starting information on our topic. After we had read we wrote out a guide sheet and bibliography for the class, and then we made plans for our own individual projects. After working through our projects and checking on the reading done by the whole class, we began to report and make demonstrations. The class got so interested that they set up other problems on machines and worked through them with the help of our group!

By the end of the third week group reporting and demonstrating were well under way. The group on electricity gave demonstrations with magnets, motors, vacuum tubes, and radio sets. They used charts and moving pictures to clarify concepts about the nature of electricity and the working of electrons in television. The group on the gas engine used a working model that had been made by a previous class to demonstrate the gas engine cycle. The principles of energy change and transfer were explained by the use of moving pictures followed by discussion. The group on light added novelty by giving demonstrations with a telescope borrowed from a hobbyist and by arranging for a work period in the University Spectroscopy Laboratory.

. . . during the eighth week, all students but one selected a project, went ahead planning it with the aid of the teacher or some other available resource person, and settled down to the job of working it out under guidance. Their projects included setting up a balanced aquarium and terrarium, dissecting frogs and studying physiological effects, building a periscope, work in table-top photography, making projection prints, studying the characteristics of vacuum tubes, purifying water, and the fractional distillation of petroleum.[1]

This is a picture of a general science class at work, or more accurately, of pupils at work. This is individualized instruction rather than mass education. The project method is a recognized instructional technique which should be in every science teacher's repertory.

THE NATURE OF THE PROJECT METHOD

The use of projects is not new in education. Teachers of academic subjects have assigned library research projects for generations. Teachers of vocational subjects have used projects as basic assignments ever since their courses were first developed. Science teachers, however, have in recent years brought out the potentialities of projects most fully by combining the elements of the practical problem and the academic problem.

What is a project? The term project is used simply to indicate a problem, usually involving the use of apparatus and materials, undertaken by an individual or a group. A problem may be as simple as making a collection of leaves. It may be as difficult as developing an original process for controlling electrolytic corrosion.

Projects are as varied as the pupils who undertake them. Most projects are simple; some call for little more than the ability to follow directions, to use elementary manipulative and academic skills, and to bring a job through to completion. But sometimes pupils do amazing work.

A project need not be new or original. Although a student may appear to be copying the design of some device or experiment, he will most likely inject new ideas of his own. Also it must not be forgotten that a discovery or invention that is well known in the scientific world may be original to an adolescent; he can benefit as much by his work as he would if his achievements were completely new.

Who should work on science projects. Any secondary school pupil may work on a science project no matter what his talents and interests may be.

---

[1] Fonsworth, Emile C., "The Functional Approach in General Science," *Ideas for Teaching Science in the Junior High School,* National Science Teachers Association, Washington, D.C., 1963.

Projects represent one method of helping young people explore their special interests in depth.

There are projects that will challenge pupils of the highest scientific aptitudes; there are projects in which nonreaders may find satisfaction.

Special encouragement should be given to pupils of high scientific ability. These young people are not sufficiently challenged by the conventional program. They can work on projects during the part of their class time that they would otherwise sit through without benefit. The project method is an excellent way, perhaps the best, for helping talented young people make the most of their potentialities.

The publicity that exceptional youngsters receive for their achievements should not blind teachers to the fact that projects are good for all pupils. Pupils who have little interest in science find pleasure in projects that combine science with their special interests. Pupils who are considered "slow," which usually means that they are retarded readers, find in project work the satisfaction that is denied them in most of their school work; they may learn more from their science projects than from all other classroom activities combined.[2]

Pupils who have expressed an intention of entering some scientific occupation should be given special encouragement to work on related projects. Thus they can learn much about the type of activity in which they will be engaging and they will discover much about their interests and aptitudes for this type of work. This knowledge will help them in making final decisions.

How the project method operates.   An actual project begins with something a pupil wants to do—a device he wants to construct, a collection he wants to make, an experiment he wants to perform. But the project method begins earlier; it begins with the teacher's plans. It cannot be assumed that pupils begin work on projects spontaneously. They need help and guidance and occasional prodding if the project method is to be effective.

Most of the suggestions for project work originate with the teacher. During regular classwork he may point out possible ways to follow up certain topics. He may note a special interest and encourage a pupil to develop this interest. He may provide lists of suggested projects or take pupils to science fairs so as to see what other pupils are doing.

However, the teacher must not dictate what a pupil is to do or how he is to do it. Should he do so, he is merely making another assignment. Part of the value in project work comes from the opportunities to make choices and plan methods of attack.

Although newspaper stories give the impression of pupils spending long hours of their own time on their projects, most science projects are initiated and carried out during regular class periods. Sometimes one or two pupils work apart from the others who continue with their regular classwork. Sometimes the teacher permits all pupils to work on projects during portions of the class time.

Many science projects are carried out by two or more pupils working together. Sometimes an entire class works on a special project. Adolescents like to work together; they feel more secure. Many a pupil who would not undertake a project alone gladly teams up with a close friend.

Once pupils begin work, the teacher must give continued help—providing special materials, instructing in troublesome techniques, suggesting new approaches, pointing out progress and praising achievements. His role is not passive; he is as active as in any other type of teaching.

After projects are completed, the teacher has one more important

---

[2] For a description of a project approach to science used for the underachiever, see Bennett, Leroy C., "Livonia's Project Science—A Reality Centered Curriculum," *School Science and Mathematics,* 66:247–254, 1966.

responsibility. He must see that pupils receive deserved recognition for their achievements. He may arrange classroom displays and reports to other pupils or set up exhibits in school corridors and showcases. He can enter projects in science fairs and congresses, and contact local newspapers and radio and television stations to keep them informed of notable achievements.

The contributions of project work. The contributions of science projects are as broad as the science program as a whole. The subject matter learnings constantly amaze judges at science fairs. Equally important as the facts and principles learned are the changes in ways of thinking and acting. These contributions may be summarized as follows:

1. Stimulating an interest in science.
2. Satisfying scientific curiosity.
3. Developing problem-solving techniques.
4. Encouraging independent thinking.
5. Giving practice in critical thinking.
6. Developing an appreciation for the work of scientists.
7. Making scientific principles more meaningful.
8. Helping develop each individual to the utmost.
9. Increasing self-confidence.
10. Giving experience with tools and techniques of science.
11. Filling leisure time to good advantage.

INITIATING PROJECT WORK

Project work is almost always initiated by teachers. Occasionally an exceptional individual begins work on a project spontaneously, but such instances are rare. In some schools pupils are constantly at work on projects. In other schools there is never a project worth looking at twice. The difference stems from the difference in teachers.

Consideration for the nature of adolescents. It is not enough for the teacher to want to put the project method in effect. He must know how to make the method appeal to his pupils and how to attain worthwhile results from their work. He must know the nature of his pupils.

Adolescents have a number of characteristics that impel them to undertake project work enthusiastically: they like the freedom of action permitted them; they like the distinction of working on a problem apart from others in the class; they enjoy the status a successful project gives them with their peers and with adults; they like the favorable recognition and the publicity their projects earn for them. They also like to work with their friends.

In general adolescents like manipulative work and favor projects that enable them to make things. Most of them like to produce tangible things that they can look at with pride. They like the excitement of experiments. Many like animals. They enjoy making and operating mechanical models.

On the other side of the picture, adolescents have a few traits that discourage them from project work. They have many immediate and pressing problems that take precedence in their minds over any form of school work. Young adolescents in particular are little concerned with the remote future and are apathetic about tasks that cannot be completed within a short time.

Adolescents are apt to underrate themselves and, although they might wish to duplicate some of the projects described to them, they feel inadequate to do so. They are afraid of failure and ridicule. They are particularly sensitive to criticism from leaders in their peer groups and may remain aloof from project work if the leaders refuse to undertake it.

Recognition of these adolescent traits makes it possible to introduce the subject of project work with reasonable expectations of success. However, not every pupil reacts favorably at the very beginning; different approaches are needed to fit different personalities.

Stimulating pupils to undertake projects.   Any number of ways may be used to encourage pupils to begin projects. With mass methods all pupils are appealed to at once; these are most successful when pupils are accustomed to doing project work. With individual methods one or two or three pupils are dealt with apart from the others.

The individual conference approach is often successful. The teacher notes through some contact with the pupil the existence of some special interest. The teacher arranges a conference with the pupil and explores this interest. The teacher may need do no more than propose ways the pupil may follow up this interest. But if the pupil is unaccustomed to individualized work of this nature, the teacher may need to give concrete suggestions for procedures.

In a second form of individual approach, the teacher describes to one or two pupils the nature of some project that would be useful in his classroom teaching. This may be the repair of some piece of equipment, the construction of some special device, or the creation of a chart or model. Many pupils enjoy being thus singled out and respond favorably. They usually prefer to work with close friends on such projects.

Science club work provides opportunities for individual contacts with pupils. Projects may be suggested on a service basis, as just described. Pupils with special interests may be encouraged to follow up their interests.

Some teachers call for volunteers to do project work. During the progress of a lesson they outline one or more follow-up studies and ask if any pupils would like to undertake them. Again pupils often volunteer more willingly if allowed to work with friends.

Pupils are apt to be influenced by the examples of others. If a single pupil or a group of two or three pupils has undertaken a project and is working on it where others can watch, perhaps during a portion of the regular class period, the remainder of the class becomes favorably inclined toward project work. Perhaps at first they are more influenced by the consideration the others receive but once started it is possible that they will become interested in the project for its own sake.

The influence of example can also be utilized by requesting pupils who are working on projects to make interim reports. This awakens interest in the projects early and keeps interest high until the completion of the reports.

Pupils who are working on projects for other teachers or for science clubs may be invited to describe their activities to a class. This may not be so effective as reports from members of the class but certain pupils might be challenged by some of the more elaborate projects.

Some teachers retain projects made by former students. Introduced at the beginning of the year they help pupils see the possibilities for similar efforts by themselves.

Many teachers set aside one unit in their programs for individual project work. They encourage pupils to propose their own problems but they also supply lists of possible projects that pupils may choose to work on. Such a unit is commonly placed rather early in the school year so that pupils may if interested follow up their projects through the remaining months. Other pupils, once acquainted with the project method, may find in following units possibilities for projects that will hold their interests.

It is always good motivation to take pupils to see science fairs. Schools often send bus loads of pupils to community and regional fairs. Many pupils are inspired by the entries. Most pupils come away feeling that they too could develop projects the equivalent of many of those they saw. However, science fairs usually come late in the school year and pupils do not feel any encouragement to begin projects at once. By the time fall has come the pupils have forgotten the impact of the fair, other interests have intervened, there may have been a change of teachers, and so the value of the fair has been lessened. Some way for reviewing the fair is needed, perhaps some of the programs, newspaper clippings, and photographs on the bulletin board, or a viewing of colored slides may be effective.

Perhaps the one thing that teachers should not do is assign a project to a pupil. Such a project would be no different than any other assignment. It might, if properly chosen and if the pupil were receptive, stimulate the pupil to spontaneous efforts. The chances are, however, if the teacher has not been able to appeal to the pupil in one of the ways just described, that he will resent the assignment and no good will result.

Providing ideas for projects.   It has already been mentioned that many ideas for projects will arise from regular classwork and from a knowledge of a pupil's special interests. It is helpful, however, to know something of what pupils have done in the past in order to make suggestions. Many of these projects will be suitable for repetition and many will need only alteration to fit special needs.

Programs of science fairs give hundreds of suggestions. Lists and ideas for science projects have been published by several sources, including the National Science Foundation, Science Service, Biological Sciences Curriculum Study, and many industries. (See list of Suggested Readings at the end of this chapter.)

Science teaching journals contain descriptions of many projects that have been carried out by pupils. These usually represent exceptional achievements that lie beyond the abilities of most secondary pupils but they can serve as inspiration for the specially talented. Sometimes with modification they are useful for other pupils as well.

Textbooks often contain suggestions for projects; these are usually appropriate for pupils of average ability. Also valuable are the "do-it-yourself" science books written in increasing numbers for boys and girls. The familiar materials, the simple techniques, and the clear-cut directions make these books appeal to young people.

FITTING PROJECT WORK INTO THE PROGRAM

Class and group projects carried out as part of the regular classwork are fitted into the program just as are other standard teaching techniques. The problem of encouraging completely independent work is somewhat different.

One or more pupils may be permitted to work on projects while other pupils carry out regular assignments. Rarely are these special pupils given all of a class period for project work. Instead they participate in most of the general activities of the class and spend only part of a period on their own interests.

The practice of excusing pupils from uniform class participation has been criticized on the grounds that these pupils miss important work.

Actually the loss is negligible. These pupils do participate in the most important of the learning activities. If they are superior students, and many project workers are, they grasp the new material much more rapidly than the others and do their project work in the time that they would usually waste if forced to work with the others.

Occasionally the retarded reader is excused from certain activities to work on his project. He may learn little from textbook or notebook, but he will probably learn a lot from his project work. As for the other pupils— each is a special case and only the teacher can decide whether he will profit more from regular class activities or from special project work.

As has been described previously, teachers also set aside class time for all pupils to work on projects. This does not mean that full periods are used for project work. It is usually better to begin each period with general reviews, summaries, drills, tests, or the presentation of new material. Only the last half hour or so is given over to project work. Adolescents find it difficult to concentrate intensely for much longer than twenty minutes and to hold them at their tasks for a greater length of time may result in waste of class time. However, all situations are different and there are occasions when general interest is so high that a full period may be utilized profitably.

During the remainder of the school day, pupils may find time for project work during study periods, noon recesses, and activity periods. When a teacher finds a pupil of special ability eager to work on a project it sometimes pays to make arrangements to have him excused from some of his study periods. This type of pupil usually has a good academic record and there is little difficulty in making the arrangements. This pupil may then work on his project in the science laboratory even if a class is present. The presence of a pupil working by himself is rarely disturbing.

Senior high school science is sometimes scheduled during the last period of the school day. This permits students who are involved in laboratory work to continue their activities without interruption. Students are not required to remain after school, but those who prefer to remain find that they can profit a great deal. This extended time has been used with success in many schools, particularly when many students are involved in individual project work.

In some schools, the use of computerized flexible scheduling programs allows students to spend one-third or more of their weekly time unstructured. In other schools, students may request released time for independent study. Either of these programs, plus the availability of resource centers and open laboratories, allows science students to utilize school time profitably on projects or research.[3]

[3] Cawelti, Gordon, "Innovative Practices in High Schools: Who Does What—and Why—and How," *Nation's Schools*, 79:56–88, 1967.

Science clubs usually provide time for individual project work. After the business, if there is any, is out of the way, the remainder of the meeting becomes a laboratory period. This may happen two or three times a month.

As pupils develop genuine interest and skill with project work they begin to use time out of school on their projects. Many of them are willing and eager to stay after school if the teacher will let them. Whenever possible a teacher should keep his laboratory doors open in the late afternoon. He need not supervise the pupils closely. He may even leave the room for short intervals or go to faculty meetings if the work being carried on is not dangerous. His presence as a person to refer to in case of trouble is usually all that is needed.

Pupils will also put a great deal of time into their projects at home if they are sufficiently stimulated. The top winners in the national contests have probably put in three or four hours of outside time to every hour of school time. Such high interest does not come spontaneously. The teachers of these boys and girls have given them class time until they were started on their projects. Then they gave them special encouragement and permitted them to work in the science laboratories during extra-class time and after school. The more the pupils worked the more challenging became their problems and soon their project work began to dominate much of their waking hours. And so the teachers really provided out-of-school time without setting aside hours or making schedules for their pupils.

PROVIDING FACILITIES FOR PROJECT WORK

Many pupils do not engage in science project work simply because they have no place to operate. They live in small apartments or underprivileged homes. Occasionally parents forbid them or at least discourage them from activities that involve construction or experimentation. A number of pupils have possible facilities at home but do not know how to take advantage of them. It is the science teacher's responsibility to help pupils find places to work.

Science classroom facilities. To provide adequately for science project work a classroom needs free floor space, ample table space, special facilities such as electricity, gas, and running water, and storage space. Many classrooms are not well adapted for project work but alterations can often be made without destroying the usefulness of the room for regular class work.

Floor space is needed when pupils wish to lay out large sheets of paper for charts and friezes, and when they wish to utilize large pieces of panel board. Movable tables and chairs permit needed floor space to be provided in a few moments.

A large amount of table space is also desirable. Movable tables already referred to can provide part of this space. Wall benches can provide the remainder. The ideal table is solid, and not easily damaged by the activities that it will be used for.

> Mr. Davenport built for his science classroom two tables patterned after picnic tables. The tops were of two-inch planks firmly attached to sturdy legs. When not in use for laboratory and project work, pupils sat at them as they would sit at the desks the tables replaced.

Almost any kind of project work could be done at these tables. They were not harmed by carpentry work; nails or drills passing through boards only made holes in the tops. Pounding did not loosen the joints or mar the oiled finish. Water did not stain them. Acid stains could be sanded off with a power sander. When the top became too battered it could be sanded off or turned over.

The tables were adaptable for many uses. If an overhead support was desired, a framework of boards could be nailed to the table. If a hole through the top was needed, a pupil could get on top and bore the hole. Strings could be attached with thumbtacks. Wires could be attached with staples or screw eyes. No other type of laboratory table has ever been so useful.

A good workbench with a carpenter's vise is essential, together with a set of tools in a cabinet that can be locked. A pair of sawhorses has numerous uses. A second workbench fitted for metal work is also desirable.

Storage space is always a critical need. Space is needed for the raw materials essential for project work—cans, bottles, lumber, wire, junk. Space is needed for the projects that are in various stages of completion— space where they can be kept out of the way of classes and yet be readily available when pupils want to work on them. Space is needed for storage of completed projects pending a science show in which they will be exhibited.

Architects almost never think of the storage problem. When facilities have not been provided the teacher may be able to requisition lockers and cabinets. Sometimes he can build cabinets. If there is a closet nearby, the administration might be receptive to the idea of its use by the science teacher. If there is unused space in the basement or attic, projects may be put into "dead" storage by encasing them tightly in shipping cartons.

Other possible facilities for project work.   Many pupils can work at home in their own rooms and in game rooms or workshops. They sometimes need advice about using their specific facilities, and they may need cautions about the use of fire, acids, and other potentially hazardous items. If parents understand the importance of project work they sometimes help their children with the needed facilities.

In some cities, the museums, zoos and other science centers make available on a regular schedule workrooms for pupils with special interests. A teacher should investigate these possibilities and tell his pupils about them.

Unusual boys and girls, who have demonstrated high interest and competence in science work, have been invited by industrial laboratory heads and college science instructors to carry on project work in their institutions. While these are exceptional cases, a teacher, should he encounter one of these unusual pupils, may investigate similar possibilities in his own community.

Many students attend summer camps. While school projects are not a part of the summer camp program, the collection of specimens of insects, leaves, rocks, and the like is often part of the nature study activity. These collections can be used during the school year as the basis of pupil projects.

WHAT TO DO WITH PROJECTS

Pupils need recognition for their accomplishments. Ideally, perhaps, pupils should work on special science problems just because they are interested; but boys and girls are human, and it is human to desire recognition for what one does.

Reporting student projects.   Some form of reporting on projects is needed so that the whole class can benefit from the experience of those who worked on the project. The length and type of the report is determined by the objectives of the project method. Sometimes the primary reason for projects is to give the pupil experience in working with materials and in planning and thinking in terms of scientific principles and applications. In such a case, a brief written or oral report will be sufficient.

Often the teacher considers the report to be an important part of the project and considerable planning and preparation are involved. A well-planned oral report will be informative to the class and will also help the student who is reporting to gain a degree of poise and self-confidence. Under most circumstances, the report should not be read to the class because first, most students have little or no experience in reading to a class and tend to be self-conscious, and second, the students have a tendency to copy the material for reports from an encyclopedia, college text or technical book and this results in the use of many difficult and unfamiliar words and a style unsuited to oral presentation. These factors will make the reading of reports a painful and monotonous experience for the class and the reader, with no satisfactory learning experience derived.

Instead of writing out the report, a few notes can be put on a card to guide the speaker, or a short outline can be put on the chalkboard where the student can refer to it and the class can use it for note-taking. The report should be given informally. It should deal with the purpose of the project, the materials used, the manner of construction and the problems encountered. The report should include a demonstration or explanation of the project and the scientific principles involved, and include practical application of the principles.

Interim reports as well as final reports are valuable. Interim reports enable pupils working on projects to organize their work more carefully because of the criticisms and suggestions of others. Interim reports help awaken interest on the part of classmates as problems are outlined and methods of attacks are proposed.

Written reports on projects may be required by the teacher, and can be useful training to future scientists in the preparation of technical reports. A general outline that may be modified by the student or teacher for the special requirements of the report is given as follows:[4]

TITLE

ABSTRACT

I. *Introduction*
   A. Statement of the topic or problem investigated.
   B. Purpose, scope, and method of investigation.
   C. Important results or information gained from the investigation.

II. *Materials and Methods*
   A. Description of the equipment and materials used.
   B. Description of the methods used (detailed enough so that the experiments may be repeated by another student.)

III. *Experiments and Results*
   A. Description of the experiments.
   B. Descriptions of the results, including any tables and graphs.

[4] Adapted from Trelease, Sam F., *How to Write Scientific and Technical Papers*, The Williams and Wilkins Company, Baltimore, 1958.

IV. *Discussion*

    A. Relevant background material.
    B. Interpretation of data.
    C. Main principles or generalizations shown by results.

V. *Summary or Conclusions*

    A. Main conclusions.
    B. Supporting evidence and reasoning upon which the conclusions were based.
    C. Suggestions for further investigation.

Providing opportunities for demonstration and display. Reports in the classroom need not be formal. An exhibition of a collection, a demonstration of an experiment, or the operation of a model, attended by a few words of explanation may be all that is needed. Pupils viewing the presentation should have opportunities for questioning and for suggestions.

Some types of project work lend themselves to static display. Flat materials such as charts, paintings, and leaf print collections may be tacked on a bulletin board. Many other items—models, results of experiments, collections of rocks—may be placed on side tables. It is often wise to exhibit one project at a time to center attention on one pupil's work and to avoid the inevitable comparisons that result when two or more projects are placed side by side.

Unusually good static exhibits—those that do not need demonstration—should be displayed to the entire school. Many schools have wall cases in the corridors for just such displays. Projects exhibited should be accompanied by labels explaining them.

When show cases are lacking there may be ways to provide opportunities for display.

> Two of Mr. Appleby's general science classes made a study of a beaver dam a short distance out in the country. They collected evidences of the beaver's work and took pictures of dam and house.
>
> Mr. Appleby put a table in the main foyer of the school, out of the main stream of traffic but accessible to everyone. Specimens were placed on the table and photographs were tacked to a panel of fiberboard behind the table.

Certain types of projects lend themselves to presentations at all-school assemblies. The projects should be of general interest. Materials displayed should be large enough to be visible from all parts of the auditorium. Special lighting and projection facilities may be needed. Programing should provide plenty of action, variety, change of pace, and humor.

The all-school science show, which will be described in a later chapter, provides excellent possibilities for suitable recognition. The date for the show is usually set for the spring so that all pupils will have opportunities to work on entries. Some teachers insist that all pupils provide at least one exhibit; other teachers make exhibition optional.

It is desirable that parents and other adults visit the show as well as pupils. For this reason the show may be given in conjunction with a P.T.A. meeting or an open house. The exhibits are set up during the day and all the pupils in the school are given opportunities to look at them. The exhibits are then left up for the evening meeting. All exhibits are more effective if the pupils who prepared them can be present to explain them.

Some science project work is newsworthy and photogenic. Local newspapers usually assign reporters to cover school activities. These reporters are happy to be informed about unusual projects and school science shows. They commonly bring cameramen with them to photograph the exhibits and the pupils involved. The resulting publicity is gratifying to pupils and to their parents.

Radio and television news reporters are also happy to learn about school science shows, winners in competition, and any special recognition that pupils achieve. Commonly, television cameramen visit science shows to record the activities, and program directors often invite pupils to bring their projects to the stations for interviews.

Superior project work should always be entered in regional, state and national competition. At these science fairs and congresses, pupils see what other pupils are doing and they talk with experts who point out the strengths and weaknesses of their work. Winners in such competition receive substantial rewards that may help them in furthering their scientific study.

Finally, pupils should be given opportunities to write up their projects for publication. Brief accounts may be accepted by the school newspaper. A science newsletter may be planned specifically for printing reports of projects. Local and state science teachers' associations usually publish a newsletter or bulletin in which pupils' projects may be reported briefly. Junior academies of science may have special bulletins for this purpose. On the national level there are the journals of the several science teachers associations and the organ of the Future Scientists of America, an organization set up to foster pupil research.

Evaluating and grading projects. As pupils work on their projects the teacher should keep clearly in mind what project work he is trying to accomplish. He will evaluate each pupil's work in terms of these objectives.

His evaluation is necessarily subjective. He can set up no rigid standards for judging the work of all pupils. Nor should he want to. Project work is important because it encourages individuality. Evaluation then must be in terms of the individual. A piece of work that represents a real accomplishment on the part of one pupil may be unworthy of the talents of another. Each project should be evaluated on its own merits not in competition with other projects, and with the abilities, interests, and background of the pupil given full consideration.

SUGGESTED ACTIVITIES

1. Plan a project-centered unit in which the pupils work as one group or in small groups.
2. Carry out a project of the experimental research type that secondary school pupils would be interested in doing. Present a report of your findings to your methods class.
3. List titles of projects in biology, with short descriptions of each, which you would suggest to pupils with (a) high academic ability, (b) average ability, (c) low academic ability.

SUGGESTED READINGS

Biological Sciences Curriculum Study, *Laboratory Blocks*, D. C. Heath Co., Boston, 1963.

————, *Research Problems in Biology, Investigations for Students*, Series 1 & 2, Doubleday & Co., Garden City, N. Y., 1963.

————, *Research Problems in Biology, Investigations for Students*, Series 3 & 4, Doubleday & Co., Garden City, N. Y., 1965.

Huffmire, D. W., "Critical Appraisal of the Independent Study Project in Science," *Science Education*, vol. 49, April, 1965.

————, "Teacher Demonstration, Laboratory Experiences, Projects" *Science Education*, 49:264–267, 1965.

Koelsche, C. L. "Characteristics of Potential Scientists," *Science Education*, vol. 49, February, 1965.

National Science Foundation, *Ideas for Science Projects*, Washington, D. C., 1962.

National Science Teachers Association, *Vistas of Science*, Scholastic Book Services, Englewood Cliffs, N. J.

Science Materials Center, Inc., *Guide to Science Projects*, New York, 1963.

Science Service, Inc., *Science Clubs of America Sponsor's Handbook*, Washington, D. C., 1963.

————, *Thousands of Science Projects*, Washington, D. C., 1957.

Showalter, Victor, and Irwin Slesnick, "Student Investigations," *The Science Teacher*, February, April, October, November, December, 1964.

Wolff, Nigel, *Your Science Project*, Bulletin 47, Edmund Scientific Company, Barrington, N. J., 1960.

Chapter 18

Science Fairs and Congresses

CAN YOU VISUALIZE AN AREA ABOUT THE SIZE OF AN ATHLETIC FIELD, FILLED to capacity with over 1500 boys and girls, each with table space about two feet deep? Each of the 1500 boys and girls comes from schools within a 100 mile radius and each has his or her own exhibit on one of the tables. The projects submitted by each of the participants have been judged as outstanding by the teachers in their own school. In addition, visualize in the athletic field hundreds of visitors, who may be the parents of the participants, teachers, prominent scientists, pupils, or just individuals interested in what is taking place. From the outside looking in, one might think it was a church bazaar on a large scale. Actually, a science fair is difficult to describe. It must be seen to be appreciated.

Some science fairs involve not only exhibits but also lecture-demonstrations. This type of science fair which involves both the line-up of projects and lecture-demonstrations has been called a science congress. This is a fine distinction, for many school science fairs include the presentation of talks along with the exhibits. In general, a congress stresses the lecture-demonstration rather than the individual exhibit.

THE PURPOSES OF SCIENCE
FAIRS AND CONGRESSES

The most important purpose of the fair or congress is to stimulate and encourage interest in science on the part of young people. This may be brought about in a number of ways. The actual presentation of the project by a pupil may bring to this pupil a deep sense of satisfaction and accomplishment resulting in a strengthened science interest. The participation in the fair, with the opportunity to see the work of other pupils, meet and talk with the judges and other adult scientists may stimulate the young pupil's interest in science. Finally, if the pupil is fortunate enough to be a prize winner in the fair, his success may do much to start him on his way to successful science studies.

Values of science fairs. Science fairs provide an excellent method of sharing the science projects of individuals, small groups, or entire classes with the other students within the school, other schools, in a community, parents and other members of the community, and the schools of the entire regional area.

Science fairs can be a motivating force for individual projects as well as for class work. Many of the classroom activities come to an end with only the class members seeing the results. To some pupils it must seem like a "hollow victory" not to have the other boys and girls praise a successfully completed project. A boy who makes a motor out of wire, nails, and a battery swells with pride as his classmates praise it. Much the same feeling can result from exhibits and demonstrations at a science fair. Teachers may also be stimulated in their work as a result of the science fair.

Another value of the fair is that it utilizes the time of youth in a constructive way. With an excess of leisure time, especially in urban centers, juvenile delinquency has increased. Science fairs are not the total cure, but they can be one of the ingredients that will help effect a cure.

Fairs provide a wonderful opportunity for discovering and encouraging science talent. The participants in the state and national fairs have a chance to win prizes of part or full college scholarships or to be recognized and given aid by organizations, colleges or industries that are looking for talented people. Thus we have in fairs an excellent device for insuring that scientifically minded youths have the opportunity to continue their education and to become the scientists of tomorrow.

Science fairs and congresses provide one of the best means of sharing science projects with other pupils and with the community.

DEVELOPMENT AND PRESENT STATUS
OF FAIRS AND CONGRESSES

The growth of science fairs and congresses lies in the increasing popularity of the project method in science. In the 1920's a few of the larger communities carried on science fairs, the essential idea being for students to make exhibits showing the facts and principles as they were taught in science. About 1938, a trend developed toward having a meeting place where pupils could come together to read papers on their individual work, report their findings, and demonstrate their equipment. Thus we see the advent of a lecture-demonstration program apart from the simple exhibit of previous times.

One of the originators of the "congress" idea was a chemistry club whose enthusiasm spread to neighboring communities and whose success then spread to the general public as participation was further encouraged.

Impetus was added in 1938, when the American Institute of Science and Engineering Clubs established aids for young science students.

Today science fairs and congresses are conducted on a local, county, state, and national scale. On the local level, we may find that a single school is having a science day or a school fair. The pupils who have made projects display these in the science rooms or in the school gymnasium. Residents of the community are invited to attend the affair. There is no formal judging by science experts. The teachers do the judging and the awards are simple—a certificate, a plaque, or merely a ribbon. The winners are sent to a local fair that may be city-wide or county-wide. On a county-wide basis, the competition is keener. Experts in the various fields of science, who have had experience as judges before, evaluate the entries. They may be research scientists from industry or college professors. The awards may range from a trip through an industrial plant to a $50.00 bond.

A number of state teachers' organizations have established regional fairs or congresses. These are usually one-day affairs. The regional congress may involve a particular geographical area. In some cases as many as two hundred high schools are contacted. These schools are invited to enter competitive exhibits and demonstrations in this regional affair. The winners from these regional science fairs or congresses are invited to attend the state science congress to compete for scholarships.

Each regional science congress has its own director and planning committee, which formulates the policies of the region. Usually the sponsoring body is an affiliate of the state science teachers' association. In New York State, the Science Teachers Association sponsors the Annual State Science Congress. The association is interested in bringing together the outstanding high school scientists of the state. The participants must be in either the junior or senior year in high school. There are approximately twenty-five participants in the state congress each year. Each of the participants represents one of the regional congresses. Also on the state level, we find junior academies of science. These groups are sponsored by the respective state academy of science. Science fairs or science days are sponsored by the state organization, at which time participants from districts in the state compete for awards.

The Science Clubs of America sponsors the National Science Fair. This fair was started in May, 1950, at which time there were thirteen affiliated regional fairs.[1] In 1961, the number of regional fairs had grown to 200. A follow-up study shows that 92 percent of the finalists of the

---

[1] An affiliated fair is one which has been organized in a specific geographic area and is registered with the Science Clubs of America. These regional fairs send their outstanding entries to National Science Fair.

National Science Fair make science, engineering, or education their profession.[2]

The Science Clubs of America also conducts the Annual Talent Search in cooperation with the Westinghouse Educational Foundation. This is a scholarship competition which is held during the spring of the year in Washington, D.C. Forty high school seniors are selected to participate on the basis of a science aptitude examination, a 1,000 word report on a science project, and information gathered from transcripts and a data form. Five scholarships are awarded which range from $3,000 to $7,500, and 35 awards of $250 each are also given.[3]

ORGANIZATION OF SCIENCE FAIRS AND CONGRESSES

The following[4] may serve as detailed information on the procedures to be followed in organizing and administering a science fair or congress:

Financing. It is essential that sufficient funds be forthcoming to cover all expenditures adequately. Such expenditures have varied from $200 to $2,500. Possible financing sources include newspapers, merchants, professional organizations, schools, theatrical and musical groups, and others.

Sponsorship. Whether one or more sponsors should be secured will depend on many factors. There are many advantages to single as well as multiple sponsors. It is recommended that a local newspaper be secured as a sponsoring body. Personnel to do the work of directing will be easier to secure if there is a local or metropolitan area organization of science teachers.

Committees. The number of committees is governed by the needs of the particular plans for the fair but they will probably include the following:

Honorary or advisory committee. Many public spirited leaders will lend encouragement and serve in an advisory capacity. Suggestions include major school officials and community service clubs.

Central committee. The duties of this committee are to develop plans for staging the event. The actual production of the fair or congress will be in the hands of this group.

[2] *Science Clubs of America, Sponsors Handbook,* 1961–62 Supplement, Science Service, Washington, D.C.

[3] *Ibid.*

[4] Prepared by J. Stanley Marshall, Professor of Science Education, Florida State University, Tallahassee.

Executive committee. This small group, composed of members from each sponsoring body, approves plans developed by the central committee.

Resource committee. This group will assume responsibility for arranging for advertising and conducting area meetings of teachers and children to advertise and clarify the whole fair enterprise.

Promotion committee. Their job is to aid in general advertising through newspapers, radios, brochures, and posters, to provide application blanks, and to cooperate with the resource committee.

Placement committee. This committee procures and arranges tables, utilities and other facilities and manages the dismantling of the fair.

Clerical record committee. This committee has charge of mailing out all registration materials, of enrolling exhibitors at the location, and of keeping all records during judging of the exhibits.

Judging committee. They secure the judges, assign judges to the proper areas, see that all exhibits are judged before being dismissed, and prepare and present the awards and prizes.

Student aid committee. These individuals organize the student helpers to assist in placement of exhibits, act as ushers and do "foot work" during the fair.

Awards committee. This group secures any prizes, certificates, or other awards desired by the central committee.

Program committee. They arrange for opening and closing programs and making awards.

Supervisory committee. In cooperation with the student aid committee, the supervisory committee formulates a schedule that provides proper supervision at all hours of the public exhibition of projects.

Subcommittees. If it is necessary, these may be created to aid the committees' work load.

Factors in planning a fair or congress.   *Area.* The territory from which entries are to be accepted must be determined.

Date. The best time for holding the fair is as late in the school year as possible. Easter vacation is a recommended time.

Publicity. An announcement must be developed so that the students may be informed as to the many procedures to be followed. Community agencies will handle well-prepared releases. School art departments and school papers are able to assist, and the duplicating and printing can be done in the school departments. A central agency for publicity is recommended.

The fields of entry. The divisions for entries on elementary, junior and senior levels must be determined.

Printed material. Brochures, posters, entry blanks, registration cards, scoring cards, exhibition badges, certificates of award, and stationery are a few of the printed materials necessary.

Time element. At least three weeks to a month should be allowed for the receipt of entry blanks. One or two days should be set aside for arranging exhibits and one complete day for judging all exhibits.

Exhibit space. The layout of the space allotments in the exhibit rooms is very important. In planning exhibit space, the planning committee should consider the school cafeteria, gymnasium and the auditorium.

Pupils' part in planning science fairs.   Many teachers permit their pupils to plan and execute a science fair as a student activity. In this instance the teachers serve as consultants only, while students manage the science fair. Great emphasis is placed on securing a student leader whose qualifications include ability to work with people, intelligence, initiative, and administrative ability.

Criteria for judging.   Procedures for judging science fair projects vary. In general, certain basic criteria are used and a given number of points are assigned for each of these criteria. This kind of breakdown tends to avoid great inconsistencies among judges when they are evaluating a science project. It also gives the judge some guidance as to the relative importance of each criterion. Weaver[5] recommends the following criteria and associated point breakdown:

1. Originality   30
2. Scientific thought   30
3. Thoroughness   30
4. Workmanship   10
5. Clarity   10
6. Dramatic value   10

Other lists of criteria which are available are basically the same as the above. Some lists include such items as social implications and ingenuity of construction.

Evaluation of a given project by a number of judges can differ greatly. These inconsistencies are sometimes so great that judges have been open to severe criticisms. Care must be taken to select judges who have the qualifications to evaluate the specific types of projects represented at the fair. The scientific background of the judge is very important. He should also know children and realize what levels of performance are to be expected from them.

[5] Weaver, Elbert C., "Chemistry Projects and Science Fairs," *Chemistry*, 37:27–29, 1964.

Awards.   Awards at science fairs and science congresses have included $10 and $50 bonds, donated by a local industrial concern, science books on various topics donated by publishers, and trips to industrial plants outside the community, sponsored by industry. Generally supplementing these awards are certificates or ribbons. On a larger scale, national science fairs and state congresses award full tuition or part tuition scholarships to various universities and colleges.

Awards given to winners on the local level are usually bonds, money, ribbons, certificates, books or small pieces of science equipment. Industrial concerns have the tendency to offer to schools bonds or money as awards. Such awards should be discouraged. Industry should donate money to support the fair in general but not in the form of bonds or money to be given as awards. In the estimation of many individuals who are experts in organizing science fairs, money and bonds more or less commercialize the fair and distract from its true meaning. Industry can certainly play a part in the fair by paying the expenses of the winners of a local fair for a trip to visit the research facilities of the concern located in another city. The General Electric Company, for example, provides such an opportunity to winners of local science fairs.

On the local level, it may be best to have a science day rather than a science fair, to avoid giving out extensive awards. If the affair concerns a single school, a science day is more appropriate. In such a case, the teachers in the school do the judging and awarding. The awards should be simple—perhaps just ribbons or certificates. The reasons for this are evident. A local fair may include ninety exhibits of which five are worth considering for competition on a regional level. The remaining eighty-five may be exhibits which the teacher forced the pupils to make. If competent judges are asked to make the awards, much of their time is wasted in evaluating a number of exhibits that are the work of pupils who were not interested in entering the fair in the first place.

A number of schools faced with the problem of presenting science day awards have experimented with various procedures. One school decided to preselect a number of the projects submitted for local exhibition. All of these projects selected were then presented to the student body, parents, and the community. There were no ribbons or certificates awarded; each student who presented a project received a small pin. This signified that he had completed his project satisfactorily in terms of certain criteria that had been established by the science staff.

In regional fairs, state congresses and national congresses, awards involving money should also be eliminated. Books, pieces of science equipment and other prizes which are connected with science are more meaningful to the boy or girl who is science-minded. These awards, along with certificates and ribbons, are treasured by these boys and girls in later years, and frequently serve as incentives for additional project work and individual study.

Scholarships awarded by universities, colleges, and industrial concerns are important awards. Universities and industries should be encouraged to continue this practice. These scholarships have given a number of boys and girls the opportunity to attend college. They may not have had this opportunity for further education without the scholarship award.

In summary, awards on the local level, in a single school, should be made by teachers and not outside judges, especially if the purpose of the local fair is to select participants for regional or district fairs. Awards on this level should be simple—certificates or ribbons. On the regional or state or national level, scholarships, field trips, books, and equipment are appropriate.

AN EXAMPLE OF A FAIR ON THE LOCAL LEVEL

The following description by Belle Cooper of an actual science fair illustrates in detail the functioning of a fair on the local level.

The science fair was a definite project of the science club of North Fulton High School, a five-year community high school. With an enrollment of 1200 students, the school has approximately 460 students registered in some science class, with 240 more in eighth grade health classes. All members of the science club were expected to enter an exhibit. Exhibits from nonmembers were welcomed.

There were six definite steps in organizing the fair: (1) planning, (2) publicity, (3) working up projects, (4) actual conduct of the fair, (5) judging and awards, (6) financing.

I. **Planning.**   The dates for the fair were selected after a conference with science teachers, principal, and P.T.A. president and executive board. The opening date was chosen to coincide with a P.T.A. meeting so that parents might visit the fair before and after their evening program. This date was selected to avoid conflict with tests or examinations, and in order to allow time for students to add improvements to projects and enter them in the state science fair.

Soon after the time was selected, the executive committee of the science club and the science teachers met to plan further. Each teacher and student volunteered for definite work, and other club members were invited to help. Committees were arranged for publicity, setting up exhibits, registering and protecting exhibits, judging, and awards. Each committee knew its responsibility and carried out its duties well.

II. Publicity. The publicity committee prepared and mimeographed a folder announcing fair dates, rules and regulations, and items to be considered in judging. The reverse side of the folder served as an exhibit entry blank. Suggestions for these items came from the Georgia State Fair and Science Service. On a given date, science club members appeared in every home class immediately after roll call, made oral announcements of the fair, delivered a mimeographed folder to each student, and answered questions.

At least once a week, the president of the science club or a selected student made some ingenious announcement of the fair over the public address system. The *Scribbler*, the school newspaper, carried a prospectus of the fair, as well as a splendid article at the time of the fair. The art department made enough posters to keep the fair before the eyes of the students in both of our buildings.

III. Working up projects. With plans well laid and publicized, the students were ready for the important phase of preparing projects to exhibit.

Each teacher used his own method for stimulating interest. Students were allowed to substitute a project for some required work, such as textbook study, reference work, or even a test. Some class time was allowed for work on projects; no additional homework was assigned.

One method of arousing interest was to start with a class discussion of problems suggested by the students. Students were then sent out to read, experiment, and discuss subjects in which they were interested. This suggested lines of research, and they were on the mark ready to go. Several catalogs of suggested projects had been placed on reference in the library, and students drew ideas from these and other sources.

There followed hours of work after school for science teachers, experimenting or planning with students, lending equipment, providing supplies, helping engineer the building of complicated apparatus, or suggesting authorities to interview. Interest, once aroused, was contagious, and students furnished all needed energy and ingenuity.

IV. Actual conduct of the fair. Four days before the fair, each exhibitor sent in his entrance blank with the entrance fee of ten cents. Besides aiding in the financing of the fair, this fee served to place greater value on the production by removing it from the "free" list. On opening day, on presenting his exhibit, each student received an exhibit card properly filled out, serially numbered, and colored across the corners with red, yellow, blue, or black paint, according to the subject area of his exhibit. The card used is approximately like that used in the national science fairs.

The five subject areas were: biological sciences; physics and its applications; chemistry and its applications; other sciences; and social applications of science.

Chemistry and physics laboratories with extra tables added served as exhibit halls, since they provided outlets for water, gas, and electricity. There were approximately 90 exhibits representing 130 students, including those working in groups.

The fair was opened to visitors first at 7:30 in the evening. It remained open all the next day, and local students poured in to visit it during their study halls. It was also open to outsiders. A detail of guards and hosts was scheduled from study halls to be on duty each period of the day.

V. Awards. Judging took place as soon as exhibits had been placed, before the fair was opened to the public. Judges included two chairmen of science departments from other community high schools and a doctor from the communicable disease center of the Public Health Service.

Items considered in judging were the same as those used in national fairs:

1. Advancement of science
2. Social implications
3. Timeliness
4. Scientific thought
5. Originality
6. Dramatic value
7. Thoroughness
8. Ingenuity of construction
9. Technical skill and workmanship

Any student who wished to demonstrate a working exhibit was allowed to do so before the judges. Judges were instructed to omit prizes in any area where there was no exhibit worthy of award. Ribbons were pinned to all prizewinning exhibits. In each subject area there was a first prize of $4.30, a second prize of $2.00 and an honorable mention. There was one overall prize for the best ninth grade exhibit.

VI. Financing. Financing the fair, strangely enough, was probably the easiest part. Since mimeograph paper was furnished by the school, and enough exhibit cards were left over from the 1951 fair, expenses were few.

Assets

Donation from school $20.00
From science club treasury (dues) 13.50
From exhibit registration fees 9.00
                        Total $42.50

Expenditures

Prizes $37.50
Supplies (thumb tacks, scotch tape, prize ribbons) 5.00

Total .... $42.50[6]

STIMULATING PUPILS TO ENTER SCIENCE FAIRS

The chapter entitled "Projects in and out of school" suggests a number of devices which the teacher can use to motivate his pupils to do projects. Encouraging the students to work on projects is the first step before the actual fair. Projects are an important activity and should be encouraged as part of classroom work and science club activity as well, but this does not mean that they should all be entered in a fair. Many science teachers have the idea that all projects should be included in a fair, local or regional, regardless of the caliber. As a result they force their pupils to work on projects to be entered in the fair by making the grade on the project part of the final grade.

Teachers should not force their pupils to enter projects in fairs; this practice defeats the purposes of the fair. It also discourages the pupils who would ordinarily be interested in continuing science study. In addition, judges and other outside visitors receive a bad impression of the science taught in a particular school. It lowers standards of the fair and robs it of its real function.

There are ways, however, in which the teacher can stimulate voluntary participation:

1. In a school where science fairs are not established, pupils can be taken to schools where science fairs are being conducted.

2. Pupils who are doing projects can give a great deal of stimulation and encouragement to those who are not engaged in projects. Lecture-demonstrations during a regular class by these students may stimulate pupils to work on a project for science fairs.

3. A teacher should give recognition and praise to those who have done anything outstanding in the line of projects. Mention can be made that the project represents excellent work and that it is good enough to enter in a fair but pupils need not be forced to enter the fair, even though a project is good. The pupil should feel that it is an honor and a reward to enter the fair.

4. If the boy or girl is college material, the teacher should mention that the fair can be a good avenue to obtain a college scholarship.

[6] Cooper, Belle, "The North Fulton Science Fair," *Selected Science Teaching Ideas of 1952*, National Science Teachers Association, Washington, D.C., 1952.

5. Teachers should bring their pupils in contact with outstanding scientists. This can be done by inviting the scientist to school where he may suggest possible projects. Scientists in universities and in industry are interested in working with talented science pupils. Not only may they suggest projects to these talented people, but in some instances the scientists provide space and equipment at a university or a local industrial plant for these pupils, and even guide them in their research.

Although the individual teacher is the person responsible for encouraging students, cooperating with them, and providing guidance when needed, the responsibility for the success of a science day or a science fair rests with the entire science staff. In some schools a committee of science teachers and other cooperating members of the school coordinate their efforts for this activity. The burden of the arrangements for a successful science day is therefore assigned to different persons. When the science students of the school have "their day" it should be an affair that has been as thoroughly planned and efficiently executed as possible.

SUGGESTED ACTIVITIES

1. Visit a science fair or congress with other members of your methods class. Obtain a judge's evaluation form at the fair. (This should be arranged by your methods teacher.) Independently evaluate a preselected number of projects. Compare your evaluations with those of other members of your methods class.
2. Set up a science fair of the projects that you and the other members of your class made during the year. Provide these with labels that would interest nonscientifically trained people in the exhibits.
3. Cooperate in setting up and conducting a local or regional science fair.
4. Debate the values of science fairs or congresses in the science program.

SUGGESTED READINGS

Barry, D. G., "Science Fairs in Perspective," *Journal of Chemical Education,* 36:309–310, 1959.

Green, H. S., "New Breed of Science Exhibits," *Educational Screen and Audio Visual Guide,* 42:22–24, 27, 1963.

Harbeck, R. M., "Science Fairs and School Public Relations," *School Life,* 42:10–12, 1960.

Jones, N. R. D., "Science Fairs—Science Education in the Community," *Science in Secondary Schools Today*, Bulletin of the National Association of Secondary School Principals, 37:165–169, January, 1953.

McCarley, Mary F., "Planning for a Science Fair," *The Instructor*, 76:119, 1967.

"Science Fairs," special issue of *The High School Journal*, vol. 39, no. 5, February, 1956.

Weaver, Elbert C., "Chemistry Projects and Science Fairs," *Chemistry*, 37:27–29, 1964.

Chapter 19

Science Clubs

SCIENCE CLUBS HAVE MADE IT POSSIBLE FOR LARGE NUMBERS OF YOUNGSTERS to find expression for their scientific interests. Young people are able to delve into special areas much more deeply than they can in regular classroom activities, receiving help and encouragement that they might not find were they to work independently.

Science clubs form the backbone of school-sponsored extracurricular activities in science. In fact, about one half of the public junior high schools of the country sponsored science clubs during 1963.[1] Considerable evidence supports the belief that science activities out of class compare favorably with regular curriculum work in terms of educational outcomes. In some instances the former may actually be superior.[2]

The science club presents a less formal atmosphere in which to work than does the usual classroom. With increasing informality comes a higher degree of cooperation between pupils and teacher. Work is more apt to proceed on a basis of mutual understanding.

[1] U.S. Office of Education, *Science Teaching in the Public Junior High School*, U.S. Government Printing Office, Washington D.C., 1967.

[2] National Society for the Study of Education, "Science Education in American Schools," *Forty-sixth Yearbook*, Part I, University of Chicago, 1947.

In the science club, much more than in the classroom, learning is fitted to the abilities and interests of the individuals. There is no reciting and memorization of predigested material, and emphasis is upon independent study and individual initiative, liberally seasoned with opportunities for cooperative work.

What is gained from the science club often carries over to the classroom. Club members bring to their classes increased enthusiasm which tends to spread to nonmembers; they share their special learnings. Sometimes they present reports and exhibit their projects, all of which have teaching value to their classmates.

Within the club there are opportunities for adolescents to mature in their attitudes and their relationships to each other. They work together in program planning, by sharing responsibilities, and in developing special club projects. They have numerous contacts with adults in making arrangements for trips, inviting and entertaining speakers, and arranging for special help on their projects.

ORGANIZING A SCIENCE CLUB

Sponsorship of a club is not a responsibility to be undertaken lightly. A sponsor must be willing to devote considerable time and energy to the club, especially during the initial stages. He must expect to provide all the early planning himself; never can he expect the club to operate well if he gives it no thought from one meeting to the next.[3]

The sponsor cannot expect to be recompensed in any tangible way for what he puts into a club. His reward is the satisfaction gained from helping young people develop their interests and special abilities. Most club sponsors find this experience sufficiently gratifying.

Facilities needed.   Before a science club can be established, the administration must be willing to grant the use of certain facilities and to provide time for meetings and other activities. The club will need the use of one or more classrooms, depending upon the size of the club. It will need access to such special rooms as darkrooms and growing rooms. It will need occasional access to school shops. The club will utilize science department equipment and materials. The administration must grant permission for such use and be willing to underwrite the extra cost involved.

The administration must also provide time for club meetings, perhaps

[3] Publications useful in organizing and maintaining a science club are listed at the end of the chapter.

The science club is more than a classroom situation. It provides opportunities for pupils to engage in independent study and stimulates individual initiative.

during the school day, perhaps after school, or in the evening, whichever is most practical. In the latter instances it must make arrangements with the custodial staff to cooperate with the club sponsor. The administration must also be willing to provide time for special activities—special assembly programs, science fairs and the like.

The administration can help greatly by freeing the sponsor from other responsibilities of an extracurricular nature. It can provide a small sum to supplement the club budget. It can provide stenographic supplies for correspondence and programs. It can allot a limited amount of school time for club trips and allow the use of school buses for such trips. Above all, it can give encouragement and show interest in club activities.

Type of club. The sponsor must make an early decision as to whether the club will deal with a wide range of science interests or be confined to a limited area. Generally speaking, the club which deals with science in its broadest aspects will succeed better than an electronics club or a chemistry club or a nature study club. The general science club fits the needs and interests of the greatest number of pupils, thus broadening the potential membership and insuring better selection of sincerely interested young people. Pupils interested in such narrow fields as radio, airplane, and photography can operate within the structure of the general science club and still work on these special interests.

Some of the primary goals that a multifunctional science club can accomplish are stated by Keiser.[4]

1. *Cultivation of an Awareness of Science.*

   The club should cultivate in its members a knowledgeable awareness of the role of science in everyday living.

2. *Familiarization of Students with Scientific Research.*

   Ideally, a core program of the science club should involve participation of the more scientifically minded members in research projects and research papers. Students not interested in involving themselves in research projects may contribute by offering ideas or criticisms. Occasional visits by area scientists, research presentations by gifted students, and sponsor explanations of research techniques will be of interest to most members of the organization.

3. *Encouragement of Critical Thinking.*

   Many facets of the club programs can contribute to the development of an attitude of constructive, alert thinking on the part of the students.

4. *Involvement of Students in Scientific Activities.*

   An integral part of any learning situation is the stimulation of students in the material involved. The science club offers a valuable medium for the encouragement of student interest in hobbies involving knowledge of some branch of science. Many sponsors will encourage their club members to form or join research groups, conservation organizations, radio clubs, rock hound societies, or other science related groups.

5. *Provision of Outlets for Student Talents.*

   This is a key point on which the success of the multifunctional science club may rest. Many of the members will have talents only indirectly related to scientific endeavors. These students may wish to participate, but have little interest in scientific research. Suitable talent

[4] Keiser, E. D., "The Multifunctional Science Club," *The Science Teacher,* 31:29–32, December, 1964.

outlets should be provided for these students. Although sponsors often disagree on this, it is the contention of this writer that such talents contribute immeasurably to the success of the club and the individuals' sense of feeling a valuable part of the group.

In larger schools, specialized clubs may be set up if there seems to be enough interest. Always, however, there will be pupils who do not share in these interests and are then denied participation in a science club even though they would benefit from such participation.

Size of club. The number of members in a club has an appreciable effect upon its operation. Too few members limits the special projects the club may undertake. Too many makes an unwieldy body that is too large for close contact with the sponsor and requires formal operating procedures.

Twenty to twenty-five members are considered by many sponsors to represent the best size but clubs with as few as ten or twelve are often successful. It is better to have a small club made up of genuinely interested members than to have a large club which contains inactive members.

If a large number of pupils wish to join a science club, and their interest seems sincere, attempts should be made to find a sponsor for a second club. In this situation it may be possible to set up a special interest club.

Selection of members. In forming a new club a sponsor may find it wise to select a nucleus of pupils who have demonstrated special interests in scientific work. This is better than broadcasting an appeal for membership which is apt to bring forth a number of pupils who are attracted only by the novelty of a new club and who make later operation difficult.

This carefully selected nucleus, which is in effect an executive committee, will help set up the general organizational pattern. These founding members may determine the qualifications for initiation and standards for continuing membership—usually much higher than the sponsor himself would set. They assist in planning the general program and developing patterns of procedures to serve as guides in later years. From their ranks come the first officers, who are much more likely to be dependable than officers elected by a large, unconsolidated group.

Time for meetings. Meeting times vary in different clubs over the country. Some meet weekly, some only once a month. It would seem that monthly meetings should be supplemented by other activities to keep interest from cooling off between times.

Many clubs meet after school hours. Under some conditions this is practical and has the advantage of limiting attendance to truly interested youngsters. However, pupils who have jobs or who travel far on school buses are denied full participation.

CHECKLIST FOR THE FORMATION AND MAINTENANCE OF SCIENCE CLUBS*

I. First Meeting
  a. Temporary officers—at least a president and secretary—selected
  b. A committee is appointed to formulate a constitution

II. The Meeting of the Constitution Committee
  a. What shall be the aim and purpose of the science club?
  b. What shall be its name?
  c. Membership
    1. Who can become a member?
    2. What must a boy or girl do to become a member?
  d. Meetings
    1. When shall they be held?
    2. Where?
    3. How often?
    4. Who shall call special meetings?
  e. Money
    1. Shall we pay dues?
    2. How much?
    3. Can we levy taxes?
    4. How? How much?
    5. For what shall the money be used?
  f. Expelling members
    1. For what reason or reasons?
  g. The business program
    1. How long shall it be?
    2. What shall be the procedure?
  h. The club program
    1. What kinds of activities shall the club have?
    2. Who shall decide upon and arrange these programs?
  i. Officers
    1. What officers shall the club have?
    2. What will be their qualifications?
    3. When shall elections take place?
    4. What shall be the officers' duties?
    5. Can an officer be removed from office? How?
    6. Shall officers filling positions left vacant be appointed or elected? And how?
  j. Any other regulations you think important to put into the constitution

III. Second Meeting (and probably the third)
  a. Presentation of the constitution
  b. Discussion and revision if necessary
  c. Adoption by majority vote
  d. Election of officers
  e. Business meeting to get the club's program underway
  f. Setting up a year's program

---

* Adapted from an outline prepared by Morris Meister, in *Modern Science Teaching*, by Elwood D. Heiss, Ellsworth Obourn, and Charles Hoffman, Macmillan, New York, 1950.

Most administrators believe that an extracurricular activity of high educational value deserves a place in the regular school program. They try to provide meeting times for clubs in a special activity period. A club sponsor must then be careful lest pupils attend meetings because these seem the least unattractive of the alternatives offered them.

Planning organization meetings.   The first meeting of a new club serves to introduce prospective members to the type of activities in which the club might engage. Its purpose is to stimulate the enthusiasm of youngsters who are energetic and easily challenged by intellectual problems. This meeting needs careful planning, not to oversell the club, but to hold the attention of the young people who will benefit most by the club.

Examples of special projects may be displayed, or field trips described. Slides and films of typical activities are excellent; these may be borrowed from sponsors of other clubs and sponsors of science fairs.

The general organization of other science clubs may be described, not as patterns to be followed, but to illustrate how science clubs operate. From these illustrations future members will gain suggestions they may wish to incorporate into their own organization.

During the first several meetings of a club, the members must be concerned with details of club organization. This is a phase that does not appeal to many adolescents, particularly to those who are eager to begin experimenting, doing photography, and taking field trips. It may be wise to do much of the organizational work through committees who report their decisions to the membership at the regular meetings.

On page 571 are suggestions for the business to be taken up in the first two or three meetings. This business could well be apportioned out over many more meetings, with but ten or fifteen minutes of each meeting devoted to consideration of a limited number of topics. In the meantime, the club may take a field trip, see a special film, watch the sponsor demonstrate a Geiger counter, participate in printing pictures, and be entertained by a committee presenting a "Chemical Magic" show.

PLANNING THE CLUB PROGRAM

Club members should be responsible for the program almost from the beginning. If the initial membership is small, all members may sit in on the planning, otherwise a special program committee should be appointed. This committee should have the power to appoint temporary committees to take responsibilities for special meetings and special events.

Preliminary decisions.   The first meeting of the program committee each year must give attention to organizational problems. The list given on page

571 can serve to set the agenda for the meeting that organizes a new club. It may be used in succeeding years to call attention to matters needing reconsideration. From the discussion of the items on the agenda the committee may set general or special meetings to deal with the problems raised.

Setting up a program for the year.   A science club needs a forward look; it cannot succeed with day-to-day planning. On the other hand, adolescents cannot work out details for months in advance; their interests tend to be more immediate. It is better to prepare a skeleton which will be filled out as the year proceeds.

One procedure that has worked well with adolescent planning groups is to encourage them to prepare a calendar on which is listed one special project or meeting for each month. If advance arrangements must be made for any of these special events, responsibilities are delegated immediately. Otherwise details are worked out a month in advance by the planning committee at its regular meetings.

The sponsor may make suggestions for these special events but decisions should be left up to the members. The sponsor is an advisor, not an officer in the club.

Among the special events that may be listed are special films, guest speakers, and visitations. Committees may be appointed to select the films and order them, to contact possible speakers, and to make arrangements for visitations. This should be done well in advance.

The club may undertake service projects, perhaps for the science department, such as helping with an inventory, or for the school, such as planting bulbs. A club may take on occasionally such a project as preparing Christmas decorations for the foyer of the school; one club decorated a tree with flasks of colored water and other science materials to produce a novel but effective display.

The club may set up special science exhibits; it may produce an assembly program; it may sponsor a school science fair. It may add regular services such as the maintenance of a science bulletin board in the corridor of the science department, the preparation of a science column for the school newspaper, or the presentation of a regular series of science radio programs.

A club may wish to raise money for some special purpose. It may ask for the refreshment concession at athletic events or sell things by house-to-house canvass. One club, in keeping with its science theme, dipped pine cones in various salts and sold them to people to burn in fireplaces for special displays of color. The social needs of adolescents should not be neglected. The science club may well have at least one party a year.

Below are the special events in which two science clubs engaged during a school year:

A chemistry club. The activities of one chemistry club included the following places visited in one year:

1. A rubber mill
2. A brewery
3. A modern hospital
4. The medical laboratories at the Mayo Clinic
5. A patent medicine and food products manufacturing plant
6. A sewage disposal plant
7. A modern farm implement factory
8. A plant which produces heating units and air conditioning systems
9. A soft drink factory
10. Two ice cream factories and a milk plant
11. Local gas factory
12. A modern foundry

All visitations were preceded with at least one discussion and preparatory meeting and followed by a discussion of the principles and applications of chemistry that were observed.

The club presented two programs—one before the pupil body and one before the Mothers' Club or P.T.A. A quarter hour of the assembly program was presented over a local radio station.[5]

A general science club. A general science club carried out the following activities in the course of a year:

1. Attended annual Dahlia Show.
   a. Group then discussed how flowers shows were conducted.
2. Attended a "Bird Lecture."
3. Visited Franklin Institute and Fels Planetarium.
4. Had a picnic which included a "Nature Hunt," races, games and a "Treasure Hunt."
5. A geologist visited the group and told them about volcanoes and earthquakes.
6. A herpetologist visited and brought some snakes which he talked about.
7. Had a movie party where the students brought their own movies and operated the projectors.
8. Took a trip to the Maryland Academy of Science.
9. Visited a zoo and had a contest on animals.

[5] Hoff, Arthur G., *Secondary-School Science Teaching*, Blakiston, Toronto, 1949.

10. Visited an airport and took a ride in an airplane.
11. Took a trip to Hopkins Botanical Gardens.
12. Took a sight-seeing trip to Washington, D.C.
13. Held a "Hobby Show."
14. Prepared own flower show.
15. Had a lecture on birds and bird calls.
16. Held a "Science Experiment" afternoon.
17. Arranged displays for the school bulletin boards.
18. Had a "Curiosity Meeting."[6]

Planning general meetings.   The basic program for the year determines in advance the nature of a number of regular meetings. One meeting, for instance, is usually needed for the initiation of new members. Visitations take up other days. A science show, if one is sponsored by the club, occupies another day. All such meetings will be in the hands of special committees.

Portions of other meetings will also be determined in advance by the master schedule. Films and guest speakers take up the major part of the meetings in which they are employed; again special committees would have made arrangements in advance for these features. Portions of a number of meetings will be used in preparations for other events—assembly programs, initiations, and the like. These meetings will be guided generally by the respective committees.

The business portion of general meetings is in the hands of the president of the club. The sponsor may help him prepare the agenda for these meetings, giving advice as to which matters may go to committees for action and which should go before the membership body for discussion and vote. The sponsor should try to keep the agenda from becoming cluttered with trivia that result in idle chatter. He should try to hold the business to one or two matters per meeting, recommending several short business sessions rather than a few long ones.

The sponsor is usually responsible for the first meeting of the year. This meeting should proceed with vigor to set a pattern for later meetings. Films or slides of work done the year before interest pupils, who enjoy seeing themselves on the screen, and stimulate them to try to better previous achievements.

Some of the same considerations that govern good lesson planning should govern the plans for club meetings. No one activity should be carried on for too long a time. A ten-minute business meeting and a twenty-

[6] Moody, Rosalie, "A General Science Club," *Baltimore Bulletin of Education*, March–May, 1951.

five minute film make a good pairing. After a fifteen-minute talk by a guest speaker there may be a ten-minute question period; the remainder of the time may be used by one or two demonstrations by club members to show the guest what the club does. A committee may present general plans for a club project for ten minutes, a free discussion period may follow as long as needed, after which pupils volunteer for sub-committees and break up to begin planning their activities in the project.

Variety in programing is always desirable. One week a field trip may take up the meeting time. The next week might be devoted to work on special projects. The next week some bit of entertainment might enliven part of the meeting. One week might be very serious; the next week the meeting might include some humor.

MAJOR CLUB PROJECTS

Young people find much satisfaction in activities that bring everyone together for constructive work. Such projects do much to weld membership together into a loyal body that takes pride in the organization.

Establishing a science museum.   Establishing a science museum is one example of a project which the science club might undertake. The science museum does not have to be a darkroom cluttered with mounted animals and obsolete equipment that is not currently in use. Nor does it have to be an elaborate exhibit of expensive apparatus. A school science museum might well consist only of simple displays placed on a table or in a glass-front cabinet. The corridor often serves as a museum, but a separate room, if available, makes a much more desirable arrangement.

One of the chief advantages of a small area for display purposes is the need to change the display at regular intervals. These frequent changes can be made by members of the science club. An exhibit that has been on display for a long period of time loses its value.

Displays attract attention and arouse questions. This in turn creates an interest which can result in improved classroom work. If the display has been collected or set up by science club members, it can be used directly in the science class. Club members can set up their exhibits in the classroom and then make up questions to be answered by the rest of the class. Displays made by club members can also serve to initiate questions from other students.

Projects and collections that become a permanent part of the museum can be used as illustrative materials for future classes. Not only does it reduce the cost of science instruction, but it also provides materials that are unobtainable at supply houses.

Science assembly programs.   One of the functions of school assemblies is to give the pupils an opportunity to plan and present programs for the rest of the student body. The science club is often in the best position to assume the responsibility for such programs. Science classes and clubs have the material for a host of novel as well as educational programs.

The program material can be taken from the various branches of science or it can revolve around a certain topic. A few topics that can provide material for assembly programs are:

1. Electrical household appliances
2. Air pressure
3. Uses of nuclear energy
4. Combustion
5. Science hobbies
6. Electronics
7. Dry ice experiments
8. Conservation
9. Meteorological equipment and weather observations
10. Life in a drop of water
11. Community health
12. Consumer education
13. Science and magic
14. Men of science
15. Experiments with sound, light, etc.
16. Science vocations[7]

Maintaining a bulletin board.   Science club members can be responsible for maintaining the bulletin board in a classroom. The bulletin board should be attractive and have appropriate captions. The display might enhance the regular classroom work.

Writing for the school newspaper.   Each member may be responsible for writing up a science news article that would be submitted to the school newspaper. The article should be scientifically accurate, interesting, and well written.

Presenting demonstrations or exhibits to the elementary school.   Whenever a science club has an interesting exhibit or demonstration within the realm of understanding of elementary school pupils, the members should be encouraged to present it to the lower grades. This would help to stimulate science interest in the elementary grades.

[7] Marshall, J. S., "A Program for Increasing Student Interest in Science," *School Science and Mathematics*, 54:656–662, 1954.

Making demonstration materials for the science classroom.   Science club members can make materials, such as homemade lantern slides or simple demonstrations, apparatus, microscopic preparations, preserved specimens, picture files, charts, and diagrams. These may be kept and enlarged upon from year to year for the use of the entire school.

Maintaining an inventory of science materials and equipment.   A helpful service for a club to perform is to check science supplies and provide each teacher in the building with a current inventory of equipment and materials in the building. This would not only be a time saver for teachers but would assure maximum utilization of such materials.

Repairing and maintaining science equipment.   Many pieces of equipment can be repaired without too much difficulty if the science teacher has the time. Often the equipment can be repaired by science club members who have mechanical aptitude. Along with this, science club members can help to keep science materials orderly so that they can be found when needed.

Setting up demonstrations for the science teacher.   Science club members can assume the role of laboratory assistants. They can be very helpful to teachers in setting up apparatus in preparation for a demonstration or for a laboratory period. They can also dismantle and store the apparatus after use.

Finding resource people in the community.   Many club members come in contact with outstanding scientists in industry and in universities. These individuals may be invited to speak at assemblies and regular club programs. Science teachers should evaluate these individuals before they are approached by science club members.

EXAMPLES OF SCIENCE CLUBS

A junior high science club.[8]   The Grant Science Club is the product of over fifteen years of experience. Through the years it has gradually evolved to its present form, which has proven most successful for the junior high school level. The club is limited to twenty-five members and the only basic requirement for entrance is a keen interest in science.

[8] Prepared by Charles G. Gardner of the Grant Junior High School, Syracuse, N.Y., who has sponsored the club since its origin.

Selection of new members. Prospective candidates assemble after school for a brief meeting at which they learn the story of the Grant Science Club and its activities. They are told that if they wish to join they must submit within a week's time a sample science project of their own creation—a scrap book, a nature collection, a report of work with a chemistry set, or the like.

On the assigned day, the projects are displayed after school. Each is identified only by a number. Each club member examines them and rates them from 1 to 10. The ratings are averaged and the projects are listed by rank. An arbitrary dividing line is established; this fluctuates depending upon the numbers which can be taken in to fill the membership of the club. Applicants receive notification slips and return to pick up their projects.

Successful candidates are invited to an interview by the club membership committee, which tries to find out their reasons for wishing to enter the club, their special science interests, and something of their respective personalities. The club members take this very seriously and make a careful evaluation. If a candidate does poorly on the interview he is personally interviewed by the sponsor. The sponsor talks with the home room teacher of each candidate to determine whether there is any reason why this person should not join the science club.

Personal letters signed by the club sponsor and the club president announce the decision of the club to the successful candidates and invite them to the next meeting at which they are initiated. Harmless initiation tricks are played on the blindfolded initiates, under the careful supervision of the sponsor, to the great delight of the members.

The new members are then officially welcomed into the club and given their Third Class requirement card and a mimeographed guide sheet. Later they are given a special briefing session after school.

The point system. The club operates on a point system. Members are awarded points for various types of activities. Some of these activities are listed below, but members may do many other things with the approval of the sponsor. A careful record of points earned by each member is kept in a notebook by the sponsor.

1. Perform an experiment and write it up with a drawing (5 points)
2. Give book report on scientific book or booklet (1 to 10 points)
3. Report on club trips (1 to 10 points)
4. Operate the balance scale (5 points)
5. Operate the microscope (10 points)
6. Know the 25 common elements and their symbols (10 points)
7. Construct laboratory equipment (up to 25 points)

8. Carry out a research project (up to 25 points each)
9. Do committee work (points awarded according to judgment of sponsor)
10. Participate in science show and congress activities (points determined by the sponsor)

In order to eliminate efficiently the joiners with no real interest in science, there is a requirement that new members must earn 25 points by the end of the first month and 75 points by the end of the second month, in order to remain in the club. Thus the sponsor is assured of an active group.

Through various projects and through participation in club activities, members can progress in rank. The ranks are based on both point requirements and special requirements.

A research approach club.[9] Mr. Leonard M. Krause, a general biology teacher, organized a club whose activities center around "research." The club is unique in that a team of professional scientists work with students who have an interest in science and in doing research. The following is a description of the objectives and activities of the club:

> A relatively new concept in the teaching of science to interested and able science students has been employed for the past five years at the Plymouth-Whitemarsh secondary school system, Plymouth Meeting, Pennsylvania. The project consists of a team of professional research scientists working intimately with small groups of carefully chosen students, who, through their efforts in the classroom, have demonstrated ability to cope with science as a subject and to approach problem solving scientifically. The resulting group of students and scientists, together with their sponsor, has been called the Science Research Club, an affiliate of N.S.T.A.'s Future Scientists of America.
>
> Objectives of the club are many. Major objectives include: satisfying science interests; developing an understanding of the meaning and significance of research; providing an opportunity to study areas not usually presented in class; and learning to approach problems in an organized way, such as recording data accurately and presenting this information in a properly written and/or oral form. These and other goals arose from a strong desire on the part of the sponsor and the research scientists to bring to able students a new dimension in science experiences. Research and its implications for twentieth century living were to be the cornerstones on which the structure of the club was to be built. Pure science and its natural concomitants would be set as the ideal goal.

[9] Krause, L. M., "The Research Approach Club," *The Science Teacher*, 32:36–37, March, 1965.

The club meets formally one evening a month at the school. The business of the club is conducted by a set of officers assisted by committees which are structured as needed. . . .

An evening consists of an hour long lecture, demonstration, or film followed by conference groups.

Conference groups which follow are composed of one research scientist and eight to ten students, each of whom is interested in working in a science area which lies within the professional field of his research advisor. Guidance is given to students at this time regarding the ways in which each might approach his problems.

The Alchemist, the club magazine, is deserving of such designation both because of size and content. Articles are written by members and include summaries of research projects, book reviews, current scientific developments, and art work reflecting a high degree of science insight.

Students in grades nine to twelve may gain entrance to the club. Once accepted, they maintain *active* membership by pursuing one of three types of projects.

The first is the *"original" research* activity involving laboratory procedures. . . .

The second type of project is the *construction* project which involves investigating the possibilities of improving an existing piece of apparatus. . . .

The third involves library search to gather information on a topic of interest to the student. A paper is compiled. Varying degrees of difficulty allow students of less experience to learn from those with more experience. . . .

Active members, who, in addition to their project, also have good attendance at meetings and are in good standing with the school, are eligible to attend all-day field trips to industry, to regional and state conferences such as the Junior Science and Humanities Symposium, and to participate in the monthly conference groups of the club. Nonmembers may only attend monthly lectures.

An after-school science club is in operation in the Evansville, Indiana high schools. Mr. Herschel G. Dassel,[10] the science consultant for the Evansville-Vanderburgh School corporation, describes the organization and the aims of the club as follows:

Four years of dreaming and planning by the Science Consultant and by members of the Evansville Science Teachers Association (E.S.T.A.) paid off last year when twelve After School Science Programs went into operation in three Evansville, Indiana, high schools and in seven elementary schools. Trained and able science teachers who formerly had sought extra pay for extra duty in other school programs, such as athletics, stayed in science rooms and laboratories to guide the after-school programs. For the first time in our school system, science teachers were being paid for an extra-curricular activity in their chosen field of specialized training. Knowledge

[10] Dassel, Herschel G. "After School Science: Johnny Will Stay After School", *The Science Teacher*, 32:42–43, November, 1965.

and skills in science, acquired through advanced training and study (including summer science institutes) were afforded another avenue of expression. Science rooms and laboratories which had been upgraded with the help of N.D.E.A. funds were kept open on a regular schedule with help and guidance to the science students who want to "go the extra mile in science."

The After-School Science Programs, in both the elementary and high school areas, have these common objectives:

1. To further develop laboratory skills through continued use of laboratory materials and equipment.
2. To develop and deepen interests in the field of science.
3. To provide an opportunity to pursue scientific hobbies.
4. To provide activities which are not adapted to the regular laboratory program because of time and/or equipment limitations.
5. To promote scientific research and project activities.

SUGGESTED ACTIVITIES

1. Visit a science club and observe its operation. Report your observations to your methods class for discussion.
2. Obtain a year's program of a science club. Note the variety and balance of activities. Classify the activities under headings such as the following: social and entertainment activities, field trip activities, service projects, and seminars. (Use additional headings as needed.) Propose other activities which might strengthen this program.
3. Plan the organization meeting that you might use in establishing a science club.
4. List the promotional devices you can use to stimulate membership in a science club.

SUGGESTED READINGS

Chubbs, E., "For the Gifted, A Science Club," *School Activities*, February, 1963.

Dassell, Herschel G. "After School Science: Johnny Will Stay After School." *The Science Teacher*, Vol. 32, No. 8, Nov. 1965.

Drapkin, Herbert, "Enriching Science for Youngsters," *Science Teaching Ideas II*, National Science Teachers Association, Washington, D. C., 1955.

Heiss, E. D., E. S. Obourn, and E. W. Hoffman, *Modern Science Teaching*, Macmillan, New York, 1950.

How to Organize a Science Club, American Institute of the City of New York, 60 E. 42 St., New York, 1950.

Keiser, E. D. "The Multifunctional Science Club," *The Science Teacher*, Vol. 31, No. 8, Dec. 1964.

Krause, L. M. "The Research Approach Club," *The Science Teacher* Vol. 32, No. 3, Mar. 1965.

Lawrence, F. A., "Science Club," *School Activities*, March, 1963.

Science Clubs of America, *Science Club's Sponsor's Handbook*, Science Service, 1719 N St. N.W., Washington, D. C.

Chapter **20**

Facilities for Science Teaching

THE EVOLUTION OF SCIENCE TEACHING IN THE LAST FEW DECADES HAS
necessitated a parallel evolution in the physical settings—rooms and facilities—necessary for good instruction. As science teaching has become less
concerned with presenting factual information as an end in itself, and
more with using science to bring about important changes in ways of
thinking and acting, the traditional room has become less functional.

From the room designer's viewpoint, one of the most significant
trends has been the rapid increase in the number and variety of teaching
methods. It has not been so very long since lecture-demonstration and
stereotyped laboratory exercises were virtually the sole methods of instruction. Contrast this with the wide variety of activities in the modern classroom: project work, group discussion, pupil demonstration, film projection,
the study of displays, to mention but a few. The modern room may be
used for a film at the beginning of a period and a group discussion at the
end; or for a test which is immediately followed by small group project
work; or for several types of activities going on at the same time. Such a
room must not only have the facilities for these activities but it must be
converted easily and quickly from one purpose to another. Space and
facilities must be designed with one important criterion in mind—flexibility.

THE DESIGN OF NEW FACILITIES

Room design is a complex task; in all probability no one person is capable of doing the whole job properly. Planning is best accomplished by a committee of all people concerned. The committee should include school administrators, board of education members, representatives of the architect and contractor, and the science teachers who will use the rooms. In addition, the committee may well include other members of the community, not only for the services they might bring but also to increase community participation in school affairs.

The technical and advisory services of equipment and furniture manufacturers can be called upon. The W. M. Welch Company, for example, loans scale models of room furnishings for use in room layout and design. Other manufacturers, such as the Hamilton and Sheldon companies, maintain a planning service and can bring to the planning committee years of practical experience in designing and fitting modern science classrooms. (See Appendix for addresses of supply houses.)

Information on classroom and laboratory facilities can be found in the current professional literature. Many of the national study groups have produced a variety of plans for science facilities for the modern school. Various bulletins and pamphlets which outline the recommended laboratory and classroom facilities needed for teaching the new curriculum patterns are now available to science teachers. (See Appendix for addresses of BSCS, PSSC, CBA, etc.)[1]

Site selection.   Science is the subject most concerned with the outside environment. Whenever possible, the site of a new school should be chosen to provide suitable contacts with the world of science. A forested area, a pond, a stream, a hillside, become outdoor laboratories. A park near the school is a valuable asset. Sometimes through cooperation with a city planning commission, a school may be built near the site of a future park and certain natural features may be saved for educational purposes.

Location of science rooms.   While school planning is still in the preliminary stages, some attention should be given to the location of the science rooms within the school. Biology and general science rooms, for example, should have southern or southeastern exposures to provide adequate sunlight for plants. To encourage field work, all science rooms should have either direct exit to the out-of-doors or should be close to main exits.

[1] A statement of the facilities may be found in, Richardson, John S. (ed.), *Science Facilities for Our Schools K-12.* National Science Teachers Association, Washington, D.C., 1963.

Physical science rooms may be located near industrial arts classrooms so as to take better advantage of the facilities there.

Number of science rooms.   The number of rooms required depends upon the type of program, the number of pupils, and, of course, the money available. The Richardson formula[2] may be used as a starting point.

$$\text{Number of rooms} = \frac{\text{Student-periods}}{\text{Average class size} \times \text{periods per week}}$$

The number of *student-periods* is determined by multiplying the number of students by the number of periods that the classes meet in one week. The *periods per week* is the total number of periods per week that each room will be usable.

If the number required is one or less, an all-science classroom should be considered. If the sum is two or more, various combinations are possible.

Types of science rooms.   Having decided upon the number of rooms required, the next step is determining the type of room. Science rooms may be classified as: (1) the all-science room in which all sciences are taught, (2) the semi-specialized room designed for instruction in a single area of science, such as the biological or physical science area, and (3) the specialized rooms for specific subjects such as chemistry and biology.

Room size.   Modern science teaching, with its wide variety of activities and its need for "work centers" for independent activities, demands larger rooms than were formerly given to the lecture-demonstration type of program. As a general rule 35 to 40 square feet of floor space is needed for each pupil in the largest class that will use the room; this may be considered as adequate but not generous. In addition, 10 to 15 square feet per pupil, or about 20 percent of the total is useful as accessory space for larger projects and special activities.

General characteristics.   The requirements for science classrooms are basically the same as those of conventional classrooms, with the addition of certain features peculiar to the needs of science instruction.

1. *Floors* receive a rugged and varied treatment. Chemicals and cold water damage many types of flooring; vinyl plastic makes a durable floor surface for science rooms.

[2] Richardson, John S. (ed.), *School Facilities for Science Instruction*, National Science Teachers Association, Washington, D.C., 1961.

2. *Ceiling* should be fireproof and paintable; acoustic materials are desirable.

3. *Walls* should also be fireproof and paintable; light colors brighten the room and make it more attractive; a white area on one wall makes a reasonable substitute for a projection screen.

4. *Lighting* is very important; illumination should be 35 to 40 foot candles for general work and higher in special work areas.

5. *Heating* should be sufficient to keep the room at a temperature of 68°F. with a relative humidity of 50 percent; special provisions are needed for keeping living things, as will be discussed later.

6. *Ventilation* should be adequate to carry away all odors produced by experiments and by organisms; in the chemistry room a fume hood is essential.

General work space.   The ideal classroom has an area in which the pupils meet for such activities as recitations and demonstrations, and other areas to which they are directed for experiments and project work. All this work space is flexible; seats may be reorganized for general discussions and for small group planning, and large areas of floor space may be cleared for special activities.

Within this ideal classroom there is also adequate desk, table, and workbench surface area for all activities. This flat work surface area is necessarily varied to meet the demands of the modern program and ranges from small surfaces on which to write notes to large tables on which major projects may be assembled.

The largest space investment in the science classroom is likely to be the student laboratory tables, and these units are also the most difficult to locate properly. These tables are inflexible by nature; their position cannot be varied, their surfaces, being broken up by utility services and sinks, provide little clear space, and their surfaces cannot be used for construction or other "rough" work.

Schools large enough to maintain several sections of each course often solve the problem by equipping separate laboratories and classrooms, scheduling one of the former to give laboratory facilities for three or four of the latter. Though efficient in terms of use, this is at the cost of good teaching. In the combined classroom laboratory a smooth transition from one activity to another is possible; problems arising from class discussion may be solved immediately by impromptu experiments, and experiments may be followed up immediately by films or reading.

Other schools have tried combining student laboratory and lecture positions, arranging the laboratory tables in rows facing the instructor. This practice provides such an inflexible classroom that good teaching becomes very difficult.

For a compromise that permits more efficient use of space than the ideal classroom, utility service may be provided along the walls with movable tables beneath. These tables may be used in this position when facilities are needed but they may also be pulled away from the wall and grouped in various ways.

It should also be remembered that for some courses such as general science and general biology, there is not much demand for tables equipped for all facilities. A few such tables may be put in these classrooms and different groups of pupils may carry out different activities at one time. Thus more classroom space becomes free for other uses.

Special work areas in the classroom.   The teacher needs a small section for office space in which will be his desk, a filing cabinet, and one or two extra chairs for student conferences. Special project work space is essential, preferably somewhat isolated from the room by storage walls in which equipment and supplies can be kept. One of these work areas should be provided with a workbench and tools. To these work areas individuals or small groups may be sent to engage in independent projects.

The national curriculum study groups (CBA, PSSC) have emphasized the desirability of individualized instruction. Architecturally, this would ideally be achieved by providing the science facilities with a project area that included as many student "cubicles" for project and study purposes as are financially possible. The student cubicles are separate work areas for individual or group work that connect to the supply and laboratory facilities of the science complex.

Reading space is another "must." While it is not suggested that the science room assume the function of the school library, it is desirable at certain times for students to do reading and reference work in the classroom. The reading space should be equipped with a library table, chairs and bookcases, and a bulletin board.

The responsibility for the effective organization and administration of the science library can be delegated to cooperative students or assumed by members of a science club. Student interest in keeping abreast of the latest developments in science can be effectively maintained when they have a part in contributing current articles from periodicals, newspapers, and other current literature; and they are the responsible group for the administration of the science library.

Supplementary rooms.   If a science classroom is to be in continual use by several different teachers, office space is needed outside the classroom for work on registers, planning, counseling and the like. One office may service two or three teachers but not more.

A darkroom has long been considered an essential *supplemental* room. This is usually equipped for photography but may well be used for certain types of experiments and for pupil project work.

A growing room for plants and animals enables pupils to carry on projects in biological science work in a way not possible in the regular classroom. Some schools in the past have provided small greenhouses for their biology teachers but have ignored the general science teachers who need these facilities as much or even more.

Experience has shown that special rooms set aside for individual project work are of high value in helping talented pupils. In such rooms these pupils carry out projects both in school and after school, unhampered by the demands placed on the regular classroom. These rooms may be small but should be fully equipped with utilities and with ample locker space in which the pupils may keep materials.

Storage-preparation rooms are useful for any teacher and become essential when two or more teachers in separate classrooms must share the same materials. The ideal location for a storage-preparation room is between two classrooms, with an opening into each. It should also be accessible from the main corridor.

Furniture for science rooms. Each standard classroom should be equipped with a demonstration desk located in front of the space in which pupils sit. It should be of standing height, thirty-six inches from the floor. It should have full utility service: electricity, gas, hot and cold running water. The sink should be acid proof. Sometimes a compressed air supply is useful enough to justify the cost. There should be storage space for standard demonstration equipment. In crowded classrooms if there is no room for the teacher's desk, one or two locked drawers will be needed for records.

A cart of the same height as the demonstration table is useful to transport materials to and from storage rooms, to set up demonstrations on, and even to use as a table on which to perform demonstrations. It should be made of stainless steel and have four large, rubber-tired wheels with locks. The top may have a surface matching that of the demonstration desk.

All science classrooms should be fully equipped with facilities necessary for pupils to carry out standard laboratory experiments. A number of types of laboratory desks are available; there are perimeter tables designed to fit along a wall, peninsula tables which project from the wall, and island tables which stand in the middle of the room. The latter are the easiest to supervise but reduce the amount of free floor space; they may be preferable for classrooms in which much standard laboratory work is carried out, such

A growing room for plants and animals enables pupils to carry on projects in the biological sciences in a way not possible in the regular classroom.

as in chemistry classrooms. The perimeter tables use the least amount of floor space but reduce other uses of the wall area; they may be preferred when only a few are needed, as in general science classrooms.

Student laboratory tables should be equipped with thick, acid-resistant tops—stone or specially treated wood. The sink should be of stone and the waste pipes of lead. It is useful to have two sets of electrical outlets—standard outlets for 110 volts d.c. and special outlets connected to a central control panel so that different voltages and frequencies may be supplied. There should be apparatus-support rods and sockets with each table. The type of storage space in each will vary with the courses being serviced.

A standard letter file is needed for clippings and pamphlets. A 3 by 5 inch card file having three or four drawers is needed for keeping inventories and for other records; this may be kept in a separate office if there is one.

A cabinet for charts and maps is required. These expensive items deserve good care. Neither they nor the appearance of the room is improved when they are rolled up and placed in a corner or on top of a wall cabinet.

A small, general purpose table, which may be of the folding type, will have many applications in the science room. It may be used for exhibits, displays, student conferences, project work and the like.

Special facilities.   In addition to running water, gas, and electricity, which have been mentioned before and will be taken up again, science rooms need other special equipment and facilities. One wall should hold a large bulletin board for topical displays. A small bulletin board for current events clippings is also useful.

The front wall should have a well-lighted chalkboard. One section may be ruled off in squares to simplify the construction of graphs.

Several wall racks for charts and maps should be distributed about the room. One should be at the front of the demonstration area for the teacher's use during discussions; the others are for the pupils to use during individualized study.

The ideal projection screen is a built-in feature of the science classroom. Located near the front of the demonstration area where the pupils can view it without changing their seats, it becomes a regularly used tool. A stand for a projector, either fixed in place or movable, with an adjacent electrical outlet, is also needed. Dark shades are desirable. A darkened room is necessary when using an opaque projector. Many experiments and demonstrations call for a darkened room.

No science room should be considered equipped until it has a complete first aid kit and fire extinguishers. The first aid kit should contain neutralizing solutions, burn ointment, sodium bicarbonate, and surgical dressings. One fire extinguisher may be of the soda-acid type for general fires; the others should be for chemical and electrical fires.

Window shelves are very useful in general science and biology classrooms for plants and various vivaria. All too often this valuable space is wasted with radiators and vents. Even in physics and chemistry classrooms window shelves make excellent display areas and should not be neglected.

Equipment storage.   Ordinary shelved storage cabinets are suitable for the storage of the majority of items of equipment. The problems in equipment storage are caused by the items of "difficult" size or shape: small items, long and tall ones. Special provision must be made for the storage of tall items such as Boyle's law apparatus, vertical resonance tubes and the like. Tall, narrow cabinets with cupboard type doors are available which will fill this need.

Drawer storage is suitable for long items such as Kundt's tubes and Liebig condensers, as well as small items. The storage cabinets purchased should have adequate drawer space. Partitions in drawers are seldom provided, although they are necessary for small-item storage, but they may be readily made from cardboard sheets; cardboard cartons used for shipping laboratory glassware such as beakers or flasks may be cut down and inserted in the drawers.

A rigorously logical system of equipment storage is difficult, owing to the varying sizes of the equipment. Where possible, items of a similar nature should be stored together; drawer storage may be alphabetical or topical. Labeling of drawers and cabinets with punched tape helps both students and teachers to locate equipment.

The most frequently used equipment should be stored in the most accessible places, and some equipment storage space that can be locked should be provided for fragile, expensive or dangerous equipment.

An equipment inventory is a vital part of the storage system. This inventory should be kept on 3 by 5 cards, stating the name of the item, quantity, condition, date purchased and the manufacturer. The location in the storage system should also be included.

Chemical storage.   Chemicals are used frequently in all science courses, and their storage is extremely important. Chemicals should be readily accessible; however, because of the potential, and in some cases extreme danger of chemical poisoning, some locked chemical storage space should be provided. Certain valuable chemicals also should be stored in a locked space.

Shelves in chemical storage cabinets should be surfaced with some resistant material. Owing to corrosion danger, particularly from hydrochloric acid fumes, metal equipment should be kept away from chemicals, in a separate cabinet or preferably in a different room. As a practical pointer, hydrochloric acid and ammonium hydroxide should be stored separately; the fumes react to form ammonium chloride which will collect on every available surface in the storage space.

Chemicals may be arranged in the cabinet alphabetically by element symbols, usually (in the case of compounds) the metallic element. In the case of compounds of a given metallic element they can be arranged in order of the nonmetallic ion. It is sometimes convenient, and space-saving as well, to separate bottles of liquids from jars of dry chemicals, and to separate larger containers from smaller ones.

An inventory should be kept of chemicals on 3 by 5 file cards, stating the name of the chemical, the quantity at time of inventory, and the date purchased. As the chemical is used, a notation may be made on the card and the item entered in the order book.

Storage for student purposes.   Student laboratory stations should be provided with storage space for frequently used equipment. Drawers should be provided for glassware, burners, etc., while a locker is necessary for ringstands, clean-up equipment, and the like.

There should be some provision made for the storage of student project work. Lack of such storage space is frequently a deterrent to effective project work, since projects are lost or broken by careless handling.

Storage furniture.   Many types of storage furniture are available commercially. As in the case of the other types of classroom furniture discussed, the science-room planner should familiarize himself with these types before making any final decision.

Thought should be given to obtaining storage furniture which uses otherwise "dead" space in the classroom. The space between the top of the ordinary storage cabinets and the room's ceiling, for example, may be filled with cupboard type cabinets which may be used to store infrequently used items. Storage units may be built into partitioning walls between classrooms; these units have the advantage of accessibility from either side. Storage space may also be provided behind sliding tackboards and chalkboards. By the selection of proper furniture, almost any unused volume of space in the classroom may be adapted to storage purposes.

THE DESIGN OF SPECIFIC SCIENCE ROOMS

The problems of planning science rooms and facilities have already been dealt with in a general way. These problems are very similar from room to room, but each room presents one or more problems of its own. It will be the purpose of this section to discuss in detail the problems peculiar to each type of science room.

The general science room.   All too often, general science rooms are a sort of "poor relation" when science facilities are being planned. If any thought is given to the special needs of the general science program, beyond seeing that the room is equipped with a demonstration table and one or two storage cabinets it is generally assumed that general science is a kind of miniature version of biology, and consequently the room in which it is taught may be a scaled-down, less elaborate, replica of the biology room.

This, of course, is not the case. Even fairly small schools will require a room devoted solely to general science to provide an adequate program, since general science is taken by more pupils than any of the other sciences. These rooms in their way are as specific in purpose as the senior science rooms; they have a distinct "personality" of their own. Facilities for the general science room should be as carefully planned as are the facilities for a physics room.

While it draws material from all fields of science, general science is

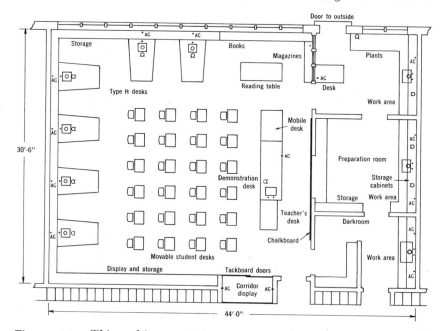

Figure 28.   *This multipurpose science room is relatively wide. The student desks are movable. The deep corridor space is made possible by the storage cabinets built into the wall and the lockers in the corridor. The preparation room has a wall table and a section of shelves from which materials can be obtained by sliding aside a chalkboard panel. The plant room serves also as a work and conference room for the teacher* (courtesy U.S. Office of Education).

not, or should not be, a "watered down" version of one or all of them; it is a science program in its own right with its own aims and values. Certain activity methods and instructional techniques are most suitable for general science, and efficient room design must take these into account.

General science activities are apt to include group discussion, committee work, project work, and all-class experimentation as well as demonstrations and use of audiovisual aids. Formal laboratory work of the traditional type is not necessary and may not be advisable. The laboratory work called for is simpler in nature and does not require the same amount or kind of furniture and equipment.

In smaller rooms that provide little work space around the room, flat-topped individual tables are best. These may be rearranged in various ways to suit the nature of the activities being carried out. Several may be pushed together to provide large work surfaces. Tablet-arm chairs and slanted-top desks are not at all satisfactory. In a large room that provides additional work space, tablet-arm chairs may be used in the demonstration area.

In addition to these tables there should be one fully equipped laboratory unit of the physics or chemistry type, and another of the biology type. These may be along the wall or at the rear of the room. One or more additional sinks may be located at the rear or side of the room. There should be standard electrical outlets near all work surfaces.

Making and displaying projects is an important part of the general science program. Adequate tackboard space should be provided in readily visible portions of the room. Wall display cases are needed for collections and other exhibits. A display table was mentioned in a previous section. A combination sand table and display table has many uses.

Living materials form an important part of the general science course. The general science room should have an aquarium, one or more terrariums, animal cages and the like. A special project room may have facilities for growing plants also. These facilities are discussed more fully in the section on the biology room.

The storage problem in general science can be particularly vexing because the needs of the course are not anticipated. Since the course covers such a variety of topics, an equal variety of materials and equipment is needed. All of this must be stored carefully. Some of it must be locked up to keep it away from inquisitive and thoughtless pupils. In addition to cases in the classroom, a preparation-storage room with many additional cases is a necessity.

The biology classroom.   Fundamental in the design of a biology classroom is provision for ready access to the out-of-doors and for bringing things found outdoors back inside for study. There should be adequate window space for plants and certain types of terrariums. There should be a few cages for animals brought in for temporary study.

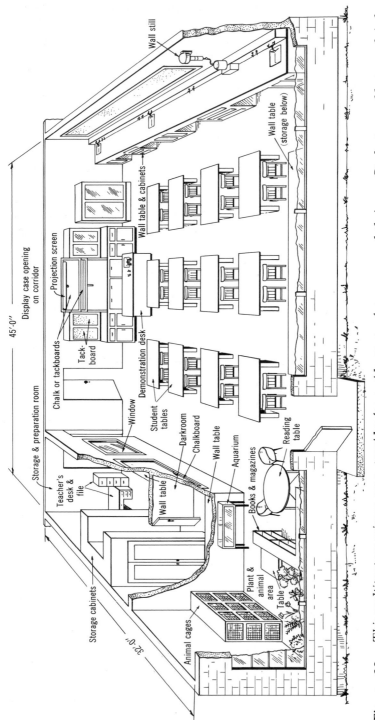

Figure 29. This multipurpose science room provides for a wide range of resources and their use. Students are able to work independently without disturbing classes that are in session. A glass partition can be created to separate the plant and animal area entirely from the class area. An ion exchange apparatus can be used instead of the wall still (courtesy The Ohio State University and National Science Teachers Assoc.)

Wall still

Wall table (storage below)

Wall table & cabinets

Display case opening on corridor

45'-0"

Projection screen

Chalk or tackboards

Tack-board

Demonstration desk

Window

Storage & preparation room

Teacher's desk & file

Wall table

Student tables

Darkroom

Chalkboard

Wall table

Aquarium

Books & magazines

Reading table

Plant & animal area

Table

Animal cages

Storage cabinets

32'-0"

A shelf should be provided for aquariums, with electrical outlets for aerators and heaters. Overhead lighting with fluorescent lamps adds to the attractiveness of the aquariums; this is to be preferred to sunlight, which promotes the growth of algae.

Special equipment that is to be desired for the study of living things includes an incubator, a sterilizer, and a refrigerator. The first two may be moved from room to room as needed; the last named may be kept in a preparation room that is available to all.

Tables make the best work space for pupils; these may seat two or four pupils each. Tops should be acid resistant. There should be storage space for pupils' books and for frequently used materials. Electrical outlets will be needed if the pupils use microscopes a good deal. If microscopes are used only occasionally, pupils may work at side benches or move their tables to wall outlets. Without electric service the tables may be movable to add to the flexibility of the room.

Gas, running water, and electricity should be provided at one or two work centers, perhaps at standard laboratory tables. In addition, one or two large sinks are needed for washing equipment; these should have strainers that are easily removed, drainboards, and pegboards for drying glassware.

Display cabinets and tackboards are needed for exhibits. Models and specimens may be kept on permanent exhibit except when being used. Microscopes are best kept in locked cabinets. A few other cabinets will take care of chemicals, glassware and miscellaneous supplies.

For teachers interested in BSCS biology, a complete report on the basic needs for classroom and laboratory presentation has been prepared[3] The report presents a comprehensive and excellent treatment on the many considerations for providing an efficient work area in biology. Teachers should be aware of the fact that an effective BSCS course does not require an elaborate laboratory facility. Many excellent courses are taught in so-called out-dated laboratories.

The growing room.   The growing room is a valuable adjunct for biology and general science classrooms. In it may be kept living things that will be used for study in the regular classrooms. In it talented pupils may carry on special projects.

One growing room may service several classrooms. It should be near them but have separate entrances from the main corridor. A door to the outside is useful for bringing in or taking out bulk materials such as soil.

[3] Abraham, Norman, and Alfred Novak, "Observations on Laboratory Facilities for BSCS High School Biology," BSCS Newsletter No. 9, Biological Sciences Curriculum Study, Boulder, Colorado, 1961. More recent lists may be found in BSCS Newsletters, Nos. 18, 21, 25, and 29.

The growing room needs thermostatic temperature control and reasonable control of the humidity. There should be proper ventilation to take away odors. One end of the growing room should be fitted with a germinating bed, racks for garden flats, and storage bins for soil and fertilizer. Some large Wardian cases are needed for plants with high humidity requirements.

If the growing room is located on the south or east side of the school building and is partially enclosed by glass, artificial lighting may not be necessary. However, in lieu of the above, satisfactory lighting may be provided by use of daylight fluorescent bulbs.

The shaded portion of the room should be equipped with shelves for aquariums, terrariums, and animal cages. Some dark closets are useful for keeping living things that avoid or do poorly in the light. In addition to the above, the growing room should have work space for potting plants and for cleaning animal cages. Running water and a sink should be available at this work center.

The physical science room.   The physical science room may be planned specifically for chemistry or for physics, or it may be planned for joint use and for the physical science course now coming into favor. The requirements for all these courses are somewhat similar, differing only in emphasis; a physics room, for instance, may need more elaborate electrical facilities than does the chemistry room.

Laboratory tables should have chemical resistant tops, apparatus-support rods and sockets, gas, electricity, hot and cold water, and stone sinks with lead drains and traps. In a room specifically designed for chemistry, the advantages of stone tops should be weighed against the added cost; they may be more economical in the long run.

There should be easily accessible master valves for all gas and water services and a master switch for the electricity. A masterbreaker switch is needed to guard against overloads and it is well for each student desk to be similarly protected. It is helpful to have each student laboratory table equipped with a special outlet that is connected with an electrical control center. These outlets may then be serviced with electricity of different voltages and frequencies as needed.

Distilled water is used in large quantities. A wall still, permanently installed with its own water and waste connections, may be used, or an ion-exchange apparatus may be used. The latter is more expensive, but it is more convenient and produces purer water with one treatment.

Facilities for earth science.   Earth science is becoming more popular as a science offering in the secondary school. A few schools which are offering the course have a planetarium and a weather center. Usually, these resources are provided for when planning new facilities. A planetarium can be installed in existing areas but the space requirement is rather excessive. Field weather stations can be set up on the school grounds and protected by a large screened cage. Project work and laboratory work in earth science require large working areas. Separate storage areas for materials collected on field trips should be considered. Areas for storage cabinets for rock samples, physics apparatus, chemicals, and charts, as well as field materials, should also be included when setting up an earth science laboratory.

Facilities for advanced placement courses.   The traditional type of laboratory facility found in most schools for teaching biology, chemistry, and physics is not satisfactory for teaching advanced placement courses. The experiments that are performed in these programs are more complex than those in traditional courses; they emphasize discovery in science and are open-ended in design. Provision should be made so that each student in this course has a large working area where experiments and project work can be performed and not disturbed. Many experiments in these courses require more time than is provided by two laboratory periods. It is not unusual to find pupils working on one experiment for several weeks. Ample storage space for equipment and chemicals, and a well-equipped darkroom in the vicinity of the working area should be provided.

The science darkroom.   Photography is a valuable activity at all levels of science instruction, both as a subject for study in itself and as a valuable tool in instruction. For these reasons a darkroom makes a valuable addition to the science suite. The darkroom need not be large, but it should be accessible. If circumstances dictate that it be located in a specific room with no other access, the logical place for it is the physics room or the general physical science room.

Furniture for the darkroom should consist, at a minimum, of two benches, one equipped for wet work and one for dry. The dry table may be simply a folding classroom table, but the wet bench should be one of the type designed especially for photographic work, equipped with hot and cold running water, a flat space for developing trays and a large, stainless steel sink. Storage space for chemicals and at least one light-tight storage space for film and paper may be provided under the dry bench or in a wall storage cabinet.

A good quality of photographic work may be done with a surprisingly small amount of equipment. A start may be made with a quite simple set-up, and more complicated and expensive items of equipment added as funds become available.

Individual study carrels.   As the use of individualized instruction materials for various subdisciplines of biology and other sciences increases, a facility which has become more valuable in the science program is the individual study carrel. These carrels may be located in a school learning laboratory, a small room adjacent to the science laboratory, or in the laboratory itself.

Some carrels are nonprogramed, and merely provide areas for the students to work on individual projects or handle laboratory materials. An example of this type of carrel is the individual study center used in Littleton High School, Littleton, Colorado, to provide a work area where all of the material needed by a biology student is at hand, and, at the same time, to eliminate duplication of all of the material for every student. The study center is a circular structure consisting of six individual work stations surrounding four central shelves—one fixed and the other three revolving like a lazy susan. The shelves and individual carrels together contain all necessary equipment: reference books, specimens, charts, microscopes, strip film projector, and screen.[4]

Other carrels contain audio-tape units for use in individual programed instructions. At Ridgewood High School in Norridge, Illinois, each subject area has a learning laboratory, stocked with tape decks, appropriate books and reference materials and audiovisual equipment. The labs are manned by teachers from the subject areas, and most have study carrels and areas for group conferences. Students come to the laboratories to work individually or in groups on teacher-prepared assignments or to work on independent study projects.[5]

IMPROVING EXISTING SITUATIONS

Very few teachers find themselves teaching in situations where they have designed all the facilities themselves. Most teachers will be teaching in rooms that they will find unsatisfactory to some degree. Good teaching can take place in spite of unsuitable conditions. Teachers should work constantly toward a betterment of these conditions.

The first step is an analysis of existing shortcomings as compared with ideal conditions. The second step is planning what may be done. The third step is setting a schedule of the order in which improvements may best be made. The fourth step is "action"—selling the plans to the administration and beginning such changes as lie within the teacher's powers.

[4] Nimnicht, Glendon P., and Arthur R. Partridge. *Designs for Small High Schools.* Educational Planning Service, Colorado State College, Greeley, Colorado, 1962.

[5] Cawelti, Gordon, "Innovative Practices in High Schools: Who Does What—and Why—and How," *Nation's Schools*, 79:56–88, 1967.

Remodeling a classroom.   Sometimes the school administration is willing to provide proper facilities in a room where none exists. Though this may be an expensive procedure, proper planning and wise purchasing will help hold costs down.

The orientation of the room—that is, the location of the demonstration table and the student tables, will depend upon the utilities. Sometimes the utilities may be tapped at the end walls, sometimes at the corridor walls, rarely at the outside wall. Sometimes they may be tapped through the floor to rooms or basements below.

For science courses that do not require extensive use use of the utilities, one or two sinks may be located along walls containing water pipes, and gas and electricity may be supplied to wall tables only. Should utilities at pupil laboratory tables be essential, wall and peninsula type tables against the walls containing the piping represent the cheapest installation.

Electricity and gas can be supplied to wall tables with comparative ease. Pipes and electrical conduits can follow along the walls and be tapped where needed.

If no gas line exists in the school, bottled gas may be installed with small expense. It is even possible to use the small portable bottles for demonstration purposes, although these would be expensive for laboratory use by all pupils.

A fume hood, if needed, may be set up by a window with a blower to carry off the fumes. Perhaps a ventilating duct, if one exists in the walls of the room, can be tapped. The Kewaunee Manufacturing Company produces a portable fume hood which can be very useful in such a situation.

Aside from installation of the utilities, the remaining requirements for a good classroom should cost little more than for a new classroom. Some of the furniture might have to be built to special dimensions, but usually this is not necessary.

Minor room modifications.   Many improvements can be made in a science room by rather minor changes. Imagination is needed. In one case, for example, an amazing increase in room flexibility was obtained through the simple process of exchanging the tablet arm chairs with which the room was equipped for the one-pupil tables in an English room. The increased flat space in a room previously deficient in working space permitted a great increase in the number of activities possible.

Room rearrangement can often lead to valuable results. For example, one of the first things a science teacher should do if the furniture in his room is fixed in position is to remove the screws and make the furniture movable, if its construction permits. Particularly in older classrooms, which were often larger than considered necessary by today's standards, enough space can be gained by rearranging to provide needed accessory space. For example, if six feet along one end of the room can be gained in this fashion, it may be partitioned off to provide useful, even if cramped, accessory space.

Much is to be gained from improving the appearance of a room; there is no need for the science room to be a dark, dreary place. The paint-roller has simplified painting to the extent that anyone with a roller and a free weekend can effect a complete change in the appearance of his room.

Many other room modifications will occur to the perceptive teacher. A science room is never so good that it needs no changes—or so bad that it must be abandoned as hopeless.

Constructing laboratory facilities. Construction skills of the teacher and the pupils may be put to good use as a source of needed furniture and equipment, particularly when funds are limited. In many cases, articles may be produced which are as good as commercially available counterparts at a fraction of the cost. Even where funds are not severely limited, construction by teachers and pupils provides a method for getting the most use of money and for getting articles specially designed for a particular situation. Such construction has learning value as well, although it is not necessary to justify all such construction on the basis of learning value. Building a special-purpose table for the physics room may not contribute a great amount of direct experience in physics, but the table itself is a substantial achievement for the student.

Where funds are very limited, school construction sometimes becomes the only method of obtaining many needed articles. In this case, the wisest use of funds is investing in tools; with tools and a little ability to hunt up needed materials, limitations are imposed only by the skill and ingenuity of teachers and pupils. Without tools, very little is possible.

If the decision is made to begin an extensive school construction program, a few points should be considered. The first of these is to *insist on careful work*. The teacher who begins his construction program with the feeling that anything he can produce is just a poor substitute for "Store-bought" materials is doomed from the start. The purpose of such a program will not be accomplished unless the items constructed are, within their limitations, as good as those available commercially. This does not mean they must be as elaborate or as finished in appearance; it does mean that they must be of equal utility. If the equipment constructed by pupils or teacher will not serve its intended purpose adequately, it is better to save what money is available until the needed articles can be purchased.

If the requisite care is taken, however, there is no reason why, over a period of years, the school construction program cannot provide the school with well-designed, useful equipment, in much greater quantity than would be possible if the same amount of money had been used for direct purchase.

A second rule is to *keep it simple*. Cleated joints in woodworking, for example, are not as good looking as dado or mortise-and-tenon joints; but they are as serviceable and more easily produced. Resist the temptation toward ornamentation, or toward tackling too elaborate projects, particularly in the beginning phases of the program. The reasons for this rule should be fairly evident; simplicity reduces costs and construction time. Pupils, as well as the teacher, are likely to tire of elaborate projects, with the result that the project remains in a corner somewhere unfinished, or else is finished off in a slap-dash fashion.

A third rule is to *design for solidity and utility*. Science room furniture and apparatus is likely to lead a rugged life. This should be kept in mind when plans are being made. If wooden construction is employed, be sure that the stock selected is of adequate size; better to err on the large size than on the small.

ORDERING AND MAINTAINING MATERIALS AND EQUIPMENT

The science teacher, in any situation, is responsible for ordering and maintaining science equipment. This means that the teacher has to know what is on hand as well as the condition of the materials and equipment. From this point, the teacher can determine what has to be purchased— either to replace what has been used up or to replace equipment which has been damaged.

Determining the inventory.   A teacher, in a new teaching situation, is confronted with the chore of determining the inventory of equipment, materials and supplies. If the new teacher is fortunate enough to have had a predecessor who was conscientious enough to keep a current record of materials the inventory creates no problem. Most teachers who arrive in new situations are not this fortunate.

A preliminary inventory accomplishes two purposes; not only does it inform the teacher of what is on hand, but it gives him an opportunity to become familiar with apparatus that he has not come in contact with before.

Mr. James accepted a teaching position at Cherry Valley Central School. He was supposed to report to his new teaching position on September 4th. During the month of July, Mr. James decided to spend two or three days at the school to take an inventory of supplies and equipment. The preceding science teacher kept no records so Mr. James' job was overwhelming. He first made an inventory of the chemical supplies. For each chemical he made out a 3 by 5 index card.

On the card, he placed the name of the chemical and the amount on hand and also the date of the inventory. He also took an inventory of the apparatus and equipment and made out a 3 by 5 card on each piece. On each card he placed the name of the equipment, the purpose, its condition, the name of the equipment company that sold it, the date of the inventory and the place where it is stored so it could be readily located.

This was a monumental job, but when he finished he knew exactly what was available to teach his courses.

A card system to keep an up-to-date record of what is available may serve a number of purposes:

1. It is a ready reference file for supplies that have to be purchased.
2. Equipment can be located easily, since each card indicates the place of storage.
3. The annual inventory can be taken without difficulty.

The following is a suggested form for an inventory card. The back of the card can be used for remarks.

INVENTORY CARD

Item of equipment:
Ordered from: Catalogue no.:   Cost:
Place of storage:

Date of inventory	Number on hand	Condition	Date ordered	Number ordered	Cost

Points to consider in ordering equipment.   Knowing what is on hand is only a stepping-off point to determine what has to be purchased. Before ordering, the following have to be considered:

1. The budget for materials and equipment.
2. The number of pupils that will be in a particular course.
3. The amount of individual laboratory work which will be done by the pupils.
4. The number of demonstrations which will be performed by the teacher.
5. The equipment and supplies required by a textbook, workbook, laboratory manual, or the teacher's own course of study.

Budget.   In most schools, funds are limited for the purchase of materials and equipment. For this reason, the teacher will have to weigh the importance of various items before ordering them. That is, items which are essential should be first on the list of purchases. Items which are not as important can be purchased at a later date or when money is made available. In considering the purchase of certain items, the teacher should remember the cost involved in conducting individual laboratory work.

If a particular item costs $100 and ten items are needed for individual laboratory work, and the total overall budget is $1200, the teacher may want to think twice before ordering ten pieces. He may have to order one item rather than ten so that he can at least use it in a teacher demonstration. If, on the other hand, an item costs $10 and ten items are needed for pupils to do individualized laboratory work, the teacher should consider the advantages of laboratory work over the teacher demonstration, since the cost involved here is not too great.

The use of expensive equipment in individual laboratory work should not be overlooked because of cost. The teacher should consider the purchase of a microscope each year, for example, until there are enough on hand to permit each pupil to handle and use a microscope. The amount of laboratory work to be performed by the pupils, the number of teacher demonstrations, and the number of pupil experiments can be determined only from a course of study, a textbook, workbook, or laboratory manual that are to be used.

If the teacher decides to use a particular laboratory manual, the equipment and materials needed to conduct a laboratory experiment is clearly indicated in the manual. One procedure which has been followed by some teachers is as follows:

The teacher determines which experiments in the manual or textbook are to be conducted by the pupils. For each experiment, a list of the items needed per pupil is made. After this list is made, he can determine the size of his class by getting from the guidance director an estimate of the registration for this course. If the teacher is going to teach in a new situation, the principal has a reasonably good idea of what the registration will be for a particular course. By simple multiplication (number of pupils in the class times the items per experiment) the teacher can determine how much is to be ordered.

Where to order equipment.   In ordering equipment, the teacher should purchase from equipment companies that are reliable and close to the school. The closer the company is to the school, the cheaper the cost for transportation—for the school has to pay the cost of mailing and express charges. An equipment company in California may sell an item for ten cents less than one in New Jersey, but the cost for shipping such an item to a school in New York would probably result in a total cost of $.50 more than its cost in New Jersey.

It is also wise to order, in so far as possible, from a single reliable equipment company. Many schools have found that better service is obtained if the company regards the school as a regular customer. Being a regular customer may result in purchasing equipment at a discount.

Some school systems have purchasing departments which designate the company from which an item should be purchased. In such a case, the teacher should very clearly indicate in detail a description of the item so that the quality of the item is exactly as the teacher desires.

When to order materials and equipment.   The science teacher should have a long range plan for ordering materials and equipment. Live material, for example, should be ordered at a specified time during the year to assure its arrival when it is needed. Ordering live material during the summer months for use in the month of January is impractical unless it can be maintained during the summer months. The teacher should record the ordering date on the 3 by 5 inventory cards, so that he will be reminded to order such material enough in advance.

Expendable material has to be ordered yearly or each semester. During the summer months or before school closes, the teacher should indicate the needs to the principal or purchasing agent so that the material is available for fall. At this time, equipment which has been broken and has to be replaced should be ordered, together with new pieces of equipment that have never been part of the science inventory.

Maintaining science equipment.   In order to make certain that equipment is in good repair, the science teacher should check it after use. Many pieces of equipment get out of adjustment after use by pupils and should be inspected when the pupils are finished using them.

A number of simple repairs can be done in the classroom if the science department is equipped with tools. It is not important to have elaborate tools, but certain basic ones are essential.

Shop tools for science teaching.   Even if an extensive construction program of the sort outlined earlier in this chapter is not undertaken, the science department should have its own set of tools. It is not satisfactory to depend on the shop department except for occasional use of power tools; there is no assurance that the tools will be available when needed; and sending students to the shop every time tools are needed imposes an extra burden on the shop teacher.

Science projects cover such a wide area that a fairly comprehensive selection of tools is needed. Such tools may be divided into three categories: in the first are tools that represent the basic minimum; in the second group are tools that permit a wider variety of project work; in the third group are tools needed for elaborate projects. All tools should be of good quality. Cheap tools break easily, dull quickly, and are a handicap to good workmanship.

Good tools represent a large investment. They should be stored carefully in locked cabinets which show at a glance whether or not items are missing. Tools left around have a way of disappearing; sometimes they are stolen, more often just borrowed and not returned. Not only is the financial loss serious but the loss of the tools handicaps the instructional program.

A few power tools are very useful. An electric hand drill has innumerable uses, especially if suitable accessories are provided. A power grinder permits tools to be serviced immediately without taking them to the industrial arts shops. Power saws, drill presses and lathes are usually available in school shops.

SUGGESTED ACTIVITIES

1. Suppose that the principal of your school has suggested that you use a standard classroom to provide for the science activities of a group of especially talented pupils. Plan the facilities you would like in this room for this purpose.
2. Assume that you are assigned a drab, dreary room for your science program. Develop plans for making this room an attractive place for young people to work.
3. Arrange a field trip to several new secondary schools in your area. Study the science facilities provided in each. Discuss among your classmates how the facilities in each school could be improved.

SUGGESTED READINGS

Barthelemy, Richard E., *et al.*, *Innovations in Equipment and Techniques for the Biology Teaching Laboratory*. Biological Science Curriculum Study, D. C. Heath and Company, Boston, 1964.

Grobman, Arnold B., *et al.*, *BSCS Biology—Implementation in the Schools*. Biological Sciences Curriculum Study Bulletin No. 3, BSCS, Boulder, Colo., 1964.

"How to Design Science Laboratories that Work," *School Management*, March, 1966, p. 109–12.

Murray, Darrel L., "A Design for an 'Open' Laboratory," *The American Biology Teacher*, 28:788–796, 1966.

"New Laboratory Design," *The Times Educational Supplement*, No. 2661, Friday, May 20, 1966.

Nimnicht, Glendon P., and Arthur R. Partridge, *Designs for Small High Schools*, Educational Planning Service, Colorado State College, Greeley, Colo., 1962.

Richardson, John S. (ed.), *School Facilities for Science Instruction*, 2nd edition, National Science Teachers Association, Washington, D. C., 1961.

―――, *Science Facilities for Our Schools K-12*, National Science Teachers Association, Washington, D. C., 1963.

Vyvyan-Robinson, A. F., "The Ideal Laboratory," *The Times Educational Supplement*, No. 2609, Friday, May 21, 1965.

Chapter 21

Continuing To Grow

Professionally

Upon graduation from college, the teacher should not consider him-self a finished product. He must keep informed about the new develop-ments in science and new methods and materials which will make his teaching more effective. Participation in in-service workshops, attending professional meetings, enrolling in graduate programs, and reading profes-sional journals are some of the activities which help a teacher to keep abreast of new developments. It is the responsibility of the individual teacher to find the best means to permit him to grow professionally.

PROFESSIONAL ACTIVITIES WITHIN THE SCHOOL

Programs can be offered in a school setting which will contribute to the professional growth and development of experienced and inexperienced teachers as well as converted science teachers (teachers who have had no formal training in science but are now teaching science.) These programs may involve workshops, credit, or noncredit courses offered by a university professor, courses and workshops conducted by the science teachers themselves, and clubs for science teachers. Programs are set up because the science teachers of a system have indicated a need. Effective programs must have a purpose, they must be needed, and they must be carefully planned. The planning may involve the science teachers alone or science teachers working with administrators.

Courses.   In-service courses can be offered to acquaint teachers with new approaches and methods such as BSCS biology and PSSC physics. They are sometimes set up to bring teachers up to date on recent developments in particular science areas and to provide a science background for converted science teachers. These courses can be offered weekly, biweekly, or monthly, after school hours. They can run for one month or even for the full academic year, depending on what must be accomplished. The person who conducts an in-service course should be a science teacher who has acquired an excellent background by having attended a National Science Foundation summer session or academic-year institute and has had a great deal of teaching experience in the subject.

Credit or noncredit university courses may be taught on the school premises by a college professor. Through their extension branches, a number of universities offer school systems courses in the subject matter of science or in science methods. Arrangements concerning college credit must be made when the course is in the planning stage.

Workshops are similar to courses in that they can be conducted by qualified science teachers or university personnel. However, workshops involve more active participation on the part of the individuals who are enrolled. Generally a workshop is centered around a curriculum improvement program or some other central theme. In these courses teachers may work together in small groups on separate phases of a curriculum problem. The group results are gathered and collated into a final report which may be used as a basis for improvement of the science program.

Science teacher clubs.   In large cities it is not unusual for science teachers to organize themselves into clubs according to certain science disciplines. Meetings are held to improve the curriculum or to solve problems of mutual concern. Such organizations can provide an invaluable means of sharing thoughts on methods, activities, and resources, as well as the scope and sequence of courses. Meeting together can benefit all teachers, especially the inexperienced. Science teacher clubs can also be established in rural districts by involving all the science teachers within a certain radius. The number of science teachers may be small in rural areas, but the contact with other teachers can be a valuable source of information to improve science instruction.

Industry days. Many communities have cooperated with industry by setting up visiting days in various industrial plants. All classes are canceled for one day in the entire district, and teachers visit one or two plants within the area. Teachers learn how science and technology are related. They can see and learn how certain scientific principles have been used in an industrial process. This experience in turn enriches the science curriculum in the classroom.

GRADUATE STUDY

Many school systems require their teachers to enter graduate work. In some instances these systems pay the tuition for any course which benefits the teacher in his teaching situation. In other school systems, a certain number of graduate credits place a teacher in another step on the salary scale. In most states, a master's degree or its equivalent is required for permanent certification in a subject matter area. These are all incentives for the teacher to take work which will improve him professionally. The beginning or the experienced teacher will see the need for more study to enrich his knowledge of science and to improve his teaching methods. The incentives mentioned should not be needed to encourage the competent teacher to better himself.

Graduate programs leading to a master's degree for science teachers vary considerably from university to university. A number of universities have instituted general science programs which lead to a master of science degree in general science. In these programs, the teacher has an opportunity to extend his knowledge into areas such as astronomy, genetics, and geology, which were not included in his undergraduate work. One such program is given below:

Entomology	3 credits
Water biology	3 credits
Ornithology	3 credits
Field botany and ecology	3 credits
Heredity and evolution	3 credits
Descriptive astronomy	3 credits
Microbiology and man	3 credits
Physical geology	3 credits
Radiation biology	3 credits
General science comprehensive paper	3 credits
	30 credits

One of the best ways for teachers to learn about new curriculum approaches is to attend workshops which are set up especially for this purpose. This group of teachers is attending an IPS workshop.

The same type of program may give the teacher a chance to concentrate in one or two science areas in order to add to his competence in these fields.

Some universities and colleges have programs for science teachers leading to a master's of science in science education. In general these programs require nine semester hours of courses in education, three semester hours in science education, and eighteen semester hours in science content courses. These are well-balanced programs offered through schools of education.

A well-balanced graduate program should include field courses as well as courses in bacteriology and microbiology. General science teachers need field work to be able to answer the variety of questions which arise in their classes. Biology teachers who are involved in teaching BSCS versions need courses in biochemistry, statistics, and genetics as well as courses in field biology. In addition, microbiology courses are important since the advances in this area during the past decade have been so significant.

At institutions where general science programs are offered, a library or laboratory research paper is required to obtain the master's degree. The paper is supervised by a professor in the field in which the paper is to be written. The following are titles of some papers that have been written by teachers with master's degrees in general science:

1. An Investigation of Several Properties of Liquid Ammonia Solutions.
2. A Study of the Effects of Some Antithyrotoxic Agents on the Absorption of I^{-131} Labeled Thyroxine from the Intestinal Wall of the Rat.
3. A Survey of Metal Carbonyls.
4. Factors Influencing the Life-span of Seeds.
5. Comparative Thermo-regulation in Selected Genera and Species of the Family Heteromyidae.

GOVERNMENT SPONSORED PROGRAMS

In order to encourage science teachers to improve their professional competence, a number of programs offering subsidized graduate study have been established by the National Science Foundation at various universities and colleges. The best known of these are the academic year and summer institutes. Each participating university plans its own institute, but all are designed to increase the competence of teachers by improving and updating their subject matter knowledge. Emphasis is placed upon basic science principles and the impact of current scientific developments upon the secondary school curriculum.

During the summer of 1966, approximately 21,000 experienced high school science and mathematics teachers participated in 457 summer institutes. During the year 1966–67, about 1,500 persons attended academic year institutes at some sixty-five participating colleges and universities. It seems probable that in the future the number of opportunities to participate in the academic year institutes will decline somewhat, while the summer session opportunities will increase commensurately.

Nevertheless, the academic year program will continue to provide opportunities to a significant number of experienced teachers. Such institutes generally last one school year, although some include one summer session as well. Sometimes teachers can meet the requirements for a master's degree in science or mathematics or in the teaching of these subjects through an academic year institute or sequential summer institute.

Participants in this program must meet the following requirements. They must be a teacher or supervisor of science or mathematics in grades seven to twelve, with three years of experience. Science and mathematics teachers in junior colleges are eligible for a few of the institutes. Ordinarily they must not have been participants either in a previous academic year institute or in three or more National Science Foundation summer institutes.

The amounts of the grants are as follows. The maximum stipend is $3,000 plus $450 for each dependent up to four, plus waiver of all tuition and fees. In addition substantial travel and book allowances are provided.

Applications are made directly to the participating institutions, whose own admission requirements will have to be met by participants.

The summer institutes are of two types. One type called the unitary institute is a single summer experience for a particular group of teachers. Usually the institute is offered once, but it may be repeated for several summers. However, each individual teacher is eligible to participate in this institute only one time. He may of course attend a unitary institute at another institution if he qualifies.

The other type is called the sequential institute and is designed to offer a coordinated sequence of work so that participants may return each summer to the same institution to work toward a specific goal, such as a master's degree. The length of the sequence varies, but generally four summers are needed to complete the requirements.

In general, any teacher or supervisor of secondary science or mathematics is eligible to participate in both types of summer institutes. However, there are some complex eligibility requirements for persons who have previously participated in other summer or academic year institutes, so one should check carefully to be certain of eligibility.

The amounts of the grants vary with the institution, but in general they are as follows. The grant pays for all tuition, enrollment, and health fees as well as a travel allowance and a basic stipend. The latter varies but in no case exceeds $75 per week plus $15 per week for each dependent up to four. If a participant lives at home while attending the institute, he will probably receive less than these amounts.

The National Science Foundation also supports in-service institutes in science and mathematics. This program permits a teacher to enroll in selected universities for one course each semester of the academic year. The courses usually meet on Saturdays or in the evening. Tuition is provided as well as a travel allowance. Other programs which may be of interest to science teachers include the National Science Foundation Fellowship Program for science and mathematics teachers and a Research Participation Program for science teachers. Brochures describing these programs as well as others can be obtained by writing to the program director of the particular program, National Science Foundation, Washington, D.C. 20550. It is best to inquire early in the academic year, as deadlines for applications are usually during the early spring.

Brochures listing the universities and colleges which offer academic year institutes, summer institutes, and in-service institutes can be obtained by writing to the

> Operations Unit AD/E
> National Science Foundation
> Washington, D.C. 20550

Under Title V-C of the Higher Education Act of 1965, the federal government awards hundreds of fellowships each year to experienced teachers who are pursuing a career in elementary or secondary education. The government awards the money directly to the participating universities who then select the recipients. The stipend is for $4,000 per year plus $600 for each dependent. For more information and names of participating universities write:

> Division of Educational Personnel Training
> Bureau of Elementary and Secondary Education
> United States Office of Education
> Washington, D.C. 20202

PROFESSIONAL ORGANIZATIONS

Professional organizations of science teachers in this country are numerous. Of national importance and scope are the National Science Teachers Association and the National Association of Biology Teachers.

Large science teaching associations include regional groups, the best known of which is the Central Association of Science and Mathematics Teachers. There are state associations, county or state regional groups, and even associations of science teachers in some large cities.

Members of these associations receive the various magazines, bulletins, and other publications of the association. They are also given the opportunity to participate in the activities and meetings of the group. The meetings of these associations are beneficial to the science teachers. The meetings may include lectures, reading of papers, round table discussions, forums, clinics, and demonstrations of teaching materials and techniques. At many of the meetings, the manufacturers and publishers of teaching equipment and materials will have displays of their products for the inspection of the members.

The meetings bring together science teachers from different schools and often from different school systems. The discussions and "shop talk" among the teachers is a valuable source of ideas and philosophies of science teaching for all concerned.

If a teacher becomes an affiliate of an organization, he should not merely be a joiner. He should participate fully in the activities of any organizations to which he belongs. This is especially true if he belongs to state or local organizations. In most cases, state organizations are divided on a regional basis with each region having its own officers and members.

WRITING FOR PROFESSIONAL GROWTH

Writing is an important means of continuing professional growth of the science teacher. The teacher can learn to improve his ability to communicate with other teachers and to express his ideas by writing. The teacher's own classroom, with its activities and projects, can furnish the subject matter. By writing about his own classroom, the teacher can analyze his teaching methods and try to improve them. The science teacher can describe effective techniques and teaching aids which he has developed; these are of interest to science teachers in general. If the science teacher has made experimental studies or has developed new ideas to improve teaching methods or revised the science curriculum, these should be reported, for they may be useful to other teachers and administrators.

The teacher's writing can be interesting to many different types of individuals. The pupils and parents will be interested in matters pertaining to student activities in the local classrooms. The school and local newspapers publish articles on these topics. Professional bulletins and journals at the local, state, and national level provide the means for the teacher to publish articles of interest and concern to the profession as a whole.

Articles written by science teachers can be submitted to the editors of various professional journals in the field of science teaching. The names of the editors can be found in each copy of these journals. Each journal has a specified format to follow in preparing an article for publication. For example, most journals require that the article be submitted on 8 by 10 paper, typewritten and double spaced. In some cases, the editors state that photographs should not be dispersed throughout the article but all placed on one page, properly numbered, with the captions on the bottom of the page. They may also require that the photographs occupy a certain area on the page so that the page can be more easily reproduced. The journals may also limit the number of photographs. Usually additional photographs can be incorporated beyond a specified number as long as the author assumes the expense. If a single photograph is to be submitted along with the article, it should be 8 by 10 in size and of exceptional quality.

In general, diagrams and line drawings should be drawn in India ink. They should be clear and properly labeled. Pencil drawings are not accepted unless the journal provides an artist to draw the diagram for the author. This usually is not the case.

OTHER MEANS OF PROFESSIONAL GROWTH

Contacts with other teachers. A beginning science teacher finds that other teachers are one of his most valuable sources of information and inspiration. Another science teacher can be especially helpful in selecting objectives, methods, materials and sources of information. Even the well-qualified teacher finds his fellow teachers to be important resources in his professional growth. By working with other teachers who are not in the field of science the science teacher learns to see the relationship of his subject to other subjects. This may bring about better coordination between subjects and improve instruction within the school.

The science teacher can grow professionally by his contacts with teachers in other schools during visitations, conferences, or meetings. The teacher can broaden his outlook on teaching methods and philosophies through insight gained by these contacts. The importance of visiting other science teachers cannot be overemphasized. Beginning teachers should see experienced science teachers in action. Whenever a science teacher is known to be outstanding, he should be observed insofar as possible by the inexperienced.

Travel. The science teacher can use travel not only to provide relaxation and pleasure, but also to gather much information, experience, and material that will help him to improve his teaching. A camera, preferably 35 mm, can be used to take photographs for use in the classroom. Advanced planning is needed to obtain the greatest benefit from travel. Tourist bureaus, chambers of commerce, and travel agencies can provide information and literature about the places to be visited. Visits within the United States provide great opportunities to collect plant and animal specimens for biology teaching. Animals and plants can be studied in their natural habitats. Visits to museums can give a teacher many new ideas concerning exhibits and collections. Visits to local industries, and places of geological importance and general scientific interest can be utilized fully by taking photographs, obtaining samples, and collecting descriptive literature. A science teacher can acquire a great deal of information and material for his classroom without detracting from the enjoyment of his travels.

Summer employment. Industry in some instances has helped science teachers grow professionally by providing science-related summer jobs. These enable the teacher to gain an understanding of the applications of science in industry. The teacher may work in a laboratory where he will develop skills and understandings in the methods of research which will be used in the school to improve instruction.

Some universities have established a practice of hiring teachers as research assistants through the summer months. As assistants, the teachers can help on routine operations until they develop the skill and knowledge to do more advanced work. In many cases, the teachers take courses at the university while working. In this manner the teacher not only acquires up-to-date knowledge and methods, but also develops skills and attitudes toward research that he will carry back to the classroom and laboratory to stimulate his students.

Science hobbies. Teachers can enrich their curriculum by having science hobbies that may be directly or indirectly associated with their teaching area. For example, many science teachers are ardent entomologists or ornithologists. Many are excellent water biologists. It is not uncommon to find a chemistry teacher who is an enthusiastic bird watcher or a biology teacher who is an excellent geologist. Physicists frequently are amateur astronomers or radio amateurs. Such hobbies as these not only help to enrich the curricula, but they stimulate pupils to undertake science-related projects.

Research. Many science teachers have excellent backgrounds in a particular science area; some have advanced degrees, a fact which means that they have the necessary background to do research. Teachers with extensive backgrounds in an area of science should be engaged in research. Teachers who think that they do not have the space, the equipment, or the materials to do research should solicit the help of a near-by university. University professors will generally cooperate with teachers on a research project by providing space and equipment. Teachers should not neglect to use this source of aid.

Pupils who know that teachers are actively engaged in a research project may be stimulated to work on projects of their own. If the teacher reports his findings to the pupils, he may find that many of the exceptional pupils may be interested in helping him on the project.

High school teachers who publish their research in recognized journals receive recognition from their colleagues as well as their pupils. These teachers will be regarded as specialists and authorities in their science area. Members of the community will also recognize them as outstanding teachers and scientists. They will be recognized as the teachers under whom parents would like their children to study.

Reading. Such a vast amount of valuable and interesting literature is available that no teacher could ever hope to read it all. Nevertheless, there is no excuse for a teacher not spending at least one hour a week reading for his own professional growth.

Every science teacher should read regularly and preferably subscribe to some professional science education journal, such as the *Science Teacher, Science Education, Journal of Chemical Education, The American Biology Teacher, The Physics Teacher, Journal of Geological Education, Journal of Research in Science Teaching,* or any of the state journals.[1] These contain valuable articles on major innovations in curriculum and materials, as well as short descriptions of specific new instructional materials and books of interest to science teachers. The science teacher who wants to grow professionally should keep himself informed on the latest developments in his profession. There is no better way than by regularly reading one of the journals.

In addition, every science teacher should regularly read one or more science journals not specifically aimed at science teaching. Outstanding examples of these are *Scientific American, Science, Science World, Chemistry, American Scientist, Earth Science,* and *Science News Letter.* Frequently, the popular magazines (such as *Life*) or major newspapers (such as *The New York Times*) will publish feature stories on scientific topics. These can also be valuable sources of pictures for science room bulletin boards.

---

[1] See Appendix for listing of professional journals.

Besides these periodicals, the science teacher should frequently read books on his major field and related topics. College textbooks are a good source of information for the science teacher who wants to broaden his knowledge of a particular subject.

For the names of books on more specific topics, consult the Appendix herein. For detailed reports on most recent publications, consult the book review sections in *Scientific American, The Science Teacher, Science,* and *Science News Letter* or any scientific journals.

SUGGESTED ACTIVITIES

1. List the books and periodicals that should be found in a science teacher's professional library.
2. Join the National Science Teachers Association and your state science teacher's organization. If possible, attend some of their conventions.
3. Investigate the various types of institutes and grants available to you as a science teacher to continue your professional growth.
4. Read various articles in the *Journal of Research in Science Teaching* and *The Science Teacher* and list the areas of research that are emphasized today.

SUGGESTED READINGS

Association for the Education of Teachers in Science, "Guidelines for the Doctorate in Science Education," *The Science Teacher,* 33:32–35, 1966.

Breukelman, John, and W. A. Reynolds, "Writing Articles for Publication," *The American Biology Teacher,* 28:552–559, 1966.

Brouty, H. S., "Relation of the New Curriculums to the Professional States of High School Teaching," *Secondary Education,* January, 1963.

Fox, Fred W., "Education and the Spirit of Science—The New Challenge," *The Science Teacher,* 33:58–59, 1966.

Glass, H. Bentley, "The Most Critical Aspect of Science Teaching," *The Science Teacher,* 34:19–23, 1967.

Gores, H. B., "Facilities for the Future: Science Facilities," *Liberal Education,* 49:34–47, 1963.

Goslin, W. E., "Forces Undermining Professional Dignity," *Child Education,* February, 1963.

Gross, Leo, N. Molomut, and E. A. Simendinger, "A Summer in Science Research," *The Science Teacher,* 31:31–34, 1964.

Kane, Julian, "Junior High Faculty Holds Science Seminars," *The Science Teacher*, 31:27, 1964.

National Society for the Study of Education, "Rethinking Science Education," *Fifty-ninth Yearbook*, Part 1, University of Chicago Press, Chicago, 1960.

Orr, David B., and A. T. Young, Jr., "Who Attends N.S.F. Institutes?," *The Science Teacher*, 30:39–40, 1963.

Pascarella, Carl J., "Local Industry—an Educational Resource," *The Science Teacher*, 33:45–47, 1966.

"Preparation of Manuscripts, The," *The Science Teacher*, 32:7–8, 1965.

Schenberg, Samuel, "Inservice Training in a Large Urban School System," *The Science Teacher*, 34:36–37, 1967.

Stapp, William B., "Inservice Teacher Training in Environmental Education," *The Science Teacher*, 34:33–35, 1967.

Verbalow, Theodore H., "A Unique Program in Support of Teacher-Student Science Research in the High School," *The American Biology Teacher*, 28:616–617, 1966.

Winslow, J. Leon, "Teaching Science Abroad," *The Science Teacher*, 33:45–47, 1966.

Wood, Hugh B., "What Science Teachers Can Learn from Our Urban Job Corps Experiences," *The Science Teacher*, 33:42–43, 1966.

Appendix

A. REFERENCE BOOKS FOR THE SCIENCE LIBRARY

Bennett, H., *Chemical Formulary*, Chemical Publishing Co., Tudor, Vols. 1–13, $8.00 each (Gives detailed directions for making thousands of various chemical products)

Beveridge, W. I. B., *The Art of Scientific Investigation*, Morton Press, rev. ed., 1957, $4.25, PB, Vintage (V129), $1.25

The Book of Popular Science, The Grolier Society, Inc., 2 West 45th St., New York 36, N.Y. (Ten volumes concerning all junior and senior high school sciences), revised annually, $89.50

Conant, J. B., *Science and Common Sense*, Yale University Press, New Haven, Conn. $6.00, PB, $1.95, 1951

Gabriel, M. L., and S. Fogel, *Great Experiments in Biology*, Prentice-Hall, 1955, $4.95

Hodgeman, Charles (ed.), *Handbook of Chemistry and Physics*, Chemical Rubber Publishing Co., 2310 Superior Ave. N.E., Cleveland, Ohio, 44114

Johnson and Abercrombie, *Dictionary of Biology*, Aldine, $5.00

Knobloch, I. W., *Readings in Biological Science*, Appleton-Century-Crofts, $3.00

Lange, Norbert (ed.), *Handbook of Chemistry*, 10th ed., 1961, $11.00; text ed., $9.50; rev. 10th ed., $12.00; text ed., $10.00, McGraw-Hill

McGraw-Hill Encyclopedia of Science and Technology, McGraw-Hill (An international reference work in 15 volumes including an index), $295.00

"How to Know . . ." Series, William Brown Co., Dubuque, Iowa (This series consists of several separate, spiral bound, inexpensive volumes on many specific biological subjects including freshwater algae, grasses, immature insects, fall flowers, trees, protozoa, beetles, insects, land birds, spiders, and mammals)

Sullivan, J., *The Limitations of Science*, Mentor, New American Library, $0.60

Uvarov, E. B., and Chapman, D. R., *Dictionary of Science*, 4th ed., 1960, PB, $0.95, Penguin

Van Nostrand's International Encyclopedia of Chemical Science, Van Nostrand, $32.50

Van Nostrand's Scientific Encyclopedia, 3rd ed., Van Nostrand, $29.75

JOURNALS FOR THE SECONDARY-SCHOOL SCIENCE LIBRARY

Aquarium

Audubon Magazine

Consumer Reports

Field and Stream

Flying

Life

Mechanics Illustrated

National Geographic Magazine

Natural History

Popular Mechanics

Popular Photography

Popular Science

Radio Electronics

Science Digest

Science World

Scientific American

Sky and Telescope

B. PROFESSIONAL SCIENCE EDUCATION BOOKS

Blough, G., and M. Campbell, *Making and Using Classroom Science Materials in the Elementary School*, Holt, Rinehart & Winston, 1954, $4.95

Brandwein, Paul, *The Gifted Student as Future Scientist*, Harcourt, 1955, $2.00

————, et al., *Teaching High School Science*, Harcourt, 1958, $7.95

Fitzpatrick, F. L. (ed.), *Policies for Science Education*, Columbia University Press, 1960

Freeman, K., *et al.*, *Helping Children Understand Science*, Holt, Rinehart & Winston, 1954, $5.50

Jersild, Arthur T., *Psychology of Adolescence*, illus., 2nd ed., Macmillan, 1963, $7.25

National Science Teachers Association, *Science Facilities for Our Schools*, National Education Assoc., 1963, $1.50

Joseph, A., *et al.*, *Teaching High School Science: A Sourcebook for the Physical Sciences*, Harcourt, Brace & World, 1961, $7.95

Lynde, Carleton J., and Lieb, Floyd, *Science Experiences with Home Equipment*, illus., 3rd ed., Van Nostrand, 1949

————, *Science Experiences with Inexpensive Equipment*, illus., 3rd ed., Van Nostrand, 1950

Miller, D. F., and Blaydes, G., *Methods and Materials for Teaching the Biological Sciences*, McGraw-Hill, rev., 1962, $7.95

Morholt, Evelyn, *et al.*, *Teaching High School Science: A Sourcebook for the Biological Sciences*, illus., Harcourt, Brace & World, 2nd ed., 1966, $9.75

Moulton, F. R., and Schifferes, J., *The Autobiography of Science*, illus., Doubleday, rev. ed., 1960, $6.95

National Academy of Sciences, *Geology and Earth Science Sourcebook*, Holt, Rinehart & Winston, 1962, $3.60

National Science Teachers Association, published by National Education Association:

> *Ideas for Science Projects*, 1962, $1.00
> *Ideas for Teaching Science in Junior High Schools*, 1963, $4.00
> *Career for You as a Science Teacher*, 1965, $0.25
> *Cumulative Index to the Science Teacher*, 1965, $2.50
> *Experimentation and Measurement*, 1962, $0.50
> *How to Care for Living Things in the Classroom*, 1965, $0.35
> *How to Utilize the Services of a Science Consultant*, 1965, $0.35
> *Keys to Careers in Science and Technology*, 1964, $0.50
> *Teaching of a Concept*, 1966, $0.75
> *Theory into Action in Science Curriculum Development*, illus., 1964, $1.50
> *Tested Overhead Projection Series: Tops in Chemistry*, 1962, $1.50
> *You & Your Child & Science*, 1963, $0.75

New York Bureau of Secondary Curriculum Development, *Handbooks: General Science, Biology, Physics, Chemistry*, rev. ed., 1960–62

Richardson, J., *Science Teaching in Secondary Schools*, Prentice-Hall, 1957, $10.60

Schwab, J. J., *The Teaching of Science as Enquiry*, Harvard University Press, 1962, $3.25

Sutton, R., *Demonstration Experiments in Physics*, McGraw-Hill, 1938, $8.95

Swezey, K., *Chemistry Magic*, gr. 8–12, illus., McGraw-Hill, 1956, $5.50

Patterson, M. E., and J. H. Kraws, comps., *Thousands of Science Projects*, 5th ed., Science Service, 1957, $0.25

Merrill, Helen L., *Science Teacher in Action*, Christopher Publishing House, 1956, $2.25

Nedelsky, Leo, *Science Teaching and Testing*, Harcourt, Brace & World, $7.25

Washton, Nathan, S., *Science Teaching in the Secondary School*, Harper, 1961, $6.75

C. PROFESSIONAL JOURNALS, MAGAZINES, AND PAMPHLETS

JOURNALS AND MAGAZINES

American Biology Teacher, National Association of Biology Teachers, write Dr. Jerry P. Lightner, Great Falls High School, Great Falls, Mont., monthly, $10/yr.

American Journal of Physics, American Association of Physics Teachers, American Institute of Physics, Inc., 335 E. 45th Street, New York 17, N.Y., monthly, $10/yr.

American Scientist, Society of Sigma Xi, 51 Prospect Street, New Haven, Conn., 06511, quarterly, $3.50

Canadian Nature or *Canadian Audubon*, Audubon Society of Canada, 46 St. Clair Ave., Toronto, Canada, bimonthly, $3

Chemical and Engineering News, American Chemical Society, 1155 16th St., N.W., Washington, D.C. 20036, weekly, $6/yr.

Cornell Rural School Leaflets, New York State College of Agriculture, Cornell University, Ithaca, N.Y.

Current Science and Aviation, American Education Publications Inc., 1250 Fairwood Avenue, Columbus, Ohio 43216, weekly, $1.40

Journal of Chemical Education, 20 & Northampton Sts., Easton, Pa., monthly, $4/yr.

Journal of Geological Education, National Association of Geology Teachers, c/o M. B. Rosalsky, Geology Dept., City College of New York, New York, N.Y. 10031, 5 times/yr., $5

Junior Astronomy News, Junior Astronomy Club, 100 Washington Square E., New York, N.Y. 10003, bimonthly, $2/yr.

Mathematics Teacher, National Council of Teachers of Mathematics, 1201 16th St. N.W., Washington, D.C. 20036, monthly $5 or $7/yr.

National Geographic, National Geographic Society, 17 and M Sts. N.W., Washington 6, D.C., monthly, $8/yr.

Natural History, American Museum of Natural History, Central Park W. and 79th St., New York, monthly, $5/yr.

Nature, Macmillan Co., St. Martin's St., London, W.C. 2, weekly

The Physics Teacher, American Institute of Physics, 335 E. 45th St., New York, N.Y. 10017, 8 times/yr., $5/yr.

Popular Science Monthly, Popular Science Publishing Co., 355 Lexington Ave., New York City 10017, monthly, $4/yr.

Review of Educational Research, American Educational Research Association, 1201 16th St. N.W., Washington, D.C., nonmember, $7/yr.

School Science and Mathematics, Box 108, Bluffton, Ohio, monthly, $6/yr.

School Science Review, J. Murray, 50 Albemarle St., London, W.I., England

Science, A.A.A.S., 1515 Massachusetts Ave. N.W., Washington 5, D.C., $8.50/yr.

Science Counselor, Duquesne Univ., 901 Vickroy St., Pittsburgh 19, Pa.

Science Education, University of Tampa, Tampa, Florida, 5 times/yr., $5/yr.

Science News Letter, Science Service, 1719 N. St. N.W., Washington 6, D.C.

The Science Teacher, National Science Teachers Association, 1201 16th St. N.W., Washington, D.C.

Science Teachers World, Scholastic Magazines, Inc., 50 W. 44th St., New York, N.Y. 10036, 30 issues with each ed. of *Science World,* $4.50

Science World, Scholastic Magazines, Inc., 50 W. 44th St., New York, N.Y. 10036, (In 2 editions) Edition 1, $1.25; Edition 2, $1.50

Scientific American, Scientific American, Inc., 415 Madison Ave., New York 17

Sky and Telescope, Sky Publishing Corp., 49 Bay State Road, Cambridge, Mass., monthly, $6/yr.

Turtox News, General Biological Supply House, Inc., 8200 Hoyne Ave., Chicago, Ill. 60620, monthly, free

Weatherwise, American Meteorological Society, 45 Beacon St., Boston, Mass. 02108, bimonthly, $5/yr.

PAMPHLETS

AIBS Bulletin, American Institute of Biological Sciences, 2000 P St. N.W., Washington 6, D.C.

BSCS Newsletter, quarterly, free, Biological Sciences Curriculum Study, University of Colorado, Box 930, Boulder, Colorado 80301

Education for All American Youth, Educational Policies Commission, National Education Association, 1201 16 Street N.W., Washington, D.C. 20036.

Program for Teaching Science, Thirty-first Yearbook, Part 1, National Society for the Study of Education, University of Chicago Press, 1932

Redirecting Science Teaching in the Light of Personal-Social Needs, W. C. Croxton (ed.), National Education Association, 1201 16 Street N.W., Washington, D.C. 20036.

Reorganization of Science in Secondary Schools, U.S. Office of Education, Bulletin 26, Washington, D.C.

Report of the Committee of Ten on the Reorganization of Secondary Schools, New York World Book, 1894

Science Education in American Schools, Forty-sixth Yearbook, Part I, National Society for the Study of Education, University of Chicago Press, 1947

Science in General Education, Progressive Education Association, Appleton-Century-Crofts, 1938

Science in Secondary Schools Today, National Association of Secondary School Principals Bulletin, vol. 37, no. 191, 1953

Supervision for Quality Education in Science, Alexander, U.S. Dept. of Health, Education and Welfare, Office of Education (OE29039) Bulletin No. 3, 1963

D. PAPERBACKS AND INEXPENSIVE BOOKS FOR THE SCIENCE TEACHER

American Association for the Advancement of Science (in collaboration with the National Science Foundation), *An Inexpensive Science Library,* 1515 Massachusetts Ave. N.W., Washington 5, D.C. (Note: Revised yearly; an exhaustive and up-to-date review of paperbound books in all branches and levels of science)

E. LIST OF PUBLISHERS

Because of the frequent appearance of new textbooks in science and the revision of existing texts, no attempt has been made to list texts. The following list of publishers includes textbook publishers (*), review and workbook publishers (**), as well as most of the publishers mentioned in the reference section.

Abelard-Schuman, Limited, 6 W. 57 St., New York 10019

Academic Press, Inc., 111 5th Ave., New York 10003

Aldine Publishing Co., 64 E. Van Buren St., Chicago 60605

*Allyn and Bacon, Inc., 470 Atlantic Ave., Boston 02210

*American Book Company, 55 5th Ave., New York 10003

American Meteorite Laboratory, 7891 Osceola, Box 2098, Denver, Colo. 80201

**Amsco School Publications, Box 315, Canal St. Station, New York 10013

Appleton-Century-Crofts, 60 E. 42 St., New York 10017

Barnes & Noble, 105 5th Ave., New York 10003

**Barron's Educational Series, Inc., 113 Crossways Park Drive, Woodbury, N.Y. 11797

Basic Books, Inc., 404 Park Ave. S., New York 10016

Brown, William C. & Co., 135 S. Locust, Dubuque, Iowa 52003

**Cambridge Book Company, 45 Kraft Ave., Bronxville, N.Y. 10708

Chemical Publishing Co., Inc., 212 5th Ave., New York 10010

Chemical Rubber Company, 2310 Superior Avenue, Cleveland, Ohio 44114

Children's Press, Inc., 1224 W. Van Buren Street, Chicago 60607

Christopher Publishing House, 1140 Columbus Ave., Boston 02120

**College Entrance Book Co., 104 5th Ave., New York 10011

Collier, P. F. Inc., 640 Fifth Ave., New York 10019

Creative Educational Society, 515 N. Front St., Mankato, Minn. 56001

Thomas Y. Crowell Co., 201 Park Ave. S., New York 10003

Crown Publishers, Inc., 419 Park Ave. S., New York 10016

John Day Co., Inc., 62 W. 45th St., New York 10036

Dell Publishing Co., Inc., 750 3rd Ave., New York 10017

Didier Publications, 660 Madison Ave., New York

Dodd, Mead & Co., Inc., 432 Park Ave. S., New York 10016

Doubleday & Co., 501 Franklin Ave., Garden City, New York 11531

Dover Publications, Inc., 180 Varick St., New York 10014

E. P. Dutton & Co., Inc., 201 Park Ave. S., New York 10003

The Exposition Press, 386 Park Ave. S., New York 10016

Follett Publishing Co., 1010 W. Washington Blvd., Chicago 60607

Garden City Books, 277 Park Ave., New York 10003

*Ginn & Company, Statler Bldg., Back Bay P. O., 191, Boston 02117

Golden Press, 850 Third Ave., New York 10022

Grolier, Inc., 575 Lexington Ave., New York 10022

Grosset & Dunlap, 51 Madison Ave., New York 10010

Hale, E. M. & Co., 1201 S. Hastings Way, Eau Claire, Wisc. 54702

*Harcourt, Brace & World, 757 Third Ave., New York 10017

Harper & Row, Publishers, 49 E. 33rd St., New York 10016

Harvard University Press, Kittridge Hall, 79 Garden St., Cambridge, Mass. 02138

D. C. Heath & Co., 285 Columbus Ave., Boston 02116

Holt, Rinehart & Winston, Inc., 383 Madison Ave., New York 10017

Houghton Mifflin Co., 2 Park St., Boston 02107

International Publishers Co., Inc., 381 Park Ave. S., New York 10016

International Textbook Co., 1001 Wyoming Ave., Scranton, Pa. 18515

Alfred A. Knopf, Inc., 501 Madison Ave., New York 10022

J. B. Lippincott Co., E. Washington Sq., Philadelphia 19105

Little, Brown & Co., 34 Beacon St., Boston 02106

Lothrop, Lee & Shepard Co., Inc., 419 Park Ave. S., New York 10016

McGraw-Hill Book Co., Inc., 330 W. 42nd St., New York 10036

David McKay Co., Inc., 750 3rd Ave., New York 10017

The Macmillan Co., 60 5th Ave., New York 10011

University of Michigan Press, 615 E. University, Ann Arbor, Mich. 48106

William Morrow & Co., Inc., 425 Park Ave. S., New York 10016

Mortons Press, 201 E. Walton Place, Chicago 60611

National Audubon Society, 1000 5th Ave., New York

National Education Association of the United States, 1201 16th St. N.W., Washington, D.C. 20036

New American Library, 1301 Avenue of the Americas, New York 10019

Norton, W. W. & Co., Inc., 55 5th Ave., New York 10003

**Oxford Book Co., Inc., 71 5th Ave., New York 10003

Oxford University Press, Inc., 417 5th Ave., New York 10016

Pantheon Books, Inc., 22 E. 51 St., New York 10022

Penguin Books, Inc., 3300 Clipper Mill Rd., Baltimore, Md. 21211

Pocket Books, Inc., 630 5th Ave., New York 10020

Prentice-Hall, Inc., Englewood Cliffs, N.J. 07632

G. P. Putnam's Sons, 200 Madison Ave., New York 10016

Random House, Inc., 457 Madison Ave., New York 10022

Roy Publishing, Inc., 30 E. 74th St., New York 10021

Science Service, 1719 N. St. N.W., Washington, D.C. 20006

Scholastic Book Services, Scholastic Magazines, 50 W. 44th St., New York 10036

Charles Scribner's Sons, 597 5th Ave., New York 10017

*Scott, Foresman & Co., 433 E. Erie St., Chicago 60611

Sentinel Press, 194 E. 76th St., New York 10021

*Silver Burdett Co., Park Ave. and Columbia Rd., Morristown, N. J. 07960

*The L. W. Singer Co., Inc., 249 W. Erie Blvd., Syracuse, N.Y. 13202

Simon and Schuster, Inc., 630 5th Ave., New York 10020

Vanguard Press, 424 Madison Ave., New York 10017

*D. Van Nostrand Co., Inc., 120 Alexander St., Princeton, N.J. 08540

The Viking Press, Inc., 625 Madison Ave., New York 10022

Franklin Watts, Inc., 575 Lexington Ave., New York 10022

John Wiley & Sons, Inc., 605 Third Ave., New York 10016

*The John C. Winston Co. (Now Holt, Rinehart & Winston)

World Publishing Co., 2231 W. 110th St., Cleveland, Ohio 44102

Yale University Press, 92a Yale Station, New Haven, Conn. 06520

PUBLISHERS OF PAPERBOUND BOOKS IN SCIENCE

Addison-Wesley Publishing Company, Inc., Reading, Mass. 01867
Affiliated Publishers, Inc., 630 5th Ave., New York 10020
Allyn and Bacon, Inc., 470 Atlantic Ave., Boston 02210
Anchor (*see* Doubleday and Company)
Ann Arbor, University of Michigan Press, Ann Arbor, Mich.
Apollo Editions, Inc., 425 Park Ave. South, New York 10016
Bantam Books, Inc., 271 Madison Avenue, New York 10016
Barnes & Noble, Inc., 105 Fifth Avenue, New York 10003
Beacon Press, Inc., 25 Beacon Street, Boston 02108
Cambridge University Press, 32 East 57th Street, New York 10022
College Outline (*see* Barnes & Noble)
Dell Publishing Company, Inc., 750 Third Avenue, New York 10017
Dolphin (*see* Doubleday and Company)
Doubleday and Company, Garden City, New York 11530
Dover Publications, Inc., 180 Varick Street, New York 10014
Evergreen—Grove Press, Inc., 80 University Place, New York 10003
Harper & Row, 49 East 33rd Street, New York 10016
Holt, Rinehart and Winston, Inc., 383 Madison Avenue, New York 10017
Macmillan Company, 60 Fifth Avenue, New York 10011
McGraw-Hill Book Co., Inc., 330 West 42nd St., New York 10036
Mentor Books (*see* New American Library)
Meridian Books, The World Publishing Co., 119 West 57th St., New York 10019
Noonday Press, 19 Union Square West, New York 10003
Oxford University Press, Inc., 417 Fifth Avenue, New York 10016
Penguin Books, Inc., 3000 Clipper Mill Road, Baltimore 21211
Permabooks (*see* Pocket Books)
Phoenix, University of Chicago Press, 5750 Ellis Ave., Chicago 60637
Pocket Books (*see* Affiliated Publishers, Inc.)
Popular Library, Inc., 355 Lexington Avenue, New York 10017
Prentice-Hall, Inc., Englewood Cliffs, N.J. 07632
Signet and Signet Key (*see* New American Library)
Simon & Schuster, Inc. (*see* Affiliated Publishers, Inc.)
Universal Library, Grosset & Dunlap, Inc., 51 Madison Ave., New York 10010
Viking Press, 625 Madison Avenue, New York 10022
Wisdom, Philosophical Library, Inc., 15 East 40th St., New York 10016
Yale University Press, 920 Yale Sta., New Haven, Conn. 06520

F. A SOURCE LIST OF AUDIOVISUAL AIDS

TRANSPARENCY MAKING EQUIPMENT

Chart-Pak, Inc., River Road, Leeds, Mass. 01053

Commodore Business Machines, Canada, Ltd., 946 Warden Ave., Scarborough, Ontario, Canada

T. J. Donohue, Co., Kimberton, Pa. 19442

, *Gestetner Corp.*, Dept. A-32, 216 Lake Avenue, Yonkers, N.Y. 10702

Honeywell Incorporated, Photographic Division, 27-1 4th Ave. South, Minneapolis, Minn. 55408

Keaffel and Esser Co., Educational/Audiovisual Division, Hoboken, N.J.

Minnesota Mining and Manufacturing Co., Dept. DFK-116, St. Paul, Minn. 55119

Viewlex, 4 Broadway, Holbrook, Long Island, N.Y.

PREPARED TRANSPARENCY SETS

Only those companies known to have transparencies dealing with science and mathematics topics are listed.

Allyn and Bacon, Inc., Audiovisual Dept. A., 470 Atlantic Ave., Boston, Mass. 02210

Audio-Visual Division, Popular Science Publishing Co., Inc., 355 Lexington Avenue, New York, N.Y. 10017

Black Box Collotype Studios, Inc., 4840 West Belmont Ave., Chicago, Ill. 60641

John Colburn Associates, Inc., Dept. AVI, 1122 Central Ave., Willmette, Ill. 60091

Colonial Films, Inc., 71 Walton St. N.W., Atlanta, Ga. 30303

Denoyer-Geppert Company, 5235 Ravenswood Ave., Chicago, Ill. 60640

Educational/Audio-visual Division, Keuffel and Esser Company, Hoboken, N.J.

General Ariline and Film Corporation, 140 West 51 St., New York, N.Y. 10020

Ginn and Company, Sales Office, New York, N.Y. 10011

C. S. Hammond and Company, Maplewood, N.J. 07040

Hubbard Scientific Co., P.O. Box 105, Dept. S3, Northbrook, Ill. 60062

Instructo Products Co., 1635 N. 55th St., Philadelphia, Pa. 19131

Minnesota Mining and Manufacturing Co., Dept. OHO-47, St. Paul, Minn. 55119

A. J. *Nystrom and Company*, 3333 Elston Ave., Chicago, Ill. 60618

Technifax Corporation, Visucom Division, 20 First Ave., Chicopee, Mass. 01020

Tweedy Transparencies, 338 (A) Hollywood Avenue, East Orange, N.J. 07018

OVERHEAD PROJECTORS

American Optical Co., Instrument Division, Buffalo, N.Y. 14215

Applied Science, Inc., 12345 Euclid Ave., Cleveland, Ohio

Bausch and Lomb, Inc., Instrument Sales Division, 635 St. Paul St., Rochester, N.Y.

Charles Beseler Co., 219 S. 18th St., East Orange, N.J. 07018

Buhl Optical Company, 1009 Beech Ave., Pittsburgh, Pa. 15233

Graflex, 3750 Monroe Avenue, Rochester, N.Y. 14603

Happman Corporation, 5410 Port Royal Rd., Springfield, Va. 22151

Keystone View Company, Meadville, Pa.

E. Leitz, Inc., 468 Park Ave. S., New York, N.Y. 10016

Laboratory Furniture Co., Inc., U.S. Route 1 North, Ashland, Va. 23005

Minnesota Mining and Manufacturing Company, 2501 Hudson Road, St. Paul, Minn. 55119

Ozalid Division, General Ariline and Film Corporation, Johnson City, N.Y.

Projection Optics Co., Inc., 271 Eleventh Avenue, East Orange, N.J.

Technifax Corporation, Holyoke, Mass.

Victorlite Industries, Inc., 130 Q Street N.W., Washington, D.C. 20002

Visual Impact Materials, Inc., 812 East Apache Boulevard, Tempe, Ariz. 85281

Wilson Corporation, 456 W. 119th Street, Chicago, Ill. 60628

SINGLE CONCEPT FILM LOOPS AND EQUIPMENT

PROJECTORS:

Fairchild Camera and Instrument Corp., Industrial Products Division, 221 Fairchild Avenue, Plainview, L.I., N.Y.

Jayark Instruments Corporation, 10 East 49th St., New York, N.Y. 10017

Technicolor Corporation, Dept. AV 116, P.O. Box 517, Costa Mesa, Calif. 92627 (Technicolor also has a comprehensive listing of filmstrips available for use in their projectors)

FILM LOOPS:

Only those companies known to have film loops dealing with science and mathematics topics are listed.

Cambosco Scientific Co., Inc., 342 Western Avenue, Boston, Mass. 02135

Cebco Company, 104 Fifth Avenue, New York, N.Y. 10011

Cenco Educational Films, 1800 Foster Ave., Chicago, Ill. 60640

Central Scientific Co., 1700 Irving Park Rd., Chicago, Ill. 60613

College Entrance Book Company, 104 5th Ave., New York, N.Y. 10011

George F. Crain Company, 730 E. Washington Street, Indianapolis, Ind. 46206

DCA Educational Products, Inc., Dept. C-2, 4865 Stenton Avenue, Philadelphia, Pa. 19144

Encyclopaedia Britannica Films, 425 North Michigan Ave., Chicago, Ill. 60611

Film Associates, 11559 Santa Monica Boulevard, Los Angeles, Calif. 90025

General Biological Supply House, 8200 South Hayne Ave., Chicago, Ill. 60620

Harcourt, Brace and World, New York 10017, Chicago 60648

Jayark Instruments Corporation, 10 East 49th St., New York, N.Y. 10017

Macalester Scientific Corporation, 60 Arsenal St., Watertown, Mass. 02172

McGraw-Hill Book Co., Inc., Text-Films Division, 330 W. 42nd St., New York, N.Y. 10036

Modern Learning Aids, 1212 Avenue of the Americas, New York, N.Y. 10036

Ohaus Scale Corporation, 1050 Commerce Ave., Dept. DK, Union, N.J.

Rand McNally and Company, P.O. Box 372, Chicago, Ill. 60645

Science Research Associates, Inc., 259 E. Erie St., Chicago, Ill. 60611

Scope Productions, Educational Division, Bullard Professional Center, 1425 West Shaw Ave., Fresno, Calif. 93705

Walt Disney Nature Library, available in: "Standard 8" from *Communication Films* 870 Monterey Pass Road, Monterey Park, Calif. 91754
"Super 8" from *Ealing Film Loops*, 2225 Massachusetts Ave., Cambridge, Mass.

Wards Natural Science Establishment, Inc., P.O. Box 1712, Rochester, N.Y. 14603 or P.O. Box 1749, Monterey, Calif. 93942

MOVIE PROJECTORS

Bell and Howell, 7100 McCorcack Rd., Chicago, Ill. 60645

Eastman Kodak Co., Motion Picture and Education Markets Division, Rochester, N.Y. 14650

Graflex, 3750 Monroe Ave., Rochester, N.Y. 14603

Honeywell Photographic, 4800 E. Dry Creek Rd., Denver, Colo. 80217

Kalart/Victor, Dept. AV3, Plainville, Conn. 06062

Movie-Mite Corporation, 8311 Puritan Ave., Detroit, Mich. 48238

Radio Corporation of America (RCA), 30 Rockefeller Plaza, New York, N.Y. 10020

FILMSTRIP AND SLIDE PROJECTORS

Key: Filmstrip—FS   Slide (2″ × 2″)—S

Airequipt, Inc., 20 Jones St., New Rochelle, N.Y. 10802   S

American Optical Company, Projector Sales, Buffalo, N.Y. 14215   S

Bausch and Lomb, Inc., 635 St. Paul St., Rochester, N.Y. 14625

Bell and Howell, 7100 McCormack Rd., Chicago, Ill.   FS & S

Charles Beseler Company, 219 S. 18th St., East Orange, N.J. 07018

Brumberger Company, Inc., 68 34th St., Brooklyn, N.Y. 11232   S

Camera Optics Manufacturing Corporation, C.O.C. Industrial Division, 23-53 Steinway St., Long Island City, N.Y. 11105   FS & S

DuKane Corporation, Audiovisual Division, St. Charles, Ill.   FS & S

Eastman Kodak Company, Motion Picture and Education Markets Division, Rochester, N.Y. 14650   FS & S

Genarco, Inc., 97-04 Sutphin Blvd., Jamaica, N.Y. 11435   FS & S

Graflex, Inc., 3750 Monroe Ave., Rochester, N.Y. 14603   FS & S

Honeywell Photographic, 4800 E. Dry Creek Rd., Denver, Colo. 80217   S

Kalart/Victor, Dept. 19, Plainville, Conn. 06062   FS & S

La Belle Industries, 510 S. Worthington, Oconomowoo, Wisc. 53066   FS & S

E. Leitz, Inc., 468 Park Ave. S., New York, N.Y. 10016   S

Picture Recording Company, 121 W. 2nd St., Oconomowoo, Wisc. 53066   S

Spindler and Sauppe, Inc., 1329 Grand Central Avenue, Glendale, Calif. 91201   S

Standard Projector and Equipment Co., Inc., 7433 North Harlem, Chicago, Ill. 60648   FS & S

Strong Electric Corp., 6 City Park Ave., Toledo, Ohio 43601   S

Viewlex, 4 Broadway, Holbrook, L.I., N.Y.   FS & S

MICROPROJECTORS

Bausch and Lomb, Inc., 78027 Bausch St., Rochester, N.Y. 14602

Broscope Manufacturing Company, P.O. Box 1492, Tulsa, Okla. 74101

Elgeet Optical Company, Inc., 838 Smith St., Rochester, N.Y. 14606

Graflex, Inc., 3750 Monroe Ave., Rochester, N.Y. 14603

Hudson Photographic Industries, Inc., S. Buckhout and Station Rds., Irvington-on-Hudson, N.Y. 10533

Ken-A-Vision Manufacturing Co., Inc., 5615 Raytown Road, Baytown, Mo. 64133

E. Leitz, Inc., 468 Park Ave. S., New York, N.Y. 10016

Radio Corporation of America, 30 Rockefeller Plaza, New York, N.Y. 10020

OPAQUE PROJECTORS

American Optical Co., Instrument Division, Buffalo, N.Y. 14215

Bausch and Lomb, Inc., 635 St. Paul St., Rochester, N.Y. 14625

Charles Beseler Company, 219 S. 18th St., East Orange, N.J. 07018

Projection Optics Company, Inc., 271 11th Ave., East Orange, N.J. 07018

Squibb-Taylor, Inc., 10807 Harry Hines Boulevard, Dallas, Tex. 75229

LISTINGS OF AVAILABLE AUDIOVISUAL AIDS

A Composite List of Conservation and Related Subjects Film Titles (more comprehensive than the "A Critical List . . ." below), Conservation League, 110 71st St., New York, N.Y. 10023, 65¢

A Critical Index of Films and Filmstrips in Conservation, free from Conservation Foundation, 30 East 40th St., New York, N.Y. 10016

Department of Audiovisual Instruction, complete list of all DAVI publications, free from Publication Sales, National Education Association, 1201 16 St. N.W., Washington, D.C. 20036

Directory of Geoscience Films, American Geological Institute, 2101 Constitution Ave., Washington, D.C., 1962, $1.00, 63 pp.

A Directory of 16mm Sound Feature Films Available for Rental in the United States, Educational Film Library Assoc., Inc., 250 W. 57th St., New York, N.Y., 1966, $5.00, 102 pp.

Educational Film Guide, H. W. Wilson Co., 950 University Ave., New York 52, N.Y., 1954–58, with supplements through 1962, $5.00

Educators Guide to Free Films, 26th ed. Educators Progress Service, Randolph, Wisc., 1966, $9.50, 722 pp.

Educators Guide to Free Filmstrips, 18th ed., Educators Progress Service, 1966, $7.00, 163 pp.

Educators Guide to Free Science Materials, Educators Progress Service, 1966, $8.25, 358 pp.

Educators Guide to Free Tapes, Scripts and Transcriptions, 13th edition, Educators Progress Service, 1966, $6.75, 177 pp.

Film Guide on Chemicals, Chemistry, and the Chemical Industry, Manufacturing Chemists' Association, Inc., 1825 Connecticut Ave. N.W., Washington, D.C., 1956–1966, 21 pp.

Films and Filmstrips for the Space Age, Educational Film Library Assoc., Inc., 250 W. 57th St., New York, N.Y., 1958, $1, 11 pp., ("EFLA Service Supplement")

BOOKS ON THE USE OF AUDIOVISUAL AIDS

GENERAL

Brown, James W., and Richard B. Leris (eds.), *A-V Instructional Materials Manual*, 2nd ed., McGraw-Hill Book Co., New York, 1964

Brown, James W., Lewis, and Harcleroad. *A-V Instruction Material and Methods*, McGraw-Hill Book Co., New York, 1964
(A basic and complete textbook for teachers who want to improve their use of audiovisual aids)

DeKieffer, Robert E., and L. W. Cochran, *Manual of Audio-Visual Techniques*, Prentice-Hall, Englewood Cliffs, N.J., 1955

Erickson, C. W. H., *Fundamentals of Teaching with Audiovisual Technology*, Macmillan Co., New York, 1965

Minor, Ed., *Simplified Techniques for Preparing Visual Instructional Materials*, McGraw-Hill, New York, 1962

Morlan, John E., *Preparation of Inexpensive Teaching Materials*, Chandler Publishing Co., San Francisco, 1963

Oates, Stanton C., *Audio-Visual Equipment—Self Instruction Manual*, Wm. C. Brown Book Co., Dubuque, Iowa, 1966

Wittich, Walter A., and Charles F. Schuller, *Audio-Visual Materials: Their Nature and Use*, 4th ed., Harper and Row, New York, 1967

SPECIFIC

Hartzell, Horace D., and W. L. Veenandaol, *Overhead Projection*, Henry Steward, Inc., 210 Ellicott St., Buffalo 3, New York, PB, $2.95

Schulz, M. J., *The Teacher and the Overhead Projector*, Prentice-Hall, Englewood Cliffs, N.J., 1965

PERIODICALS REVIEWING FILMS AND FILMSTRIPS

Audio-Visual Equipment Directory, 13th ed., National Audio-Visual Association, Fairfax, Va., 1967

Business Screen, 7064 Sheridan Road, Chicago 26, Ill., every 6 weeks, $3.00/yr.

Educational Film Library Association Bulletin, 250 W. 57th St., New York 19, N.Y., monthly, $5/yr.

Educational Films, Audiovisual Center, Kent State University, Kent, Ohio 44240, every 3 years, with annual supplement, $2.00/copy

Educational Screen and Audio-Visual Guide, monthly, $/yr., annual compilation $1.00, Trade Periodicals, 434 South Wabash Ave., Chicago, Ill. 60605

Film Library Catalogue, Dept. of Commerce, Albany 1, N.Y.

Film News, 250 W. 57th St., New York, N.Y. 10019, bimonthly, $5/yr.

Film World and AV World, Sidale Publishing Co., 672 S. Lafayette Park, Los Angeles, Calif. 90057, $4/yr.

Films, Filmstrips, Slides on Worldwide Programs of UNESCO and Agencies with Related Programs, National Commission for UNESCO, U.S. Dept. of State, Washington, D.C., 1961, 12 pp.

Films, Recordings, and Slides, N.Y. State College of Agriculture, Cornell University, Ithaca, N.Y.

Films on Oceanography, 1st rev. ed., Naval Oceanographic Office, U.S. Department of Defense, Washington, D.C., 1964, $.50, 72 pp.

Filmstrip Guide, H. W. Wilson Co., 950 University Ave., New York 52, 1955–58 with supplement to 1962, $14.00

Filmstrips: A Descriptive Index and User's Guide, Falconer, McGraw-Hill Book Co., New York, $5.00

Free and Inexpensive Learning Materials, 1966–67, available for Division of Surveys and Field Services, George Peabody College for Teachers, Nashville, Tenn. 37203

Mental Health Motion Pictures, U.S. Department Health, Education, and Welfare, Washington 25, D.C., $.35

Modern Index and Guide to Free Educational Films from Industry, Modern Talking Picture Service, Inc., 45 Rockefeller Plaza, New York 20, N.Y.

National Tape Recording Catalogue, 1962–1963, National Association of Educational Broadcasters, University of Colorado, Boulder, Colo., 1963, $1.50, 38 pp. (also available for $1.50 from NEA at 1201 16th St. N.W., Washington, D.C. Catalogue is of tape recordings which are available from the National Tape Repository. Any individual group, educational institution, firm, etc., may order recordings of the thousands of tapes available. Only a limited number of tapes dealing with mathematics are available, but there are dozens of tapes on scientific subjects. Many are dramatized biographies of great scientists; others tell of great discoveries and inventions. Some are instructional.

Programmed Instructional Materials, 1966, rev. ed., Teachers College Press, 525 W. 120th St., New York, N.Y., 1965, $2.50, 163 pp.

Reviews of Films: Report of Some Reviewing Committees, National Council of Teachers of Mathematics, Washington, D.C., 1963, $.40

Selected Films and Filmstrips on Food and Nutrition, Food and Nutrition Council of Greater New York, Bureau of Publications, Teachers College, Columbia University, New York, N.Y., 1961, *Supplement,* 1964 (both for $1.25)

Supplement 1, Available from NEA, 1201 16th St. N.W., Washington, D.C., 1965, $1.00, 38 pp.

Space Science Educational Media Resources: A Guide for Junior High School Teachers, North Carolina Department of Public Instruction, available from the Bureau of Audiovisual Education, 111 Abernathy Hall, Chapel Hill, N.C., 1965, $3.50

United States Governmental Films for Public Educational Use, Reid & Grubbs, Office of Education, 1963, available from Superintendent of Documents, U.S. Government Printing Office, Washington, D.C., 1964, $3.00, 532 pp.

G. TEACHING MACHINES, PROGRAMED INSTRUCTIONAL MATERIALS AND BOOKS

Key: Materials—Mat   Machines—M

Accelerated Instruction Methods Corp., 175 N. Michigan Ave., Chicago, Ill. Mat

Addison-Wesley Publishing Co., Inc., Reading, Mass. Mat

Appleton-Century-Crofts, Lyone and Carnahan, 34 West 33rd St., New York, N.Y. M and Mat

ASTRA, 19 Burton Ave., Norwich, Conn. M and Mat

Center for Programed Instruction, 365 West End Ave., New York, N.Y. Mat

Central Scientific Company, 1700 Irving Park Road, Chicago, Ill. Mat and M

Coronet Instructional Films, 65 E. South Water St., Chicago, Ill. Mat

The Deverux Foundation, Box 717, Devon, Pa. Mat

Dorsett Electronics, Inc., 1143 S. 71st East Ave., Tulsa, Okla. M

Doubleday & Co., 575 Madison Ave., New York, N.Y. Mat

DuKane Corporation, 103 N. 11th Ave., Saint Charles, Ill. 60174 M

Education Engineering, Inc., 381 West 7th St., San Pedro, Calif. M and Mat

Educational Aids Publishing Corp., Carle Place P. So., Long Island, N.Y. Mat

Educational Development Associates, 2302 J. Street, Eureka, Calif. Mat

Educational Development Laboratories, 74 Prospect Street, Huntington, N.Y. Mat

Encyclopaedia Britannica Press, 425 N. Michigan Ave., Chicago 11, Ill. Mat

General Education, Inc., 96 Mt. Auburn St., Cambridge, Mass. 02138   Mat

General Programmed Teaching Corporation, 1719 Girard N.E., Albuquerque, N.M.   Mat

Ginn and Company, Statler Building, P. O. Box 191, Boston, Mass. 02117   Mat

Harcourt, Brace & World, 750 Third Ave., New York, N.Y.   Mat

D. C. Heath and Co., 285 Columbus Ave., Boston, Mass. 02116   Mat

Holt, Rinehart and Winston, 383 Madison Ave., New York 17, N.Y.   Mat

Honor Products Company, 20 Moulton St., Cambridge, Mass.   M and Mat

Inrad, P. O. Box 4456, Lubbock, Tex.   Mat

Learning Foundations Institute, Inc., 271 North Avenue, New Rochelle, N.Y.   M and Mat

Learning Incorporated, 1317 W. Eighth St., Tempe, Ariz.   Mat

The Macmillan Company, 60 Fifth Ave., New York, N.Y.   Mat

Mast Development Company, 2212 E. 12th St., Davenport, Iowa 52803   M

National Education Association, Publication Sales, 1201 16th St. N.W., Washington, D.C. 20036   Mat

New York Institute of Technology, 500 Pacific Ave., Brooklyn, N.Y.   Mat

Prentice-Hall, Inc., Englewood Cliffs, N.J.   Mat

R.C.A. Educational Services, Camden, N.J.   Mat

Roto-Vue, 211 North 7th St., 1212 Holland Bldg., St. Louis, Mo.   Mat

Science Research Associates, Inc., 259 East Erie St., Chicago, Ill.   Mat

Teaching Machines Incorporated, 221 San Pedro, NE, Albuquerque, N.M. 87108   M

Teaching Materials Corporation, 575 Lexington Ave., New York 22, N.Y.   Mat

Universal Teaching Machine Institute, 510 Hudson St., Hackensack, N.J.   M and Mat

Varian Associates, 611 Hansen Way, Palo Alto, Calif.   Mat

Videoscope Division, Centinela and Teale, Culver City, Calif. 90230   M

Viewlex, Inc., 4 Broadway, Holbrook, L.I., N.Y.   M

Welch Scientific Co., 1515 Sedgwick St., Chicago, Ill.   Mat

Wiley, John and Sons, Inc., 410 Fourth Ave., New York, N.Y.   Mat

Young, Jay, Kings College, Wilkes-Barre, Pa.   Mat

BOOKS ON THE USE OF PROGRAMED INSTRUCTIONAL MATERIALS

Lysaught, Jerome P., and Clarence M. Williams, *A Guide to Programmed Instruction,* John Wiley and Sons, New York, 1963

Pipe, Peter, *Practical Programming*, Holt, Rinehart & Winston, New York, 1966

Ryan, William F., *A Handbook for Programed Learning Information*, Division of Educational Communication, University of the State of New York, State Education Department, Albany, N.Y. 12224

H. SOURCES OF LABORATORY EQUIPMENT AND SUPPLIES*

Ainsworth & Sons, 2151 Lawrence St., Denver 5, Colo. 80205   (equipment)

Allied Chemical & Dye Corp., 40 Rector St., New York 6, or Box 111, Ashland, Ky. 41101

American Hospital Supply Corp., 40-05 168 St., Flushing, N.Y., or 2030 Ridge Ave., Evanston, Ill.   (equipment and supplies)

American Optical Co., Buffalo, N.Y. 14215   (equipment)

American Type Culture Collection (bacteria), 12301 Parklawn Dr., Rockville, Md.   (supplies)

Bausch and Lomb Optical Co., 635 St. Paul St., Rochester, N.Y. 14625 (equipment)

BICO Scientific Supply Co., Div. of National Biological Supply Co., 2325 So. Michigan Ave., Chicago, Ill. 60616   (chemistry, physics, biology, equipment)

Brunswick Corp. Biological Research, Inc., 1831 Olive St., St. Louis, Mo. 63124 (laboratory equipment)
243 W. Root St., Chicago, Ill. 60609 (biological supplies)

Carolina Biological Supply Co., Highway 100, Elon College, Burlington, N.C. (biological supplies)

Cambosco Scientific Co., 342 Western Ave., Brighton, Mass.   (equipment)

Central Scientific Co., 1700 N. Irving Park Road, Chicago, Ill.

Certified Blood Donor Service, 146-16 Hillside Ave., Jamaica, N.Y. 11435

Chemical Rubber Company, 2310 Superior Ave., Cleveland, Ohio 44114 (chemistry laboratory equipment)

Clay-Adams Co., 141 E. 25th St., New York, N.Y. 10010   (equipment)

Cole-Parmer Instrument and Equipment Co., 7330 North Clark Street, Chicago, Ill. 60626 (equipment)

Corning Glass Works, Corning, N.Y. 14830   (glass equipment)

Denoyer-Geppert Co., 5235 N. Ravenswood Ave., Chicago, Ill. 60640   (globes and charts)

Difco Laboratories, Inc., 920 Henry St., Detroit, Mich. 48201   (supplies)

* For special chemical lab equipment and supplies, see the annual "Buyers Guide Issue" of *Chemical Week* magazine, McGraw-Hill, N.Y.

Dow Chemical Co., Midland, Mich. 48232   (chemical supplies)

Ealing Corporation, 2225 Massachusetts Ave., Cambridge, Mass. 02140

Eastman Kodak Co., Motion Picture and Education Markets Division, Rochester, N.Y. 14650

Edmund Scientific Company, Barrington, N.J. 08003   (equipment)

Fisher Scientific Supply Co., 711 Forbes Ave., Pittsburgh, Pa. 15219   (laboratory equipment and supplies)

General Biological Supply House, Inc. (Turtox), 8200 S. Hoyne Ave., Chicago, Ill. 60620

Gradwohol Laboratories, 3514 Lucas Ave., St. Louis, Mo.

Graf-Apsco Co., 5868 N. Broadway, Chicago, Ill. 60640   (equipment)

Harshaw Chemical Co., 6265 Wiche Rd., Cincinnati, Ohio 45237   (supplies)

Harvard Apparatus Co., Inc., Dover, Mass. 02030   (physiology laboratory apparatus)

Kaud K. Laboratories, Inc., 121 Express St., Engineers Hill, Plainview, N.Y. 11803   (rare chemicals and serums)

Kaufman Glass Co., 1209-21 French St., Wilmington, Delaware   (plastic and glass laboratory materials)

Klinger Scientific Apparatus, 83-45 Parsons Blvd., Jamaica, N.Y. 11432   (imported science apparatus)

Lab-Line Instruments, 15th and Bloomingdale, Melrose Park, Ill. 60160

Labindustries, 1802 2nd St., Berkeley, Calif. 94710

Lab Com Co. Incorp., Box 14466, Houston, Tex. 77021

Laboratory Equipment, Box 1511, Saint Joseph, Mich. 49085

Laboratory Metalware Corp., 429 W. Superior St., Chicago, Ill. 60610

Lab Research Manufacturing, Northwest Blvd., Vineland, N.J. 08360

Lab Sciences, Inc., 604 Park Dr., Boca Raton, Fla. 33432

Charles Lane Corp., 105 Chambers St., New York, N.Y.

Lederle Laboratories, Div. American Cyanamid Co., No. Middletown Rd., Pearl River, N.Y. 10965   (biological supplies)

Macalester Scientific Corp., 60 Arsenal St., Watertown, Mass. 021072

Marine Biological Laboratories, Woods Hole, Mass.

Merck and Co., Inc., Lincoln Ave., Rahway, N.J. 07065   (chemical supplies)

Monsanto Chemical Co., 1700 S. 2nd St., St. Louis 63104   (chemical supplies)

New York Scientific Supply Co. (branch of Welch Scientific Co.), 331 East 38th St., New York City, N.Y.   (general science supplies)

Nutritional Biochemicals Corp., 21010 Miles Ave., Cleveland, Ohio 44128

Nystrom, A. J. & Co., 3331-41 N. Elston Ave., Chicago, Ill. 60618   (maps, anatomical models)

Scientific Kit Co., 402 Greentree Rd., Pittsburgh, Pa. 15220   (general laboratory equipment and supplies)

Polaroid Corp., 730 Main St., Cambridge, Mass. 02139

Charles Pfizer & Co., 11 Bartlett St., Brooklyn, N.Y. 11206   (chemical supplies)

E. H. Sargent and Co., 4647 West Foster Ave., Chicago, Ill. 60630   (chemistry laboratory equipment)

Scientific Kit Co., 402 Greentree Rd., Pittsburgh, Pa. 15220   (general laboratory equipment and supplies)

Sprague-Dawley, Inc., P.O. Box 2071, Madison, Wisc.   (laboratory rats)

Standard Scientific Corp., 34 W. 4th St., New York, N.Y.   (laboratory supplies)

Teaching Materials Corp., 575 Lexington Ave., New York, N.Y.

Testa Manufacturing Co., 10126 Rush St. S.E., Los Angeles, Calif.

Arthur H. Thomas Co., Box 779, Philadelphia, Pa. 19105   (general laboratory supplies and equipment)

Science Electronics, Division of General Electronic Laboratories, Inc., 1085 Commonwealth Ave., Boston, Mass. 02215   (physics and apparatus)

Science Kit, Inc., Box 69, Tonawanda, N.Y.   (general elementary and junior high science equipment)

Ward's Natural Scientific Establishment, P.O. Box 1712, Rochester, N.Y., Box 1749, Monterey, Calif. 93942   (biological supplies and equipment)

Welch Scientific Co., 1515 N. Sedgwick St., Chicago, Ill.   (general science supplies and equipment)

Will Scientific, Inc., Box 1050, Rochester, New York   (laboratory equipment and supplies)

Windsor Biology Gardens, Moor's Creek Rd., Bloomington, Ind.   (specimens)

Kimble Glass Co., Owen-Illinois, Inc., P.O. Box 1035, Toledo, Ohio   (glass)

Keystone Plastics Co., 701 Painter St., Media, Pa. 19063   (animal cages and supplies)

Lapine Scientific Co., 6001 S. Knox Ave., Chicago, Ill. 60629   (chemistry, biology, and physics equipment and supplies)

Ohaus Scale Corporation, 1050 Commerce Ave., Union, N.J.   (scales and balances)

Torsion Balance Company, Clifton, N.J. 07013   (balances and general physics equipment)

Southwest Scientific Co., 319 E. Indian Plaza, Scottsdale, Ariz. 85251   (mineralogy specimens and supplies)

I. SOURCES OF LABORATORY FURNITURE

Browne-Morse Co., 111 Broadway, Muskegon, Mich. 49444   (furniture)

Chemical Rubber Co., 2310 Superior Ave., Cleveland, Ohio 44114

E. H. Sheldon and Company, 716 Nims St., Muskegon, Mich. 49442   (furniture)

Equipment & Furniture Co., Inc., 116 E. 32nd Street, New York, N.Y. (furniture and equipment)

Fisher Scientific Co., 711 Forbes Ave., Pittsburgh, Pa. 15219

Hamilton Manufacturing Company, Columbus Street, 1935 Evans Street, Two Rivers, Wisc. (furniture)

Kewaunee Manufacturing Company, 700 S. Center Street, Adrian, Mich. 49221 (equipment)

Maurice A. Knight Co., P.O. Box 111, Akron, Ohio 44309 (equipment)

Lab Fabricators Co., 1540 E. 49th St., Cleveland, Ohio 44103

Laboratory Furniture Co., Inc., 3720 Northern Blvd. U.S. Rte. 1, N., Long Island City, N.Y. (furniture)

Metalab Equipment Corporation, 270 Duffy Avenue, Hicksville, N.Y. 11802, (furniture and equipment)

Leonard Peterson & Co., Inc., 1222 Fullerton Ave., Chicago, Ill. 60614

E. H. Sheldon and Company, 716 Nims St., Muskegon, Mich. 49442 (furniture)

W. M. Welch Manufacturing Co., 7300 N. Linder Ave., Skokie, Ill. 60076

Will Scientific, Inc., P.O. Box 1051, Rochester, N.Y.

J. CURRICULUM PROJECT ADDRESSES*

Biological Sciences Curriculum Study   (BSCS)
    University of Colorado
    P.O. Box 930
    Boulder, Colorado 80302

Chemical Bond Approach Project   (CBA)
    Earlham College
    Richmond, Indiana 47375

Chemical Education Material Study   (CHEMS)
    Wing B, Gayley Road
    University of California
    Berkeley, California 94720

Earth Science Curriculum Project   (ESCP)
    P.O. Box 1559
    Boulder, Colorado 80301

Harvard Project Physics   (HPP)
    Pierce Hall
    Harvard University
    Cambridge, Massachusetts 02139

* For a complete listing see: Report of the International Clearing House on Science and Mathematics Curricula Developments; J. David Lockhard (ed.), Commission on Science Education, AAAS, University of Maryland, College Park, Maryland, 1967.

Introductory Physical Science   (IPS)
    Education Development Center, Inc.
    55 Chapel Street
    Newton, Massachusetts 02160

Physical Science Study Committee   (PSSC)
    PSSC-ESI
    164 Main Street
    Watertown, Massachusetts 02172

The Portland Project
    Portland State College
    P.O. Box 751
    Portland, Oregon 97207

Secondary School Science Project   (SSSP)
    Princeton University
    171 Broadmead Avenue
    Princeton, New Jersey 08540

K. K–12 CURRICULUM PROJECTS

Arlington County K–12 Curriculum Development Project
    Associate Superintendent for Instruction
    4751 North 25th Street
    Arlington, Virginia 22207

Conceptual Schemes in Science: A Basis for Curriculum Development
    Biology Department of Boston University
    2 Cummington Street
    Boston, Massachusetts 02215

Conservation Curriculum Improvement Project
    School of Education
    University of South Carolina
    Columbia, South Carolina 29201

K–12 Science Design
    Elementary Curriculum Coordinator
    Las Cruces School District No. 2
    301 West Amador Avenue
    Las Cruces, New Mexico 88001

Pennsylvania Science in Action Program
    Department of Public Instruction
    Bureau of General and Academic Education
    Box 911
    Harrisburg, Pennsylvania 17126

The Reorganized Science Curriculum—Minneapolis Public Schools
    807 N.E. Broadway
    Minneapolis, Minnesota 55413

Index